D0618091

ADVANCES IN WATER QUALITY IMPROVEMENT

Water Resources Symposium

Number One

ADVANCES IN WATER QUALITY IMPROVEMENT

Edited by

EARNEST F. GLOYNA

and

W. WESLEY ECKENFELDER, Jr.

UNIVERSITY OF TEXAS PRESS, AUSTIN AND LONDON

Library of Congress Catalog Card No. 68–63334

Manufactured in the United States of America

FOREWORD

The special lectures on water pollution control were designed to focus attention on the most recent advances in wastewater renovation and management. These contributions are now included in this first of a series of volumes on water resources, to be published by The University of Texas College of Engineering.

The conservation of water resources has become a matter of increasing concern at all levels of industry and government.

Research and engineering now being applied to water quality management, toward maintaining and improving man's environment, are having a profound effect upon entire industries and populations. The importance of this subject has been highlighted by The Honorable Stewart L. Udall, secretary of the Department of the Interior, who wrote "Conservation and Man's Environment" for this volume.

The current special lecture series on advances in water quality improvement has significant relevance to one of the most crucial problems of our time, a problem whose solution depends in substantial measure upon the ingenuity, resourcefulness, and leadership of the engineering profession.

John J. McKetta, Jr., Dean
College of Engineering

PREFACE

The purpose of this special lecture series is to present the most advanced thinking on wastewater handling, treatment, and disposal. The authors have been carefully selected for their notable work in a specific area. The organization of the topics is such that wastewater disposal to streams and wastewater treatment prior to release could be considered in detail without neglecting the overall water resources management concept.

Water pollution control is one of the major aspects of water resource management. Organic substances are becoming more prevalent in the waterways, and both natural and man-made inorganic salts are increasing the salinity of these waters to levels which ultimately will require costly treatment. As population centers grow, as industry develops to support the demands of the people, and as agriculture becomes more efficient through controlled irrigation, the amount of polluted waters will become greater. The demand for pure water will increase. The strain on the water budget for high-quality surface waters and groundwaters will become more acute. Only through use of the most effective water management measures will it be possible to provide the amount and quality of water required.

Wastewater management embraces virtually every water resources activity. To the water resources administrator, waste handling may imply local, river basin, regional, state, national, or even international resources planning. To the water quality oriented engineer, wastewater treatment and disposal may suggest broad conceptual synthesis, perhaps denoting analysis and evaluation of segments of the water system. To the socioeconomist and demographer, wastewater management may imply an array of statistical tools that permits the consideration of wastewater re-use and return flows in terms of material wealth and human welfare. To the jurist, water resources may be construed in terms of the difficult problems of appropriations versus reparation rights, adjudication, and other legal matters. To the scientist, water resources and, more specifically, wastewater may be too broad a concept to be meaningful. To the educator, water resources and wastewater treatment may mean not only training specialists in principles sanctified by time but also encouraging the removal of some of the traditional barriers that hinder the development of a program of study that may encompass the best of several disciplines. To the water pollution control specialist, management of the water resources implies a certain degree of wastewater treatment, prior to release or as renovation for some specific use. The handling, treatment, and disposal of wastewaters thus become of utmost significance to the water resource management team. Each specialist may help bridge the gap between the basic understanding of the problems involved in developing a wastewater handling plan and the eventual execution of the plan.

Section One in this book is devoted to the broader aspects of water resource conservation, specifically the transport of wastes in streams and the ecology of the aquatic environment. The latest in water pollution control technology is illustrated.

It is logical that the first section of this lecture series should focus attention on the aquatic environment, the stream, and the manner in which wastewaters may be dispersed. The stream is the central artery through which water resources are channeled to meet the needs of industry, municipalities, and agriculture. Significantly, the stream or body of water becomes valuable only through actual use by people, and the distribution of this commodity to the people involves problems in economics, management, hydraulics, stream ecology, and the mathematical modeling of various mixing phenomena.

Section Two is specifically directed to the latest concepts in advanced biological waste treatment. The articles in this section are highly specific with respect to biological wastewater treatment. The newest technological advancements for the removal of organic materials from wastewaters by biological processes are discussed. The theories of biological waste treatment are examined, and the most recent improvements in process design are illustrated.

Section Three pertains to current trends in low-cost treatment practices. Current practices in the use of waste stabilization ponds for biological treatment of waste containing organic pollutants are considered. Advances in the development of design criteria, as well as special new innovations, are described in detail. A compilation of similar material on the family of waste stabilization ponds has not previously been assembled.

ACKNOWLEDGMENTS

The success of this Special Lecture Series on Advances in Water Quality Improvement and the publication of these proceedings were made possible through the efforts and the assistance of many people. The University of Texas was indeed fortunate in obtaining the cooperation of both nationally and internationally recognized authorities. These men gave freely of their time and resources toward the development of these proceedings.

Without the assistance of a number of University organizations and people, it would have been impossible to undertake this Lecture Series. Financial contributions were made by the College of Engineering. The assistance provided by Mr. Dean Griffith, engineering program director, in preparing the announcements is gratefully acknowledged. Dr. Norris Hiett, assistant dean, and the staff of the Division of Extension of The University of Texas were most helpful in the preparation and distribution of conference brochures and in the operation of many other conference arrangements. The faculty and staff of the Environmental Health Engineering Division of the Civil Engineering Department devoted much time and effort to further this Special Lecture Series. Finally, without the assistance of the staff of the Center for Research in Water Resources, particularly Mrs. Linda Green, it would have been impossible to coordinate the material for all the twelve hundred registrants who attended the Special Lecture Series.

The full cooperation of the University of Texas Press in undertaking the editing and publication of this volume is most gratefully acknowledged.

TABLE OF CONTENTS

Section Three: Waste Stabilization Pond Practices

CONSERVATION AND MAN'S ENVIRONMENT

The Honorable Stewart L. Udall
Secretary, Department of the Interior

I have spent my time in Texas looking at phases of conservation—and I hope you share my enthusiasm for wilderness, wild rivers, park conservation, and the preservation of historic places.

From Big Bend National Park and old Fort Davis, I bring you the greetings of the First Lady, Mrs. Lyndon B. Johnson, and, from Washington, I bring you best wishes for a most fruitful conference from a President who is enlarging the conservation aspirations and performance of the Nation each month.

The President has pointed out that:

> We live with history. It tells us of a hundred proud civilizations that have decayed through careless neglect of the nature that fed them.
>
> We live with the certain future of multiplying populations, whose demands on the resources of nature will equal their numbers.
>
> We are not immune. We are not endowed—any more than those perished nations of the past—with a limitless natural bounty.
>
> Yet we are endowed with their experience. We are able to see the magnitude of the choice before us, and its consequences for every child born on our continent from this day forward.

President Johnson recently had me head a fact-finding mission to West Germany to study the approach there to urban planning and environmental pollution. Our report will be of great interest, I believe, to conservationists in both countries.

Because our environmental pollution problems are man-made, it follows that man can solve them if he is willing to try—and willing to pay the cost of restoring the quality of the American environment.

Thanks to you and other scientists like you, we are making progress in gaining the technical know-how necessary for better water quality management, and other techniques necessary to improve man's environment. We also have a greatly enhanced public awareness of the relationship between the burgeoning population and our limited natural resources.

Under a broad and amplified concept of "conservation," attempts are being made to soften the impact of the problems posed by population increase. The people must have opportunities to relate to the land that cradled and nurtures them, whether that relationship comes through fishing a secluded trout stream, hiking a mountain trail, plowing a contoured furrow, or just looking at a sunset through a car window.

Each person must have elbow room and opportunity for occasional solitude. He must be spared excessive noise and pollution. He needs clean, pleasant surroundings, with touches of beauty.

In a truly Great Society, conservation takes a new orientation, reaching out to encompass the quality of the total environment; considering the rivers that once graced and now often disgrace our cities, pitting a critical eye and a creative brain against the mounting tide of litter and contamination; pondering how to stretch our resources to cover the demands of a mushrooming population while still preserving the quality of existence.

In 1965, the need for planning to assure that we achieved a sound balance between the demands of a growing population and the need for a quality existence came crowding in on all fronts. Great sections of the nation suffered devastating floods; other sections underwent withering drought. Endangered species slipped still farther down the slope toward extinction. Prime park areas experienced such heavy visitation that in many cases they lost their original flavor.

We still have with us, however, those who give lip service and nothing else to solving the problem, and, even worse, we have those who profess that they can't see what all the hollering is about. The women, bless them, under the leadership of the First Lady, are in action all across the country with their varied beautification programs.

So I challenge the civic clubs and chambers of commerce to get in—with both feet—the fight for a clean and fresh and appealing country.

Let them go to the city dump--and let the sight and the smell of soil, air, and water pollution smite their senses—and I am confident they will act.

They should inspect and take interest in sewage disposal systems—and I'm confident they will give strong support to local pollution abatement efforts.

They should walk along the rivers around the industrial plants and judge for themselves what is being turned into the streams and what this refuse is doing to the fish and plant life of the stream. I hope—for contrast—some of them knew the streams in earlier years when nature was in charge.

They should keep an eye on the city's smokestacks and insist that air pollution be controlled.

They should determine if the filth of the streets and the pesticides washing straight through storm sewers add to river pollution.

Then they should see what they can do to help the municipal and state authorities take corrective action.

I think I can guarantee that those who take such trips will no longer ask what all the furor is about.

The cleanup of the environmental pollution of a nation begins in a single alley or with a single storefront or alongside a single road.

Some bright spots are in this picture, I'm glad to say, some of them right here in Texas.

My Department is particularly pleased with the aggressive manner in which the state is approaching its water pollution problems--especially since we are so concerned with the effect that polluted Texas streams, discharging into the Gulf of Mexico, are having on commercial marine life in the bays and estuaries along the coast.

The newly created Texas Water Development Board, as some of you may know, is well into a comprehensive study of water supply, fish and wildlife aspects, flood control, pollution control, and recreational facilities. And the Texas Water Rights Commission is cutting into the tangled situation of water rights.

The coordination between state and federal bodies is quite remarkable, and my personal compliments go to the state and to Governor John Connally for the way—administratively and technically—Texas has organized to handle the many facets that affect solution of a water problem anywhere.

Unlike my native state of Arizona, where the water shortage exists in all directions, Texas' supply problem is overabundance in East Texas contrasted with a deficit in West Texas. I transmitted to Governor Connally last year on a provisional basis Departmental views on transfer of the surplus East Texas water to the deficient areas in West Texas. The Bureau of Reclamation of the Department still is working closely with the Texas Water Development Board to help that body develop a sound statewide water plan.

Water is the common thread that sews together the various bureaus that make up my Department, and in them we consider six great types of water problems: pollution, inadequate supply, uneven distribution, floods, variability of supply and demand, and chemical and sediment problems. Most of the states and all of the major geographical regions have at least several of the six problems.

For the nation as a whole there is no absolute shortage of water. If spread uniformly over the United States, our supply of water would measure nine inches deep. We are using only about one fourth of the seven thousand gallons per person per day that are available.

The problem comes down to providing the right amount of water, of the right quality, at the right time, at the right place, at the right cost. Another way of looking at it is the matching of population needs with the supply of resources on a regional basis, both within the regions and among the regions.

Some areas of the United States are suffering right now under a shortage of fresh water from natural resources. Others are threatened.

If ways to increase available supplies are not forthcoming, these areas are face to face with stunted economic and demographic growth, with increased public health risks, with decreased opportunities for and increased costs of outdoor recreation—or even with forced shifts of population and industry.

We must combine all the means at our disposal--federal, state, local, and private—progressively to find the right answers.

Guidelines for action can be taken from some concepts that have gained relatively wide acceptance:

1. The nation's water problems will never be solved by taking the parochial viewpoint.
2. The provincial approach to water problems must be replaced by the regional and even the national approach.
3. The area of origin must be more than merely protected when water is taken from one area and transferred to another.
4. Federal laws and programs have "profound implications" for regional water plans.
5. There is a national and international community of interest in all water programs.
6. Recreation is a strongly growing and very important use of water; however, it requires well-planned capital investment programs, as any other business venture with extensive and lasting appeal. Otherwise we destroy natural beauty and the overall quality of the environment. Pretty scenery, clear and beautiful streams, and picture-book lakes quickly lose their appeal with the encroachment of shabby, short-lived, inadequately financed, and poorly constructed facilities.

More than one solution to an inadequate water supply problem should be considered.

First of all, more efficient use can be made of available supplies. New York City, facing the summer with only 68 percent of reservoir capacity filled, has tapped the Hudson River and is augmenting its supply with lower grade, more heavily chlorinated Hudson water.

Philadelphia saw the problem coming several years ago and installed a water metering system—a step that New York is still loathe to take. Now Philadelphia has one of the most efficient systems in the country.

Some municipalities are reclaiming wastewater and re-using it for recreational facilities.

Water desalting may be an economic solution where saline or brackish water is available. Key West, Florida, is putting in a desalination plant to supplement existing supplies, since alternative sources of supply would be as or more expensive. Los Angeles, my Department, and the Atomic Energy Commission are studying a desalting-electric powerplant for that California city.

Water resources research has made this progress possible and it continues to be the essential ingredient of advancement. Nearly five hundred research projects are now under way in the fifty-one state water research centers (that extra center is in Puerto Rico).

I believe that this cooperative water research program will contribute to the achievements in its field just as the agricultural research program has brought American agricultural efficiency and productivity to unprecedented levels. My confidence is based in part on the fact that already more than 550 advanced undergraduate and graduate students are receiving training in water resources research under the guidance of able scientists. Such a continuing trained manpower pool bodes well for our nation's future.

When the President sent his environmental pollution message to the Congress, February 23, 1966, he said:

> To sustain an environment suitable for man, we must fight on a thousand battlegrounds. Despite all of our wealth and knowledge, we cannot create a Redwood forest, a wild river, or a gleaming seashore.
>
> But we can keep those we have.
>
> The science that has increased our abundance can find ways to restore and renew an environment equal to our needs.
>
> The time is ripe to set forth a creed to preserve our natural heritage—principles which men and women of good will will support in order to assure the beauty and bounty of their land. Conservation is ethically sound. It is rooted in our love of the land, our respect for the rights of others, our devotion to the rule of law.
>
> Let us proclaim a creed to preserve our natural heritage with rights and the duties to respect those rights:
>
> The right to clean water—and the duty not to pollute it.
>
> The right to clean air—and the duty not to befoul it.
>
> The right to surroundings reasonably free from man-made ugliness—and the duty not to blight.
>
> The right of easy access to places of beauty and tranquility where every family can find recreation and refreshment—and the duty to preserve such places clean and unspoiled.
>
> The right to enjoy plants and animals in their natural habitats—and the duty not to eliminate them from the face of this earth.

SECTION ONE
EFFECTS OF POLLUTANTS ON STREAMS

WATER RESOURCE VALUES

Allen V. Kneese*
Resources for the Future, Inc., Washington, D.C.

It will not come as a surprise to anyone here that the effects of pollution on water resource values have received strong recognition over the past few years. The net value of water quality in our water courses is a function of both the benefits resulting from improved water quality and the cost of attaining it.

Interest in the problem of water quality is, of course, intense. Congressional hearing after Congressional hearing has been concerned with the matter. A few years ago a special committee of the Senate made a massive study of water resources with heavy emphasis on quality. Over the last couple of years almost every newspaper and magazine has carried feature articles stressing water quality problems. Many of these accounts, in their search for spectacular material, have emphasized striking, but comparatively easy to solve, problems instead of building an understanding of the more subtle but often also more challenging problems. Still, they offer the strongest evidence of the immense public concern with water quality values.

Major legal and administrative developments have reflected this concern. A succession of stronger national laws dealing with federal participation in pollution control have been passed in recent years. We have seen within the year a new federal law which greatly expands federal authority in the field. In addition to setting stream quality standards if the states don't set their own within a two-year time limit, the complex of federal legislation now provides for inclusion of water quality control storage in federal reservoirs, making of comprehensive water quality control plans by the Federal Water Pollution Control Authority, subsidies to municipalities for construction of waste treatment plants, and extensive enforcement powers against individual polluters. Recommendations contained in President Johnson's natural resources message of February 23 and in the resulting Clean Rivers Restoration Act of 1966, introduced in the Congress on February 28, would strengthen the trend of federal initiative. Special recognition is given to the opportunities for effective and efficient action on a regional basis. Demonstration projects in entire river basins are proposed. These would, at first, be financially assisted by the federal government, but they are meant to help establish technically and financially viable regional or river basin agencies. Clearly we will see much further attention being given to the systems approach to water quality control in entire water sheds. This trend will be strongly reinforced by certain state and interstate activities. For example, the state of Texas, through its Water Pollution Control Board, has shown great interest in taking a regional systems approach to the waste disposal problems in several areas, perhaps most notably in the Houston-Galveston Bay complex. Elsewhere, the creation of the Delaware River Basin Compact Commission through interstate compact is a landmark in institutional development in regard to regional water management. These various developments place great emphasis on the importance of research which permits us to understand the biology and chemistry of entire stream systems and how particular water quality control devices will fit into larger control systems. They also stress the need for improved economic and systems analysis, which will let us search more effectively for levels and techniques of control that will permit us to obtain the maximum benefit from our water courses.

---

*Opinions expressed are those of the author and not necessarily those of his organization.

The recent rush of rather spectacular activity, however, can easily obscure the fact that pollution control efforts which have been underway for some time at a state and interstate level have already borne considerable fruit. Despite the pronouncement of the more lurid popular articles, over the last decade the conditions on many heavily used streams have improved markedly. In the Eastern United States this achievement has been somewhat overshadowed by the extraordinarily low flow of rivers over the past few years. Nevertheless, in the Delaware, the Ohio, and the Potomac, for example, many highly offensive materials that once floated down these rivers are now removed from effluents before they enter the stream. This improvement is no doubt in some measure a result of the activities of interstate pollution control bodies on the streams. For instance, INCODEL, which is the predecessor of the Delaware River Basin Compact, wrote an impressive record of getting basic treatment facilities built by most municipalities and many industries. The record of ORSANCO, the Ohio River Sanitation Commission, was even more impressive. When ORSANCO was formed in 1948, less than 1 percent of the sewered population in the basin had any form of treatment. Currently, over 90 percent are treating their wastes, mostly by mechanical means which remove at least the grosser material. It should also be realized that virtually all of this was accomplished before federal subsidies were available to municipalities. Many individual states and municipalities elsewhere also made great progress, especially in the matter of keeping the raw sewage solids, oil, blood, hair, animal carcasses, and other highly offensive solids so beloved to the newspaper storywriters, out of their streams. It is my impression that Texas has gone quite far in this direction.

Nevertheless, serious problems of water quality still confront the nation. They are of various kinds. In some places raw sewage still enters streams—but this will be comparatively easy to eliminate. More difficult are the residuals which remain after primary or secondary treatment. More difficult still are industrial wastes which often enter water courses with little or no treatment and which are technically difficult and economically costly to control. In the final analysis, the most difficult of all may turn out to be the pollutants which are contained in the runoff from our watersheds. The solution of these problems will lie in part in the fields of biological, physical, and engineering sciences—the fields which are in the main focus of the present series of lectures. But their solution will also require the very best efforts of lawyers, public administrators, economists, and systems analysts as well.

Presently, pollution control programs place almost their entire emphasis on conventional treatment (by techniques fifty years old) at individual points of outfall. In a few instances a certain amount of flow regulation for multipurpose federal reservoirs has also been provided. There is reason to believe that as urban and industrial growth demands ever higher levels of pollution abatement, much more economically efficient modes of attack could be devised, especially in our more densely developed watersheds. One important possibility grows out of the fact that all available evidence shows that waste treatment plants exhibit substantial economies of scale, that is, as the amount of waste treated increases, the unit cost falls.

Another widely noted fact is that industrial wastes which present difficult treatment problems by themselves can often be much more effectively treated in combination with municipal or other types of industrial wastes. These factors suggest that the systematic search for the best ways to combine wastes and conduct them to large central treatment plants could yield major economies.

Combining waste treatment into fewer and larger plants opens up an additional possibility: to design and operate such plants to make better use of the naturally occurring assimilative capacity of the rivers, while maintaining desired stream quality standards. For example, it might be possible to design such plants so that they are able to tailor their treatment effect to the actual needs of the stream. As is well known, the assimilative capacity of waters varies greatly with hydrologic and climatic conditions. One might design plants which could operate with high treatment effect (perhaps by means of chemical application) during really critical periods, and could operate at considerably lower cost at times when the full effect is not needed. Because small isolated plants are often operated very ineptly and because there ordinarily is not a central authority to monitor the stream quality and to program the levels of treatment needed, this alternative cannot be viewed as realistic in the present institutional context. Clearly, however, the Clean Rivers Restoration Act contemplates regional or river basin agencies which could systematically search for and implement the most efficient means of control. These agencies could realize scale economies in treatment plant construction and operation, and achieve economies from combining municipal and industrial wastes. This is a most constructive new orientation in federal policy.

Further elements in a regional systems approach to water quality management may be mentioned. Using reservoir capacity to augment low flows is a well-recognized technique. If it is to be effectively and efficiently utilized, however, it must be closely coordinated in design and operation with all the other elements that might enter into a regional systems approach. Other regional-scale measures to improve river quality have been implemented abroad. These involve treatment of entire streams in one fashion or another, as in the case of the Ruhr and Emscher Rivers. If a suitable regional agency exists to manage the matter it may even prove desirable to have a certain amount of stream specialization, in which certain streams are kept at very high quality for recreational and water supply purposes while others have their assimilative capacity used to a greater extent. It is possible that such an approach would provide greater utility to the residents and industries of the area than could be obtained from an equivalent expenditure which left all streams in a mediocre condition. But stream specialization implies planned control, not haphazard and capricious circumstance.

In our more densely developed areas, especially, it would be desirable to move toward the establishment of regional agencies with broad powers to design, construct, operate, and finance regional systems of waste disposal. Such regional systems would be the result of a full and flexible identification and evaluation of all applicable techniques and their coordinate implementation and operation. Federal policy appears to be turning in this direction. While this development is most constructive, it does pose a massive challenge to those interested in systems analysis, economics, and institutions. They must improve their ability to design and operate such regional systems and to create institutions capable of implementing them, but which at the same time are consistent with our political heritage. Moreover, it means that those who are working on particular treatment processes and the improvement of technology in regard to waste management must begin to orient their work toward the place of particular types of facilities and processes in a larger systems context. The question may no longer be so much, "Is this or that facility best?" But rather, "How can this or that facility be devised to yield its maximum comparative advantage in view of the whole quality management system?"

Decisions concerning appropriate water quality standards for water courses cannot rationally be made on the basis of the techniques available for control alone—however sophisticated and well articulated they may be. The benefits associated with improved water quality must be defined in a quantitative way. For it is only by considering gains as well as costs associated with pollution control that one can find a proper balance in the use of the water resource and realize maximum net value from it. It is clear that one of the most useful attributes of the resource is its ability to receive, assimilate, and transport wastes. Scientists can ill afford not to use this resource to some extent. Although research has shown that any desired degree of reduction of impurities in municipal and industrial waste streams can be achieved, costs rise very rapidly when 100 percent removal is approached. For example, municipal waste treatment costs about double when removal from municipal effluent increases from about 90 percent to 96 or 97 percent. Costs about triple again if one wished to go from 97 percent to about 100 percent. The cost increase appears to involve an exponential function. While per capita real costs of municipal sanitation probably have not risen much if at all over the past seventy-five years, even though standards of treatment have gradually improved (from an unpublished table prepared by Harold Thomas, Harvard University), they could increase sharply should municipalities try to move rapidly toward highly purified effluents—or to put it differently, should they seek to abandon any dependence on the waste assimilative capacity of the surface waters. Doing this might add something like twenty billion dollars a year to national costs for disposing of wastes. This is on the order of what is spent for primary and secondary education combined. Thus, use of the assimilative capacity of water courses is of extremely high value. Deciding how much to use them must therefore depend on both the costs of waste management and the benefits which arise from water quality improvement. Another way of putting this is that loss functions must be defined showing the relationship between deteriorating water quality and damages that occur. The water quality research program at RFF has made some progress toward defining such functions. While results are still tentative and the studies have been spotty, some rough conclusions can be drawn.

Several industry studies are underway that, among other things, seek to assess the damage which industries suffer when they have to use low-quality water, or to put it another way, the benefits that would accrue to them if water quality improved. Since a variety of adjustments to differing water quality are possible, the problem becomes complex. Some results, however, are available for the pulp and paper, petroleum refining, canning, thermal power, and sugar beet industries. In all these instances, industrial costs turned out to be surprisingly insensitive to water quality within comparatively wide ranges—especially in regard to aspects of quality that are usually influenced by prior uses and discharge of effluents. Sensitivity is greater to pollutants, which in most cases are of natural origin, such as chloride and magnesium. One important reason for the comparative insensitivity is that the vast proportion of industrial water use is for purposes that can readily accommodate low quality—cooling, for instance. A second reason is that the really sensitive processes—high-pressure boilers, for example—ordinarily need water of such quality that extensive treatment is necessary if any kind of river water is used; water of distinctly low quality can be used with only minor incremental costs. High-pressure boiler feed water must be distilled and the cost of distillation is not particularly sensitive to the quality of the intake water. The moral of this is that not much pollution control can be justified by benefits to industrial users. Or, to put it another way, the value of improved water quality for industrial purposes often will not match the costs of achieving high levels of water quality.

The situation appears to be surprisingly similar for municipal water supplies. Much of what has been said about the need for high-quality water supplies as a basis for preparation of potable water is more the product of emotion than of logic. Water of the much-discussed Hudson River, which allegedly should not be used for municipal supply because of its poor quality, is actually not worse than that at the Toresdale intake of the city of Philadelphia. This water has, for many years, using the very well-understood technology, been prepared for acceptable drinking water—albeit at the expense of some extra chemical applications. Furthermore, a water treatment plant at Düsseldorf, Germany, using activated carbon and ozone, makes aesthetically pleasing drinking water from the Rhine, which is in far worse shape than either the Delaware or the Hudson. Poor water quality does impose extra costs for municipal water treatment but, except in cases of extremely toxic or evil-tasting substances, it ordinarily cannot justify very high levels of waste effluent treatment.

This point is brought out in a recent study of a synthetic stream system along the shores of which are municipal waste dischargers and municipal water users. This study involved a very careful gathering of cost data and even the generation of new cost information. It also developed a sophisticated technique for tracing by means of computer simulation the interrelationship between water quality at waste outfalls and at water intakes. The study found that vast amounts of re-use are required to justify the additional costs of advanced sewage treatment for municipal waste disposal (1). For example, it turned out that water withdrawal for municipal water treatment downstream required to justify additional upstream sewage treatment costs solely on savings to downstream water treatment plants was on the order of 16-250:1 for small sewage treatment plants, and 10-30:1 for large sewage treatment plants. Again, it appears that the need to prepare drinking water cannot justify particularly high standards of stream water quality. In another study, that of the Delaware Estuary by the Public Health Service, a similar result emerged. Costs of water quality improvement are very high in this area, which now suffers from highly degraded water. Quantifiable benefits to municipal and industrial users appear to be comparatively small and far less than would be needed to justify high levels of water quality control (2).

It must be remembered, however, that persons place value on water not only for withdrawal purposes but also for use within the rivers themselves. Indeed, it appears that the major justification for high quality stream water is found in the aesthetic and recreational values—if indeed such a justification exists.

Of course, clear evidence exists of a relationship between water quality and human satisfactions. It does not seem so much to arise from a feeling that health is really endangered to any great extent or that the cost of manufactured goods has been substantially increased because manufacturers have had to provide costly treatment to the water they use. Rather, it is seen in the reactions of fishermen who have experienced aesthetically displeasing water (perhaps with dead fish in it) and of persons who just prefer to see a clear stream and might even be willing to put up with something else (higher local taxes or higher prices for manufactured goods) to get it. Politicians have been sensitive to these feelings which have permitted if not induced the progressively stronger federal legislation and federal initiative in recent years. But politically expressed discontent is a highly generalized phenomenon. It cannot tell whether action is justified in a particular instance and, if so, how much. From it cannot be infered what standard for a water body will balance costs and gains in a particular instance. Clearly it depends on circumstances. How much, then, does it cost to improve quality? What present and future uses does the water have? What alternatives are there? Economic analysis can go some distance in helping to answer all these questions, but certainly further work is needed, and most urgently in regard to the value that people attach to water in the stream itself.

While research results are scanty in this area, there is evidence that in certain instances persons may attach a high value to water quality for recreation purposes, and decisions concerning water quality must often, if not usually, turn on this kind of value. A useful study of the recreational value of water quality is underway in the Delaware Estuary, on whose shores is perhaps the greatest urban industrial complex in the United States. To raise the presently low dissolved oxygen in the Estuary is a very expensive matter. An investment of $80,000,000 or more might be required to raise it to two parts per million and $300,000,000 or more to lift it to four parts per million. Imposing as these costs are, an econometric study of potential increases in recreation participation rates in the Estuary area shows that these higher oxygen levels might be justified on recreational grounds alone. Preliminary results suggest that placing a value on increased boating of about $2.50 a day might justify maintaining three parts per million of dissolved oxygen, even if no other benefits were considered (3). At today's levels of discretionary income, $2.50 does not seem to be an extravagant value to attach to a day of boating. More and better studies of this kind are badly needed if our water quality objectives are to have any rational basis.

CONCLUSIONS

1. Much progress has been made in pollution control, but difficult problems remain—among them the problem of residual substances in municipal waste and the control of industrial waste.

2. The main hope for dealing effectively and efficiently with these problems, at least in our more highly developed areas, is through a regional systems approach. This approach has been given strong emphasis in the President's resources message and in the Clean Rivers Restoration Act.

3. Realizing the maximum net value from water courses requires consideration of both the costs and the gains of quality improvement. What little research exists on gains or benefits suggests that high-quality water usually must be justified on the basis of instream values if it is justified at all. An urgent need exists for learning how to better assess these values.

4. If scientific and engineering developments are to be applied in a systematic and rational manner, the ability to understand their economic and institutional implications must be improved. Institutions must be designed that are consistent with the country's democratic heritage but capable of obtaining and using information on technology and values in the implementation of optimal water quality management programs.

REFERENCES

(1) Frankel, Richard. "Water Quality Management: Engineering Economic Factors in Municipal Waste Disposal," *Water Resources Res.*, *1*, 2, 2 (1965).

(2) *Delaware Estuary Comprehensive Study—Report on Alternative Water Quality Improvement Programs*. Washington, D.C.: Department of Health, Education and Welfare, Federal Water Pollution Control Administration (February 1966).

(3) Davidson, Paul, F. Gerrard Adams, and Joseph Seneca. "The Social Value of Water Recreational Facilities Resulting from Improvement in Water Quality in an Estuary," *Water Research: Resources for the Future*. Baltimore: Johns Hopkins Press (1966).

ECOLOGICAL CHANGES IN A POLLUTED ENVIRONMENT

John H. Austin and R. S. Engelbrecht
University of Illinois, Urbana, Illinois

INTRODUCTION

The biological literature is replete with reports of studies of the aquatic environment and its inhabitants. In addition, many of the physical and chemical factors have been investigated. More recently, an interest has developed in the interrelationship of many of these factors.

With respect to waters receiving pollution, the effect of dispersion on the rate of degradation of organic wastes, the effect of velocity on reaeration, the effect of benthic activity on the oxygen resources, and the effect of suspended solids on the aquatic flora and fauna, are but a few of the relationships that are being studied. Other relationships could be added to this list, depending on the investigator's particular interests. As essential and as enlightening as these varied studies may be, however, it is nevertheless judicious to step back and evaluate the overall problem. That is, how might the information available today be used to predict the effect of a waste on a given stream? If the knowledge available today is not adequate, what additional information is needed?

One way to accomplish this evaluation is for the researcher to withdraw from his position as an economist, a biologist, a chemist, or an engineer and collectively evaluate the efforts of his fellow investigators and his own work. Just as Ecology is the study of the interrelationships of organisms with one another and with the environment (Fig. 1), so also is the study of the ecological changes in a polluted aquatic environment an experiment in the interrelationships of the scientific disciplines that can contribute knowledge to the problem.

Figure 1 represents one possible pyramid of the nutritional groups and the trophic levels in an ecologic community. A similar pyramid could be constructed using the various disciplines represented in water resources, such as sanitary engineering, chemistry, limnology, toxicology, physics, microbiology, virology, hydrology, and economics.

It is possible in this paper to review only a few of the ecological investigations which have been reported and, by means of these, to point out the need for more comprehensive research and the evaluation of this information in terms of existing and future pollution problems.

ECOLOGICAL FACTORS

The innumerable factors that might be considered in an ecological investigation of the aquatic environment can quite conveniently be divided into three major categories: physical, chemical, and biological.

The physical factor that often has the most dramatic effect on stream ecology is velocity. A well-established benthic community can be entirely removed during periods of high velocity. Generally accompanying high velocity is high flow. These high flows often arise from excessive runoff, which brings additional pollution to the water course. A major pollutant is suspended solids, either of natural or man-made origin, which not only reduce light transmittance for the

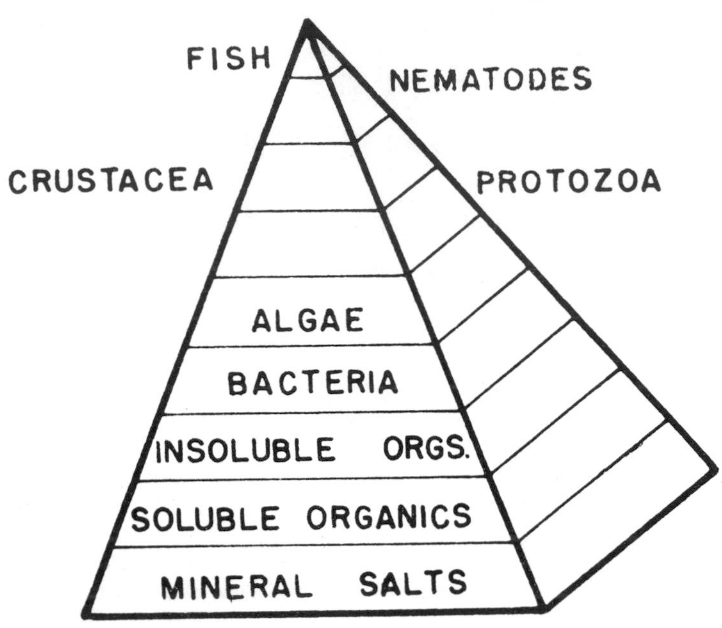

Figure 1. Nutritional groups and trophic levels in an ecologic community.

aquatic flora, but also may submerge the benthos with such a blanket of solids that the entire population is obliterated. Another major man-made physical factor is temperature pollution from industrial operations.

The chemical factors perhaps have been investiagted to the greatest extent. The effects of dissolved oxygen, ionic composition, toxic compounds, and trace elements have been studied for many types and communities of organisms. The addition of a chemical to a water course may be a pollutant per se, in that it may impair the quality of the water for some future, legitimate use. On the other hand, it may exert its effect through the metabolic activity of the organisms of the ecological community. The stability or toxicity of a chemical, or its rate of biological degradation is of utmost importance in determining the immediate and the long-term effects on the ecological community.

LONG-TERM ECOLOGICAL CHANGES

In the archives of the Natural History Survey at Urbana, Illinois, it is possible to review the changes that have taken place in one of Illinois' historic natural assets, the Illinois River. Stephen A. Forbes began his studies of this river in 1877. In 1894 he was instrumental in having the University of Illinois and the Illinois Natural History Survey establish an experimental station on the river (1). Stephen Forbes was a man of vision and knew the importance of evaluating every facet of the problem, that is, the interrelationships of the organisms and their environment. Forbes (2) deplored the condition of the Illinois River in a later comprehensive report.

In early 1900 the city of Chicago began to use the Illinois River as a convenience for the discharge of its municipal wastes. By 1913 the river was showing definite impairment of its natural beauty. In this report, Forbes stated:

> These are temporary conditions, however, and the time seems now at hand when the people of Illinois will learn to appreciate and develop this great gift of nature in the various directions in which it may be made to serve their interests and their pleasures. Its frequently beautiful and occasionally picturesque scenery is attracting more attention every year; and when, as is sure to happen in due time, a superior highway follows its course between Chicago and St. Louis; when the attractive building sites on its banks are relieved, as they now might generally be, from the midsummer plague of mosquitoes; when its most interesting situations are converted into public parks, and its fisheries are protected and enriched by means of state reservations for the breeding and feeding of fishes; and when, as must eventually come to pass, it becomes once more an indispensable central link in a principal line of traffic between the Great Lakes and the Gulf,—it will take for all time, for the state at large, the place which Lake Michigan now holds for our greatest city.

These same thoughts have been expressed by others, about other streams. In most cases, their visions have not materialized. In the above-mentioned reports by Forbes and in later publications (3), the ecologic changes of the stream are described.

Forbes (1) noted that the Illinois River contained 128 of the 150 species of fish known to be present in the state. Of commercial value were 36 species, and 6 of the species were among the best freshwater fishes in the country. He also noted the beneficial effect of Chicago's waste as food for the fish. The annual yield from the Illinois River in 1910 was over 24,000,000 pounds of marketable fish. This decreased to about 1,000,000 pounds by 1964. Figure 2 shows the trend for a 70-year period. A recent United States Public Health Service report on the

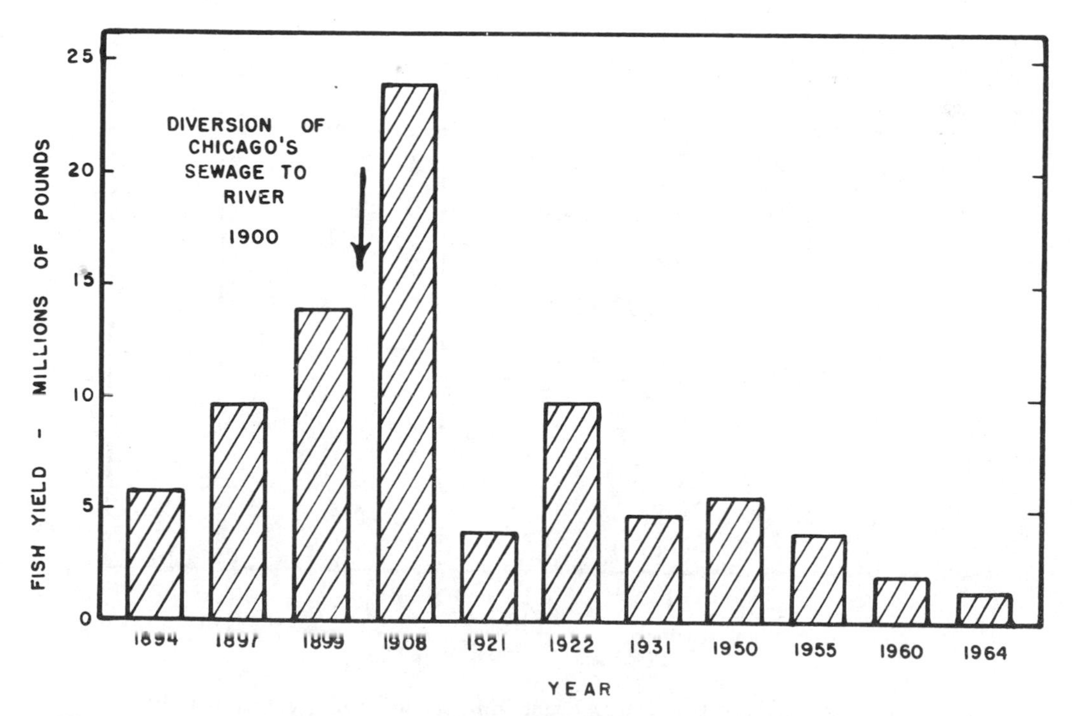

Figure 2. Commercial fish yields from Illinois River, 1894–1964. After Starrett (5).

Illinois River (4) and a report from the Illinois Natural History Survey (5) discuss the present degraded condition of the river. Although the Public Health Service report is concerned with the biological aspects of pollution, only brief mention is made of the fish population in the Illinois River. The upper reaches of the river were so polluted that it was difficult to find fish.

FLOW FACTORS

Velocity of flow and stage in the stream are important parameters not only because of their effect on the mixing and concentration of pollutants in the stream, but also because of their influence on the response of organisms to the pollutant. Chaudhuri *et al.* (6) reported that the nematode concentration in a rural stream showed marked variations with flow conditions (Fig. 3). The 20-mile section studied contained no known source of nematodes other than surface and subsurface rural runoff. The studies revealed that flows less than 100 cfs were maintained by seepage flow. Flows above 100 cfs resulted from overland runoff. The low numbers of nematodes in the stream at flows less than 100 cfs were interpreted to be due to the relatively inefficient manner in which seepage water can carry nematodes to the stream. In addition, the low velocities in the stream allowed nematodes to settle to the stream bottom. With flows between 100 and 1000 cfs the overland runoff was quite efficient in scouring nematodes

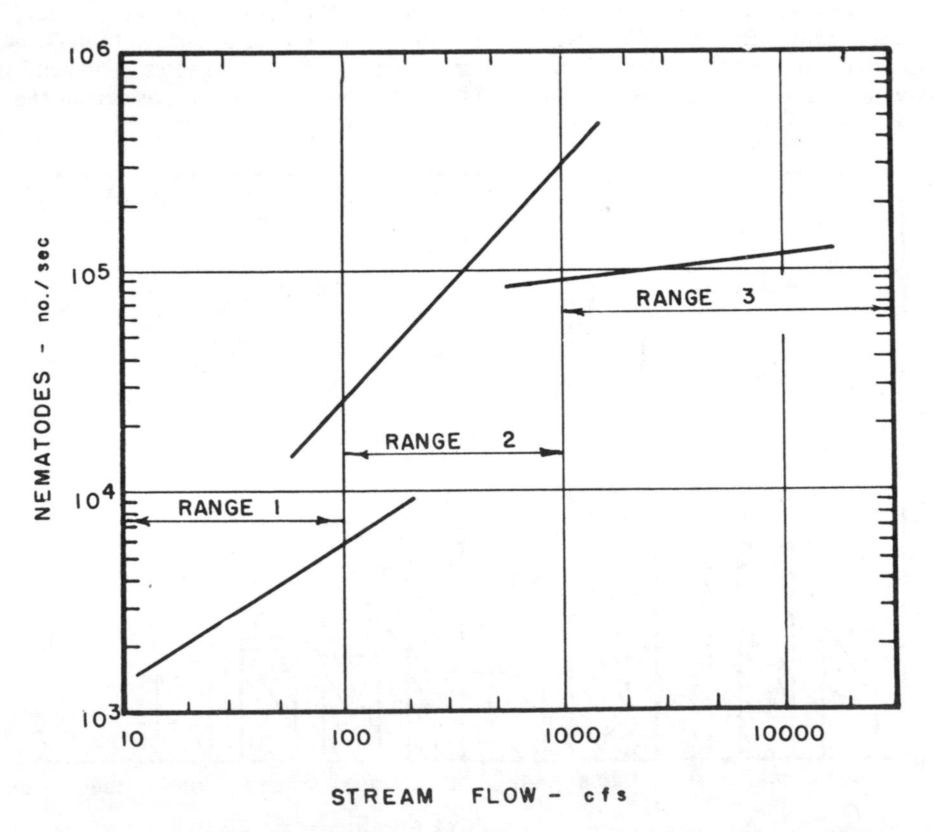

Figure 3. Variation in nematode count with stream flow in Sangmon River. After Chaudhuri (6).

from the surface layers of soil. In addition, relatively high velocities were maintained, keeping the nematodes in suspension. At flows greater than 1000 cfs the river overflowed into its flood plane. This increased depth of flow not only reduced the effectiveness of scour but also reduced the velocity so that the nematodes would again settle to the benthos. Also, by this time, many of the nematodes in the surface layer of soil had been scoured away.

Chaudhuri *et al.* (6, 7) and Baliga (8) have noted that municipal wastewater treatment plants are the principle source of nematodes in surface waters. Baliga (8) has shown that there is little relation between the nematode concentration in the overlying water and that in the benthos. Rather, in any one cross section the benthic concentration depended on the velocity across the section. The highest benthic concentrations were found in the sluggish water areas and the lowest concentrations in the channel. Flood flows accompanied by high velocities scoured out appreciable quantities of the benthic community. Subsequent periods of low flow allowed a build-up of organisms.

Jaag and Ambuhl (9) have recently reviewed the subject of the effect of flowing water on the ecological make-up of a stream community. Any observer of a polluted water course may note the luxuriant growth of *Sphaerotilus natans* in flowing water. However, this organism is not found as a rule in standing or pooled water. This difference in the ecologic communities of flowing streams has achieved a practical significance among the fishermen of Central Europe. Jaag and Ambuhl (9) state it as follows: "Within any given biogeographical region, flowing streams that have the same width and depth as well as similar gradients possess analogous biological properties especially as regards fishing." Although this rule was postulated for fish, Jaag and Ambuhl feel that it can be applied to the entire aquatic community. Of course, temperature is the dominant factor in determining the inhabitants of the aquatic community, that is, tropical versus temperate conditions. The oxygen content is also significant in an aerobic system. Jaag and Ambuhl, however, substantiated the investigations of earlier workers that the oxygen content per se is not always the critical parameter. The respiratory rate of some organisms is determined in part by the rate at which oxygen is supplied to the organism. Thus, cognizance must be taken of not only the oxygen content of the water, but also the rate at which the water passes the organism. An aquatic organism could have the same oxygen resources available in a slow-moving water with a high dissolved oxygen content as in a fast-moving water with a low dissolved oxygen content.

Some organisms thrive in fast-moving streams and tend to increase in numbers as the velocity increases. The May fly (*Baetis vernus*), black fly (*Simulium* sp.), and caddis fly (*Hydropsyche angustipennis*) represent organisms in this category. Others proliferate over a wide range of flows, but their numbers decrease at both low and high flows. This phenomenon is represented by the scud (*Gammarus pulex*) and the two different May fly larvae (*Ephemerella ignita* and *Habroleptoides* sp.) in the lower part of Figure 4. Still others flourish over only a narrow range of flows, as indicated by the two caddis fly larvae (*Rhyacophila dorsalis* and *Hydropsyche fulvipes*) in Figure 5.

The oxygen consumption of certain freshwater organisms varies with water velocity. The upper curve of Figure 6 represents an organism, for example, a caddis fly (*Rhyacophila*), whose morphological features are such that it cannot maintain a maximum supply of oxygen under low velocity conditions. In other words, it relies on the mechanical action of the flowing water to bring the oxygen to it. On the other hand, the lower curve represents an organism, for example, another caddis fly (*Hydropsyche*), which has the required morphological features to move the necessary quantity of water past itself to meet its oxygen requirements.

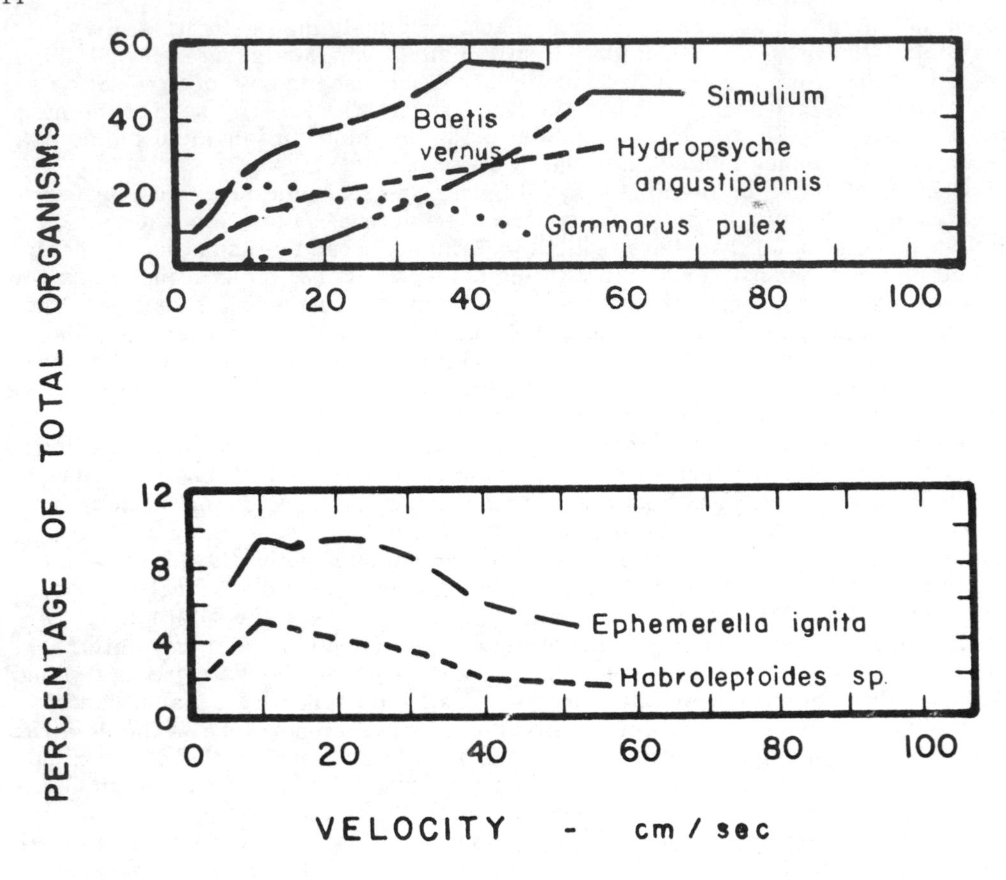

Figure 4. Effect of current on the occurrence of certain animals in an aquatic environment. After Jaag and Ambuhl (9).

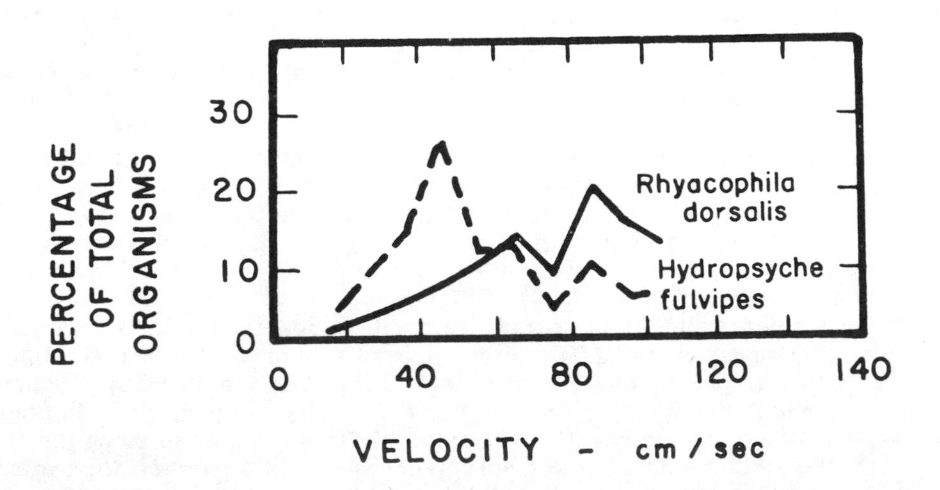

Figure 5. Effect of current on the distribution of two Trichoptera larvae (caddis fly). After Jaag and Ambuhl (9).

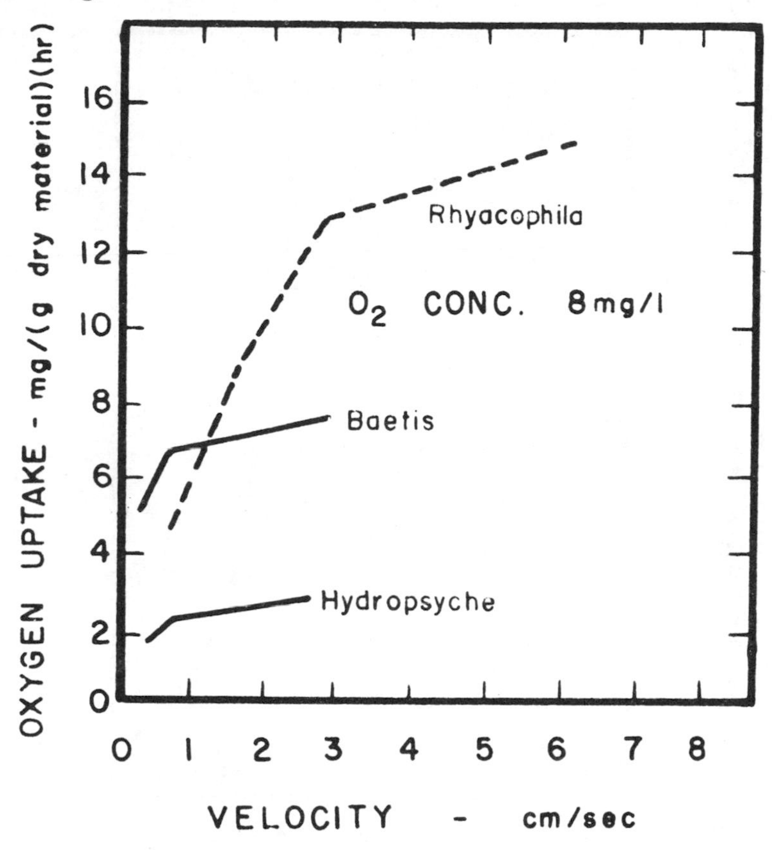

Figure 6. Effect of velocity on the oxygen consumption of certain animals. After Jaag and Ambuhl (9).

These interesting results of Jaag and Ambuhl indicate the desirability of considering not only the temperature, oxygen tension, and velocity of a stream, but also their interrelationships. Only in this way can the investigator begin to understand the complex phenomenon occurring in the aquatic community.

PERSISTENCE OF BACTERIA

The persistence of bacteria in streams receiving waste-water effluents has been of considerable interest to many users of the aquatic environment. The sanitary engineer has used this information to estimate the purification capacity of streams, and to determine the location of water intakes, the degree of treatment required for municipal water supplies, or the suitability of a reach of stream for recreational purposes. The early work by the USPHS in Cincinnati (10) indicated that there could be a considerable increase in number of bacteria in the stream immediately below the discharge to a stream. Some workers recommended chlorination in order to reduce the numbers of bacteria. Rudolfs and Gehm (11), however, showed that even this practice would not assure a low bacterial content in the stream (Fig. 7). They attributed the increase in bacterial numbers with chlorination to the removal of the fauna which feed on the bacteria.

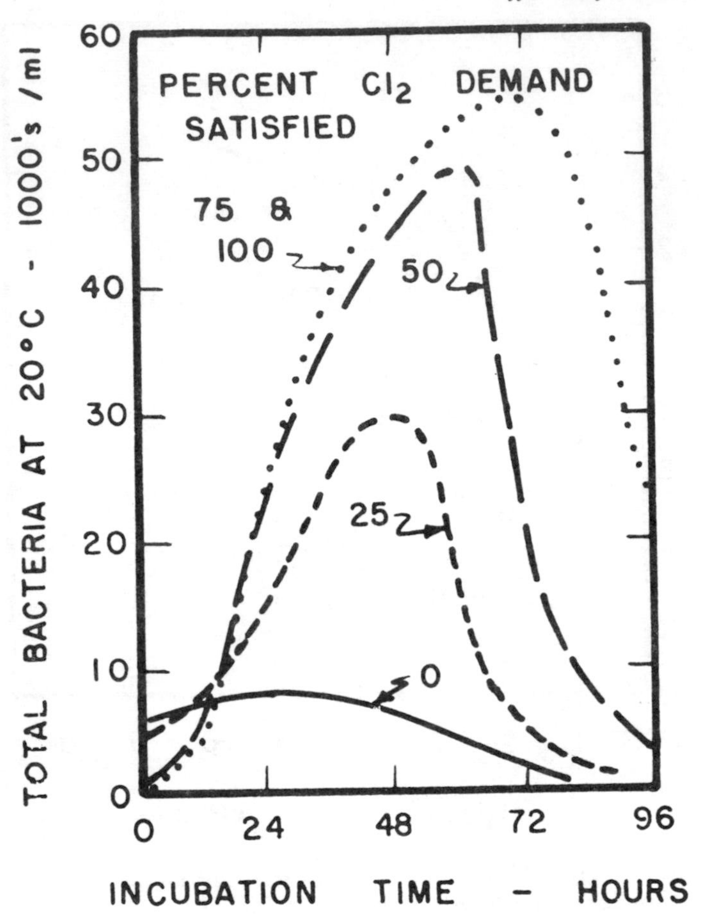

Figure 7. Growth of bacteria after partial and complete chlorination of sewage. After Rudolfs and Gehm (11).

For example, the protozoa that feed on the bacteria are more sensitive to chlorine. Also, they are present in much smaller numbers and multiply more slowly. Thus, their lag period before rapid reproduction is longer than that of the bacteria and during this period of slow recovery bacteria increase at a rapid rate. Allen and Brooks (12) have substantiated these findings, as has Heukelekian (13).

The above data indicate the problem of using various indicator organisms as a measure of the pathogens present in the stream. Limited information is available on the extent of survival of pathogenic organisms in the aquatic environment. Kabler *et al.* (14) indicated that members of the genus *Salmonella* survive for varying lengths of time in nature, depending on the composition of the ecologic community and the environmental conditions. In general, there was an inverse correlation: the greater the pollution, the shorter the survival time.

McCoy (15) has reported on the occurrence and persistence of Salmonellae in a stream receiving wastewater after various types of treatment. The flow regime in the stream varied in a similar manner each year over the 6-year study period. The sources of Salmonellae showed no evidence of change over this period. Thus, the findings (Table I) were interpreted in light of the three types

TABLE 1

SEASONAL ISOLATION OF SALMONELLAE FROM THE RIVER HULL[a]

Treatment Received and Period	Sampling Point	Percentage of Samples Positive
Sedimentation	Outfall	12.8
April 1954	2 mi. below	—
to	4 mi. below	3.8
March 1956	6 mi. below	5.6
None	Outfall	51.4
April 1956	2 mi. below	24.2
to	4 mi. below	8.7
March 1958	6 mi. below	3.9
Complete treatment[b]	Outfall	74.7
April 1958	2 mi. below	8.7
to	4 mi. below	0.9
March 1960	6 mi. below	1.9

[a]After McCoy (15).
[b]Treatment consisted of coarse screens, grit chambers, sedimentation, trickling filters, and sludge digestion.

of treatment that were used during the period of investigation. McCoy attributed the greater percentage of positive samples in the treated effluent to the fact that the organisms were present in suspension and each organism could produce one positive sample, whereas in raw sewage many organisms could be in or on a solid particle and yet produce only one positive sample. Because the organisms were in suspension in the treated effluent, they were removed readily by the various mechanisms of natural purification. The organisms bound in sewage particles, however, would not be readily attacked by these natural purification forces.

The occurrence and persistence of bacteria in streams has been used extensively in the past as an indication of the quality of the water. Kittrell and Furfari (16) have recently reviewed the fate of coliforms in streams and stressed the need for further study in this area. The data available today indicate, however, that much needs to be done to delineate the ecological relationships in the aquatic community.

BACTERIOPHAGE AND VIRUS

The viruses constitute one biological group found in the aquatic ecological community that should receive more attention. Limited information is available on these organisms because of difficulty in isolation and identification. However, recent work by Gilcreas and Kelly (17), Ware and Mellon (18), and Carstens (19) indicates that the use of bacteriophage may be a useful tool in ecological studies. Gilcreas and Kelly noted that *Bacterium coli B* bacteriophage survived longer under a variety of environmental conditions than did *B. coli*. Thus, the use of phage as an indicator of biological pollution might be more desirable than the present coliform organism. It is very likely that the environmental conditions that reduce the numbers of phage particles also reduce the numbers of pathogenic viruses such as polio and hepatitis. The false sense of security of using coliform data as a measure of the quality of water has been indicated by the recent outbreak of infectious hepatitis at New Delhi, India (20), and of salmonellosis at Riverside, California (21).

The persistence of virus in the environment appears to be a function of the water quality. Clarke *et al.* (22) have shown a significant correlation between Coxsackie virus survival times in natural waters and the extent of the pollution of the water. Organic polluting material appeared to offer some protection to viruses and thus prolong their survival. However, other factors were important in determining the survival time. Distilled water or autoclaved river waters yielded quite long survival times (Table 2), as did the addition of organic pollution to a river water. Natural waters with limited pollution yielded the shortest survival times. Virus inactivation appeared to be in some way related to the normal microbiological content of a natural water. Alteration of this natural flora by autoclaving, distillation, or addition of pollution tended to increase the survival of the virus.

TABLE 2

TIME NECESSARY TO REDUCE 1,000 LD_{50} OF COXSACKIE VIRUS TO 1 LD_{50}[a,b]

Sample	Temperature °C.	Relative Pollution	Time Days
Sewage	8	Totally	Approximately 50
Sewage	20	Totally	Less than 20
Distilled water	8	None	More than 272
Distilled water	20	None	41–135
Ohio River	8	Moderate	12–16
Autoclaved Ohio River	8	—	150–171
Ohio River	20	Moderate	Approximately 6
Autoclaved Ohio River	20	—	Approximately 102
Little Miami River	20	Little	Less than 4
Ohio River	20	Moderate	Approximately 4
Licking River	20	Considerable	4–16
Mill Creek	20	Gross	Approximately 47

[a]After Clarke *et al.* (22).

[b]One LD_{50} is the amount of virus lethal to 50 percent of the inoculated mice. The material titering 1,000 LD_{50}, therefore, could be diluted 1,000 times and still have the effect. The authors used Group A, Type 2, Coxsackie virus, in the form of a 20-percent tissue suspension. The stock suspension was added to each water or sewage sample to give an initial titer of 1,000 LD_{50} per 0.02 ml.

Table 3 shows additional information on the limitations of the coliform test as an indication of the quality of the water. Both virus and bacteria have longer survival times as the temperature decreases. The survival time of the virus was in most instances less in the moderately polluted Ohio River than in sewage or in the relatively clean Little Miami River. On the other hand, bacterial survival times were directly related to the degree of pollution. In both the Little Miami and sewage, the viruses tended to persist longer, while the bacteria survived longer in the Ohio River and sewage than in the Little Miami. Thus, generalizations of survival times regarding these two groups of organisms are difficult to make.

SUMMARY

The individual efforts of chemists, biologists, engineers, and others have been presented to indicate the desirability of correlating their efforts in order to

TABLE 3

AVERAGE TIME IN DAYS FOR 99.9 PERCENT REDUCTION IN ORIGINAL TITER OF INDICATED MICROORGANISMS AT THREE TEMPERATURES[a,b]

Microorganism	Little Miami River			Ohio River			Sewage		
	28° C.	20° C.	4° C.	28° C.	20° C.	4° C.	28° C.	20° C.	4° C.
Poliovirus	17	20	27	11	13	19	17	23	110
ECHO 7	12	16	26	5	7	15	28	41	130
ECHO 12	5	12	33	3	5	19	20	32	60
Coxsackie A9	8	8	10	5	8	20	6	—	12
A. aerogenes	6	8	15	15	18	44	10	21	56
E. coli	6	7	10	5	5	11	12	20	48
S. fecalis	6	8	17	9	18	57	14	26	48

[a]After Clarke *et al.* (23).
[b]Average coliform content of three waters before addition of the indicated microorganism:

Little Miami River	54/ml
Ohio River	197/ml
Sewage	208,000/ml

understand the ecological changes in a polluted environment. A biochemical process such as oxygen utilization may be controlled in part by a physical process such as the velocity of the stream in which the organism lives. The coliform titer of a stream may be greater in a stream receiving a chlorinated wastewater effluent than in a stream receiving a comparable, but unchlorinated effluent. The accepted bacteriological indicators of pollution may give a false impression of the viral content of the water. Only by detailed analysis of many facets of the entire ecological picture are some of the complicated problems of the polluted environment going to be solved.

REFERENCES

(1) Forbes, S. A. *Biological Investigations on the Illinois River.* Urbana: Illinois State Laboratory of Natural History (1910).

(2) Forbes, S. A., and R. E. Richardson. "Studies on the Biology of the Upper Illinois River," *Bul. Illinois Nat. Hist. Surv.*, *9*, 481 (June 1913).

(3) Forbes, S. A., and R. E. Richardson. "Some Recent Changes in the Illinois River Biology," *Bul. Illinois Nat. Hist. Surv.*, *13*, 139 (April 1919).

(4) Keup, L. E., W. M. Ingram, J. Geckler, and W. B. Horning. *Biology of Chicago's Waterways.* Public Health Service Publication No. 999-WP-32 (October 1965).

(5) Mills, H. B., W. C. Starrett, and F. C. Bellrose. "Man's Effect on the Fish and Wildlife of the Illinois River," Illinois Natural History Survey, *Biol. Notes No. 57* (1966).

(6) Chaudhuri, N., R. Siddiqi, and R. S. Engelbrecht. "Source and Persistence of Nematodes in Surface Waters," *J. Amer. Water Works Assoc.*, *56*, 73 (January 1964).

(7) Chaudhuri, N., R. S. Engelbrecht, and J. H. Austin. "Nematodes in an Aerobic Waste Treatment Plant," *J. Amer. Water Works Assoc.*, *57*, 1561 (December 1965).

(8) Baliga, K. Y. "Benthic Sampling, Analysis, and Ecological Studies of Nematodes," M. S. Thesis, University of Illinois (1964).

(9) Jaag, O., and H. Ambuhl. "The Effect of the Current on the Composition of Biocoenoses in Flowing Water Streams," *Adv. Water Poll. Res.*, *1*, 31 (1964).

(10) Butterfield, C. T. "Observations on Changes in Numbers of Bacteria in Polluted Water," *Sewage Works J.*, *5*, 600 (July 1933).

(11) Rudolfs, W., and H. W. Gehm. "Multiplication of Total Bacteria and *B. coli* after Sewage Chlorination," *Sewage Works J.*, *7*, 991 (November 1935).

(12) Allen, L. A., and Eileen Brooks. "Destruction of Bacteria in Sewage and Other Liquids by Chlorine and by Cyanogen," *J. Hygiene*, *47*, 320 (March 1949).

(13) Heukelekian, H. "Disinfection of Sewage with Chlorine. IV. Aftergrowth of Coliform Organisms in Streams Receiving Chlorinated Sewage," *Sewage Ind. Wastes*, *23*, 273 (March 1951).

(14) Kabler, P. W., S. L. Chang, N. A. Clarke, and H. F. Clark. "Pathogenic Bacteria and Viruses in Water Supplies," *Proceedings*, Fifth Sanitary Engineering Conference, Quality Aspects of Water Distribution Systems, Urbana, University of Illinois Engineering Experiment Station Circular No. 81, 72 (1963).

(15) McCoy, J. G. "Salmonellae in Crude Sewage, Sewage Effluent and Sewage-Polluted Natural Waters," *Adv. Water Poll. Res.*, *1*, 205 (1964).

(16) Kittrell, F. W., and S. A. Furfari. "Observations of Coliform Bacteria in Streams," *J. Water Poll. Cont. Fed.*, *35*, 1361 (November 1963).

(17) Gilcreas, F. W., and S. M. Kelly. "Significance of the Coliform Test in Relation to Intestinal Virus Pollution of Water," *J. New England Water Works Assoc.*, *68*, 255 (1954).

(18) Ware, G. C., and M. A. Mellon. "Some Observations on the Coli/Coliphage Relationship in Sewage," *Amer. J. Hygiene*, *54*, 99 (1956).

(19) Carstens, M. J. "Bacteriophages and Their Possible Use in Sewage Purification," *J. Ins. Sewage Purif.*, *5*, 467 (1963).

(20) Dennis, J. M. "1955–1956 Infectious Hepatitis Epidemic in Delhi, India," *J. Amer. Water Works Assoc.*, *51*, 1288 (October 1959).

(21) Ross, E. C., K. W. Campbell, and J. H. Ongerth. "*Salmonellae typhimurium* Contamination of Riverside, California, Supply," *J. Amer. Water Works Assoc.*, *58*, 165 (February 1966).

(22) Clarke, N. A., R. E. Stevenson, and P. W. Kabler. "Survival of Coxsackie Virus in Water and Sewage," *J. Amer. Water Works Assoc.*, *48*, 677 (June 1956).

(23) Clarke, N. A., G. Berg, P. W. Kabler, and S. L. Chang. "Human Enteric Viruses in Water: Source, Survival and Removability," *Adv. Water Poll. Res.*, *2*, 523 (1964).

OBJECTIVES, TECHNOLOGY, AND RESULTS OF NITROGEN AND PHOSPHORUS REMOVAL PROCESSES

Karl Wuhrmann
Swiss Federal Institute of Technology, Zurich, Switzerland

OBJECTIVES OF NUTRIENT REMOVAL PROCESSES

Background of Problem

The fertilizing effect of wastes that have been treated with the best biological methods presently available is of increasing concern for water pollution control agencies and the public. There is general agreement that the chain of events, called eutrophication, usually is released by concentration increases of available nitrogen and phosphorus in the water, at least in regions of moderate climates and where cultivated or uncultivated organically rich soils are dominant in a watershed. Other nutrient elements or essential growth factors are assumed to be in sufficient supply for primary producers in these pedological situations.

From investigations by various authors the concentration range of total dissolved phosphorus and nitrogen compounds in surface runoff of uninhabited areas can be estimated. Based on specific runoff per square kilometer, a rough estimate of the relative weight of nutrients in sewage, in comparison to "natural" nutrient sources, can be made (Table 4). The human nutrient supply with sewage,

TABLE 4

NUTRIENT TRANSPORT TO A LAKE FROM ONE SQUARE KILOMETER WATERSHED

	With Domestic Sewage			With Natural Affluents Spec. Runoff = 30 $l/km^2/sec$	
				Nutrient Content*	
	Untreated	Biol. Treat.	Biol. Treat. + N+P— Elimination	30 μg P/L 800 μg N/l	50 μg P/l 1000 μg N/l
Phosphorus					
g. P/cap/day	3	1.5	0.15		
Population density = $100/km^2$: kg $P/km^2/a$	109.5	54.7	5.5	28.4	47.5
Population density = $50/km^2$: kg $P/km^2/a$	54.7	27.3	2.7		
Nitrogen					
g. N/cap/day	12	5.5	0.8		
Population density = $100/km^2$: kg $N/km^2/a$	400	200	29.0	755	945
Population density = $50/km^2$: kg $N/km^2/a$	219	100	14.5		

*Common range for surface waters from uninhabited lands in Central Europe north of the Alps.

having been submitted to nutrient removal processes, is included (third column). The following obvious facts may be indicated: (a) Even in watersheds with a modest population density (e.g., $50/Km^2$), the human contribution of nutrients to the water makes up a large part (N) or exceeds (P) the natural runoff; (b) this proportion increases rapidly with increasing population density; (c) biological treatment alone does not change the situation fundamentally; and (d) effluents from nitrogen and phosphorus removal plants, as described in this paper, diminish human nutrient aports to an almost negligible (N) or at least tolerable (P) amount in proportion to natural runoff. From this, a pertinent conclusion evolves: an ecologically significant revenue of nutrient removal procedures can be expected only with treatments pushed to the highest possible efficiency. Imperfection in this tertiary treatment would mean thriftiness in the wrong place.

Types of Nutrients To Be Removed

Eutrophication is principally a question of growth rates and optimal metabolism of phototrophic microphytes. It is primarily a matter of cell physiology and cell nutrition, therefore, to decide whether phosphorus or nitrogen compounds or both are the more relevant factor for excessive algae growths. In this context, concentrations of available nitrogen and phosphorus normally found in surface waters are far below the necessary amounts for maximum growth rates and cell yields. Both elements are severely growth limiting in nature. Within this suboptimal range of concentrations, however, one of the two elements may be less available than the other, depending on the rate of consumption and of supply to the ecosystem.

There has been a strong tendency by some limnologists to exclusively discriminate against phosphorus as a causal agent for eutrophication in most lakes. It seems that this belief is based on a misleading oversimplification in the interpretation of (uncontestable) limnological observations. Growth rates and multiplication rates of primary producers depend as well on the concentration and availability of the essential nutrients in the medium. In a dynamic system like a lake, the rate of nutrient supply to the trophogenic layer from outside sources (hypolimnion or watershed) is an additional factor for cell production.

Observations in lakes prove that phosphate, ammonia, or nitrate can be used "to the last ion" by algae. From physiological experiments one concludes that the critical concentration limiting the uptake rate of phosphate must be much lower than that for nitrate. Ketchum (1) found, for instance, with *Nitzschia closterium* an order of magnitude of 15 to 40 μgP/1 and about 300 μgN/1, respectively. With *Scenedesmus quadricauda* these concentrations are around 100 μgP/1 and 1,000 μgN/1, according to Rodhe (2). Nitrate has to be present, therefore, in concentrations about ten times higher than phosphate to be absorbed at the same rate. In algae the proportion of N:P atoms is between 15 and 20. Hence, a physiologically equilibrated growth requires the uptake of about twenty times more nitrate ions than phosphate ions. All these arguments lead to the conclusion that nitrogen, at the concentration levels normally found in the trophogenic layers of lakes, must be relatively less available in comparison to phosphorus for phototrophic cells. Nitrogen easily may be, therefore, the true limiting factor for growth kinetics of algae in at least as many instances as phosphorus. Eutrophication abatement has to consider the removal of nitrogen compounds as well as the removal of phosphorus compounds.

Objectives and Perspectives of Nutrient Removal Procedures

The second topic of dispute is the amount of nutrients to be removed and the perspective success of tertiary treatment. It must be clearly understood that any waste discharge into a lake increases the quantity of the already existing natural (and inevitable) nutrient inflow. Where oligotrophy is representing the steady state according to pedological, morphological, and climatological conditions, any waste inflow will, therefore, endanger this steady state. An already occurring eutrophication by "natural" nutrient sources will be reinforced by wastes. It is exclusively a matter of proportions as to the rate by which eutrophication will be developed or will be increased by waste discharges. The limnological development will be unidirectional in any case.

Understandably, engineers will ask for figures indicating nutrient concentrations that are characteristic, for instance, of oligotrophy or moderate or strong eutrophy. There is only one honest answer to this request: we ignore. In fact, a lake or stream represents such a complicated system of nutrient flows that the above question implicates an inacceptable simplification of the true situation. Fortunately it is not even necessary to produce such figures, because in any water body the current nutrient supply from external sources will define the steady state of the trophic level or the rate and direction of its changes. As has been demonstrated in Table 4, human nitrogen and phosphorus contributions may already exceed 10 percent of the runoff from land, when the (sewered) population density in a watershed is around 10–20 persons/km^2 (extreme nutrient runoffs from heavily fertilized lands are not considered in this discussion). Eutrophication as a product of human waste discharges, therefore, can be successfully abated only by complete removal of nitrogen and phosphorus from sewage. However, certain limits to this objective are set by the technical means available and also by economical considerations. It would be unwise, indeed, to stipulate elimination efficiencies as being completely academic from a practical point of view. Furthermore, the diversion of wastes from the watershed of a lake may offer an alternative to elimination processes, meriting serious economical consideration in some instances.

On the basis of present experience, it can be stated that concentrations of total nitrogen of 1–3 ppm N (or about 85–90% elimination, based on settled city sewage) and of total phosphorus of 0.2–0.5 ppm P (about 90–97% elimination) in final effluents are technically feasable at bearable costs (see Table 11).

The above discussion clearly showed that in situations where oligotrophy would be the steady state in the absence of human influence, the nutrient removal will at least slow down considerably any development of eutrophy. It is not even excluded that within a period of several years a retrogression of an already established eutrophy might occur. Lake Washington (Seattle), recently relieved from sewage discharge and having been oligotrophic not too long ago, will be an excellent demonstration of possible effects of preventive measures against nutrient inflows (3). A similar example will be the Zellersee in Austria (4). In all situations where eutrophy was already existing before any sewage was flowing, no nutrient elimination from wastes will turn the wheel back. Logical deduction indicates, however, that in these circumstances nutrient removal from wastes may at least diminish extreme conditions within the range of eutrophy or polytrophy. How far such effects will be an evident relief for various uses of the water body will depend on the individual situation. Good examples to follow will be the Madison lakes (5), the Hallwilersee in Switzerland (6), or the Tegernsee in Germany (7).

Part of the material presented below has been published earlier in the German language (8). Some experimental data may be found there in more detail; literature evaluation has also been restricted in this paper in view of the extensive citations in the previous publication.

ELIMINATION OF PHOSPHORUS FROM SEWAGE

Procedures for removing phosphorus from sewage on a technical scale have been frequently discussed. However, comparative experiments with various processes over a sufficiently long period of time and with due emphasis of the sludge problem are scarce.

Phosphorus is present in sewage in three groups of compounds: as ortho-phosphate, as phosphorus in organic compounds, and as polyphosphates of either industrial or biological origin. O-phosphate makes up about 25–30 percent of the total P in sedimented raw sewage; biological treatment shifts this proportion to about 80–85 percent. It is obvious from these figures that any P-removing process has to consider the ortho-phosphate and the other P-compounds as well.

Presently proposed P-removal procedures are mostly based on precipitation, with cations forming insoluble PO_4–salts, or on absorption by inorganic hydroxides (clear-cut distinction between these two mechanisms often is not possible). Very few possibilites for economically bearable processes exist, namely reactions with Al^{3+}, Fe^{3+}, and Ca^{2+}, or with combinations of Fe^{3+} and Ca^{2+}. In addition to these inorganic chemical reactions a biological process might be considered theoretically, using the well-known property of many microorganisms to store phosphates as polyphosphates in their cells when phosphorylation substrates are lacking (9). Shapiro and Levin (10) investigated this possibility with the activated sludge process. In view of the high removal requests, as outlined earlier, their results were not at all convincing.

In our own work on P-removal processes, only Fe^{3+} or Ca^{2+} or combinations of these cations were studied as precipitants. Alum precipitation was not considered, due to the comparatively high costs in Switzerland. Furthermore, this process has already been carefully investigated by Lea, Rohlich, and Katz (11) and by Malhotra, Lee, and Rohlich (12).

Iron (III) as Precipitant

The chemical and kinetical background of the reactions between PO_4^{3-} and Fe^{3+} have been extensively studied by Galal-Gorchev and Stumm (13). In essence they showed that the dominant reaction product at $pH > 7$ is $FePO_4$ with a solubility product of about 10^{-23} (25°C.). The colloidal particle size of the $FePO_4$ (at least under conditions prevailing in sewage treatment) requires a sufficient excess of Fe^{3+} for the formation of a well-flocculating hydroxide precipitate which includes the $FePO_4$ particles and acts as an efficient absorbent for organic P-compounds and eventually for polyphosphates. Henriksen (14) postulated on the basis of careful observations that P-removal with Fe^{3+} should be considered exclusively as an absorption process. This hypothesis contradicts the opinion of Galal and Stumm. From a practical point of view, however, both reaction mechanisms lead to the same result and require the same operation conditions.

Experience shows that for efficient P-removal with Fe^{3+} the stoichiometrical amount of Fe (1.8 ppm Fe per ppm P) has to be supplemented by at least 10 ppm Fe for hydroxide formation, when treating an activated sludge plant effluent.

Iron(III) as well as Al(III) may be applied in an activated sludge system by two methods:

1. Addition of the precipitant directly to the influent of the aeration basin. Binding of P and formation of hydroxide flocs then occurs simultaneously with the formation of the activated sludge flocs, separation of the intimately mixed organic and inorganic solids from the supernatant is accomplished in the secondary clarifier. Addition of inorganic precipitants to the activated sludge had already been proposed by the early investigators of the process (15, 16), with the intention of accelerating clarification and compacting of the sludge.

Application of this principle for P-removal is advocated by Thomas (17).

2. Postprecipitation of secondary effluents in a conventional manner, using commercial precipitation and clarification units, already applied extensively in drinking-water purification.

Both processes have been assayed in parallel activated sludge plants on a model scale. For postprecipitation a reduced-size model of the "Accellator" type was used. In three test runs 10, 20, and 30 ppm of Fe^{3+} as $FeCl_3$ were applied. In the postprecipitation unit a *p*H adjustment to *p*H 7.0–7.2 by the addition of small amounts of lime was made when necessary. Essential operation data of the six experiments are assembled in Tables 5 and 6, and experimental results may be found in Table 7. The average phosphorus concentrations in the incoming sewage and the final effluents are represented in Figure 8. Characteristic features of the two processes may be summarized as follows:

1. Both processes required the addition of at least 20 ppm of Fe^{3+}, that is,

TABLE 5

OPERATION DATA OF THE BIOLOGICAL TREATMENT PLANTS IN THE COMPARATIVE EXPERIMENT WITH SIMULTANEOUS AND POSTPRECIPITATION WITH Fe^{3+}

Process	Sim.	Conv.	Sim.	Conv.	Sim.	Conv.
Fe^{3+} mg/l	30	—	20	—	10	—
Operation Time, Days	63	63	29	29	42	42
Hydraul. load m^3/m^3, day	12.00	12.00	12.00	12.00	12.00	12.00
Mixed liquor conc. mg dS/l	3035 ± 803	3540 ± 980	2380 ± 228	2240 ± 310	3080 ± 624	2620 ± 470
BOD load kg BOD_5/kgdS, day	1.65	1.65	0.24	0.24	1.56	1.56
Sludge load kg BOD_5/kgdS, day	0.54	0.46	0.10	0.11	0.51	0.62
Mixed liquor temp., °C.	13.30	13.40	12.70	12.70	11.90	11.90
*p*H final effl.	7.43	7.63	7.45	7.63	7.46	7.52
Recirc. sludge, %	100.00	100.00	100.00	100.00	100.00	100.00
Average Mohlman-Index	107.00	92.00	102.00	70.00	91.00	79.00
Excess-sludge g/m^3 sewage	147.00	66.00	164.00	75.00	133.00	108.00
l/m^3 sewage	23.90	11.00	24.40	9.60	20.30	12.80

TABLE 6

OPERATION DATA IN POSTPRECIPITATION UNIT*

	10 mg Fe^{3+} /l	20 mg Fe^{3+} /l	30 mg Fe^{3+} /l
Hydr. load of flocculation compart. m^3/m^3, day	154.00	154.00	154.00
Surface load of sedim. comp., m/h	3.12	3.12	3.12
*p*H influent**	7.54	7.62	7.65
*p*H effluent**	7.28	7.09	6.95
Excess sludge: Vol/m^3sewage	6.00	26.00	36.00
Conc. mg/l	3,475.00	2,625.00	2,680.00
Solids product. dS/m^3 sewage	22.00	66.00	93.00
Sediment volume 30 min. cm^3/l	858.00	920.00	941.00

*Slightly changed model of an "Accellator" plant Lurgi in reduced scale. All figures are average values of daily tests.

**pH-correction at all the tests by addition of $Ca(OH)_2$ in the flocc.-compt. of the "Accellator."

TABLE 7

CONCENTRATIONS AND REMOVAL OF POLLUTANTS AND PHOSPHORUS COMPOUNDS WITH IRON(III)–PRECIPITATION

Fe^{3+}-dose mg/l	Component	Simultan. Precipitat.			Postprecipitation				
		Influent mg/l	Effluent mg/l	%	Influent mg/l	Effluent Biol. Unit mg/l	%	Effluent Precipit. Unit mg/l	%
	BOD_5 mg/l	130 ± 51	19 ± 13	85.6	130 ± 51	15 ± 7	87.2	6 ± 4	95.0
10 mg/l	in solution PO_4^{3-} mg P/l	2.51 ± 0.47	0.63 ± 0.37	75.7	2.51 ± 0.47	2.04 ± 0.40	19.5	0.99 ± 0.53	60.7
	org. P + Polyph. mg P/l	1.45	0.39		1.45	0.90		0	
(14 comp. S)	solid mg P/l	2.18	0.75		2.18	1.26		1.68	
	total P mg P/l	6.14 ± 1.01	1.77 ± 0.76	71.5	6.14 ± 1.01	4.20 ± 0.71	31.2	2.65 ± 1.02	56.4
	BOD_5	48 ± 10	7 ± 3	84.8	48 ± 10	7 ± 3	82.4	1.7 ± 0.7	96.3
20 mg/l	in solution PO_4^{3-}	1.81 ± 0.22	0.21 ± 0.15	88.5	1.81 ± 0.22	1.42 ± 0.17	21.1	0.08 ± 0.04	95.5
	org. P + Polyph.	0.86	0.28		0.86	1.05		0.09	
(13 comp. S)	solid	1.18	0.35		1.18	0.53		0.27	
	total P	3.85 ± 0.69	0.84 ± 0.27	77.9	3.85 ± 0.69	3.0 ± 0.64	22.1	0.44 ± 0.31	88.3
	BOD_5	138 ± 29	12 ± 12	91.6	138 ± 29	7 ± 4	94.6	2.6 ± 2.2	98.1
30 mg/l	in solution PO_4^{3-}	3.05 ± 0.44	0.29 ± 0.94	86.9	3.05 ± 0.44	2.27 ± 0.94	26.7	0.17 ± 0.21	94.0
	org. P + Polyph.	2.10	0		2.10	1.29		0.01	
(15 comp. S)	solid	0.91	0.57		0.91	0.05		0.07	
	total P	6.06 ± 1.0	0.80 ± 0.75	87.1	6.06 ± 1.0	3.61 ± 0.58	39.7	0.26 ± 0.21	94.7

± = Standard deviations; comp. S = 24-h. composite sample (deep-freezing technique).

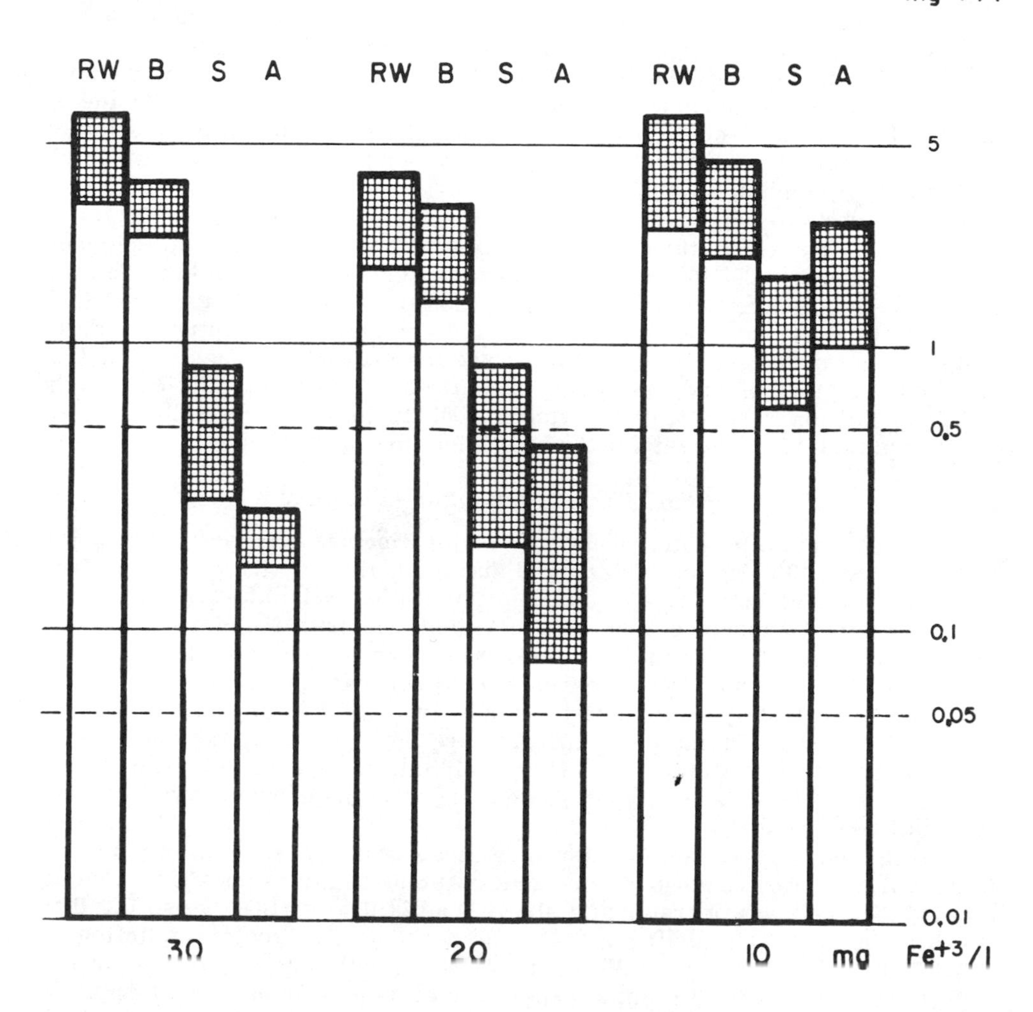

Figure 8. Average values of phosphorus concentrations in influent and final effluents in the comparative experiment with simultaneous and postprecipitation with iron(III). Compare also Table 6. From Wuhrmann (8).

roughly double the stoichiometrical amount, for decreasing the total P-content of the final effluent to 0.5 ppm or less. In fact this result was achieved with simultaneous precipitation only on a few days (in the series with 30 ppm Fe), and the average P-concentration in this unit was generally much higher.

2. $Fe(OH)_3$ flocculation in the simultaneous process was frequently incomplete, resulting in an opalescent final effluent with considerable carry-over of colloidal $Fe(OH)_3$ and phosphorus.

3. The addition of Fe^{3+} to the activated sludge resulted in a striking change of the sludge biocenosis. When the dosing was higher than 10 ppm Fe^{3+}, the protozoan fauna disappeared completely within the first two days and did not recover as long as the addition of iron was continued. In the parallel plant without iron a very rich protozoan population was found, as was to be expected for the prevailing operation conditions. It is not clear at the moment whether the adverse effect on protozoans was due to the iron itself or to some other metal in the $FeCl_3$ solution. Since technical grade $FeCl_3$ might well contain some contaminants which are toxic for certain microorganisms, this point has to be carefully considered when simultaneous precipitation is introduced.

The analytical data on the P-fractions demonstrate that an excess of iron for the formation of hydroxide flocs is indispensable in both processes for the removal of organic P-compounds and polyphosphates. In postprecipitation, however, the efficiency of the added precipitant is considerably higher than in simultaneous precipitation.

Excess sludge production in the two processes merits special emphasis. Table 5 contains excess sludge quantities and volumes in relation to the quantity of treated sewage. The remarkable increase of excess sludge volume in the simultaneous precipitation units in comparison to conventional treatment was of course to be expected. Excess sludge volumes in the postprecipitation units (Table 6), however, were also very high; and the hydroxide sludge demonstrated again its poor settling and dewatering properties. A postprecipitation process with Iron (III) for P-removal will remain a debatable procedure unless some effective dewatering process for the hydroxide sludge is invented.

Phosphorus Elimination with Lime

The process of eliminating phosphorus with lime has been proposed by Rudolfs (18) and Owen (19). Stumm (20) showed that the main reaction product at the high *p*H level necessary for efficient P-precipitation (*p*H 10.5–11) is hydroxylapatite. Practical experience has demonstrated that both the apatite and the calcium carbonate formed in the process have poor settling and flocculation properties. It was found in experiments, however, that the lime precipitation process can be greatly improved when some Fe^{3+} (1–2 ppm) is added as a flocculation aid. Sparkling clear effluents are then produced, and the excess sludge is excellently compacting. The precipitate is an efficient absorbant for organic P-compounds and polyphosphates, and thus the process satisfies the essential requirements.

A continuous experiment on a technical scale was run in the pilot plant for 74 days. All operation conditions were kept constant as far as possible. The activated sludge unit was operated at a sludge load of 0.17 kg BOD/kg solids/day, resulting in an average BOD removal of 96 percent. For postprecipitation a large experimental unit of an "Accellator" was kindly supplied by the Lurgi Company in Frankfurt. Essential experimental data are compiled in Table 8, and the average operation results and their variance may be found in Table 9. Figure 9 represents some of the main operation results. All analytical figures refer to 24-hour composite samples (deep-freezing sampling technique).

TABLE 8

AVERAGE OPERATION DATA OF BIOLOGICAL TREATMENT AND OF POSTPRECIPITATION IN P-REMOVAL EXPERIMENT WITH LIME PRECIPITATION FROM SEPTEMBER 30-DECEMBER 13, 1963

a) Biological Treatment:	
Aerat. bas. vol.	J = 6.28 m^3
Brush aeration	95 U/min. Immers. depth = 6.5 cm.
Influent	2.52 m^3/h, 60.5 m^3/day
Mixed liqu. solids	6,000 mg dS/l
O-concentration mixed liquor	4 mg O/l
Hydraul. load	9.65 m^3/m^3 · day
BOD load	1.04 kg BOD_5/m^3 · day
Sludge recirc.	211%
Excess sludge:	
Spec. volume	10.3 l/m^3 sewage
Spec. solids prod.	100 g/m^3 sewage
b) Precipitation Unit ("Accellator")	
Influent	1.08 m^3/h, 26 m^3/day
Hydraul. load of flocculat. compartm. (J = 0.418 m^3)	62.2 m^3/m^3 · day
Upflow rate in sediment, compartm. (F = 1.25 m^2)	0.87 m/h
Precipitants:	
$Ca(OH)_2$	268 mg $Ca(OH)_2$/l
$FeCl_3$	1-2 mg Fe^{3+}/l
Temperature	11.6°C. (15.4°C. → 6.0°C.)
*p*H-Influent	7.4
*p*H-Effluent	11.1
Optics, effl.	sparkling clear, colorless
Excess sludge:	
Spec. volume	63.5 l/m^3 sewage
Spec. solid product	396 g/m^3 sewage

TABLE 9

MEAN VALUES AND STANDARD DEVIATIONS OF PLANT INFLUENT AND EFFLUENT CONCENTRATION, EXPERIMENT WITH LIME PRECIPITATION. TWENTY COMPOSITE SAMPLES

	Biolog. Treatment			Postprecipitation	
	Influent	Effluent (= Influent to Precipit. Unit)	%	Effluent	%
BOD_5 mg O/l	108 ± 23	4 ± 2	91.4 ± 2.0	1.0 ± 0.2	98.9 ± 0.4
o-Phosphate mg P/l	1.63 + 0.31	2.73 ± 0.72	+ 67.5	0.15 ± 0.07	90.8
Organ. P + polyphosphate* mg P/l	4.73	0.43	90.8	0.28	94.2
Total phosphorus mg P/l	6.36 ± 1.42	3.16 ± 0.75	50.3	0.43 ± 0.14	93.4

*Difference of total P and o-phosphate.

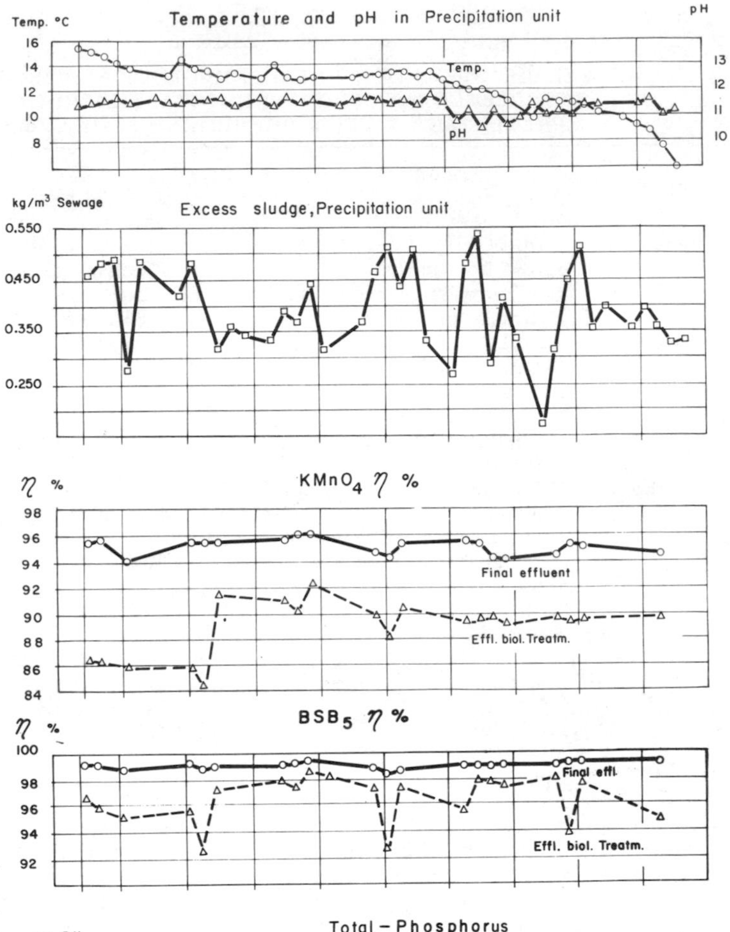

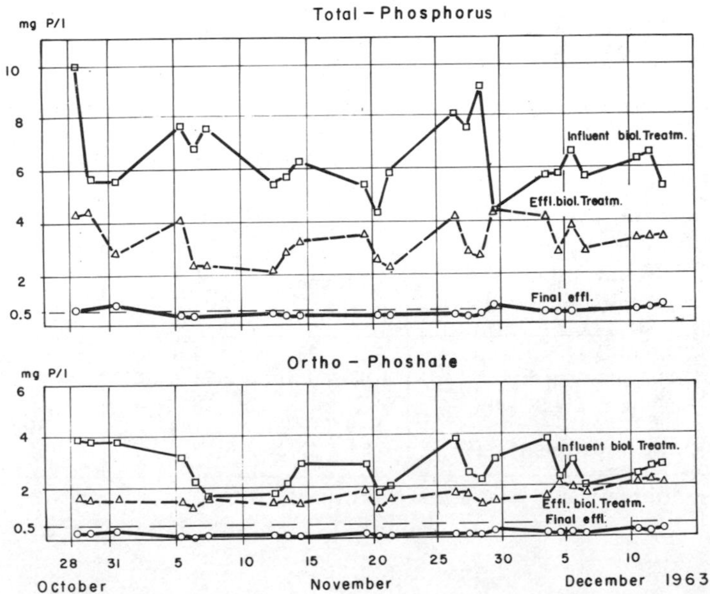

Figure 9. Operation data and results of phosphorus removal in the experiment with postprecipitation with lime. Compare also Table 8. From Wuhrmann (8).

Table 9 and Figure 17 demonstrate clearly that the requested proportion of P-removal was easily achieved, and the results correspond essentially to those of the earlier workers. It is worthwhile to mention that this process is amazingly stable and easy to operate once the appropriate amounts of the precipitants are known. The high *p*H of the final effluent is of course a great disadvantage of this procedure. Since the final effluent is completely softened, its neutralization with, for instance, combustion gases would be easy.

Lime requirements and the respective quantity of excess sludge depend largely on the alkalinity and the Ca-hardness of the treated sewage. The quantity of lime needed is approximately 1.5 times the carbonate hardness (ppm) of the sewage; and 2 ppm of Iron(III) as a flocculation aid is sufficient. These figures indicate immediately that in regions with considerable hardness of the drinking water (e.g., Switzerland, most frequently around 150–200 ppm), tremendous amounts of excess sludge will be produced by this process. Fortunately, the sludge has excellent settling properties, and in addition it might be effectively used for compacting the excess sludge from activated sludge units. Figure 10 gives some examples of settling curves of the biological excess sludge (*B*), the lime precipitation sludge (*C*), and various mixtures of both (*B* + *C*). The graph indicates the substantial increase of settleability of the biological sludge in mixture with the excess sludge from the precipitation unit.

Combined P-Removal Process with Lime and Iron (III)

In an attempt to reduce sludge solids production and excess sludge volume in the precipitation unit, a combination of P-precipitation with Iron(III) and lime was tried. Iron was dosed to about the stoichiometrical amount for 5–6 ppm of o-phosphate, and lime was added to raise the *p*H of the mixture to 8.8. It was expected that at this *p*H considerable precipitation of $CaCO_3$ would take place, which might be helpful as a thickening aid of the iron hydroxide formed; at the same time it was thought to act as an absorbent for colloidal $FePO_4$ and organic phosphate. The experiment was run for thirty days with the effluent of a complete treatment activated sludge plant. Again the "Accellator" unit was used for postprecipitation. Full account of the operation conditions of the precipitation process is given in Table 10 and Figure 11.

The results convincingly demonstrated that P-removal was equivalent to the efficiency achieved with lime or iron precipitation alone. Excess sludge quantity and volume were much smaller, however, and the settling property of the sludge was comparable to pure lime sludge (see Fig. 12). Considering actual Swiss prices for iron and lime, the costs for chemicals in this process are about 30 percent less than for the previously described methods. Sludge handling and disposal will also be considerably cheaper due to the smaller amount of solids produced and their favorable settling rate.

Essential factors for the operation of this process are the amount of o-phosphate to be removed (determining the dose of Iron[III]), the alkalinity, and the Ca-hardness of the biologically treated sewage (determining the dose of lime). We conclude from our experience that this combined process will be the most economic over a wide range of conditions and when sludge disposal is correctly included into the operation costs.

According to the solubility curve of $Al(OH)_3$, we have to expect that a combination of alum and lime precipitation will give much inferior results (see Stumm [21], Figs. 2 and 15). This is confirmed by the investigations of Malhortra *et al.* (12).

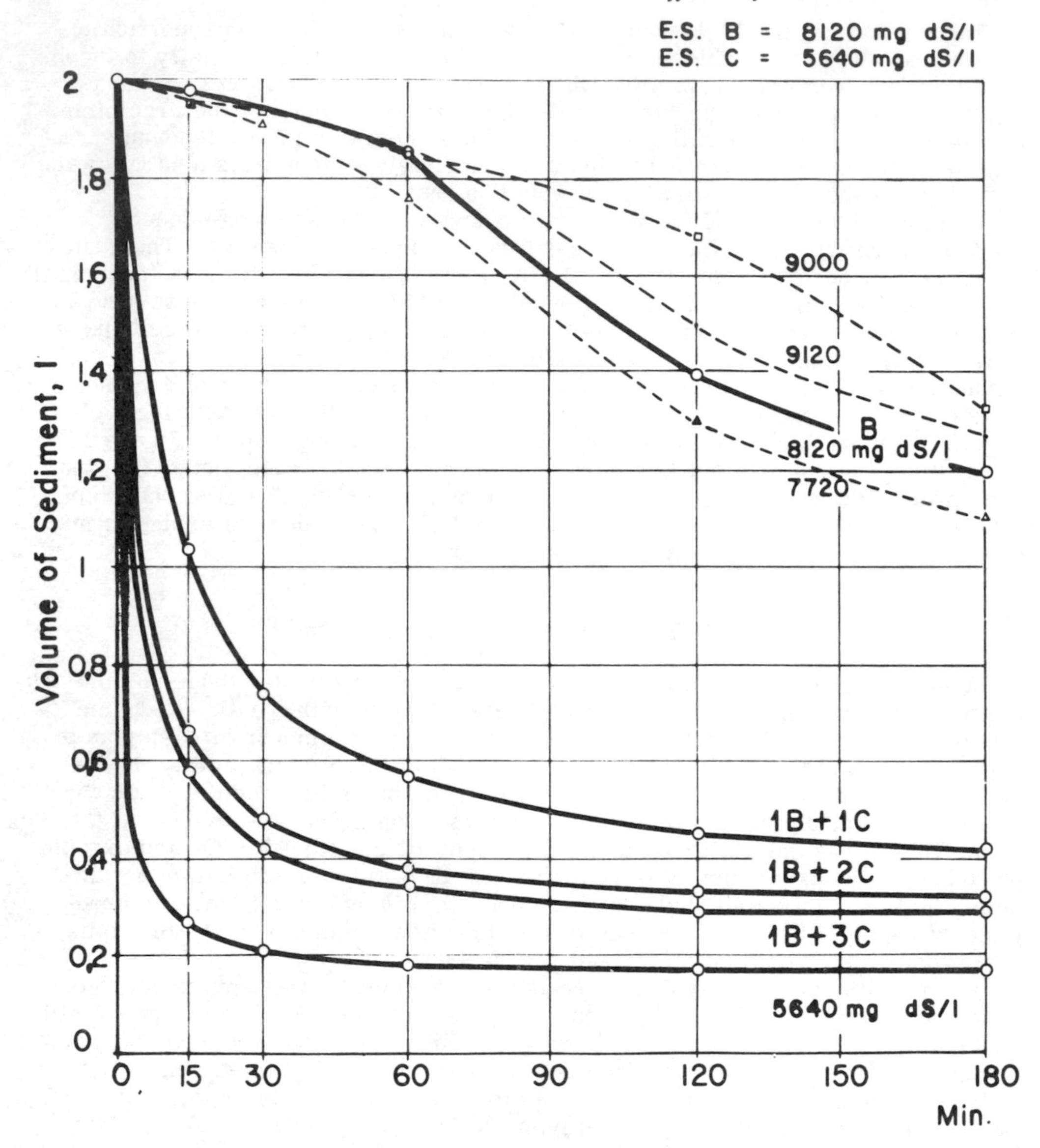

Figure 10. Sedimentation curves of biological excess sludge (B) of various initial concentrations and of excess sludge from postprecipitation with lime (C). Sedimentation curves ($B + C$) are from mixtures of the two sludges. Sedimentation under quiescent conditions in a two-liter cylinder. From Wuhrmann (8).

REMOVAL OF NITROGEN COMPOUNDS FROM SEWAGE

In settled domestic sewage nitrogen is present as NH_4-N to about 55–60 percent, as nitrogen in organic compounds to roughly 40–45 percent, and in oxidized form (NO_2 and NO_3) to 0–5 percent. In the course of biological treatment most of the organic N-compounds are degraded and the proportion in the final effluent is generally less than 20 percent of the total N. The proportion of NH_4-N to

TABLE 10

AVERAGE OPERATION DATA OF PRECIPITATION UNIT IN THE EXPERIMENT WITH COMBINED LIME-IRON(III) PRECIPITATION AT *p*H 8.8

Influent	1.08 m^3/h, 26 m^3/day
Hydraul. load, floccul. compartm. (J = 0.42 m^3)	62.2 $m^3/m^3 \cdot$ day
Upflow rate, sediment. compartm. (F = 1.25 m^2)	0.87 m/h
Precipitants:	
$FeCl_3$	10 gFe/m^3
$Ca(OH)_2$	100–150 g/m^3
Temp., floccul. compartm.	15.0 ± 1.3 °C.
*p*H influent to flocc. compt.	7.57 ± 0.18
*p*H final effluent	8.81 ± 0.18
Optics, final effluent	sparkling clear, colorless
Excess sludge:	
Concentration	4540 g/m^3
Spec. volume	53 l/m^3 sewage
Spec. solids product.	245 g/m^3 sewage

Biological treatment, see Table 8.

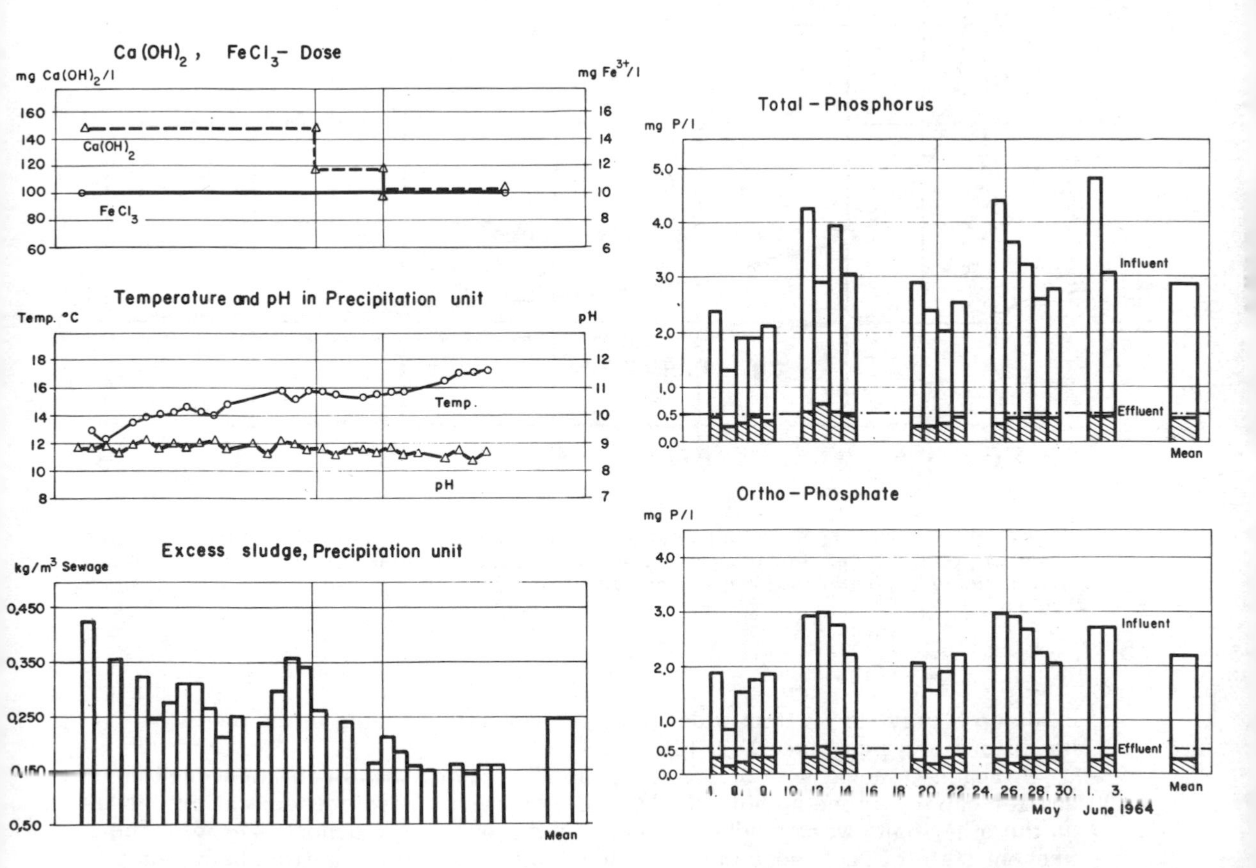

Figure 11. Operation data and results of phosphorus removal in the experiment with post-precipitation with lime plus iron(III). Compare also Table 10. From Wuhrmann (8).

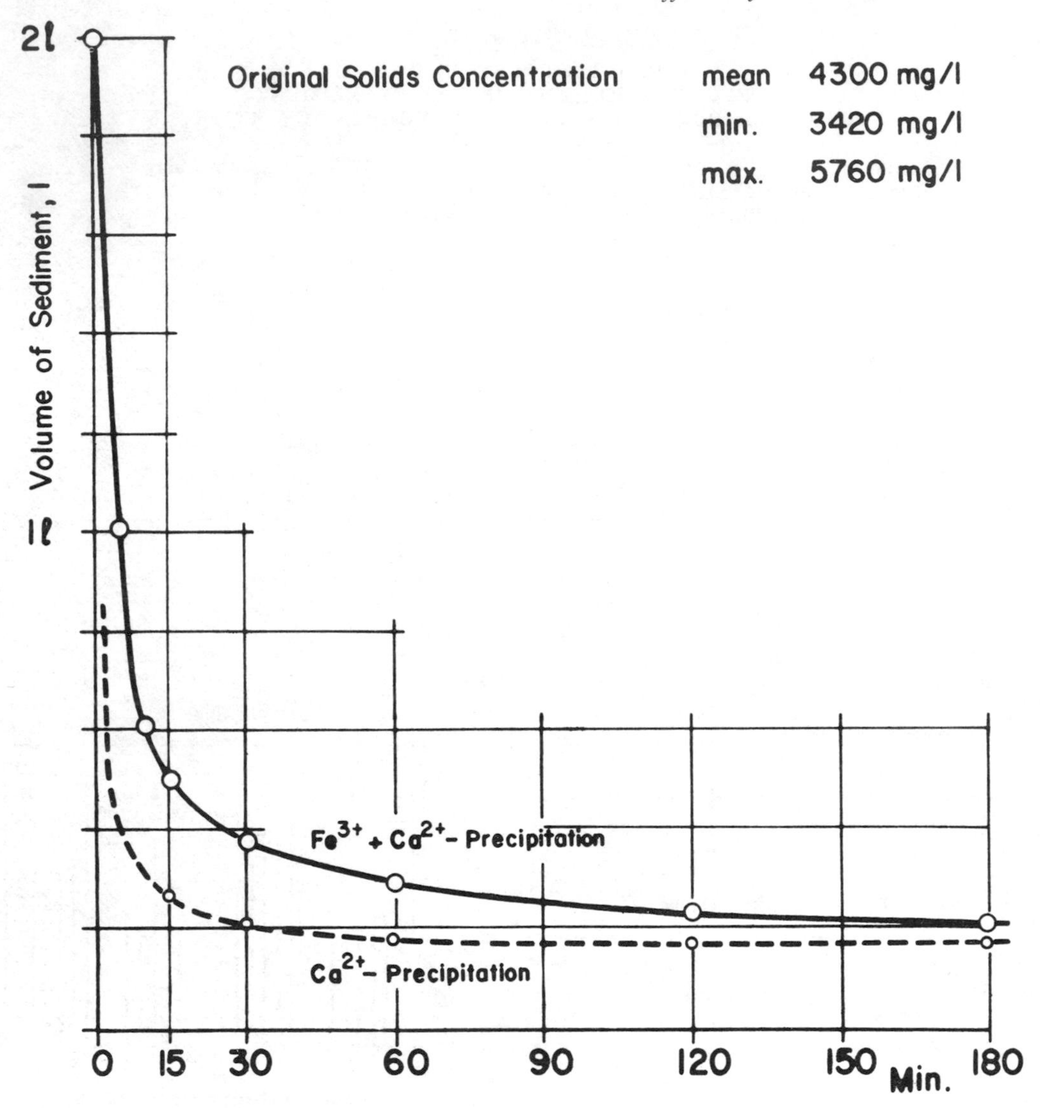

Figure 12. Average sedimentation curve (18 samples) of the excess sludge from the lime-iron(III) precipitation. For comparison the sedimentation of the lime sludge (Fig. 10) is also indicated. Sedimentation under quiescent conditions in a two-liter cylinder. From Wuhrmann (8).

oxidized N may vary within wide limits, however, according to the operation conditions of a plant (see Fig. 13).

Nitrogen removal with biological means has been extensively discussed in earlier papers by the author (22, 23) and by others. Physicochemical processes on the other hand were studied in detail by the Wisconsin school (24–26). The present state of knowledge indicates convincingly that for the time being, only biological processes will be economically bearable, and within this frame only microbial denitrification will give satisfactory results.

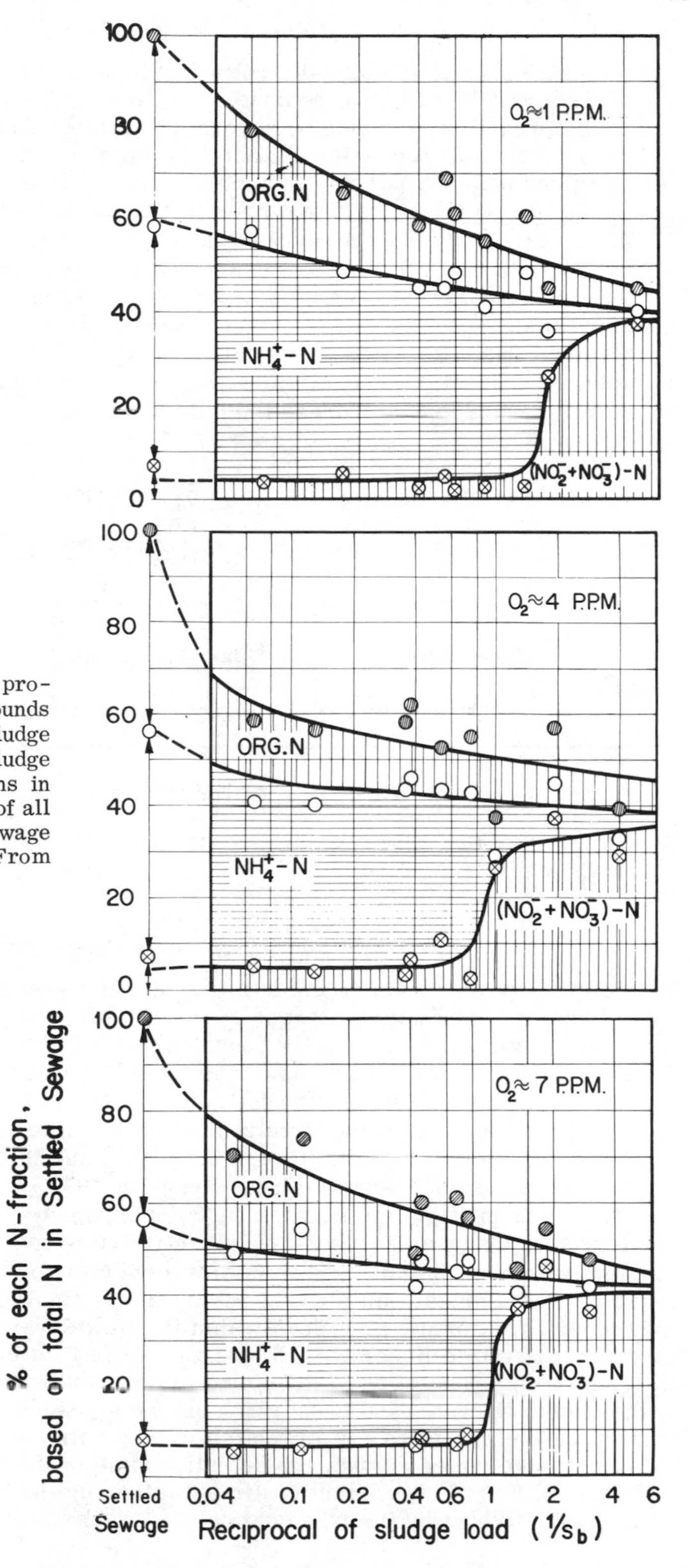

Figure 13. Shift of the proportion of nitrogen compounds in sewage by activated sludge treatment at various sludge loads and oxygen tensions in the mixed liquor. Sum of all compounds in settled sewage equals 100 percent. From Wuhrmann (8).

General Process Layout

Nitrogen losses in biological treatment plants due to microbial denitrification are well known. What has to be done, therefore, is reinforce an already pre-established reaction sequence by adequate operation conditions.

Two entirely different microbial actions on nitrogen compounds are to be combined and possibly carried to completion: (a) In a first step the nitrogen compounds in sewage must be oxidized to NO_2^- or NO_3^- ("Nitrification"); (b) these oxides may then be reduced in a second step to elementary nitrogen or eventually to N_2O. A high efficiency of both processes is possible only when they are separated from each other. It is no problem, however, to operate them in series in any conventional activated sludge plant which is supplemented with an additional basin for the denitrification reaction, as is shown in the scheme of Figure 14. Practical operation results of such a plant will be discussed later. We first have to introduce the individual reaction steps.

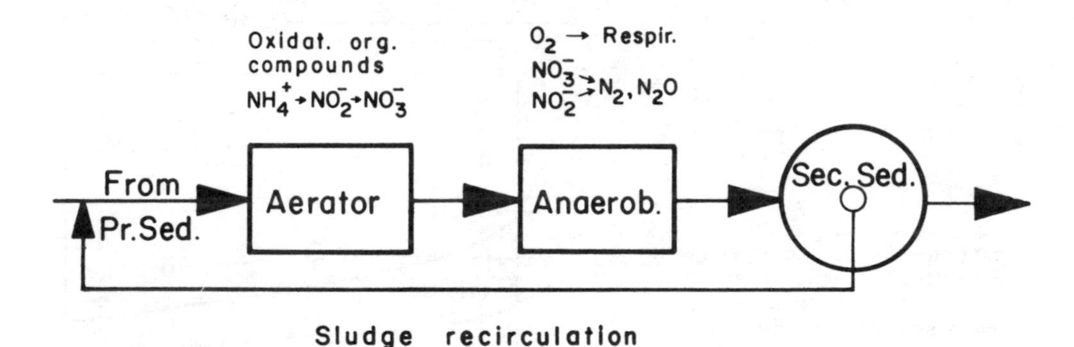

Figure 14. Operation scheme for an activated sludge plant, including microbial denitrification. From Wuhrmann (8).

Nitrification in Activated Sludge Treatment

As stated above, complete oxidation of nitrogen compounds to NO_2^- or NO_3^- is a prerequisite for efficient nitrogen removal. It is the merit of Downing and his co-workers to have elucidated the fundamentals of nitrification in the activated sludge process (27, 28), and to have indicated the essential operation conditions in a practical plant. In short, the following pertinent facts have to be considered: the strictly aerobic and chemoautotrophic ammonia oxidizers (nitrosomonas species, sole energy source: reaction $NH_4^+ \rightarrow NO_2^-$) and the nitrite oxidizers (nitrobacter species, sole energy source: reaction $NO_2^- \rightarrow NO_3^-$) are characterized by rather low multiplication rates in comparison to the heterotrophic bacterial flora making up the bulk of an activated sludge. In addition these organisms demonstrate a large temperature factor for their growth rate. In contrast to earlier assumptions, however, the critical oxygen tension in the environment for normal growth is within the limits which are conventionally maintained in mixed liquor (1–1.5 ppm O_2). The limiting factor for sustaining a sufficiently high population of nitrifying organisms in an activated sludge plant is, therefore, the detention time which can be provided for the cells in the system. Since the nitrifiers are intimately mixed with all other organisms and solids in the activated sludge, the detention time of the sludge in the plant will be decisive. The sludge detention time is given by the fraction of total solids in the plant, divided by the released solids (excess sludge plus suspended solids in the final effluent), or the sludge age. The critical sludge age for nitrification depends on all those factors which are determining (a) the growth rate of the nitrifiers (i.e., temperature, substrate concentration, concentration of eventually inhibiting compounds in the waste) and (b) the accumulation rate of sludge solids (i.e., growth rate of the heterotrophic flora, introduction of inert solids into the system). When adequate conditions for the build-up of a sizable population of nitrifiers are prevailing, nitrification is essentially an all or nothing effect. This conclusion has been verified in the experimental work of the English scientists as well as in the author's own investigations. It is obvious from the above findings that with increasing overall concentration of a sewage, an increasing sludge age has to be maintained, because the higher accumulation rate of heterotrophic sludge organisms will request a higher excess sludge release, and hence a higher loss of nitrifiers will occur. Nitrification is bound, therefore, to operation conditions leading to a minimum of excess sludge production. The large temperature coefficient of the growth rate of these organisms also makes necessary an increasing sludge age with decreasing temperature. In spite of the many factors involved, fairly reliable predictions as to the occurrence of nitrification in a plant can be made.

Denitrification by Activated Sludge

Microbial reduction of NO_2^- or NO_3^- follows two fundamentally different pathways: (a) reduction to NH_4^+ in the metabolism of nitrogen utilization (assimilation of NO_2^- or NO_3^-) and (b) reduction to N_2 or N_2O in the respiratory metabolism ("NO_2^- or NO_3^- - respiration"). Only the last sequence of reactions is of interest in the present discussion. Experience shows that a large percentage of the bacteria in conventional activated sludge systems are capable of replacing elementary oxygen by nitrogen oxides as electron acceptors in their energy metabolism. Examples of denitrification rates achieved by activated sludge under various conditions have been published previously (29).

The main problem for a rapid and complete denitrification in an activated sludge system is, therefore, to provide for those conditions which will shift the respiration of the already present flora of denitrifiers from "oxygen respiration" to "nitrate or nitrite respiration." Two rate-limiting factors have to be considered in this respect, namely, the oxygen tension in the medium and the amount of available hydrogen donors in the cells.

Oxygen as Limiting Factor

Wuhrmann and Mechsner (30) have demonstrated that oxygen acts as a powerful inhibitor for nitrite (and nitrate) respiration at *p*H values in the medium of about 6.5–7 or higher. With decreasing *p*H the detrimental effect of oxygen disappears (Fig. 15). This interaction of *p*H and oxygen tension was found with numerous bacterial strains isolated from activated sludge. In practical plant operation the *p*H value of the mixed liquor is normally found in the region of *p*H 7 or higher. This means, therefore, that efficient denitrification will be possible only under strictly anaerobic conditions. Since the organisms in the mixed liquor leaving an aeration unit are rapidly exhausting the dissolved oxygen when no further aeration occurs, anaerobiosis is easily achieved by simply storing the sludge suspension in an additional tank.

Respiration Substrates as Limiting Factors

The effluent from an aeration tank, working at the nitrification level, is practically free of easily available dissolved compounds which could be used as respiration substrates by the sludge organisms. Nitrate or nitrite respiration is

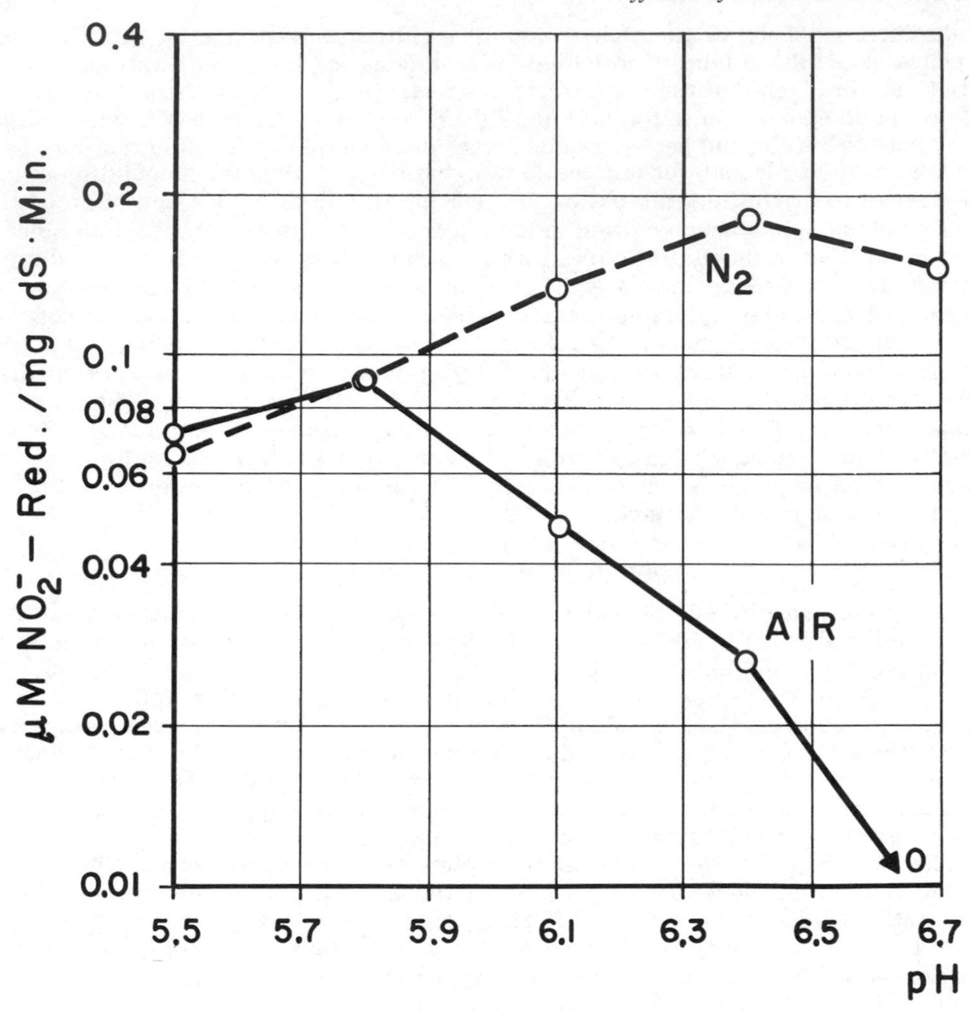

Figure 15. Endogenous rate of denitrification of NO_2^- by *Spirillum virginianum* under strict anaerobiosis (N_2) and at the oxygen tension of air in function of the *p*H in the medium. Temperature = 25°C., setting of *p*H by phosphate buffering. From Wuhrmann and Mechsner (29).

possible, therefore, only when the cells are using endogenous respiration substrates. As under normal aerobic conditions, the anaerobic nitrate respiration rate depends largely on the type and quantity of the substrates which can be mobilized by the cells. Endogenous oxygen respiration rate and nitrate or nitrite respiration rate in a denitrification basin are, therefore, closely related. Practical experience has shown that the endogenous reserve materials in bacteria are amply sufficient to maintain the respiration of activated sludge until all available nitrate or nitrite ions are reduced. It is not necessary, therefore, to add any exogenous source of hydrogen donors to the mixed liquor. This fact had not been clearly recognized when we started our first investigations on denitrification ten years ago. It was then assumed that effective denitrification would be possible only by adding some raw sewage to the mixed liquor in the anaerobic tank (22). In later experiments, Bringmann (31–33) started from the same point of view and accordingly proposed relatively complicated operation schemes. Present-day knowledge, however, permits much simpler arrangements.

Submitting the mixed liquor to a prolonged period of anaerobiosis raises the question of harmful side effects. Wuhrmann (29) and Westgarth, Sulzer, and Okun (34) found that anaerobiosis for several hours does not change the activity of activated sludge when it is aerated again. We cannot confirm, however, the statement of the latter authors that the anaerobic phase is reducing measurably the quantity of excess sludge production. As far as our experience goes, we never found any harmful or beneficial effect whatsoever which could have been attributed to the 2–3-hour anaerobiosis in our experiments. Another, more pertinent point has been submitted for discussion by Shapiro (discussion to Wuhrmann [23]) regarding the accumulation of phosphorus as polyphosphates in cells under aerobic conditions. Shapiro indicated that at least part of this incorporated phosphorus in activated sludge may be released during anaerobiosis. He assumes, therefore, that the anaerobic treatment phase will counteract the biological removal of phosphorus from sewage. We have no proof either in favor of or against this hypothesis.

Phosphorus elimination by the activated sludge under conventional operation conditions and with denitrification was never found significantly different (Fig. 16). Since nitrogen removal as a tertiary treatment process will probably always be combined with a phosphorus elimination process in a postprecipitation unit, an eventually adverse effect of the denitrification step can be tolerated.

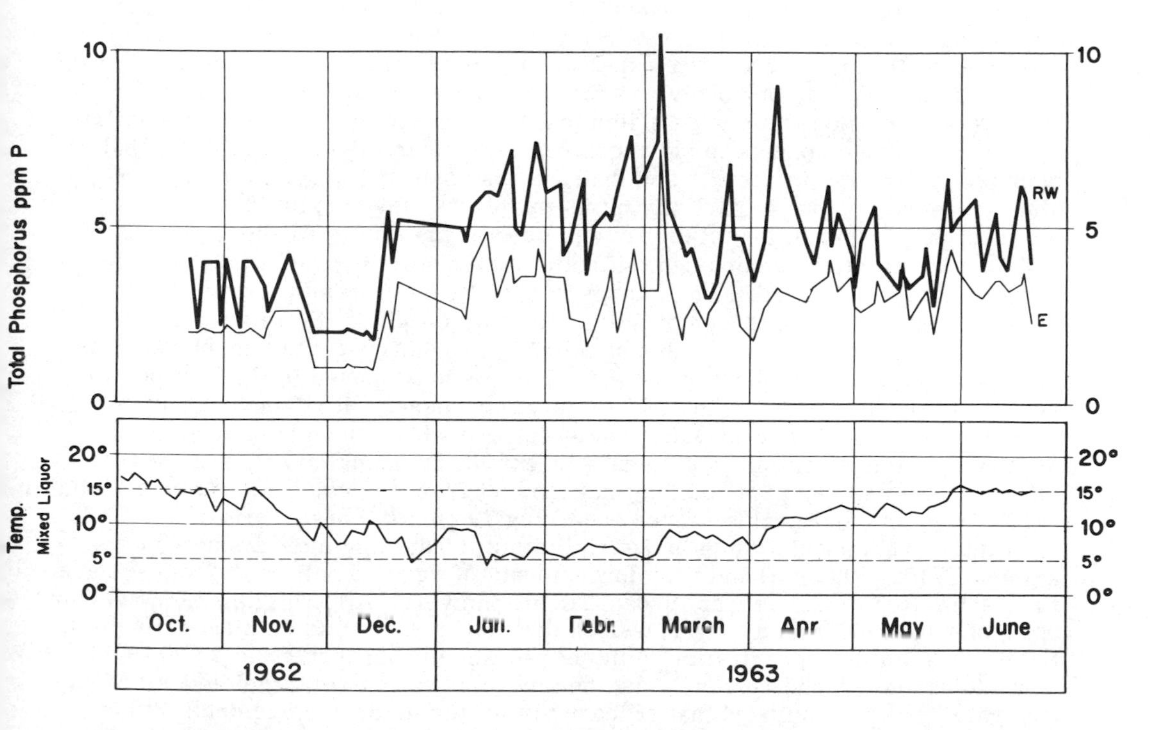

Figure 16. Total phosphorus concentration in plant influent (settled sewage) and final effluent of an activated sludge plant with denitrification (see Fig. 17).

Practical Experience with Denitrification

On the basis of several preliminary trials which have been described elsewhere (23), a pilot plant experiment on a technical scale was started in our experimental station. The total operation period comprised one year. Almost daily observations of all pertinent physical parameters and chemical analysis of three composite samples per week (24-hrs. sampling at 5-min. intervals, deep-freezing technique) of the plant influent and effluent permitted a close check of the treatment efficiency and the operation conditions.

The aeration basin ($v = 6.16\ m^3$) was equipped with a Kessener brush (immersion depth 4 cm., 113 r/min). The effluent from the aerator was transferred directly into a denitrification basin ($v = 18.8\ m^3$), in which a slowly turning paddle wheel (4 r/min) prevented the sludge from settling. From this tank the mixed liquor flowed into the secondary clarifier (upflow type, flow rate mostly 0.43 m/h), and the settled sludge was then returned to the aerator (mostly 100% return sludge).

Essential analytical results and operation conditions are assembled in Figure 17. Comparison of Graphs A and B immediately shows that a high efficiency of nitrogen removal was strictly correlated with the degree of nitrification achieved in the aerobic treatment phase (see proportion of ammonia N in the final effluent). Considering the nitrate and nitrite content of the effluent, it is evident that denitrification was quite effective at any time.

Complete breakdown of nitrogen elimination occurred during the winter months when mixed liquor temperatures fell below approximately 10°C. Since plant operation parameters were kept constant regardless of temperature, this effect was inevitable, because complete nitrification at the lower temperatures would have required a much higher sludge age than in summer time. In previous experiments it had been found, indeed, that with the sewage of the city of Zurich a sludge age of about 4 days is necessary to maintain nitrification at temperatures below about 10–12°C. The experiment leads to the general conclusion that the nitrification phase obviously was the limiting factor for elimination efficiency. Nevertheless, it can be stated that the sequence of nitrification-denitrification is a sound concept for nitrogen removal. It is of special interest that the plant was very easy to operate and that, for instance, the problem of raising sludge, frequently met in partially nitrifying plants, never existed.

About 30 percent of the total nitrogen found in the final effluent in periods of satisfactory nitrification and denitrification was due to organic nitrogen in the suspended solids. An additional postprecipitation for P-removal would completely eliminate this nitrogen quantity. We may conclude, therefore, that a complete set of tertiary treatment steps, comprising denitrification and phosphorus precipitation, will give the results which have been proposed in the introduction as a realistic first aim for nutrient removal processes. It is important to pinpoint the fact that BOD removal is not affected at all by the nitrogen removal process. In the practical experiment presented, the annual average of the plant influent BOD was 142 ppm and the final effluent from the clarifier had an average BOD of 7 ppm, single values never exceeding 10 ppm (50 observations).

A later experiment with an industrial waste, containing high amounts of ammonia (100–300 ppm) and very low amounts of organic pollutants, was successfully submitted to a nitrification-denitrification cycle. After a rather long period of sludge accumulation a bacterial flora developed which was dominated by nitrifiers. The solids concentration in the mixed liquor equilibrated to 2,000–2,600 ppm (no excess sludge release), and the sludge showed a remarkable denitrification rate. It was concluded that at least part of the heterotrophic denitrifying organisms in the sludge were using autolysis products of the nitrifiers as a

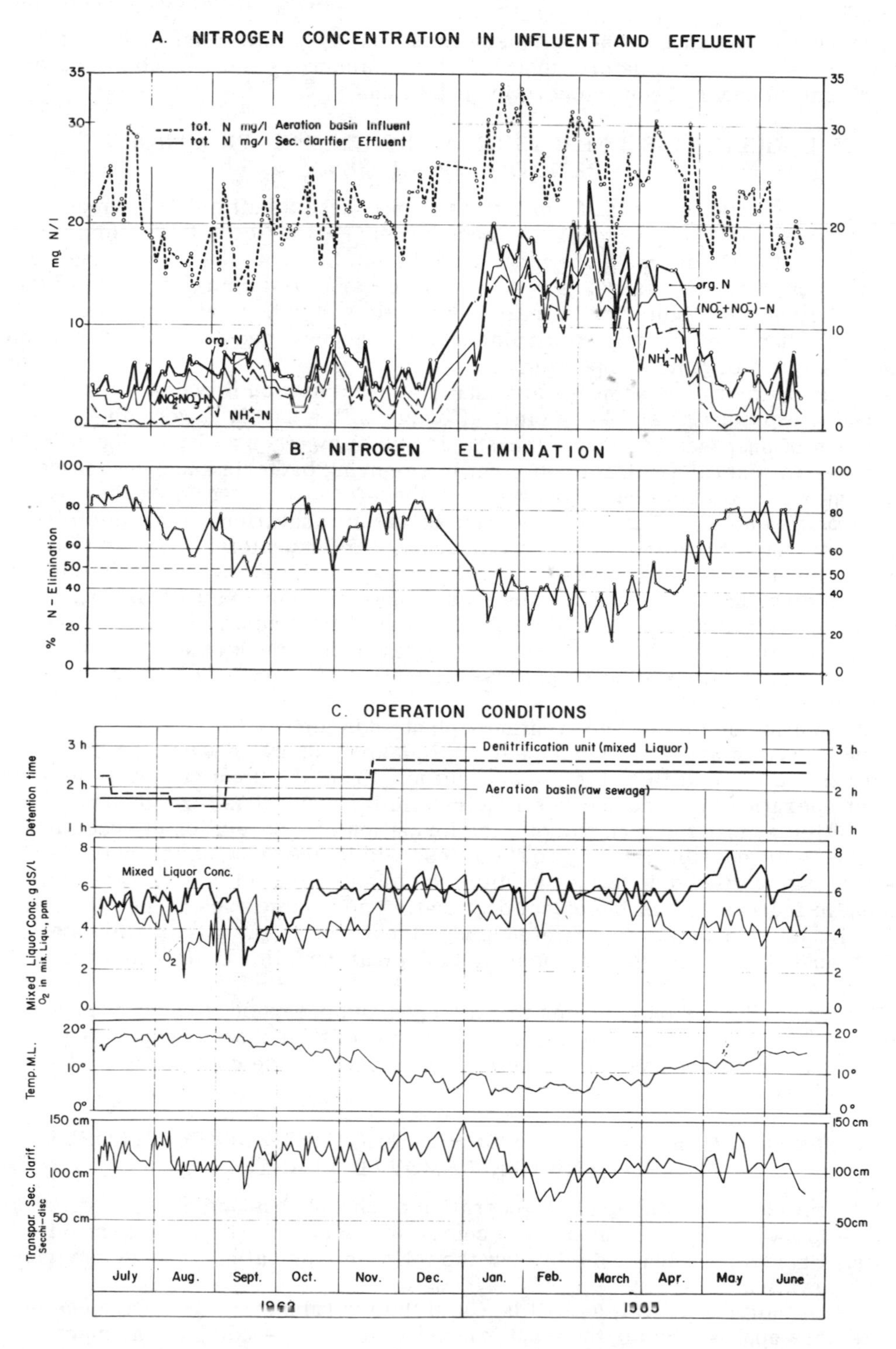

Figure 17. Record of nitrogen concentration in influent (settled sewage) and final effluent of an activated sludge plant operated with denitrification according to Figure 14. N-elimination efficiency in Graph B, operation data in Graph C. From Wuhrmann (8).

growth substrate. These observations suggest that even industrial wastes of predominantly inorganic nature, though rich in ammonia, could be submitted to denitrification under adequate operation conditions.

BENEFICIAL SIDE EFFECTS OF NITROGEN AND PHOSPHORUS REMOVAL PROCESSES

Effective nutrient removal from wastes is of course a sufficient argument for the additional costs involved by such procedures. Further beneficial effects, however, will certainly make the meal more tasteful. From the point of view of the rather high quality standards requested in regard to water re-use, one of the main deficiencies of biologically treated domestic and industrial wastes is their content of suspended organic solids (including pathogenic agents) and of undecomposed dissolved organic compounds.

Practical experience demonstrated that postprecipitation processes for P-removal are producing sparkling clear effluents with a hardly measurable concentration of suspended solids. As has been shown by other authors, flocculation processes in general are highly efficient in removing bacteria and even viruses from water. It is a reasonable expectation, therefore, that P-removal by postprecipitation implies a large step forward in water renovation, as far as elimination of various kinds of pollutants is concerned. Unfortunately, most of these beneficial side effects are lost with simultaneous precipitation, due to the intimate blending and interaction of numerous processes in one unit. It is recommended, therefore, to sacrifice the small saving of first costs, resulting from simultaneous precipitation (see Table 11), in favor of a much higher overall efficiency of a postprecipitation process (operation costs of both procedures being almost identical).

Nitrification in a biological treatment plant adds further to the removal of materials characterized by incomplete degradability or by requesting a highly specialized microbial flora for decomposition. From the point of view of fermenter operation these compounds require similar conditions for microbial decomposition as nitrification, namely, the formation of a population of specialized bacteria, with possibly small growth rates, within the bulk of the activated sludge. Due to this coincidence any nitrifying plant will lead, therefore, to an automatic increase of the biological degradation of organic substances. The traditional English practice of activated sludge treatment to the nitrification stage is fully justified in regard to a complete biological oxidation of organic compounds.

The above discussion indicates that nitrogen and phosphorus removal processes are paralleling excellently the present-day needs for increased purification effects, and by this reason their additional costs have to be considered in the right proportion.

ESSENTIAL OPERATION AND DESIGN FACTORS FOR PHOSPHORUS AND NITROGEN REMOVAL PLANTS

The critical parameters for the operation of phosphorus and nitrogen removal processes have been mentioned in the course of the description of our experiments. From a practical point of view the following indications may summarize our observations:

1. Phosphorus removal, as will be shown later (Table 11), is—regardless of the process applied—by far the most expensive step in the complete nutrient removal cycle. The operation costs are dominated by the purchase prices for the chemicals and by the costs for sludge disposal. Emphasizing both factors, experience demonstrates that the combined lime-iron process is by far the most

TABLE 11

ESTIMATE OF ANNUAL AND NET OPERATION COSTS FOR PHOSPHORUS AND NITROGEN ELIMINATION PLANTS. PRICE BASE 1964, SIZE OF PLANTS: 50,000 POPULATION, DWF = 400 l/CAP/DAY

Treatment		Mech. + Biol.	Mech. + Biol. + N-Elim.	Mech. + Biol. + P-Elim. (Sim. Prec.)*	Mech. + Biol. + P-Elim. (Post-prec.)**	Mech. + Biol. + N-Elim. + P-Elim. (Postprec.)**
First Costs	%	100	120	105	120	140
	Sfr/cap	130.00	156.00	137.00	156.00	182.00
Interest, redemption, renewal	8%	10.40	12.50	11.00	12.50	14.50
Maintenance, repair	Sfr. 40,000/a	0.80	0.80	0.80		
	45,000/a				0.90	0.90
Salaries	Sfr. 40,000/a	0.80	0.80	0.80		
	45,000/a				0.90	0.90
Electricity, without nitrif.	0.7 kWh/kg BSB_5	0.90		0.90	0.90	
with nitrif.	1.2 kWh/kg BSB_5		1.55			1.55
Chemicals	Sfr. 28.75/1000 m^3			4.25		
	26.00/1000 m^3				3.80	3.80
Service material	Sfr. 20,000.00/a	0.40	0.40	0.40	0.40	0.40
Aerobic sludge condit. + dewatering (biol. sludge)		4.40	4.40	5.00	4.40	4.40
Sludge condit. + dewatering (precipit. sludge)					1.00	1.00
Total annual costs	Sfr/cap/a	17.70	20.45	23.15	24.80	27.45
Extent over convent. treatm.	%	0	15.00	32.00	40.00	55.00
Net operation costs	Sfr/cap/a	7.30	7.95	12.15	12.30	12.95
Extent over convent. treatm.	%	0	9.00	66.50	68.00	77.00
Estimated quality of final effluent:						
BOD	ppm O	12–16	8–12	12–20	<5	<5
Susp. solids	ppm	20–25	15–20	20–30	<5	<5
Org. C	ppm C	12–16	8–12	12–20	<5	<5
Total N	ppm N	11–15	3–5	11–15	10–13	2–3
Total P	ppm P	3–5	3–5	0.5–1	≤0.5	≤0.5

*Simultaneous precipitation with 25 ppm Fe^{3+}.
**Postprecipitation, *p*H 8.8, with 10 ppm Fe^{3+} + 120 ppm $Ca(OH)_2$.

economic. The quantities of precipitation chemicals are moderate, and the sludge produced thickens rapidly and can be effectively dewatered to a highly concentrated slurry or a dry filter cake which may be dumped without danger of secondary leaching of phosphorus. The amount of lime needed is largely dependent on the alkalinity and the Ca-hardness of the biologically treated effluent and can be easily estimated in the laboratory. The iron(III) dose is stoichiometrically calculated from the average o-phosphate concentration in the biological effluent.

In conditions of low alkalinity the lime precipitation alone may prove to be cheaper than the combined process, due to the small quantity of iron(III) needed (replaceable by any other effective flocculation aid). The excess sludge has even better dewatering properties (see Fig. 12), and operation of the process is again very easy. The effluent, however, will need a recarbonation before disposal in smaller water bodies.

2. Alum and Iron(III) Precipitations have two severe disadvantages. The costs for the chemicals are relatively high and the processes lead to a sludge disposal problem which is still unresolved. In the case of alum precipitation, the recovery of the precipitant as proposed by Lea, Rohlich, and Katz (11), may lighten this burden to some degree. It is felt, however, that the complications involved will be bearable for very large installations only. The majority of the municipal plants will have to rely on more modest processes.

In regard to technical equipment for the precipitation procedures, the extended experience from water purification by flocculation can be used without restriction. Reaction kinetics and the type of precipitants applied favor strongly the combined flocculation-sedimentation units with internal sludge recirculation. In the combined lime-iron process such a unit was operated satisfactorily with a hydraulic load of the flocculation compartment of 60–63 $m^3/m^3 \cdot d$ and an upflow rate of 0.9–1.0 m/h in the sedimentation compartment. In large units this upflow rate can probably be increased considerably.

3. Nitrogen elimination, is a process for which, according to present experience and the theoretical considerations by Downing, fairly reliable indications for the dimensioning of a nitrifying activated sludge plant can be given. The sludge age will be one pertinent design factor for the practitioner, and as far as calculation of the aeration is concerned, the formula indicated by the author may be used. One major difficulty arises from the fact that sludge accumulation rates, in function of waste concentration and composition and of plant operation conditions, are still insufficiently known. The approximation given in the formula by Downing and Hopwood (28) is of some help. Much more precise information is needed, however, for design purposes, especially in critical situations such as plants with low sewage temperatures. For average American municipal sewage, the characteristics of which are closely similar to those in our experimental station, a sludge age of 2–3 days at temperatures above 14°C. and of 4–5 days at 8–10°C. will yield a stable nitrification. Higher values will be needed with more concentrated sewage, as has been demonstrated by the English investigations.

Dimensioning of the denitrification tank is much simpler. Base values are (a) the concentration of the mixed liquor leaving the aerator and being transferred to the denitrifier, and (b) the endogenous respiration rate of the sludge. It has been indicated that the endogenous denitrification rate of the sludge is theoretically strictly correlated to its endogenous oxygen respiration rate. In the course of long denitrification experiments both respiration rates have been measured frequently. Figure 18 summarizes some results. The regression of denitrification on oxygen respiration was calculated with its confidence limits. It is felt that for the range of sludge characteristics to be expected from nitrifying plants, this correlation provides adequate information for the design of a denitrification basin. Since the absolute denitrification rate of a given sludge is strictly proportional to its concentration, it is economically relevant in the design of a nitrogen removal system, in order to provide for as high mixed liquor concentrations as is compatible with secondary clarifier operation. This need coincides with the exigencies of the nitrifying treatment stage, since increasing mixed liquor solids concentrations involves an automatically increasing sludge age.

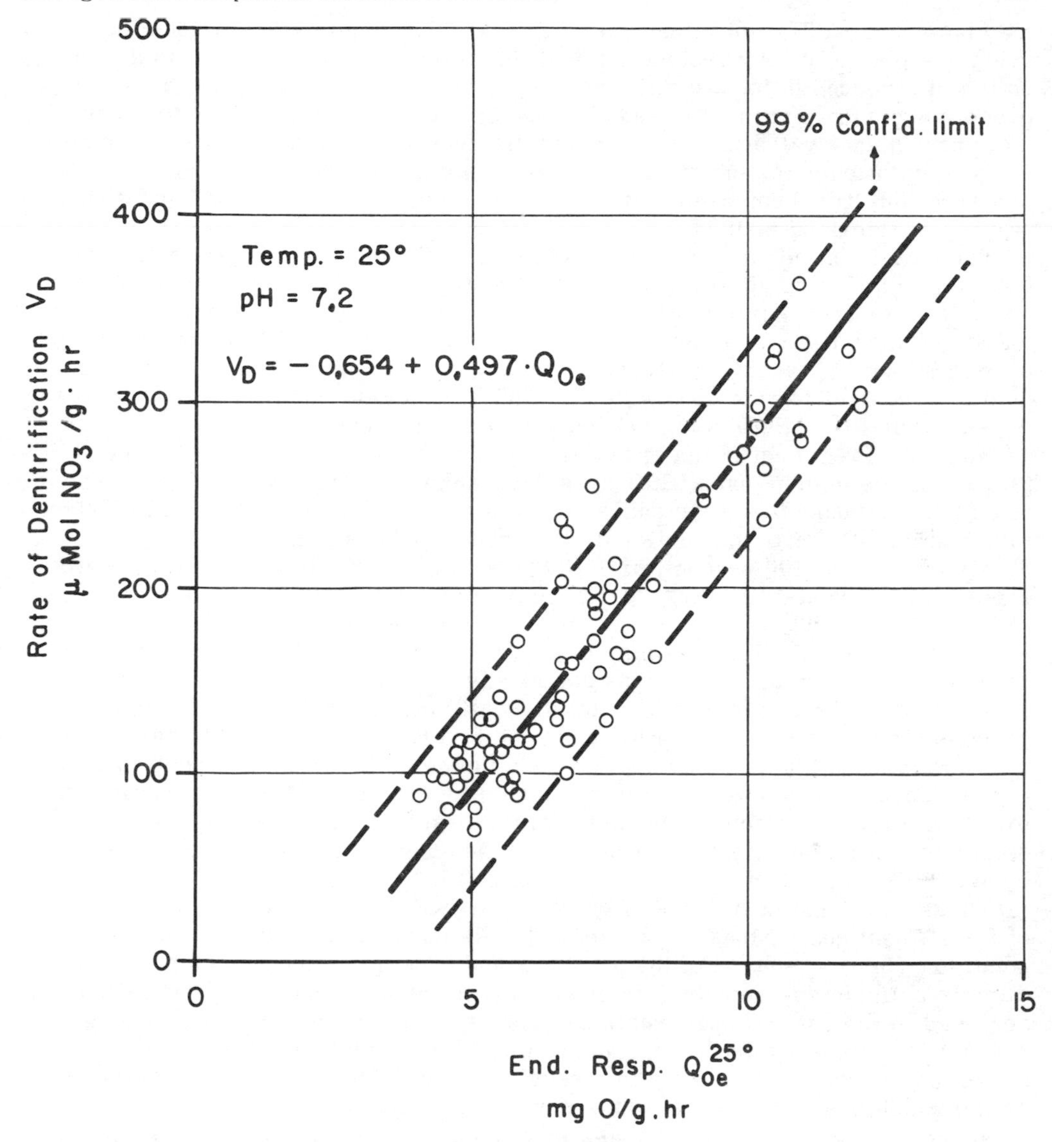

Figure 18. Endogenous denitrification rate of activated sludge under strict anaerobiosis, correlated with its endogenous oxygen respiration rate. Observations with sludges from the experiment of Figure 17 and other activated sludge plants. Temperature = 25°C., *p*H = 7.5, Warburg manometers.

COST CONSIDERATIONS

On the basis of established specific costs for conventional activated sludge plants, and with emphasis on the above indications as to the additional construction and operation requirements, an estimate of the first costs and operation costs for nutrient removal may be made. The author is fully aware of the fact that his basic assumptions, which are derived from conditions in Switzerland, may be entirely different in the United States. The general proportions, however, are probably not affected, nor will the essential final conclusions depend on the differences in local conditions. The cost estimates have been based on present experience with activated sludge plants in Switzerland. For tertiary treatment some evaluations published by Hanisch (35) and recent cost estimates for precipitation units and sludge disposal systems of a Swiss plant (now under construction) have been used. Prices for chemicals are for carload quantities valid in Switzerland in 1964.

Table 11 is based on a complete treatment activated sludge system of conventional design with no appreciable nitrification and a BOD removal in the biological unit of about 90 percent. For sludge treatment the aerobic process was choosen (about 12 days detention time) and dewatering is by filter presses to a cake of about 40 percent moisture. Dimensions of the biological plant are based on a dry-weather flow of 400 1/cap/day and a treatment capacity of 1.5 times the dry-weather flow. BOD in the settled sewage is conventionally assumed as 50 g/cap/day. Treatment of the excess sludge of the precipitation unit includes thickening, dewatering on a filter press to a cake of approximately 5 percent moisture, and dumping of the cakes at a site about 5 km. from the plant. Prices for chemicals: $FeCl_3$ in solution of 30 percent, delivered in tanks at 40.00 Sfr/100 kg $FeCl_3$ 100 percent, or 1.15 Sfr/kg Fe^{3+}; lime in 50 kg. sacks, delivered in carloads at 12.00 Sfr/100 kg. Price for electrical current is 0.07 Sfr/kWh.

The cost items in Table 11 may be subject to minor variations; obviously, however, the principle proportions can hardly be changed. It is immediately seen that the increase of capital costs is negligible for the nitrogen removal process alone; the P-precipitation units, however, require an additional 20 percent and installation of the complete cycle augments this item by about 43 percent. Operation costs are largely dominated by the expenditure for chemicals for P-removal, as is to be expected. On the basis of the prices assumed, the complete chain of nutrient removal processes causes an increase of annual costs by about 50–60 percent.

These additional costs have of course to be weighed against the improvement of the effluent quality (base of Table 11). It is undeniable, however, that the expenditure for the removal of the nutrients and of a small quantity of remaining organic pollutants is very high in proportion to the costs and the purification achieved in the conventional treatment phases. On the other hand this expense has to be compared with the total economical loss, eventually caused by an effluent of only conventional quality in a receiving water body by direct impairment or by the supplementary costs at water purification plants.

The foregoing results summarize to a certain extent the presently available information on nutrient removal processes, their economic consequences, and their supplementary beneficial effects on effluent quality. As can be seen today, the conventional biological treatment will still represent the basis of all further purification steps, both for economic and for process reasons. This is an important fact in so far as it may convincingly be stated that past scientific and monetary investment in sewage purification will certainly not lose its value, not even in view of eventual totally new procedures necessitated by the requests for much higher effluent qualities.

REFERENCES

(1) Ketchum, B. H. "The Absorption of Phosphate and Nitrate by Illuminated Cultures of Nitzschia Closterium," *Amer. J. Botany, 26,* 399–407 (1939).

(2) Rodhe, W. "Environmental Requirements of Fresh-Water Plankton Algae," *Symb. Bot. Upsaliensis, 10,* 1 (1948).

(3) Edmondson, W. T. "Changes in the Oxygen Deficit of Lake Washington," *Verh. Int. Verein. Limnol., 1^* (in press).

(4) Liepold, R. "Die limnologischen Verhältnisse des Zellersees, seine Verunreinigung und Sanierung," *Inform. Blatt Europ. Föderation f. Gewässerschutz* (in press).

(5) Lawton, G. W. "Limitation of Nutrients as a Step in Ecological Control," *Algae and Metropolitan Wastes*. Trans. 1960 Seminar, Taft Center, Cincinnati. Sec. TR W 61-63, 108-117 (1961).

(6) Baldinger, F. "Das Hallwilersee-Projekt als Beispiel einer gross-zügigen Seesanierung," *Schweiz. Z. Hydol., 19,* 18–36 (1957).

(7) Hanisch, B. "Die technischen Massnahmen zur Abwasserbeseitigung am Tegernsee," *Gas- und Wasserfach* (1963).

(8) Wuhrmann, K. "Stickstoff und Phosphorelimination, Ergebnisse von Versuchen im technischen Masstab.," *Schweiz, Z. Hydrol. 26,* 520–558 (1964).

(9) Kaltwasser, H., G. Vogt, and H. G. Schlegel. "Polyphosphatsynthese während der Nitratatmung von Micrococcus denitrificans Stamm 11," *Arch. Mikrobiol., 44,* 259–265 (1962).

(10) Shapiro, J., and G. V. Levin. "Reducing Secondary Effluent Phosphorus Concentration," *First Progr. Rep. Dept. Sanit. Engin, and Water Resources*. Baltimore: The Johns Hopkins University Press (1963).

(11) Lea, W. L., G. A. Rohlich, and W. J. Katz. "Removal of Phosphates from Treated Sewage," *Sewage Ind. Wastes, 26,* 261–275 (1954).

(12) Malhotra, S. K., F. G. Lee, and G. A. Rohlich. "Nutrient Removal from Secondary Effluent by Alum Flocculation and Lime Precipitation," *Inter. J. Air Water Poll., 8,* 487–500 (1964).

(13) Galal-Gorchev, H., and W. Stumm. "The Reaction of Ferric Iron with Ortho-Phosphate," *J. Inorg. Nucl. Chem., 25,* 576–584 (1963).

(14) Henriksen A. "Laboratory Studies on the Removal of Phosphates from Sewage by the Coagulation Process," Part 1: *Schweiz. Z. Hydrol., 24,* 253–271 (1962); Part 2: *Schweiz. Z. Hydrol., 25,* 380–396 (1963).

(15) Lockett, W. J., and E. Ardern. "Studies on the Activated-Sludge Process," *Ann. Rep.* City of Manchester: Rivers Dept. (1928).

(16) Nesmejanoff. "Untersuchungen über die Wirkungen von Eisenund Aluminiumsalzen, Belebungsvorgang des Schlammes," *Ges.-Ing., 58,* 471–476 (1935).

(17) Thomas, E. A. "Verfahren zur Entfernung von Phosphaten aus Abwässern." Schweiz. Pat. No. 361543 vom 15. (April 1962).

(18) Rudolfs, W. "Phosphates in Sewage and Sludge Treatment, II. Effect on Coagulation, Clarification and Sludge Volume," *Sewage Works, J., 19,* 178-190 (1947).

(19) Owen, R. "Removal of Phosphorus from Sewage Plant Effluent with Lime," *Sewage Ind. Wastes, 25,* 548–556 (1953).

(20) Stumm W. "Chemical Elimination of Phosphates, a Discussion," *Proceedings*, First International Conference, London (1962). *Advances in Water Pollution Research*, edited by W. W. Eckenfelder. Vol. 2. Oxford: Pergamon Press (1964).

(21) Stumm, W. "Chemical Water Quality Relations. Environmental Measurements," *PHS Publication*, No. 999-AP-15, 299–323 (1964).

(22) Wuhrmann, K. "Die dritte Reinigungsstufe, Wege and bisherige Erfolge in der Eliminierung eutrophierender Stoffe," *Schweiz. Z. Hydrol., 19,* 409–427 (1957).

(23) Wuhrmann, K. "Nitrogen Removal in Sewage Treatment Processes," *Verh. Int. Verein. Limnol., 15,* 580–596 (1964).

(24) Nesselson, E. J. "Removal of Inorganic Nitrogen from Sewage Effluents." Ph.D. Dissertation, University of Wisconsin (1954).

(25) Kuhn, P. A. "Removal of Ammonia Nitrogen from Sewage Effluent." MS Thesis, University of Wisconsin (1956).

(26) Rohlich G. A, "Methods for the Removal of Phosphorus and Nitrogen from Sewage Plant Effluents," *Advances Water Pollution Research*. Vol. 2. Oxford: Pergamon Press (1964).

(27) Downing, A. L., H. A. Painter, and G. Knowles. "Nitrification in the Activated-Sludge Process," *Proc. Inst. Sewage Purif.*, 2–25 (1963).

(28) Downing, A. L., and A. P. Hopwood. "Some Observations on the Kinetics of Nitrifying Activated Sludge Plants," *Schweiz. Z. Hydrol.* *26*, 271–288 (1964).

(29) Wuhrmann, K. "Effect of Oxygen Tension on Biochemical Reactions in Sewage Purification Plants," *Proceedings*, 3rd. Conference on Biological Waste Treatment (1960). *Advances in Biological Waste Treatment*. Oxford: Pergamon Press (1963).

(30) Wuhrmann, K., and Kl. Mechsner. "Ueber den Einfluss von Sauerstoffspannung und Wasserstoffionenkonxentration des Milieus auf die mikrobielle Denitrifikation," *Path. Microbiol.*, *28*, 99–106 (1965).

(31) Bringmann, G., R. Kühn, and B. Wagner. "Modellversuche zur biologischen Stickstoffabgasung aus Klärwässern," *Ges Ing.*, *80*, 364–367 (1959).

(32) Bringmann, G. "Optimale Stickstoffabgasung durch Einsatz von nitrifizierendem Belebtschlamm und Redoxsteuerung," *Ges. Ing.*, *81*, 140–142 (1960).

(33) Bringmann, G. "Vollstandige biologische Stickstoffeliminierung aus Klarwassern im Anschluss an ein Hochleistungsnitrifikationsverfahren," *Ges. Ing.*, *82*, 233–235 (1961).

(34) Westgarth, Sulzer F., and D. Okun. "Anaerobiosis in the Activated Sludge Process," *Proceedings*, 2nd International Conference, Tokyo (1964); *Adv. in Water Poll. Res.*, *2*, 43–54 (1965).

(35) Hanisch B. "Technische und wirtschaftliche Ueberlegungen zur Frage der Stickstoff- und Phosphorelimination," *Schweiz. Z. Hydrol.*, *26*, 559–568 (1964).

BIOLOGICAL RESPONSES TO NUTRIENTS—EUTROPHICATION: PROBLEMS IN FRESHWATER

E. Gus Fruh
The University of Texas, Austin, Texas

EMPHASIS ON EUTROPHICATION

An increasing number of impoundments are experiencing ecological upsets (1). The symptoms of such difficulties are frequent algal blooms, prolific weed growth, and depletion of oxygen in the hypolimnion of deep impoundments that undergo thermal stratification. The water quality of these impoundments may deteriorate to such a degree that the economic use of the waters for water supply, recreation, aquatic life, and agriculture is affected (2).

These water quality problems stem from the excessive activity of the photosynthetic organisms. The literature stresses the problems due to the phytoplankton. The intrinsic requirements of these algae demand a favorable environment. Physical factors include light, which serves as an energy source, temperature, and turbulence. The chemical factors are the nutrients and the toxins. The biological factors are the effects of one organism upon the growth of others.

In view of the multi-interaction of these factors in the aquatic environment, one might ask why so much emphasis is put on nutrients. The reason for the preoccupation with the nutrient influx (eutrophication) does not lie in the underestimation of the importance of the other environmental factors, but rather in the recognition that these factors are, for all practical purposes, beyond control.

For instance, little can be done to alter light or turbulence. By contrast, the nutrients which are important in plant growth are subject to at least partial control through elimination or modification of some of their sources. It should always be realized, however, that although an investigator might attempt to simplify his studies by looking only at nutrients, his results might be due to the other factors affecting photosynthesis, or to interactions between the nutrients and these factors.

It is the purpose of this presentation to provide a framework of reference on the eutrophication problems of freshwaters. Information of importance to this problem has accrued from work initiated from the different points of view of botany, limnology, and sanitary engineering. As a result, the literature is badly scattered. Naturally, all the approximations and errors of abridgment, simplification, and bias of the author's own experience arise when summarizing the literature of a broad field. Nevertheless, such a presentation points out at least a few of the areas in which our knowledge is deficient and where we meet the greatest difficulty in applying what information we do have.

NUTRIENTS

The first data on algae nutrition were gleaned from the Chlorophyceae, which had been isolated from mineral media. It was naturally concluded that inorganic elements were indispensible for algae life. The mere presence of an element in the plant, particularly if it occurred with great regularity among diverse species, was taken in itself as evidence of essentiality. It was soon recognized, however, that the algae had the capacity, within rather wide limits, of indiscriminate absorption. The algae can absorb essential as well as superfluous or even toxic elements. While every essential element must of course be present in the algae, not every element present is essential. Later, discoveries were made that an entirely new group of essential inorganic elements was overlooked because the small quantities in which the nutrients were required were usually supplied by the impurities in the nutrient medium. Magnesium sulfate, present in impure form in most media, is still a major source of these inorganic micronutrients. In order to cultivate a wider variety of species of algae, it has been found necessary for botanists in the past to add ingredients of natural origin and unknown composition, such as soil extract, soil water, lake water, yeast, or peptone, to the synthetic media. This indicates that organic compounds are required by these algae in order to grow and reproduce.

A chemical nutrient is now defined as anything that can be used for a source of energy, for the promotion of growth, or for the repair of tissue. However, the botany, limnology, and sanitary engineering literature have distinguished the requirements that nutrients fulfill. Ketchum (3) has classified these requirements into different types, as shown in Table 12. If the algae cannot grow, reproduce, or photosynthesize because a nutrient is lacking in the environment, the nutrient is termed "absolute." An "absolute" nutrient cannot be replaced by another nutrient. The "normal" nutrient requirement is the quantity of each nutrient contained in the cells produced during active growth of a population when no nutrient is limiting. The "optimum" nutrient requirement is the nutrient concentration that will permit the maximum rate of growth, or reproduction, or photosynthesis. The maximum concentration for each of these biological functions is naturally different. In all three cases, there will be nutrient concentrations higher than optimum which may be toxic or inhibitory, and nutrient concentrations lower than optimum which are limiting.

In the past, great stress has been laid upon Liebig's (4) Law of the Minimum, which states that the nutrient in the relative minimum determined the rate of growth. As pointed out by Schütte (5), this is an extremely useful law, which is completely valid and of great use in science. When carrying out experiments on limiting nutrients, one should realize from this law the importance of adding small quantities of nutrients similar to the concentrations present in the section of the aquatic environment under investigation. To culture a natural population of

TABLE 12

NUTRIENT TYPES*

a) Absolute
  1) If the nutrient is lacking, the algae cannot grow, reproduce, or photosynthesize
  2) Cannot be replaced by another nutrient

b) Normal
  1) Quantity of nutrient contained in the cells produced during active growth of a population when no nutrient is limiting

c) Optimum
  1) Nutrient concentration that will permit the maximum
    (a) Rate of growth, or
    (b) Reproduction, or
    (c) Photosynthesis
  2) Low concentration may be limiting
    (a) Under natural conditions
    (b) When all other nutrients are in excess
  3) High concentration may be toxic or inhibitory

*From Ketchum (3).

algae with the concentrations of all nutrients except one in excess of requirements, naturally, has very limited application to the natural condition. This is because the large concentrations of the macronutrients or the inorganic micronutrients added as impurities may be toxic to the algae, or antagonism and/or stimulation between elements might arise, or artificial deficiencies might be induced. Thus, Schütte (5) stresses that there is a danger that Liebig's Law does not go far enough, because it does not emphasize the influence that excess has on phenomena such as growth. This omission should be clarified by addition of Voisin's (6) Law of the Maximum, which states that the nutrient present in the relative maximum also determines the yield.

NITROGEN AND PHOSPHORUS

Based on agricultural experience, nitrogen and phosphorus were thought to be the major elements limiting primary production even before their estimation was possible. Although their measurement today still needs improvement, many studies have accumulated impressive evidence that nitrogen and phosphorus play a major part in production and periodicity, and in determining the type of community present. In fact, nitrogen and phosphorus are the only two nutrients about which we have considerable laboratory and field data.

Sources

Of all the possible nutrients, only nitrogen and phosphorus have been studied to any extent in the field. The following review presents the nitrogen and phosphorus concentrations reported in the literature for rainfall, groundwater, forest runoff, agricultural runoff, urban drainage, and wastewater effluents. A more detailed review is given by Fruh (7).

Rainfall

Table 13 shows a number of references from which nitrogen quantities in rainwater have been obtained. It is obvious that through the precipitation a significant quantity of nitrogen can enter an impoundment with a large surface area. Based on data reported by Shah (8), Fruh and Lee (9) estimated that approximately 90,000 pounds of nitrogen entered Lake Mendota, Madison, Wisconsin, by rainfall.

Table 14 presents the quantity of phosphorus found in the precipitation of various countries. The data range from an unmeasurable trace to concentrations as high as 0.1 mg/l. Depending on the phosphorus concentration used, Fruh and Lee (9) computed that the precipitation could be equal to 0.4-21 percent of the total phosphorus brought in by the surface tributaries of Lake Mendota (20).

Precipitation should also be checked as an important source of the plant nutrients in rural and urban drainage.

Groundwater

Few investigations have been conducted on the quantity of nutrients entering lakes and reservoirs via groundwater. Based on the flows reported by Cline (21) and the average nitrogen values reported by Cline (21) and Domogalla and his associates (22, 23), Fruh and Lee (9) computed that groundwater was probably the major nitrogen source for Lake Mendota. In view of the fact that nitrate concentrations in groundwater are frequently in the mg/l range throughout the country, it seems obvious that groundwater should not be overlooked as a source of nitrogen. Sylvester and Anderson (24) assumed the mean total phosphorus content to be 0.3 mg/l for the large quantity of subsurface inflow entering Green Lake, Washington. Sawyer (25) reports that the phosphorus content of groundwater is usually negligible.

TABLE 13

NITROGEN (N) IN RAINWATER

Reference	Nitrogen (N)	Concentration (mg/l)
Carroll (10)	Nitrate (U.S.)	0.16–1.06
	Ammonia (U.S.)	0.04–1.70
	Nitrate (Europe)	0.00–0.36
	Ammonia (Europe)	0.00–6.80
Larson and Hettick (11)	Ammonia plus nitrate	0.17–3.40
Weibel *et al.* (12)	Inorganic nitrogen	0.02–1.40
Gambel (13)	Nitrate	0.05–0.23

TABLE 14

PHOSPHORUS (P) IN RAINWATER

Reference	Concentration (mg/l)
Chalupa (14)	0.004
Miller (15)	0.042
Putnam and Olsen (16)	trace
Tamm (17)	0.030
Tamm (18)	0.100
Voight (19)	0.010

Forest Runoff

Sylvester (26) reported an average runoff of 0.3-0.8 lbs total phosphorus/acre/year and 1.3-3.0 lbs total nitrogen/acre/year for forested areas containing large reservoirs and insignificant human habitation. Little of the total phosphate was in orthophosphate form. At a seminar at The University of Texas, Wuhrmann (27) reported that his investigations in forested Swiss areas showed similar runoff results.

Agricultural Runoff

Based on their studies in the Yakima Valley, Sylvester (26) and Sylvester and Seabloom (28) reported significant differences in the nitrogen and phosphorus content of different types of irrigation return flow. For surface irrigation return flows, total phosphorus ranged 0.92-3.88 lb/acre/year and total nitrogen 2.45-24.0 lb/acre/year. Subsurface irrigation return flows were 2.5-8.1 lb total phosphorus/acre/year and 38-166 lb total nitrogen/acre/year. Values between those of forested areas and irrigation return flows have been reported in the literature for fertilized pasture and agricultural areas by numerous investigators (29-35). Wuhrmann (27) reported similar findings for Switzerland.

Despite these results, a number of soil chemists disagree with the statement that runoff from fertilized agricultural areas is frequently a significant source of these two elements. No doubt the quantity of the two nutrients in the solution phase of the runoff is not high. However, the quantity of nutrients on the eroded solids generally is quite high and is readily leachable upon entering a different chemical environment, such as a lake. The erosion process is selective, and the quantity of nitrogen and phosphorus is significant on the potentially erodible fine soil fraction which comprises but a small percentage of the total soil (30, 34, 35). However, it is possible that improved agricultural land management could offset the increased application of fertilizers to pastures and crop areas.

Urban Drainage

Table 15 is a tabulation of the data obtained by various investigators from 1943 to 1965. The difference in nutrient content of urban runoff before and after rains as reported by Sylvester and Anderson (24) was because of antecedent dry periods. The source of nitrogen and phosphorus is the fertilization of lawns and gardens. The data of Weibel *et al.* (12) showing runoff containing 0.8 lb total phosphorus/acre/year and 8.5 lb total nitrogen/acre/year appears appropriate for the normal urban areas. Fruh and Lee (9) reported that the storm runoff coefficient for the area studied by Sawyer *et al.* (36) in 1943 had increased three to four times. Thus, not only the concentration of nutrients, but also the quantity of urban runoff is increasing.

TABLE 15

URBAN DRAINAGE (AVERAGE VALUES)

Reference	Conditions	Total N (mg/l)	Total P (mg/l)
Benzie and Courchaine (37)	Combined sewer	3.60	2.76
	Storm sewer	0.90	0.90
Weibel *et al.* (12)	Storm runoff	2.75	0.26
Sylvester and Anderson (24)	Arterial runoff		
	Antecedent rainfall—0.42	1.05	0.19
	Antecedent rainfall—0	5.20	0.23
	Residential runoff		
	Antecedent rainfall—0.66	1.66	0.16
	Antecedent rainfall—0	2.60	0.23
Sylvester (26)	Subsurface urban drain	0.78	0.10
	Small urban creek	1.81	0.14
	Medium urban creek	1.48*	0.11
Sawyer *et al.* (36)	Storm water sewer with no dry-weather flow	1.74	0.25

*Nitrates only.

Wastewater Effluents

Considerable evidence has accumulated which shows that domestic sewage is an important source of nitrogen and phosphorus. Conventionally treated domestic sewage usually varies from 15 to 35 mg/l total nitrogen and from 6 to 12 mg/l total phosphorus (38). Comparison of the earlier data of Sawyer (39) and Owen (40) to those of Hume and Gunnerson (38) shows the contribution of detergents to the fertilizing element phosphorus. Little data are available in the literature concerning nutrients in industrial wastewater effluents.

Wuhrmann (27, 41) has made an interesting comparison of potential nutrient contribution from relatively uninhabitated areas utilized for various agricultural purposes to the contribution from cities of different population density. He assumed the rather conservative values of 3.5 g phosphorus/capita day and 12 g nitrogon/capita day. Comparison of the data in Table 16 shows that one person/acre can contribute as much phosphorus as the greatest source of runoff, while ten people/acre are needed for nitrogen to accomplish the same goal. It is obvious that domestic sewage is the most significant source of phosphorus. It is also obvious from the data in Table 16 that the nitrogen to phosphorus ratio will be

TABLE 16

COMPARISON OF NITROGEN AND PHOSPHORUS POTENTIAL FROM RUNOFF AND DOMESTIC SEWAGE*

Source	Total Nitrogen (lb/acre-year)	Total Phosphorus (lb/acre-year)
Forest runoff	1.3–3.0	0.3–0.8
Surface irrigation return flow	2.45–24.0	0.92–3.88
Subsurface irrigation return flow	38.0–166.0	2.5–8.1
Urban runoff	8.5	0.8
People (1/acre)	9.7	2.8
People (10/acre)	97.0	28.0

*From Wuhrmann (27).

below 15:1, usually cited as optimum for algal growth (42). Thus, in lakes that become eutrophic because of domestic sewage, probably nitrogen is the more critical element of the two.

Relationship of Nuisance Conditions to Nitrogen and Phosphorus

The literature abounds with numerous investigations of fish ponds and lakes which have undergone eutrophication. These investigations indicate that phosphorus and/or nitrogen are present in limiting amounts. However, there are usually three reasons why the conclusions of many of the investigators cannot be accepted at face value:

1. The nitrogen and phosphorus determinations were limited to the nitrate and orthophosphate concentrations of the water;
2. most nitrogen and phosphorus data has been obtained during "bloom" conditions, when the algae, although concentrated, have actually drawn nutrients from a much larger volume of water; and
3. the experimental work of most investigators on the change in nitrogen and phosphorus concentrations as well as changes in the quantity and species of the algae within the eutrophic body of water has been limited, in but a few cases, to studies of only a few years.

The last objection has been rectified at least in part for the Madison Lakes by the studies of Fruh and Lee (9). Based on data available at the University of Wisconsin since before the turn of the century, these investigators have shown that the standing crop of algae in Lake Mendota has increased manyfold since the earlier quantitative work of Birge and Juday (43). The dominant genera present in "blooms" have also changed, although the blue-green algae now producing nuisance conditions occasionally did occur as far back as 1854. Phosphorus and nitrogen data were also available from about 1925 to 1950. By dividing the nutrient data into four limnological seasons (the ice cover period, the spring runoff and overturn period, the warm temperature growing and temperature stratification period, and the low flow and fall overturn period), Fruh and Lee (9) found that the average phosphorus concentrations in the tributaries and in Lake Mendota have increased significantly over the years while the total nitrogen averages have remained substantially the same. However, such data still must be looked at with caution, because only orthophosphate data were obtained and because of the large variation of the nutrient data from the average computed for each limnological period.

Phosphorus

It is not known to what degree the concentration of inorganic phosphorus affects the specific composition of phytoplankton communities. One of the reasons for this has been the measurement of orthophosphate during "bloom" conditions rather than in the winter when the "total available" phosphorus can be measured, because lake and reservoirs usually are completely mixed and there is little algal growth. Yet even in "bloom" conditions, waters with high orthophosphate concentrations (50 $\mu g/l$) often have dominant genera different from waters with relatively low concentrations (1 μg PO_4-P/l). This has led Provasoli (44) to cite that phosphorus in high conditions can be considered toxic to many algae classified as oligotrophic indicators. Lund (45), however, takes objection to this statement and cites many situations involving planktonic freshwater algae which in part refute Provasoli's (44) statement. Lund (45) goes on to point out many facts that have to be considered, some of which will be reviewed here.

Although orthophosphates are the main source of phosphorus, algae vary among themselves in their ability to utilize more complex inorganic phosphates (46, 47), as well as organic phosphate (48, 45). Also, the detention time in many of our lakes and reservoirs is sufficient for the condensed polyphosphates to be hydrolyzed to orthophosphate (49).

Furthermore, although "total available" phosphorus in solution might be correlated with algal growth, the limiting concentration of this nutrient (if it ever occurs) might be unmeasurable because of the rapid turnover time (10 minutes) for phosphorus (50, 51). This indicates not only a high demand for phosphorus, but also a great efficiency of use. Golterman (52) reported that when an alga was killed under sterile conditions, 70-80 percent of the phorphorus was liberated from the cells in a few days. Only the phosphorus connected with the nucleic acids and proteins was not liberated. In comparison only 20-30 percent of the nitrogen was released under the same conditions, while a number of weeks were necessary for a similar percentage of silica and iron to be liberated. The liberation rate for phosphorus was on the order of a few hours in lake water.

Another factor which makes any correlation between "total available" phosphorus in solution and algal growth somewhat dubious is the fact of "luxury" phosphorus uptake by the algae (42, 53, 54). Fitzgerald (55, 56) has developed extractive and enzymatic techniques to measure this luxury phosphorus.

Nitrogen

A number of investigations indicate that nitrogen is the limiting nutrient in various bodies of water (42, 45, 57). In particular, Staub (58) showed that it was nitrogen rather than phosphorus which was the limiting nutrient in the growth of *Oscillatoris rubescons* D.C. in the Zurichsee. He showed also, however, the important role played by light conditions prior to blooms, by temperatures at the greater depths in the lake, and by the vertical currents.

It is important to realize that low concentrations of nitrate do not necessarily imply a lack of nitrogen. In the past, limnologists generally have neglected the measurement of ammonia, particularly, in unpolluted lakes. Significant amounts can enter via rainfall. During the winter in temperate-zone lakes ammonia is present in high concentrations under the ice cover.

Furthermore, the algae can fix gaseous nitrogen. A number of investigators (59, 60) have shown that this source of nitrogen can be significant. Generally, nitrogen fixation can occur in the presence of low concentrations of nitrate, but apparently not ammonia, which is an intermediate in the nitrogen assimilation pathway. The pathway is the same as that found for bacteria such as *Azotobacter* (61).

Many blue-green algae fix nitrogen, but most of the planktonic genera involved in "blooms," such as *Oscillatoria, Lyngbya, Coelosphaerium, Gomphosphaeria, Microcystis,* and *Aphanizomenon,* have been tested and do not do so. *Anabaena, Anabaenopsis,* and *Gloeotrichia* appear to be the main blue-green genera that fix nitrogen. The common presence of large numbers of bacteria in or around planktonic blue-green algae raises the possibility that the algae obtain their nitrogen from nitrogen-fixing bacteria. Tew (62), however, could not grow *Azotobacter* directly on the carbon available from the *Microcystis,* nor could the blue-green algae directly utilize the nitrogen from the bacteria. However, in lake water the colored *Pseudomonas* apparently transferred the nitrogen and the carbon to the *Microcystis* and *Azotobacter,* respectively. Dugdale and Neess (59) caution that the general physical and nutritional characteristics of the body of water must be such as to encourage the growth of the blue-green algae and the proper bacteria before various environmental factors operate to reduce the concentrations of the various forms of combined nitrogen to very low levels. The presence of micronutrients such as calcium, boron, and molybdenum is required.

Sawyer and Ferullo (63) studied the effect of phosphorus, nitrogen, and alkalinity on nitrogen fixation. Their results are shown in factorial design form in Table 17. In general, statistical evaluation indicates that the phosphorus effect is significant as well as the nitrogen-phosphorus interaction. Differences in alkalinity had little effect, although the alkalinity-nitrogen interaction could be important. It should be noted that rather large quantities of ammonia were added to the original waters, which contained only trace amounts of phosphorus. According to current thinking on the nitrogen fixation pathway all this ammonia would need to be utilized before fixation of atmospheric nitrogen could begin. On this basis the trace quantities of phosphorus evidently could be recycled so rapidly that the large quantities of ammonia in solution could be depleted. Unfortunately, even though five years has passed since the study of Sawyer and Ferullo (63), verification experiments have not been reported in the literature, nor has their excellent experimental approach via factorial designs been utilized.

Another factor which has received little attention in the literature is the "luxury" consumption of nitrogen by algae. Krauss (64) reported that the uptake of nitrogen proceeded almost as rapidly in cells whose growth was limited by micronutrient deficiency as in cells growing at a normal rate. This resulted in a very high nitrogen content in the cell. Gerloff and Skoog (42) and Golterman (52) reported similar results. If "luxury" nitrogen uptake is important under natural conditions, bioassay techniques in addition to chemical analyses would be needed.

MICRONUTRIENTS

In many lakes the appearance of algal "blooms" is synchronous with very low concentrations of nitrogen and phosphorus. However, some waters are so rich in these nutrients that it is doubtful that nitrogen and phosphorus could be the "limiting" nutrients. Very small quantities of inorganic and organic substances called "trace elements" are present in all matter. At one time they were regarded simply as contaminants and were not studied in great detail. Today, it is generally thought that the plants utilize the macronutrients as building materials, and the micronutrients as metal constituents of enzymes which enter into biological reactions. Thus, it is unfortunate that the term "trace element" is so widely used, since these substances function in a variety of ways, and because the sanitary engineer generally has the impression that "trace elements" do not play an important role.

TABLE 17

PHOSPHORUS EFFECT ON NITROGEN FIXATION*

July–August (N was 0.57 and 1.07 mg/l)					August–November (N was 0.92 and 1.42 mg/l)					December–February (N was 0.98 and 1.48 mg/l)				
#	alk.	N	P	ΔN (35 day)	#	alk.	N	P	ΔN (90 days)	#	alk.	N	P	ΔN (70 days)
1	-	-	-	0.21	1	-	-	-	0.31	1	-	-	-	0.57
2	+	-	-	0.20	2	+	-	-	0.38	2	+	-	-	0.34
3	-	+	-	0.31	3	-	+	-	0.84	3	-	+	-	0.07
4	+	+	-	-0.03	4	+	+	-	0.52	4	+	+	-	0.24
5	-	-	+	1.12	5	-	-	+	1.51	5	-	-	+	1.04
6	+	-	+	1.03	6	+	-	+	1.66	6	+	-	+	0.97
7	-	+	+	0.79	7	-	+	+	1.39	7	-	+	+	0.22
8	+	+	+	0.54	8	+	+	+	1.58	8	+	+	+	0.31

*From Sawyer and Ferullo (63).
Samples marked "+" were fortified with 0.2 mg/l P, or 0.5 mg/l NH_3-N, or 200 mg/l $NaHCO_3$. Light intensity was 500 foot-candles for 12 hrs/day. Room temperature.

TABLE 18

ELEMENTS REQUIRED BY GREEN PLANTS IN MACRO– OR MICROQUANTITIES*

Elements	Higher Plants	Green Algae (*Scenedesmus obliquus*)	Blue-Green Algae (*Anabaena cylindrica*)
C, H, O, N, P, S, K, Mg	Macro	Macro	Macro
Fe, Mn, Cu, Zn	Micro	Micro	Micro
Ca	Macro	Micro	Macro (?)
Mo	Micro	Micro	Micro (× 100)
Na	Micro (?)	Micro (?)	Macro
V	Micro (?)	Micro	Micro (?)
B	Micro	Micro (?)	Micro (?)
Cl	Micro	Micro (?)	Micro (?)
Cl	Micro (?)	Micro (?)	Micro

*From Arnon (65).

Inorganic Micronutrients

The inorganic micronutrients required by plants vary according to whether higher plants, green algae, or blue-green algae are being investigated. As shown in Table 18, Arnon (65) reported that all plants studied required carbon, hydrogen, oxygen, nitrogen, phosphorus, sulfur, potassium, and magnesium in macroquantities. Iron, manganese, copper, and zinc were necessary in microquantities. The requirements for the other elements were dependent on the type of plant used.

In a comprehensive review Eyster (66) made the following conclusions: (a) algae and green plants generally require manganese, iron, chlorine, zinc, and vanadium for photosynthesis; (b) those algae possessing the capability to fix atmospheric nitrogen require iron, calcium, boron, and molybdenum (some doubt remains about cobalt); and (c) various algae require manganese, calcium, boron, cobalt, copper, and silicon for various metabolic functions.

Organic Micronutrients

In a comprehensive review of organic matter, Saunders (67) showed that organic compounds may be utilized directly as energy sources or contain basic elements essential to the build-up of protoplasm. Provasoli (44) reported that of all the known vitamins and accessory growth factors only vitamin B_{12}, thiamine, and biotin have been found to be of any general importance to algae. Droop (68) reported that 60 percent of the algae strains studied (containing freshwater plankton, but mostly consisting of marine and nonplankton forms) needed an exogenous source of one or more accessory growth factors. Approximately 80 percent of these required vitamin B_{12}, 53 percent thiamine, and 10 percent biotin. Moreover, the dissolved organic material may form complexes with trace metals, thereby preventing precipitation or lowering the availability of these micronutrients (44). Similarly, organic complexes may tie up toxins or compounds which are secreted by the organisms to antagonize the metal poisons (67).

Field Studies

Considerable refinement in the measurement of algal productivity through the development of the carbon-14 bioassay method (69) has aided evaluation of the effects of the various inorganic and organic micronutrients on productivity in natural waters. Goldman (70) found that the addition of molybdenum to Castle Lake, California, increased the photosynthetic rates. Similar increases were also found upon the addition of various metal micronutrients and vitamins to lakes in Alaska and New Zealand (71). Menzel and Ryther (72) found iron to be the limiting nutrient in the Sargasso Sea, although after addition of iron, nitrogen and phosphorus quickly became limiting. Goldman and Carter (73) evaluated the relative nutrient contribution of various tributary waters to the primary productivity of Lake Tahoe and reported that iron was the critical nutrient.

NUTRIENT INTERACTIONS

As discussed previously, interactions between nutrients and various physical, chemical, and biological variables can negate any conclusions based on nutrient concentrations alone. A partial understanding of the complications arising from the multiple interaction displayed by environmental factors can be obtained from the experiments of Maddux and Jones (74). They used a continuous culture apparatus to measure the growth rates of two algae at different temperatures and light intensities and at two different levels of nitrate and phosphate enrichment of an artificial sea water medium. The two algae had a lower optimum light intensity and optimum temperature for maximum growth when cultured at the lower concentrations of nitrate and phosphorus. Thus, temperature and light-intensity data must accompany any results on "limiting" nutrients concentration. Moreover, published results on light and temperature tolerances of organisms grown on laboratory media containing nutrient levels higher than those in the aquatic environment become open to doubt.

BIOASSAYS

To avoid such nutrient interactions, a number of investigators have measured and expressed the fertility of a water in terms of growth of an alga under known conditions in the laboratory. However, often the test algae are not even components of the lake studied and frequently are not even planktonic (45). The water of the locality studied may contain substances which are growth inhibiting to the test algae. The filtration and sterilization processes in the laboratory may change many of the physical-chemical properties of the water. It is, therefore, a question whether information obtained by using such a method alone is relevant.

However, radiocarbon bioassays in conjunction with measurements of temperatures, light transmission, standing crop, and nutrient concentrations appear useful. Findenegg (75) found in oligotrophic lakes that the rate of carbon assimilation was small and did not decrease with depth. In lakes that were eutrophic, there was a distinct maximum of carbon assimilation at about 1-2 meters of depth and then a rapid decline with depth. A clear relationship existed between the decrease of carbon assimilation and of light transmission. For lakes in a transition state between oligotrophic and eutrophic conditions because of sewage, an additional peak of carbon assimilation occurred at the thermocline that may exceed the epilimnic peak.

The usefulness of such an approach for measurement of limiting nutrients is obvious.

CONTROL OF EUTROPHICATION

In addition to tertiary treatment, several approaches for control of lake eutrophication have received considerable attention in recent years. Presently, the chief method of controlling nutrient concentrations is by the diversion of nutrient-rich sources from the receiving body of water.

Fruh and Lee (9) showed the effect brought about by the diversion of domestic sewage around the Lower Madison Lakes. They indicate that the average orthophosphate and total nitrogen values at the outlet of each of the Madison Lakes steadily increased prior to the diversion, and that a substantial decrease occurred approximately one to three years following the diversion. Although the trend is evident, they caution that the average chemical data showed a large variation within each limnological period and that the average values of different investigators who obtained data during the same limnological periods were generally statistically different. Fruh and Lee (9) state that while the "blooms" continue in the still nutrient-rich waters of the Lower Madison Lakes, the nuisance conditions have become less acute. Their conclusions also took into account the changes in light penetration, depth of rooted aquatic vegetation, bottom fauna, and fish.

Oglesby and Edmondson (76) reported that by the summer of 1966 all waste-water effluents will be diverted around Lake Washington near Seattle. Although only about half of the diversion project was completed at the time of their report, their surveys during 1965 gave early indications of success.

Thomas (77) reported on the drainage system built around Lake Zurich, Switzerland. He cited from Lohr's (78) studies that the annual cost was approximately four dollars/inhabitant.

The chief difficulty with diversion is the nutrient-rich sediments within the lake. Citing the sediment leaching studies of Sawyer *et al.* (36), Fruh and Lee (9) expressed doubt that the Lower Madison Lakes would ever fully recover. Edmondson (1) agrees, but shows that not all lakes have nutrient-rich sediments during the early stages of eutrophication and, thus, predicts lake recovery following diversion.

The nutrients might also be removed from the lake itself. During summer temperature stratification, the nutrients usually accumulate in the hypolimnion of deep eutrophic lakes. Olszewski (79) successfully removed these nutrients at this time to prevent their recirculation during the fall overturn period. However, the water quality and the waste assimilative capacity of the waters downstream from the hypolimnetic release might deteriorate (80).

Harvesting of the primary and/or secondary producers is another method of removing nutrients. Fruh and Lee (9) reported that a significant reduction of nutrient in Lake Mendota could be obtained by harvesting shore-line vegetation during the summer growing season. Also, normal fish harvesting in Lake Mendota considerably reduced the nutrients. Even by using these two methods, however, the nutrient levels would be sufficient to support nuisance blooms if other environmental factors were favorable.

Other methods of control are not based on the principle of nutrient removal. Oglesby and Edmondson (76) are studying the effects of adding large amounts of nutrient-poor Seattle tap water to eutrophic Green Lake for dilution purposes. Sketelj and Rejic (81) are conducting a dilution study of Lake Bled in Yugoslavia. Bryan (82) has attempted to control many of the water quality problems arising from eutrophication by disrupting the temperature stratification by mixing or by aerating the hypolimnion.

CONCLUSIONS

One cannot state a priori what the limiting nutrients in any lake or reservoir are. They might be inorganic or organic and present in either macro- or micro-quantities. In particular, the current mental stagnation of the sanitary engineering field about the super importance of phosphorus should be broken. The best field approach to studying the critical concentrations of nutrients appears to be the radiocarbon bioassay in conjunction with measurements of temperature, light transmission, and total nutrient concentration. In evaluating significant sources of nutrients, one should not overlook rainfall, groundwater, and urban drainage.

Other than tertiary treatment, diversion of the nutrient-rich sources appears to be the most feasible solution. However, the leaching or bacterial decomposition of nutrients from the sediments appears to be the limiting factor in the rate of a lake's recovery.

Many processes in the aquatic environment are assigned to the bacteria. At this time, however, analytical techniques for quantitative evaluation of number and species of bacteria do not exist. This is the area of basic and applied research from which answers will be needed before eutrophication problems can be solved.

REFERENCES

(1) Edmondson, W. T. "Water Quality Management and Lake Eutrophication: The Lake Washington Case." Manuscript prepared for a Water Quality Management Seminar at the University of Washington (in press).

(2) Fruh, E. G., and G. F. Lee. "The Aging of Lakes," *Ind. Water Engr., 3,* 26 (1966).

(3) Ketchum, B. H. "Mineral Nutrition of Phytoplankton," *Ann. Rev. Plant Physiol., 5,* 55 (1954).

(4) Liebig, J. *Chemistry in Its Application to Agriculture and Physiology*. New York: J. Wiley & Sons, Inc. (1849).

(5) Schütte, K. H. *The Biology of the Trace Elements: Their Role in Nutrition*. London: Crosby Lockwood & Sons, Ltd. (1964).

(6) Voisin, A. "Schadet die Mineraldungung, wenn sie richtig angewendet wird, die Gesundheit der Menschen," *Munch. Med. Wschr.*, *103*, 1041, 1096, 1144 (1961).

(7) Fruh, E. G. "The Overall Picture of Eutrophication." Paper presented at the Texas Water and Sewage Works Association's Eutrophication Seminar held in College Station, Texas (March 1966).

(8) Shah, K. S. "Sulfur and Nitrogen Brought Down in Precipitation In Wisconsin." M. S. Thesis, University of Wisconsin (1962).

(9) Fruh, E. G., and G. F. Lee. "The Effect of Eutrophication upon the Water Resources Management of the Yahara River Basin." Report of the Water Chemistry Program, University of Wisconsin, Madison, Wisconsin (in press).

(10) Carrol, D. *Rainwater as a Chemical Agent of Geological Processes—A Review*. Geological Survey Water-Supply 1535-G (1962).

(11) Larson, T. E., and I. Hettick. *Mineral Composition of Rainwater*. Illinois State Water Survey Division Circular 56 (1956).

(12) Weibel, S. R., R. J. Anderson, and R. L. Woodward. "Urban Land Runoff as a Factor in Stream Pollution," *J. Water Poll. Cont. Fed.*, *36*, 914 (1964).

(13) Gambel, A. W. *Sulfate and Nitrate Content of Precipitation over Parts of North Carolina and Virginia*. Geological Survey Professional Paper 475-C, C209 (1963).

(14) Chalupa, J. "Eutrophication of Reservoirs by Atmospheric Phosphorus," *Sci. Pop. Inst. Chem. Technol., Praque, Fac. Technol. Fuel. Wat.*, *4*, 295 (1960); *Water Pollution Abstracts*, *35*, 5 Abs. No. 660.

(15) Miller, R. B. "The Chemical Composition of Rainwater at Taita, New Zealand, 1956–58," *New Zealand J. Sci.*, *4*, 844 (1961).

(16) Putnam, H. D., and T. A. Olson. *An Investigation of Nutrients in Western Lake Superior*. School of Public Health Report, University of Minnesota (1960).

(17) Tamm, C. O. "Removal of Plant Nutrients from Tree Crowns by Rain," *Physiol. Plant.*, *4*, 184 (1951).

(18) Tamm, C. O. "Growth, Yield, and Nutrition in Carpets of a Forest Moss," *Meddelanden fran Statens Skogsforkning Institute*, *43*, 1 (1953).

(19) Voight, G. H. "Alteration of the Composition of Rainwater by Trees," *Amer. Midland Nat.*, *63*, 321 (1960).

(20) Belter, W. G., and T. A. Calabresa. "The Origins and Quantities of Algal Fertilizers Tributary to Lake Mendota." M. S. Thesis, University of Wisconsin (1950).

(21) Cline, D. R. *Geology and Ground Water Resources of Dane County, Wisconsin*. Geological Survey Water-Supply Paper 1779-U (1965).

(22) Domogalla, B. P., E. B. Fred, and W. H. Peterson. "Seasonal Variations in the Ammonia and Nitrate Content of Lake Waters," *J. Amer. Water Works Assoc.*, *15*, 369 (1926).

(23) Tressler, W. L., and B. P. Domogalla. "Limnological Studies of Lake Wingra," *Trans. Wisc. Acad. Sci. Arts & Letters*, *26*, 331 (1931).

(24) Sylvester, R. O., and G. C. Anderson. "A Lake's Response to its Environment," *J. Sanit. Engr. Div. ASCE*, *90*, (1964).

(25) Sawyer, C. N. "Causes, Effects, and Control of Aquatic Growths, *J. Water Poll. Cont. Fed.*, *34*, 279 (1962).

(26) Sylvester, R. O. "Nutrient Content of Drainage Water from Forested, Urban, and Agricultural Areas," *Transactions*, Seminar on Algae and Metropolitan Wastes, R. A. Taft Sanitary Engineering Center, TR W61-3 (1961).

(27) Wuhrmann, K. Private Communication.

(28) Sylvester, R. O., and R. W. Seabloom. "Quality and Significance of Irrigated Return Flow," *J. Irrig. Drain., ASCE*, *89* (1963).

(29) Duley, F. L. "The Loss of Soluble Salts in Runoff Water," *Soil Sci.*, *21*, 401 (1926).

(30) Scarseth, G. D., and W. V. Chandler. "Losses of Phosphate from a Light Textured Soil in Alabama and Its Relation to Some Aspects of Soil Conservation," *J. Amer. Soc. Agron.*, *30*, 361 (1938).

(31) Rogers, H. T. "Plant Nutrient Losses by Erosion from a Corn, Wheat, & Clover Rotation on Dunmore Silt Loam," *Soil Sci. Soc. Amer. Proc.*, *6*, 263 (1941).

(32) Kohnke, H. "Runoff Chemistry: An Undeveloped Branch of Soil Science," *Soil Sci. Soc. Amer. Proc.*, *6*, 492 (1941).

(33) Fippen, E. O. "Plant Nutrient Losses in Silt and Water in the Tennessee River System," *Soil Sci.*, *60*, 223 (1945).

(34) Massey, H. F., and M. L. Jackson. "Selective Erosion of Fertility Constituents," *Soil Sci. Soc. Amer. Proc.*, *16*, 353 (1952).

(35) Eck, P. "Fertility Erosion Selectiveness on Three Wisconsin Soils." Ph.D. Thesis, University of Wisconsin (1957).

(36) Sawyer, C. N., J. B. Lackey, and A. T. Lenz. *Investigation of the Odor Nuisance Occurring in the Madison Lakes, Particularly Lakes Menona, Waubesa, and Kegonsa from July 1943 to July 1944.* Report to the Governor's Commission, State of Wisconsin (1944).

(37) Benzie, W. J., and R. J. Courchaine. "A Study of the Discharges from Separate Storm Sewers and Combined Sewers." Paper presented at the 38th Annual Conference of the Water Pollution Control Federation held in Atlantic City, New Jersey (1965).

(38) Hume, N. B., and C. E. Gunnerson. "Characteristics and Effects of Hyperion Effluent," *J. Water Poll. Cont. Fed.*, *34*, 15 (1962).

(39) Sawyer, C. N. "Some New Aspects of Phosphates in Relation to Lake Fertilization," *Sewage Ind. Wastes*, *24*, 768 (1952).

(40) Owen, R. "Removal of Phosphorus from Sewage Plant Effluent with Lime," *Sewage Ind. Wastes*, *25*, 548 (1953).

(41) Wuhrmann, K. "Nitrogen Removal in Sewage Treatment Processes," *Inter. Assoc. Theor. Appl. Limnol.*, *15*, 579 (1964).

(42) Gerloff, G. C., and F. Skoog. "Nitrogen as a Limiting Factor for the Growth of *Microcystis aeruginosa* in Southern Wisconsin Lakes," *Ecology*, *48*, 561 (1957).

(43) Birge, E. A., and C. Juday. *The Inland Lakes of Wisconsin, The Plankton. I. Its Quantity and Chemical Composition.* Bulletin #64, Wisconsin Geological and National History Survey (1922).

(44) Provasoli, L. "Nutrition and Ecology of Protozoa and Algae," *Ann. Rev. Microbiol.*, *12*, 279 (1958).

(45) Lund, J. W. G. "The Ecology of the Freshwater Phytoplankton," *Biol. Rev.*, *40*, 231 (1965).

(46) Clesceri, N. L., and G. F. Lee. "Hydrolysis of Condensated Phosphates-I: Non-Sterile Environment," *Inter. J. Air Water Poll.*, *9*, 723 (1965).

(47) Maloney, T. E. "Detergent Phosphorus Effect on Algae," *J. Water Poll. Cont. Fed.*, *38*, 38 (1966).

(48) Johannes, R. E. "Uptake and Release of Dissolved Organic Phosphorus by Representatives of a Coastal Marine Ecosystem," *Limnol. Oceanog.*, *9*, 224–234 (1964).

(49) Clesceri, N. L., and G. F. Lee. "Hydrolysis of Condensed Phosphates-II: Sterile Environment," *Inter. J. Air Water Poll.*, *9*, 743 (1965).

(50) Rigler, F. H. "A Tracer Study of the Phosphorus Cycle in Lake Water," *Ecology*, *37*, 550 (1956).

(51) Rigler, F. H. "The Phosphorus Fractions and the Turnover Times of Inorganic Phosphorus in Different Types of Lakes," *Limnol. Oceanog.*, *9*, 511 (1964).

(52) Golterman, H. L. "Studies on the Cycle of Elements in Fresh Water," *Acta Botanica Neerlandica*, *9*, 1 (1960).

(53) Mackereth, F. J. H. "Phosphorus Utilization by *Asterionella formosa* Hass," *J. Exper. Bot.*, *4*, 296 (1953).

(54) Kuenzler, E. J., and B. H. Ketchum. "Rate of Phosphorus Uptake by *Phaeodactylum tricornutum*," *Biol. Bull., Woods Hole*, *123*, 134 (1963).

(55) Fitzgerald, G. P. *Detection of Limiting or Surplus Nutrients in Algae.* Project WP 297, Progress Report (1965).

(56) Fitzgerald, G. P., S. L. Faust, and T. C. Nelson. "Extractive and Enzymatic Analyses for Limiting or Surplus Phosphorus in Algae" (submitted for publication).

(57) Goldman, C. R. "Primary Productivity and Limiting Factors in Three Lakes of the Alaska Peninsula," *Ecol. Monogr.*, *30*, 207 (1960).

(58) Staub, R. "Ernahrungsphysiologisch-autokologische Untersuchungen an der Planktischen Blaualge Oscillatoria rubescens DC.," *Schweiz. Z. Hydrol.*, *23*, 82 (1961).

(59) Dugdale, R. C., and J. C. Neess. "Recent Observations on Nitrogen Fixation in Blue-Green Algae," *Transactions*, Seminar on Algae and Metropolitan Wastes, R. A. Taft Sanitary Engineering Center, TR W61-3 (1961).

(60) Dugdale, V. A. and R. C. Dugdale. "Nitrogen Metabolism in Lakes. II. Role of Nitrogen Fixation in Sanctuary Lake, Pennsylvania," *Limnol. Oceanog.*, *7*, 170 (1962).

(61) Fogg, G. E. *Algal Cultures and Phytoplankton Ecology*. Madison: University of Wisconsin Press (1965).

(62) Tew, R. W. "Laboratory Studies of Nitrogen Fixation under Conditions Simulating Lake Environments." Ph.D. Thesis, University of Wisconsin (1959).

(63) Sawyer, C. N., and A. F. Ferullo. "Nitrogen Fixation in Natural Waters under Controlled Laboratory Conditions," *Transactions*, Seminar on Algae and Metropolitan Wastes, R. A. Taft Sanitary Engineering Center, TR W61-3 (1961).

(64) Krauss, R. W. "Inorganic Nutrition of Algae," *Algal Culture from Laboratory to Pilot Plant*, edited by J. S. Burlew. Carnegie Institute of Washington Publication 600 (1953).

(65) Arnon, D. I. "The Role of Micronutrients in Plant Nutrition with Special Reference to Photosynthesis and Nitrogen Assimilation," *Trace Elements*, edited by C. A. Lamb, O. G. Bently, and J. M. Beattie. New York: Academic Press (1958).

(66) Eyster, C. "Micronutrient Requirements for Green Plants, Especially Algae," *Algae and Man*, edited by D. F. Jackson. New York: Plenum Press (1964).

(67) Saunders, G. W. "Interrelationships of Dissolved Organic Matter and Phytoplankton," *Botan. Rev.*, *23*, 389 (1957).

(68) Droop, M. R. "Organic Micronutrients," *Physiology and Biochemistry of Algae*, edited by R. Lewin. New York: Academic Press (1962).

(69) Steeman-Nielson, E. "Productivity, Definition and Measurement," *The Sea*, edited by M. N. Hill. New York: Academic Press (1963).

(70) Goldman, C. R. "Molybdenum as a Factor Limiting Primary Productivity in Castle Lake, California," *Science*, *132*, 1016 (1960).

(71) Goldman, C. R. "Primary Productivity and Micro-Nutrient Limiting Factors in Some Northern American and New Zealand Lakes," *Inter. Assoc. Theor. Appl. Limnol.*, *15*, 365 (1964).

(72) Menzel, D. W., and J. H. Ryther. "Nutrients Limiting the Production of Phytoplankton in the Sargasso Sea, with Special Reference to Iron," *Deep Sea Res.*, *7* 272 (1961).

(73) Goldman, C. R., and R. C. Carter. "An Investigation by Rapid Carbon-14 Bioassay of Factors Affecting the Cultural Eutrophication of Lake Tahoe, California-Nevada," *J. Water Poll. Cont. Fed.*, *37*, 1044 (1965).

(74) Maddux, W. S., and R. F. Jones. "Some Interactions of Temperature, Light Intensity, and Nutrient Concentration During the Continuous Culture of *Nitzschia closterium* and *Tetraselmis* sp.," *Limnol. Oceanog.*, *9*, 79 (1964).

(75) Findenegg, I. "Producktionsbiologische Planktonuntersuchungen an Ostalpenseen," *Inter. Revue ges Hydrobiolia*, *49*, 381 (1964).

(76) Oglesby, R. T., and W. T. Edmondson. "Control of Eutrophication." Paper presented at the 38th Annual Conference of the Water Pollution Control Federation, Atlantic City, New Jersey (1965).

(77) Thomas, E. A. "The Eutrophication of Lakes and Rivers, Cause and Prevention," *Transactions*, Third Seminar on Biological Problems in Water Pollution, R. A. Taft Sanitary Engineering Center, Publication No. 999-WP-25 (1962).

(78) Lohr, M. "Gewasserschutzbestrebungen des Landes Bayern," *Verband Schweizerischer Abwasserfachleute*, Verband-Bericht Nr. 71/1, 195 (1961).

(79) Olszewski, P. "Versuch einer Ableitung des Hypolimnischen Wassers aus einem See," *Inter. Assoc. Theor. Appl. Limnol.*, *14*, 855 (1961).

(80) Knight, W. E. "Improvement of the Quality of Reservoir Discharges through Control of Discharge Elevation," *Transactions*, Symposium on Streamflow Regulation for Quality Control, R. A. Taft Sanitary Engineering Center, Publication No. 999-WP-30 (1965).

(81) Sketelj, J., and M. Rejic. "Pollutional Phases of Lake Bled." Paper presented at the Second International Water Pollution Conference, Tokyo (1964).

(82) Bryan, J. G. "Improvement in the Quality of Reservoir Discharges through Reservoir Mixing and Aeration," *Transactions*, Symposium on Streamflow Regulation for Quality Control, R. A. Taft Sanitary Engineering Center, Publication No. 999-WP-30 (1965).

BIOLOGICAL RESPONSES TO NUTRIENTS—EUTROPHICATION: SALINE WATER CONSIDERATIONS

B. J. Copeland and Donald E. Wohlschlag
Marine Science Institute, The University of Texas, Port Aransas, Texas

INTRODUCTION

Estuaries, bays, and lagoons, collectively termed "inland waters" in this paper, are brackish-to-saline bodies of water between the freshwater streams and the sea. These bodies of water serve as nutrient traps, and with the coming decreases in freshwater flow they are becoming much more so. In other words, without the freshwater to flush out inland waters, stagnation and decreases in mixing add to the importance of the waters as nutrient traps.

Nutrients in sea water are in very low concentrations. Increases in nutrients in the inland waters arise by several processes: (a) natural runoff from land masses via streams; (b) domestic, agricultural, and industrial pollution along the inflowing streams; (c) domestic, agricultural, and industrial pollution located on the lagoon, estuary, or bay; and (d) increases in inland waters by evaporation, expecially in shallow areas. Probably the two most important of these are industrial and domestic sewage pollution located along the streams and around the periphery of the inland waters.

There are around 1,300,000 acres of estuaries, bays, and lagoons along the coast of Texas (Fig. 19). These bays receive each day millions of gallons of effluent from the hundreds of industries and sewage disposal plants located around their periphery. With little daily tide, and sometimes little exchange of water with the open Gulf, the combined effluents are stirred by strong Gulf Coast winds to provide new ecological systems. It is these systems that will be discussed.

Five main types of nutrient-laden wastes enter Texas coastal waters:

1. *Oil Field Brine-Bleedwater.* The very hard oil field water, rich in nutrients and contaminated with some oil, combines with shallow waters to produce massive blue-green algal mats and associated sulphur bacteria. Waters in the Mexican Laguna Madre and some areas of the Laguna Madre of Texas are hypersaline and in many ways resemble the oil field brine polluted waters.

2. *Sewage.* Although various degrees of treatments are applied to municipal wastewaters, high concentrations of nutrients are in the sewage waste waters.

3. *Petrochemical Industry Wastewaters.* Wastes from the petrochemical industry are usually very high in concentrations of some types of nutrients. The wastes are sometimes toxic to aquatic animals. The impact of such a waste to saline ecological systems is great and sometimes detrimental.

4. *Seafood Packing Wastewaters.* Scattered along the entire Texas Coast are a large number of seafood packing plants. Their wastes are discharged into bays, and these highly enriched waters develop into very highly populated plankton communities. These wastewaters seem to be very high in nutrient concentrations.

5. *Pulp Mill Wastes.* The waters from pulp mills are particularly high in phosphorous and some of the other nutrients.

Considerable knowledge exists about marine pollution in Texas bays. Odum *et al.* (1) reported metabolic characteristics and nutrient concentrations for abnormal marine ecosystems of Texas affected by seafood industry, petrochemical

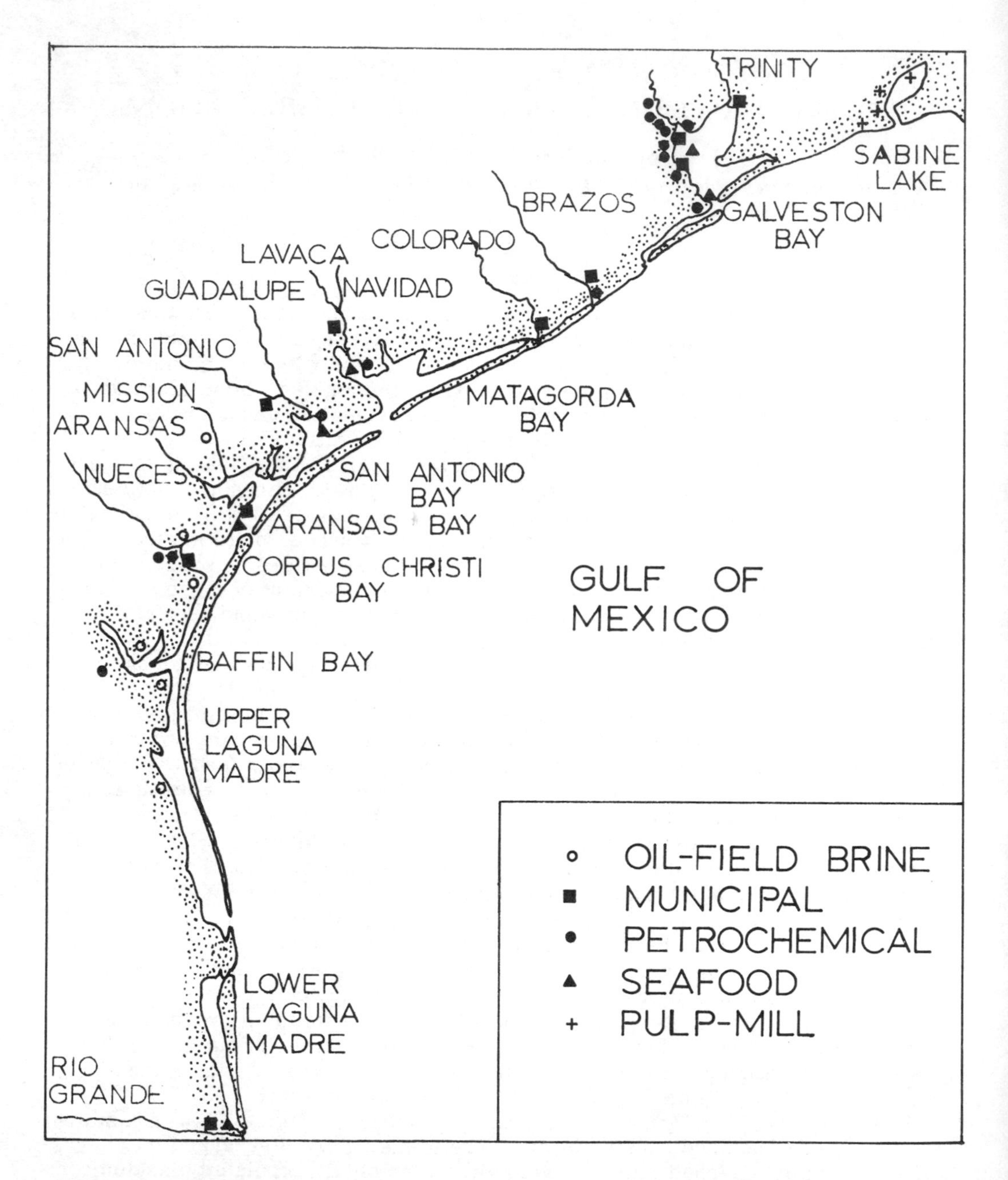

Figure 19. Outline of the Texas Coast, indicating the general location and type of wastes entering inland waters.

wastes, and oil field brine. Chambers and Sparks (2) and Hohn (3) reported biological and physical properties related to wastes in the Houston ship channel in the Galveston Bay area. Copeland (4) reported nutrient concentrations in St. Joseph Bay, Florida, which is polluted with wastes from a pulp mill complex. Hood (5) measured several chemical components of the waters of Corpus Christi Bay and its connecting water bodies. Of indirect relation to nutrient concentration or eutrophication in bays was the study of organic carbon levels in the bays of Texas by Wilson (6).

General levels of total phosphorous, a very important nutrient, have been documented in relatively unpolluted bays of Texas by Odum and Wilson (7). Phosphorous concentrations are about 40 ppb in the open Gulf and increase to about 150 ppb in the hypersaline bays. Odum *et al.* (1) found phosphorous concentrations in bays receiving wastes generally higher than previously accounted and ranging sometimes up to 2,000 ppb or more. As pointed out by Odum (8), when freshwater flow is high the concentrations of waste and the effects of waste are minimized, whereas in times of low flow (with little flushing) the effects of wastewaters and their nutrient concentrations are great.

Nutrient concentrations for San Antonio Bay, Texas, are shown in Figure 20. It should be noted that concentrations of nutrients are higher adjacent to known wastewater inputs. Figure 21 shows nutrient concentrations in St. Joseph Bay, Florida, which receives great quantities of effluent from a paper mill complex.

Existing evidence will be used in this report to pose questions whose answers are going to be urgently needed in the future. In most cases the full impact of the contribution of excess nutrients to estuarine waters is unknown, and it is possible that severely adverse effects will occur before corrective measures can be devised. There are many implications from the known evidence concerning the future use of the marine resources of Texas. The phosphorous data (Figs. 20 and 21) document the influence that wastes from one place are having on users in other parts of the bays. Waste levels are already concentrated enough to merit public efforts to separate the water receiving wastes from general release to the large bays that must also serve for nursery grounds of marine animals, recreation, and commercial fishing.

While the biological effects of intense pollution, chronic or acute, are obvious, the more subtle biological effects of slight pollution are not. The importance of these subtle effects will be emphasized.

EFFECTS ON BASIC PRODUCTIVITY

Adverse metabolic effects may occur when waters containing high concentrations of nutrients are dumped into the marine environment. A large influx of nutrient salts usually enhances the growth of primitive organisms. The ecosystem reacts to this influx of foreign material, and the results are reflected in the metabolism of the system. Thus, community metabolism may be a sensitive measure for the assessment of the extent to which the ecosystem is upset.

The criterion of community metabolism has been used to evaluate the effects of organic pollution in both fresh and saline waters (1, 4, 7, 9-11).

Generally speaking, photosynthetic and respiratory rates of whole biological communities are nearly equal; that is, the community requires all of the organic matter that is made during photosynthesis to maintain the biomass and the limited growth rates during the 24-hour period. When nutrients alone are added to the community, photosynthesis may exceed respiratory demands because of the fertilization effect in the absence of added organic loads. This example is rare in waters receiving wastes, because excessive nutrients are usually accompanied by excessive organic material.

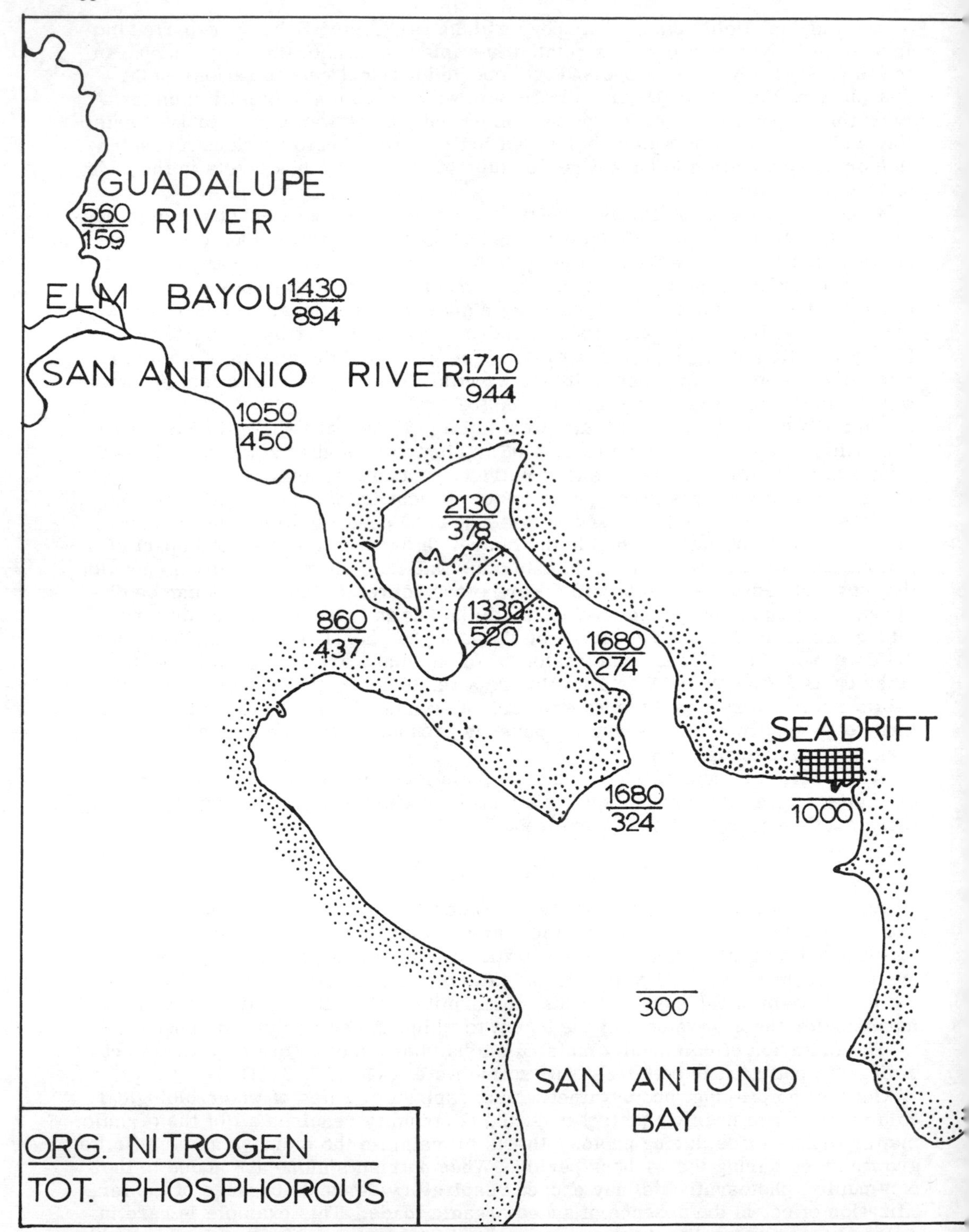

Figure 20. Concentrations of organic nitrogen and total phosphorous in San Antonio Bay and the San Antonio-Guadalupe River system. Concentrations are reported in parts per billion (ug/l).

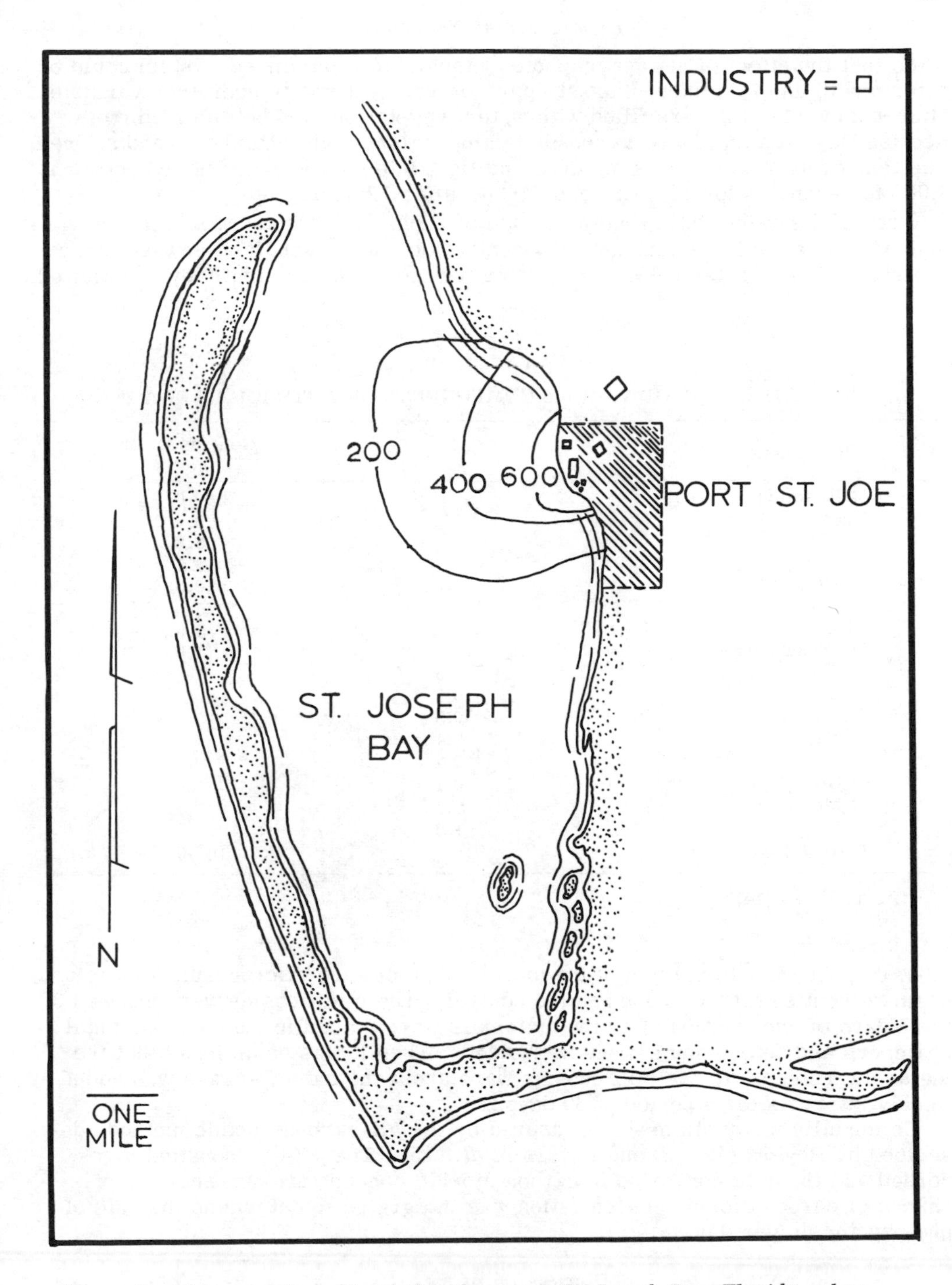

Figure 21. Concentration of total phosphorous in St. Joseph Bay, Florida, a bay influenced by pulp mill wastes. Concentrations are in parts per billion (ug/l). After Copeland (4).

Experimental Procedure

So that the effect of sewage on photosynthesis of a marine ecosystem could be determined, an experiment was set up to control light and temperature variables. Microcosms (12, 13) were filled with water, vegetation, and bottom mud from Redfish Bay, Texas, placed in constant-temperature-light chambers, and stirred. The temperature was a constant 25°C and light intensity was alternated between 3,000 foot-candles for 12 hours and darkness for 12 hours.

Artificial sewage, following the recipe of Pipes (14), was used so that the various additions would be constant. Concentrations of the artificial sewage components are shown in Table 19. Amounts of sewage were such that they constituted

TABLE 19

CONCENTRATION OF VARIOUS COMPONENTS OF ARTIFICIAL SEWAGE*

Component		Concentration (mg/1)
Milk solids		200.0
Urea		20.0
KH_2PO_4		6.8
K_2HPO_4		8.7
$KHCO_3$		250.0
$MgSO_4$		5.0
EDTA		5.0
Micronutrients		1.0 cc/1
Fe	0.5	
Ca	0.5	
Zn	0.5	
Mn	0.1	
Cu	0.1	
Co	0.1	
Mo	0.1	
B	1.0	
BOD of final solution		161.0

*From Pipes (14).

0.01, 0.1, 1.0, and 10 percent of the total volume of each microcosm. One microcosm without sewage was used as the control. The microcosms were allowed 30 to 45 days of acclimation after the materials were placed in the environmental chambers and before any sewage was added. When it was established that the metabolic rates of all the microcosms were about the same, sewage was added at weekly intervals for a period of 60 days.

Community metabolism was measured by the *p*H-carbon dioxide methods described by Beyers (12, 13) and Beyers *et al.* (15). The *p*H was constantly recorded and the data converted to carbon dioxide concentrations. The rate of change of carbon dioxide concentration was integrated to determine the rate of photosynthesis per day.

Discussion of Results

The rate of photosynthesis as effected by various sewage concentrations is shown in Figure 22. The data for 1965 (top curve) are a reflection of constant stirring, thus complete mixing and no stratification. The data for 1964 (lower curve) are a reflection of little mixing and some stratification during daylight.

In the 1965 data the photosynthetic rate was the same at 0.01 percent sewage as it was in the control. Photosynthetic rate increased to the 1.0 percent sewage level and then declined in the microcosm with 10 percent sewage. In the 1964 data the photosynthetic rate increased as the amounts of sewage were increased. It is possible that stirring, which simulates the strong Gulf Coast winds, may have some effect on the impact of sewage to an inland water ecosystem.

Although the variation of photosynthesis at each sewage concentration (indicated by the vertical lines in Figure 22 was sometimes great, there is a general effect of sewage concentration on the photosynthetic rate. As shown in Figure 23, the variation in photosynthetic rate is a reflection of the general increase in photosynthetic rate with time. Thus, the gradual accumulation of nutrients with time was reflected in the increased photosynthetic rate with time. Also, there was a fluctuation of photosynthetic rate each time that sewage was added; this fluctuation could possibly be eliminated in future experiments by the incremental addition of sewage to each microcosm.

In all cases of the increases in photosynthetic rates there was an accompanying increase in community respiration rate. The ratio of photosynthesis to respiration remained near unity during the experiment. Perhaps the production of labile organic material during photosynthesis enhanced the respiration rate of the dependent community as in other experiments (16).

The results of the above experiment indicate that the dumping of sewage into an ecosystem in inland waters will result in eutrophication and the concomitant increase in basic productivity. Unfortunately, this increase in basic productivity is seldom advantageous. The two-fold increase in basic productivity, as shown in Figure 22, does not necessarily make the estuary twice as productive in terms of man's needs. The ecosystem sometimes reacts to such an increase with the exclusion of various top carnivores because of the slight increase in toxicity or the variations in energy-flow pathways.

An example of the effects of an increase of nutrients on the production of phytoplankton in inland waters in nature is shown in Figure 24. The data included were presented by Nash (17) for the Patuxent Estuary and Chesapeake Bay area. The increase in nutrient concentration during the spring resulted in an increase in phytoplankton biomass soon after. When the phytoplankton reached its peak the nutrient concentration in the water decreased sharply because the nutrients were incorporated in phytoplankton biomass. The cycle was repeated again in the fall.

Similar effects have been observed in waters receiving industrial wastes (1, 9). However, in the case of harsh industrial wastewaters, there is usually a tremendous increase in respiratory demands of the community.

SPECIES DIVERSITY

The principle of species diversity to indicate the condition of an ecosystem was developed by Gleason (18) and has been used extensively by others (1, 19). It is based on the principle that species diversity is lowered in a community under stress. Odum *et al.* (1) used the number of species among 1,000 individuals encountered in a particular place as an index of species diversity.

The data presented in Figure 25 show the species diversity of three saline inland water ecosystems as affected by seafood packing wastes (Curve A), wastes from a petrochemical industrial complex (Curve B), and pulp mill wastes (Curve C). The species diversity for zooplankton increased as the distance from the known pollution source increased. Although this illustration involves only zooplankton, other groups should be similarly affected. Indeed, Hohn (3) showed much the same relationship for diatoms in the Houston Ship Channel, a heavily polluted system.

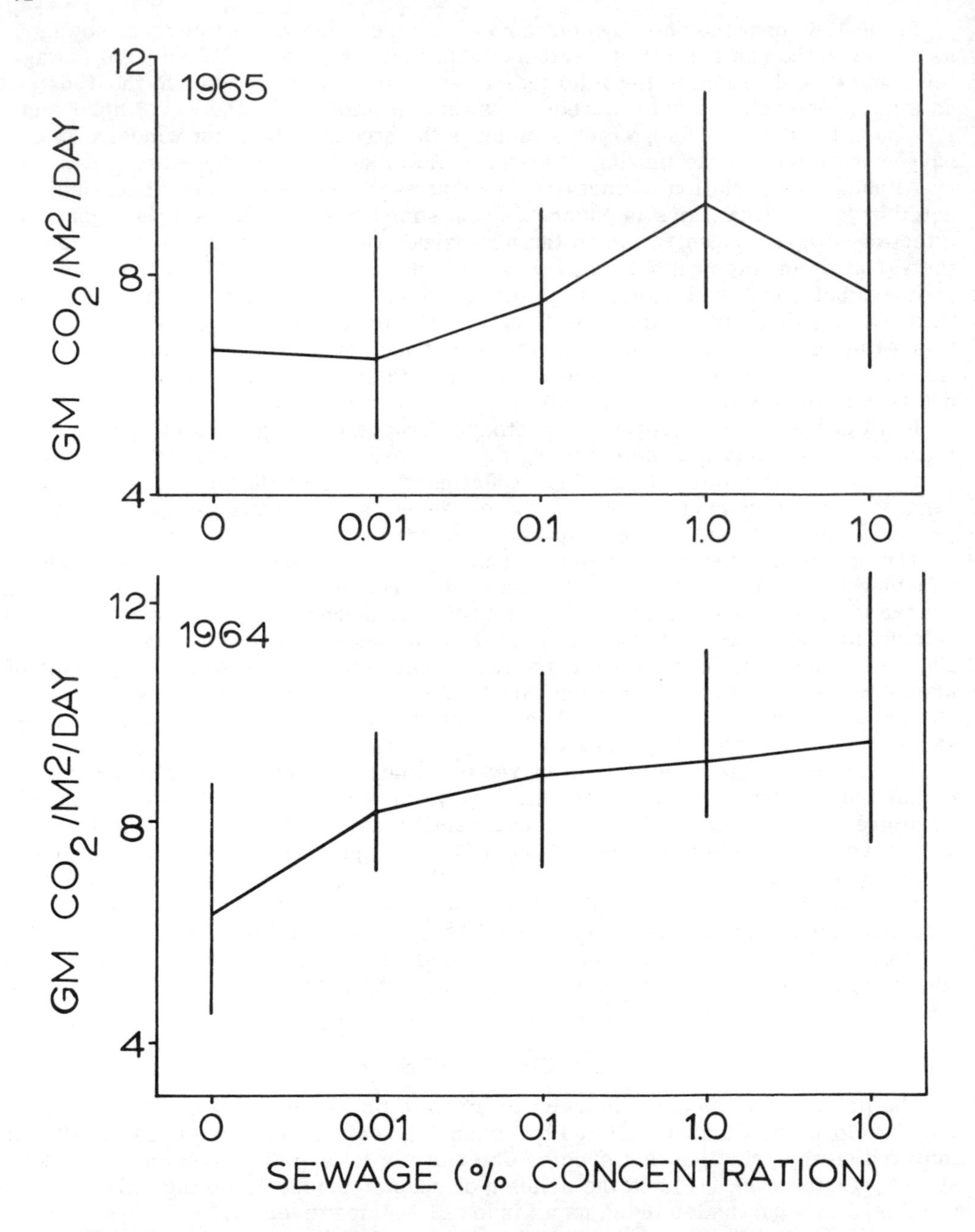

Figure 22. Photosynthetic rate of simulated estuarine systems as affected by various concentrations of sewage. Percent concentration is by volume. Artificial sewage following the recipe given in Table 19 was used in all cases. The vertical line at each point indicates the range; the horizontal line is drawn through means of 10 or more values.

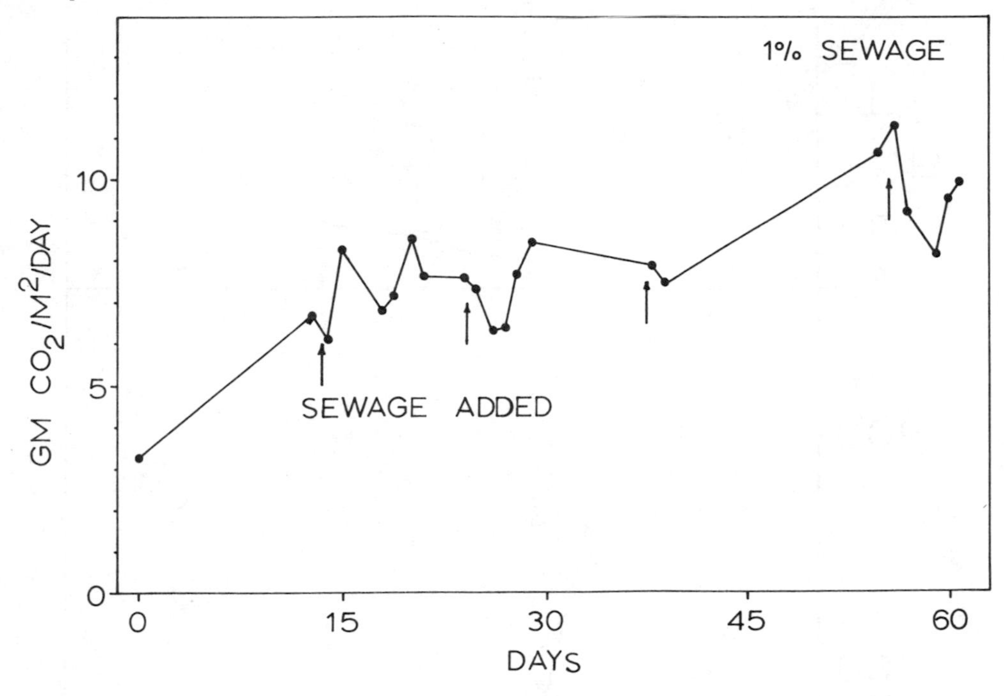

Figure 23. Photosynthetic rate of a simulated estuarine system receiving 1 percent (by volume) sewage. Sewage was added on the dates indicated by the arrows.

If one assumes that community stability is related to the number of kinds of organisms, species diversity would then indicate the complexity of community structure. In other words, the more complex (more species diversity) the community the greater the possibility for more complete pathways of energy flow. If the species diversity is lowered because of environmental stress (i.e., pollution) the number of pathways for the flow of energy through the system would be reduced. Thus, when pathways are eliminated or broken, the cyclic patterns of which they were a part are interrupted. The cost to the community to repair these broken links or to provide new pathways would be great. In either case the efficiency of the system is lowered.

Because even the simplest natural ecosystem involves a reasonably large number of plant and animal species, even detailed studies of stress on any one or several of them could hardly be expected to characterize the entire ecosystem. The following sections exemplify the problems of detecting subtle effects of environmental stresses on individual populations.

EFFECTS OF SLIGHT INCREASES OF MORTALITY ON POPULATIONS

In many areas, residents have a general "impression" that there has been a decrease in fish or other populations over a period of years or decades without any evidence of sudden declines, although adequate data are usually unavailable for proof of decline. Sometimes such declines are obviously caused by increased exploitation. But, even if a species may not have experienced exploitation pressures, long term, but slight, environmental changes such as pollution can cause population declines. Major reviews on the theories of fish population declines are by Beverton and Holt (20) and Ricker (21).

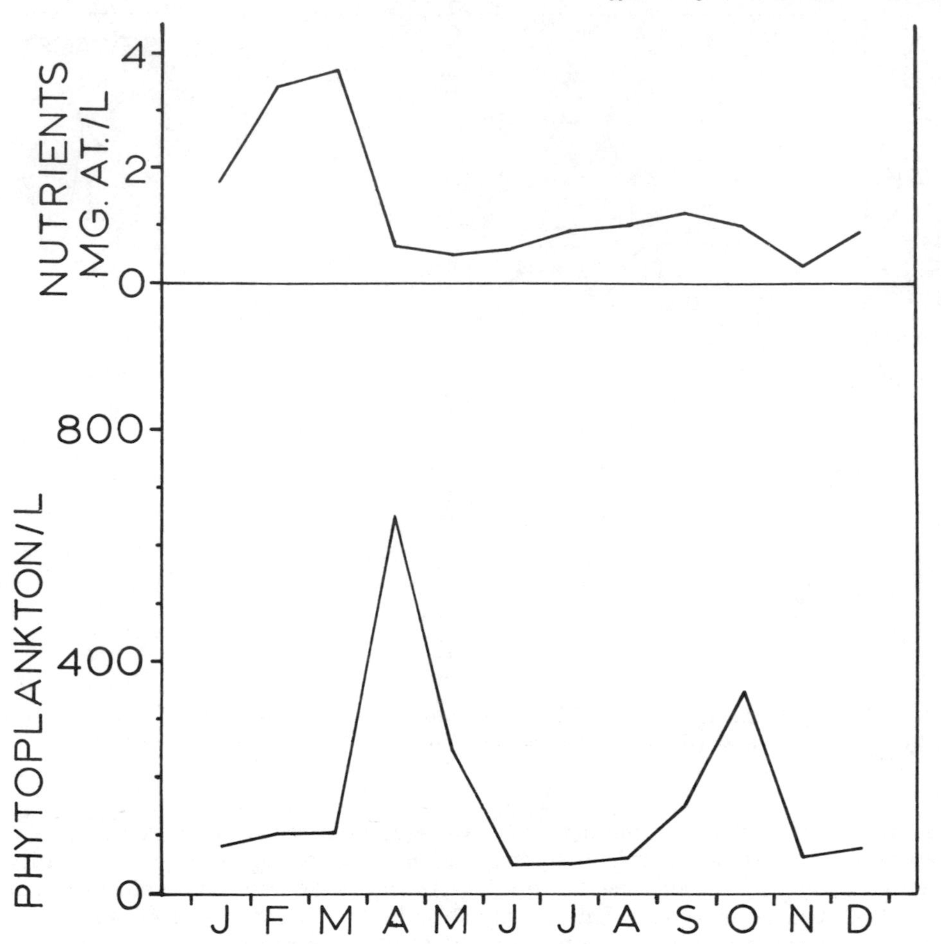

Figure 24. Nutrient concentration and phytoplankton production in Patuxent Estuary. After Nash (17).

Experimental Detection

It is often difficult or impossible to set up experiments on populations of larger animals like fish that allow for cause and effect evaluations of pollution. For example, if a population of 10,000 fish die at a uniform rate over a year so that 0.75 of the total survive, the annual instantaneous rate of death, i = 0.29, can be calculated from the relationship

$$7{,}500 = 10{,}000\, e^{-i}$$

On a daily basis, the instantaneous rate would be 0.29/365 = 0.0008, which means that from the initial population about 8 fish would die per day. If the population experienced a 0.10 increase in the fraction dying annually, the annual survival rate would be 0.65, the annual instantaneous mortality rate would be 0.43, the daily equivalent would be 0.43/365 = 0.0012, and of 10,000 fish about 12 would die in one day. It would be unreasonable indeed to expect an experiment to be sensitive enough to detect the difference between 8 and 12 deaths among 10,000

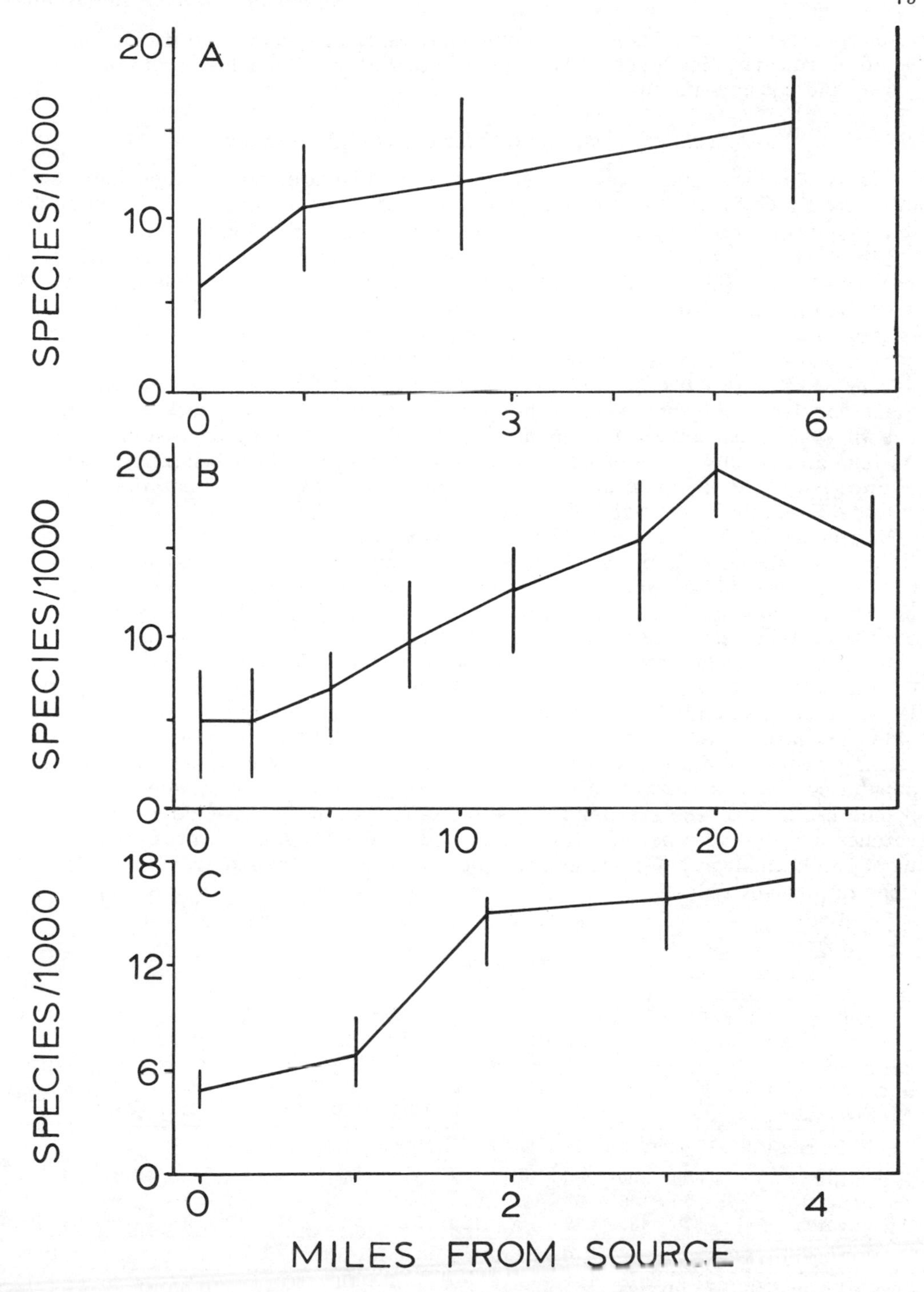

Figure 25. Zooplankton diversity in species per one thousand individuals. Curve A is from a system effected by seafood packing wastes; after Odum *et al.* (1). Curve B is from a system effected by petrochemical wastes; after Odum *et al.* (1). Curve C is from a system effected by pulp mill wastes; after Copeland (4). The vertical line at each point represents seasonal ranges.

fish, considering both the usual experimental variability and the difficulty in handling so many fish, especially larger ones, within reasonable limits of manpower and equipment.

Effects of Slight Mortality Increases on Population

The following hypothetical arithmetic model illustrates how a slight increase in mortality due to pollution can have a major effect on a population. Ricker (22) discusses the same situation on the basis of modern population theory.

To start with, consider a fish species that grows to 1.5 pounds by age III and is recruited to the fishable size range at 1,000 per year. At age IV, the fish would weigh 3.5 pounds, and so on for later years, as in the top line of Table 20. Now suppose that mortality is such that at the end of one year 25 percent die due to natural causes and 25 percent are fished out so that the overall survival is 50 percent. After the first year 500 fish survive from 1,000 recruits, and from these survivors 250 survive until the following year, and so on until (to the nearest whole fish) one survivor remains at age XIII, as in the top portion of the table. As long as recruitment is constant and the recruits are added instantly at the end of any given year, the population (to the nearest fish) will be stabilized at 1,999, with catch numbers and weights as indicated.

Suppose now that there is a decrease in survival, brought about by slight pollution that causes an increase of 10 percent in the fraction dying annually due to natural causes, while the percentage fished remains the same. From one age class to the next only 40 percent survive through the year. If at the beginning of each year recruitment is maintained at 1,000 age-III fish, it will require five years for the population to reach the stable level of 1,667 fish, as indicated in the bottom half of Table 20. Not only is the numerical size of the hypothetical population reduced slightly, but there also is a pronounced reduction in the number of older and heavier fish that reduce the weight of the catch. Thus the effect of a slight increase in mortality is obvious only after a number of years when the population reaches a new stable age composition, the numbers of older fish in the population decline, the smaller fish available to the fishery provide smaller catches and the catch becomes much reduced in weight, assuming that recruitment can be maintained in spite of the increased mortality and greater proportions of younger fish.

TABLE 20

MODEL OF A HYPOTHETICAL FISHERY, EXPERIENCING A SLIGHT INCREASE IN NATURAL MORTALITY

Age Wt/Fish (Lbs.)	III 1.5	IV 3.5	V 4.5	VI 6.0	VII 7.5	VIII 10.5	IX 13.0	X 16.5	XI 19.0	XII 21.5	XIII 25.0	Totals
Stable Population (50% Survival; 25% Fished; 25% Mortality):												
Population	1,000	500	250	125	62	31	16	8	4	2	1	1,999
No. in catch	250	125	62	31	16	8	4	2	1	—	—	499
Wt. of catch	375	438	279	186	120	84	52	31	19	—	—	1,584
10% Additional Mortality												
Stable Population (40% Survival; 25% Fished; 35% Mortality):												
Population	1,000	400	160	64	26	10	4	2	1	—	—	1,667
No. in catch	250	100	40	16	6	3	1	—	—	—	—	416
Wt. of catch	375	350	180	96	45	32	13	—	—	—	—	1,091

With the usual sampling and fishing variability accompanying any natural variability in population size that occurs from year to year, it is manifestly unlikely that small increases in mortality could be readily detected. Only major decreases can be readily recognized, and by this stage of decline in a population it is likely that recruitment would also have been adversely affected.

AN EXPERIMENT ON THE SUBTLE EFFECTS OF POLLUTION

The purpose of this experiment is to evaluate the nonlethal effects of unknown and not easily identifiable pollutants on the respiratory metabolism of the pinfish, *Lagodon rhomboides* (Linnaeus), over and above the effects of dissolved oxygen, temperature, and salinity.

Respiratory metabolism of fishes and other organisms as commonly defined by the rate of oxygen consumption per unit weight is an elegant measure of integrative physiological processes. A good general review of metabolism from experimental and theoretical viewpoints is given by Locker and Kinne (23) in a symposium that points up the multiplicity of environmental factors which can affect metabolism.

During recent years there has been an accumulation of literature on the metabolism of fishes with special reference to oxygen consumption rates. Fry (24) and Winberg (25) have excellent reviews. In the proceedings of *Biological Problems in Water Pollution*, Third Seminar, 1962, organized by Tarzwell (26), pertinent papers dealing with dissolved oxygen as a fundamental requirement for fishes were contributed by Douderoff and Warren, Bennett, Hoet, Fromm, and Alderdice. These authors cover a wide range of topics on the effects of dissolved oxygen at various concentrations, the lowest of which are usually less favorable for development and growth.

Among the commonest attributes of eutrophication and of many kinds of pollution is the general lowering of dissolved oxygen levels. One of the approaches to measuring the subtle effects of eutrophication on the physiology of fishes involves the measurement of "scope of activity" described by Fry (27). The "scope" is the difference between a standard rate of metabolism of a resting fish and the rate at the highest possible sustained swimming activity under specified environmental conditions. Fromm (28) advocates a comparative system whereby the scope for polluted conditions can be compared to those set up as norms for unpolluted environments. The large volume of literature, which indicates that there is a definite lowering of metabolism with low oxygen levels for fishes and other aquatic organisms, will not be reviewed here; but it is rather pertinent (24) that the scope of activity could also be expected to be reduced under conditions of low oxygen levels characteristic of advanced eutrophication or pollution. Over a wide temperature range, Davis *et al.* (29) showed that the swimming performance of small salmon was greatly impaired at low oxygen levels.

Herrman *et al.* (30), among others, present data to show how growth rates of fishes in the laboratory are depressed at low oxygen concentrations. Similarly, there is abundant published evidence that larval development is likewise slower, or impaired altogether, at lower oxygen levels.

Even if the oxygen level and its effect on metabolism—and ultimately, on growth—is understood, other obvious variables are important in natural environments. The metabolic and growth effects of temperature are very real and are fairly well understood. But relatively little is known of the combined effects of oxygen, temperature, and salinity on metabolism and growth of fishes. Some of the interaction effects are greatly different from the single factor effects, according to Kinne (31, 32, 33), Kinne and Kinne (34), and Alderdice (35).

By comparing polluted with unpolluted sea water at given temperatures, at constant salinities, and at near-saturation oxygen levels, it is possible that any differences in metabolism of fishes in the two kinds of water would be due to pollution of the type that could not ordinarily be established by any simple biological or chemical tests.

Methods

To evaluate the effects of polluted, but oxygenated, waters on the respiratory metabolism of the pinfish, *Lagodon rhomboides* (Linnaeus), highly polluted water from the Corpus Christi turning basin was utilized in a preliminary study of mortality effects during February-March 1966. In a 1,455-liter holding tank, pinfish and other species died within a day or so, but they survived in a one-half dilution with unpolluted sea water at a salinity of about 35 ppt for a week or more in apparently good condition when confined within a 463-liter insulated, temperature-controlled aquarium that was continuously aerated at near-saturation levels.

Fresh specimens from unpolluted sea water of about 35 ppt salinity and a temperature of about 13-15°C.were placed in the aquarium, and the temperature was lowered to about 10°C. over a period of about one day. The aquarium, similar to that described by Wohlschlag (36), was then controlled at about ± 0.05°C. for a period of three days before determination of oxygen consumption rates for six individual fish in the manner described by Wohlschlag (37). The same procedure was followed with newly caught fish raised to a temperature of about 15°C. Additional fish placed in the aquarium at 15°C. were then slowly acclimated to 20°C., held for three days, and tested for oxygen consumption rates; the remaining fish from 20°C. were acclimated to 25°C., held three days, and tested; the remaining fish from the 25°C. runs were then acclimated, and held at the 30°C. level for the final runs. The entire experiment was repeated, except that unpolluted sea water at a salinity of about 35 ppt was used. During each set of six oxygen consumption rate determinations, the swimming velocities were recorded. After each determination, the individual fish were weighed and sexed. The fish ranged in standard lengths between 87 and 203 mm. Their weights were between 16 and 221 g.

Results

The results, in mg O_2 consumed/kg/hr, expressed as the average of six determinations (five in one case) at each temperature are plotted in Figure 26. The variability at the two lower temperatures was definitely greater than at 20°C. or higher. Initial oxygen concentrations were always near saturation at the outset of a run, and after a 45-minute run ranged from about 4 ppm at 30°C. levels to about 8 ppm at 10°C. levels.

Except for the fact that the fish in polluted water at about 20°C. had inexplicably high oxygen consumption rates, the temperature responses are much the same as those for many other species. It is particularly pertinent that at all temperature ranges, except the 20°C. level, the oxygen consumption rates for the fish in unpolluted water were definitely higher than the comparable rates for fish in polluted water.

Discussion

Compared to the metabolism in polluted water, the metabolism in unpolluted water at the 10°, 15°, 25°, and 30°C. levels, the oxygen consumption rates in mg/kg/hr are respectively 116, 61, 15, and 18 percent higher. On the same basis at about 20°C. the oxygen consumption rate is 13 percent lower. It is possible that the high rate at 20°C. in polluted water might be the result of some "optimal" conditions for fish acclimated to about 13°C. in the natural environment.

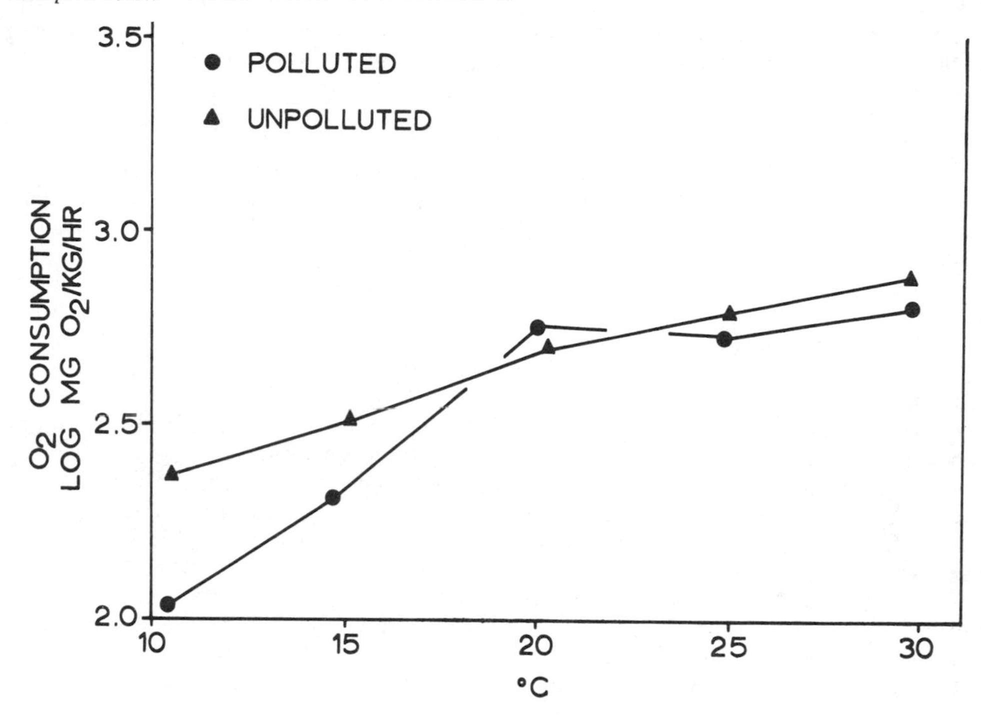

Figure 26. Metabolic rates of *Lagodon rhomboides* (L.) subjected to polluted and unpolluted waters at various temperatures.

All the metabolism levels reported here are best considered as "routine" and not "standard" (24). As such the fish represent slowly swimming fish with an average swimming velocity of the order of only 3 m/min. On this basis it is anticipated that the routine metabolic levels appear to be realistic in ecological terms of fish populations in the natural environment, insofar as direct observations of behavior are pertinent.

Why the individual rate determinations are more variable at the lowest two temperature levels is not known, but this type of variation persists in experiments on polar and north-temperate species studied by a number of workers who have utilized a variety of techniques (38).

Under conditions of pollution stress it is of importance to note that at lower temperatures the metabolic levels are comparatively quite low. Because stressful conditions in inshore waters in terms of pollution or salinity and temperature variability are more severe than in the open Gulf, it is quite possible that there is a metabolic-related explanation of the occurrence of seaward migrations of pinfish during unfavorable conditions, as reported by Caldwell (39).

Caldwell's evaluation of a large amount of data on the pinfish also leads to the conclusion that larger specimens (e.g., above 200 mm.) occur in the more open and deeper waters, where stressful conditions are less pronounced than in inshore areas. Kinne (31) and Kinne and Kinne (34) indicate that nongenetic adaptation tends to increase with increasing rates of metabolism and that for a euryplastic fish, the faster growing fish would adapt faster than slower growing fish. Whether or not this explanation would pertain to the occurrence of the larger pinfish in less stressful environments is not known without direct experiments, but the Kinne adaptation hypothesis in terms of growth and metabolism has some very important and pertinent implications.

Von Bertalanffy (40) developed a general growth theory whereby rate of change in weight is in terms of anabolic (growth) minus catabolic (maintenance) processes:

$$dw/dt = hs - kw,$$

where dw/dt is the rate of change in weight with time, hs is the anabolic or growth portion of metabolism (h is a constant and s is "metabolic surface" that would be roughly equivalent to $w^{2/3}$, and kw is the catabolic or maintenance portion of overall metabolism (k is a constant). Clearly, for very large fish growth rates tend toward zero and anabolism equals catabolism, inasmuch as the anabolic term increases with weight less rapidly than the catabolic term. The general theory of metabolism and growth is further illustrated by von Bertalanffy (41). Application of the theory to fisheries is discussed in detail by Beverton and Holt (20).

It would seem logical that lowered metabolism due to pollution would be manifested by decreased growth rates or by insufficient available energy for fish to meet maintenance requirements. In the former case the individual fish with lowered growth rates would be exposed to ordinary population mortality pressures a longer time before sexual maturity and reproduction than would be the case in populations whose individuals grow at a normally faster rate. In the latter case where a fish cannot meet maintenance requirements it would die and thus contribute directly to a higher population mortality rate than would be the case in a population whose members grew within normal limits.

In either case an environmental stress that lowers metabolism would tend to have an adverse affect on population size: in the first case normal development and fecundity would be delayed so that recruitment would be adversely affected by a time delay; in the second case the population with higher mortality rates would be smaller and younger. In either, or both, cases there would be a sensible explanation of the decline of fish populations in slightly polluted waters whose fish populations have even a minor metabolic disadvantage, even though the usual sampling or fishery statistics would be relatively insensitive in evaluating the decline.

CONCLUSIONS

1. The addition of a known nutrient source to a marine community resulted in alteration of the metabolic patterns of the ecosystem. An increase in the amount of nutrient material caused an increase in photosynthetic production.

2. Species diversity of zooplankton is reduced in marine environments receiving various types of organic wastes, which indicates an interruption of normal community structure by the addition of new nutrient materials.

3. A theoretical case was presented to demonstrate that slight toxic effects are pronounced although not detectable by conventional means of measurement. With just a slight increase in mortality rate the biomass of the fishes affected would be decreased greatly.

4. Experiments on the metabolic rate of fishes revealed that slight pollution stresses tend to lower the metabolic rates considerably. The depression was greatest when the fish were already subjected to regular environmental stress, such as low temperature.

5. Most of the effects of waste materials in the marine environment are subtle. It appears that the community approach rather than the organismic approach will be more fruitful in evaluating the impact of man-made changes in inland saline water ecosystems, notwithstanding the fact that the effects of stresses on individual populations can be physiologically quantifiable.

REFERENCES

(1) Odum, H. T., R. P. Cuzon du Rest, R. J. Beyers, and C. Allbaugh. "Diurnal Metabolism, Total Phosphorus, Ohle Anomaly, and Zooplankton Diversity of Abnormal Marine Ecosystems of Texas," *Publ. Inst. Mar. Sci. Univ. Tex., 9,* 404–453 (1963).
(2) Chambers, G. V., and A. K. Sparks. "An Ecological Survey of the Houston Ship Channel and Adjacent Bays," *Publ. Inst. Mar. Sci. Univ. Tex., 6,* 214–250 (1959).
(3) Hohn, M. "The Use of Diatom Populations as a Measure of Water Quality in Selected Areas of Galveston and Chocolate Bay, Texas," *Publ. Inst. Mar. Sci. Univ. Tex., 6,* 206–212 (1959).
(4) Copeland, B. J. "Industrial Pollution in Marine Ecosystems," *Pollutions Marines par les Microorganismes et les Produits Petroliers, Symposium de Monaco* (Avril 1964), 79–88 (1965).
(5) Hood, D. W. "A Hydrographic and Chemical Survey of Corpus Christi Bay and Connecting Water Bodies," *Texas A&M Res. Found. Rep., 40,* 1–23 (1953).
(6) Wilson, R. F. "Organic Carbon Levels in Some Aquatic Ecosystems," *Publ. Inst. Mar. Sci. Univ. Tex., 9,* 64–76 (1963).
(7) Odum, H. T., and R. F. Wilson. "Further Studies on Reaeration and Metabolism of Texas Bays, 1958–1960," *Publ. Inst. Mar. Sci. Univ. Tex., 8,* 23–55 (1962).
(8) Odum, H. T. "The Requirement for Freshwater in a General Plan for Multiple Development of the Marine Bays," *Proceedings,* 6th Annual Conference on Water for Texas, A&M College, 32–34 (1960).
(9) Copeland, B. J., and T. C. Dorris. "Photosynthetic Productivity in Oil Refinery Effluent Holding Ponds," *J. Wat. Poll. Cont. Fed., 34,* 1104–1111 (1962).
(10) Copeland, B. J., and T. C. Dorris. "Community Metabolism in Ecosystems Receiving Oil Refiner Effluents," *Limnol. Oceanog., 9,* 431–447 (1964).
(11) Odum, H. T. "Analysis of Diurnal Oxygen Curves for the Assay of Reaeration Rates and Metabolism in Polluted Marine Bays," *Waste Disposal in the Marine Environment,* edited by E. A. Pearson. New York: Pergamon Press (1960).
(12) Beyers, R. J. "The Metabloism of Twelve Aquatic Laboratory Microecosystems," *Ecol. Monogr., 33,* 281–306 (1963).
(13) Beyers, R. J. "The Microcosm Approach to Ecosystem Biology," *Amer. Biol. Teach., 26,* 491–498 (1964).
(14) Pipes, W. O. "*p*H Variation and BOD Removal in Stabilization Ponds," *J. Wat. Poll. Cont. Fed., 34,* 1140–1150 (1962).
(15) Beyers, R. J., J. L. Larimer, H. T. Odum, R. B. Parker, and N. E. Armstrong. "Directions for the Determination of Changes in Carbon Dioxide Concentration from Changes in *p*H," *Publ. Inst. Mar. Sci. Univ. Tex., 9,* 454–489 (1963).
(16) Copeland, B. J. "Evidence for Regulation of Community Metabolism in a Marine Ecosystem," *Ecology, 46,* 563–564 (1965).
(17) Nash, C. B. "Environmental Characteristics of a River Estuary," *J. Mar. Res., 6,* 147–174 (1947).
(18) Gleason, H. A. "On the Relation between Species and Area," *Ecology, 3,* 158–162 (1922).
(19) Reish, D. J. "The Use of Marine Invertebrates as Indicators of Water Quality," *Waste Disposal in the Marine Environment,* edited by E. A. Pearson. New York: Pergamon Press (1960).
(20) Beverton, R. J. H., and S. J. Holt. "On the Dynamics of Exploited Fish Populations," *U. K. Min. Agr. Fish., Fish. Invest.,* Ser. 2, *19,* 1–533 (1957).
(21) Ricker, W. E. "Handbook of Computations for Biological Statistics of Fish Populations," *Fish. Res. Bd. Canada, Bull., 119,* 1–300 (1958).
(22) Ricker, W. E. "Big Effects from Small Causes: Two Examples from Fish Population Dynamics," *J. Fish. Res. Bd. Canada, 20*(2), 257–264 (1963).
(23) Locker, A., and O, Kinne (eds.). "Quantative Biologie des Stoffwechsels," *Erstes internationał Symposium: Vorträge und Diskussionen. Helgol. Wiss. Meeresunters., 9*(1–4), 1–496 (1964).
(24) Fry, F. E. J. "The Aquatic Respiration of Fish," *The Physiology of Fishes,* edited by M. E. Brown. New York: Academic Press (1957).

(25) Winberg, G. G. "Rate of Metabolism and Food Requirements of Fishes" (Original in Russian), *Fish. Res. Bd. Canada, Translation Seris No. 194* (1956).

(26) Tarzwell, C. M. (ed.). "Biological Problems in Water Pollution," Third Seminar 1962, U.S.P.H.S. Publ. No. 999-WP-25, 1–424 (1965).

(27) Fry, F. E. J. "Effects of the Environment on Animal Activity," *Univ. Toronto Studies, Biol. Ser. 55* (Publ. Ontario Fish. Res. Lab.) *68,* 1–62 (1947).

(28) Fromm, P. O. "Physiological Considerations in Studies of the Action of Pollutants on Aquatic Animals," *Biological Problems in Water Pollution,* Third Seminar 1962, edited by C. M. Tarzwell. USPHS Publ. No. 999-WP-25, 316–319 (1965).

(29) Davis, G. E., J. Foster, C. E. Warren, and P. Douderoff. "The Influence of Oxygen Concentration on the Swimming Performance of Juvenile Pacific Salmon at Various Temperatures," *Trans. Amer. Fish. Soc., 92,* 111–124 (1963).

(30) Herrmann, R. B., C. E. Warren, and P. Douderoff. "Influence of Oxygen Concentration on the Growth of Juvenile Coho Salmon," *Trans. Amer. Fish. Soc., 91,* 155–167 (1962).

(31) Kinne, O. "Growth, Food Intake and Food Conversion in a Euryplastic Fish Exposed to Different Temperatures and Salinities," *Physiol. Zool., 33,* 288–317 (1960).

(32) Kinne, O. "Non-genetic Adaptation to Temperature and Salinity," *Helgol. Wiss. Meeresunters., 9*(1–4), 453–458 (1964).

(33) Kinne, O. "Salinity Requirements of the Fish, *Cyprinodon macularis,*" *Biological Problems in Water Pollution,* Third Seminar 1962, edited by C. M. Tarzwell, U.S.P.H.S. Publ. No. 999-WP-25, 187–192 (1965).

(34) Kinne, O., and E. M. Kinne. "Rates of Development in Embryos of a Cyprinodont Fish Exposed to Different Temperature-Salinity-Oxygen Combinations," *Can. J. Zool., 40,* 231–253 (1962).

(35) Alderdice, D. F. "Some Effects of Simultaneous Variation in Salinity, Temperature, and Dissolved Oxygen on the Resistance of Young Coho Salmon to a Toxic Substance," *J. Fish. Res. Bd. Canada, 20*(2), 525–550 (1963).

(36) Wohlschlag, D. E. "Antarctic Fish Growth and Metabolic Differences Related to Sex," *Ecology, 43,* 589–597 (1962).

(37) Wohlschlag, D. E. "Differences in Metabolic Rates of Migratory and Resident Freshwater Forms of an Arctic Whitefish," *Ecology, 38,* 502–510 (1957).

(38) Wohlschlag, D. E. "An Antarctic Fish with Unusually Low Metabolism," *Ecology, 44,* 557–564 (1963).

(39) Caldwell, D. K. "The Biology of the Pinfish, *Lagodon rhomboides* (*Linnaeus*)," *Bull. Florida State Mus., Biol. Sci., 2*(6), 77–173 (1957).

(40) Bertalanffy, L. "Untersuchungen uber die Gesetzlichkeit des Wachstums. II. A Quantitative Theory of Organic Growth," *Human Biol., 10,* 181–213 (1938).

(41) Bertalanffy, L. "Basic Concepts in Quantitative Biology of Metabolism," *Helgol. Wiss. Meeresunters., 9*(1–4), 5–37 (1964).

ECOLOGICAL ASPECTS OF STREAM POLLUTION

Neal E. Armstrong and Earnest F. Gloyna
The University of Texas, Austin, Texas

B. J. Copeland
The University of Texas Marine Science Institute, Port Aransas, Texas

An interchange of gases, nutrients, and energy occurs between the various components of the ecosystem. Gas exchanges denote the activity of plants and animals in photosynthesis and respiration. Nutrient flows describe the recycling processes. Energy exchange ties the ecosystem into a package which may be described in thermodynamic terms.

Energy may enter an ecosystem in the form of sunlight and as imported organic material, which would include pollution. Electromagnetic energy impinging on the ecosystem is converted to organic matter with an efficiency of about 2–5 percent, accompanied by a simultaneous release of oxygen and uptake of carbon dioxide. Transfer through consumer trophic levels involves losses as unassimilated material and dead organisms to the decomposer trophic level, passage to other ecosystems or trophic levels, or respiration to heat with the concurrent consumption of oxygen and evolution of carbon dioxide.

Energy is conserved in transfers, but a portion is always lost as an entropy tax: thus the first and second laws of thermodynamics are obeyed. Because an ecosystem follows the second law, self-regulating mechanisms cause ecosystems to stabilize even though they may be disturbed by natural or man-made pollution. The place where stabilization occurs depends on the energy inputs to the ecosystem and the amounts of energy associated with those inputs.

The lines of organic transfer constitute food chains, and the role of each component in the chain determines its trophic level (1). Plants, herbivores, and carnivores are the primary producers and the primary and secondary consumers, respectively. Trophic structure is measured by numbers of organisms in each level, by the weight of those organisms, or by the rate at which energy flows through each level.

The stability of a trophic level, as measured in terms of energy, depends on the rate at which food is produced in the previous level, and on the number of food chains between trophic levels. Consequently, the stability increases with increasing channels through which energy can flow. Similarly, this concept is related to the number of species in a trophic level, since each species is part of a food chain; and thus the more species present the greater the stability. Since each trophic level is influenced by the energy flow through the ecosystem, the stability of the ecosystem may be measured by the number of species in a trophic level and the number of individuals in each species. This has led to the use of biological indicators in the detection of pollutional stresses.

SPECIES-DIVERSITY INDEX

Relations of individuals to species have been used in comparing types of waters. For example, Patrick, Hohn, and Wallace (2) have used diatoms. Odum, Cantlon, and Kornicker (3) have proposed a species-individual relationship which is linear on a semilog plot instead of the truncated log-normal curve of Patrick *et al.* (2) and which follows the relation

$$dI/dS = kI \quad (1)$$

where S is the number of species and I the number of individuals. Integrating one obtains

$$S = K_D \log I + 1 \quad (2)$$

where K_D is the species-diversity index. An analogy might be occupational organization in human society. There are common occupations which serve many in a community, and a few occupations which serve relatively few in a community. As long as the rarer occupations are related to the common occupations in a fixed ratio, the relationship of occupations to individuals is logarithmic. The analogy applies to organisms when each species is considered to be an occupation.

The species-diversity index is found by counting the number of species found in the first 1,000 individuals counted. Such measurements of mollusck shells found in three different marine environments showed K_D values to be 11.3 for the Gulf of Mexico, 6.3 for a hyposaline Texas bay, and 3.3 for a hypersaline Texas bay (Fig. 27). By plotting diatom data obtained by Hohn (4) in the Houston Ship Channel, Galveston Bay, Chocolate Bay, and Mustang Bay, it becomes evident that a direct relationship exists between the changes in structure of the diatom flora and the effect of pollution, (Figs. 27, 28).

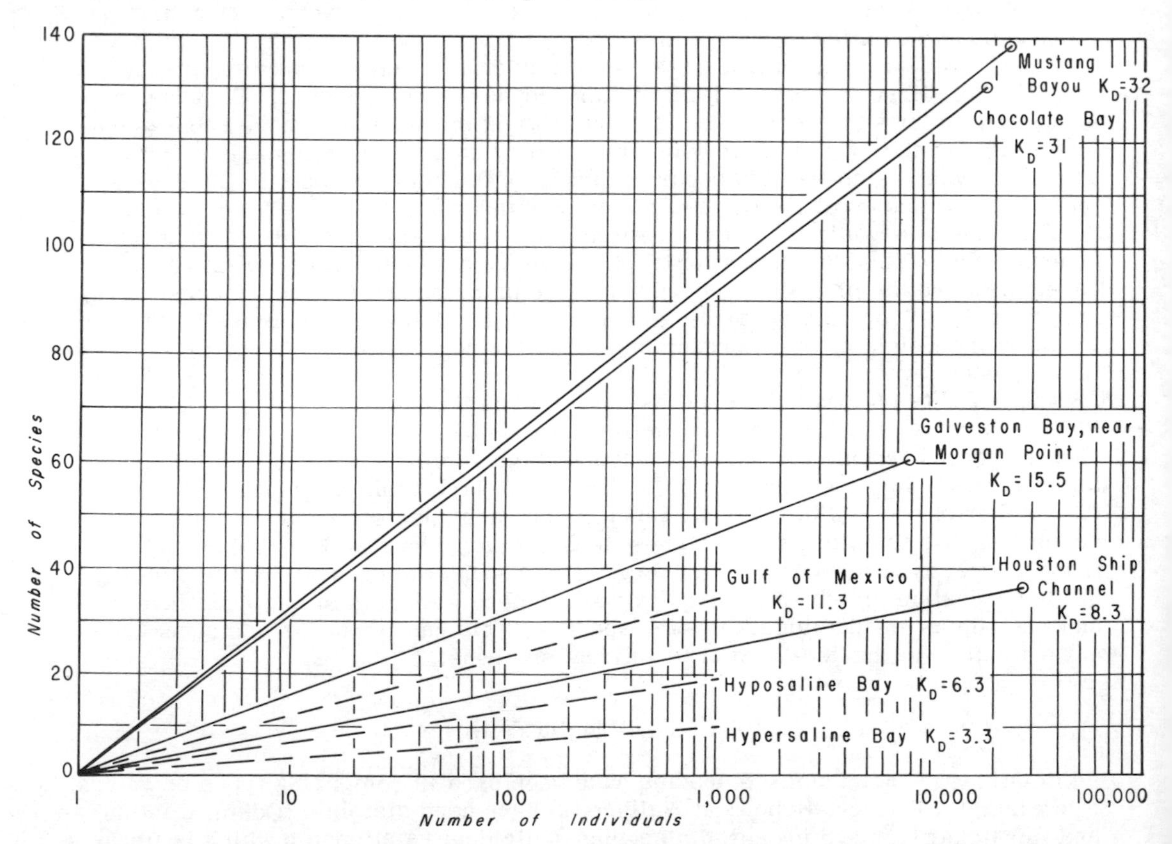

Figure 27. Species diversity in Texas bays. Determination of K_D for polluted and unpolluted waters.

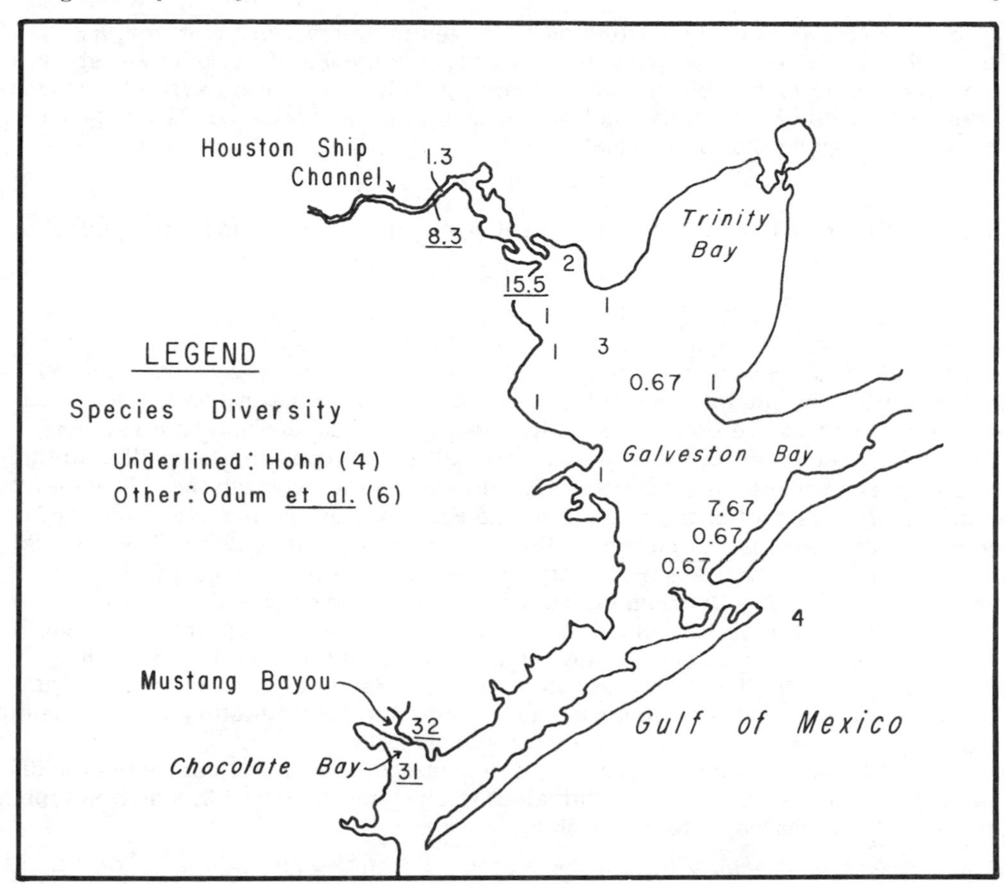

Figure 28. Species diversity in Texas bays. K_D values for diatoms and zooplankton generally increase from the polluted Houston Ship Channel to the Gulf of Mexico.

This relationship between species and individuals has been applied to the zooplankton of marine ecosystems and has proved to be a sensitive indicator of environmental stress caused by either natural or man-made pollution.

Copeland (5) obtained similar results for zooplankton in St. Joseph Bay, Florida, near the outfall of a paper mill plant. At 250 feet from the outfall, K_D = 1.3, at 1,000 feet K_D = 4.3, and at about 2,500 feet K_D = 6. Odum, Cuzon, Beyers, and Allbaugh (6) similarly found that in the Corpus Christi, Texas, ship harbor K_D = 1.6. Ten miles into Corpus Christi Bay, K_D = 3.3, and at twenty miles K_D = 6.

Unfortunately, no direct comparison has been made between the species-diversity index, K_D, and some pollution parameters such as BOD or coliforms. So far, K_D has been related only to ecological parameters which would indicate pollution. However, the ecological evaluation of pollution effects in natural waters based on indicator organisms must always be accompanied by a view of the overall community structure and physiology before definitive answers can be obtained.

DIURNAL CURVE

The diurnal curve method can be used to determine the total production and respiration of oxygen in natural waters. The rate of change of oxygen content,

dC/dt, in water is caused by diffusion of oxygen into or out of the water, $K_2(C_s - C)$: the production of oxygen by photosynthesis, p: the uptake of oxygen by respiration of plants, animals, microbes, and wastes, r; and the accrual of oxygen by groundwater and runoff (7). Usually the latter source may be neglected. The oxygen change can then be shown as Equation 3

$$dC/dt = K_2 (C_s - C) + p - r \tag{3}$$

This is valid for daylight use, but at night $p = 0$, so that Equation 4 is applicable.

$$dC/dt = K_2 (C_s - C) - r \tag{4}$$

The rate of change is obtained in various ways, depending on the type of water system involved. For a lake or estuary the diurnal oxygen curve is taken at one or several locations and the rate derived as the change in oxygen with time (8). This is called the single curve analysis. For a river, two stations are selected and diurnal curves are obtained simultaneously (7). The downstream curve is then shifted to the left on the time axis one half the amount corresponding to the time required for the water mass to travel between the two stations. The upstream station is shifted to the right on the time axis by the same amount, and the difference between the curves is the rate of change curve (9). This process insures that the water measured upstream is the same water measured downstream; the difference between the curves is then the increase or decrease in oxygen content. If a river has the same characteristics both upstream and downstream the single curve method may be used. Such is the case for the Itchen River in Figure 29. The basic assumption in the diurnal curve analysis is that the water measured at a station has had a recent metabolic history characteristic of the water measured previously at that station (10).

After the rate of change curve has been obtained, it must be corrected for diffusion gains or losses. This is equivalent to changing Equation 3, which is typical for daytime responses, into Equation 5.

$$(dC/dt)_c = p - r = dC/dt - K_2 (C_s - C) \tag{5}$$

Similarly, Equation 4 for nighttime responses can be translated into Equation 6.

$$(dC/dt)_c = - r = dC/dt - K_2 (C_s - C) \tag{6}$$

Of course the determination of K_2 is very critical to this analysis and several methods may be employed to estimate it. The previous method (10, 11) was to select two sampling periods during the night, usually at predawn and postsunset, and insert values for dC/dt, C_s, and C into Equation 4 such that Equations 7 and 8 can be written.

$$dC/dt_1 = K_2 (C_s - C)_1 - r_1 \tag{7}$$

$$dC/dt_2 = K_2 (C_s - C)_2 - r_2 \tag{8}$$

By subtracting and solving for K_2 it is possible to write Equation 9.

$$K_2 = ((dC/dt_1 - dC/dt_2) + (r_1 - r_2))/((C_s - C)_1 - (C_s - C)_2) \tag{9}$$

The units of K_2 are the reciprocal of time. This equation is similar to that developed by Odum (7), but differs in the denominator so as to give units compatible with K_2 as used by engineers. Values for K_2 may be obtained by the formulation presented by Dobbins (12) or O'Connor and Dobbins (13), which has been successful for actual stream data, or they may be determined directly from the uncorrected rate of change data. Postsunset data are plotted according to Equation 10, or Equation 4 such that K_2 is the slope of the curve (Fig. 30).

$$dC/dt = -K_2 C + (K_2 C_s - r) \tag{10}$$

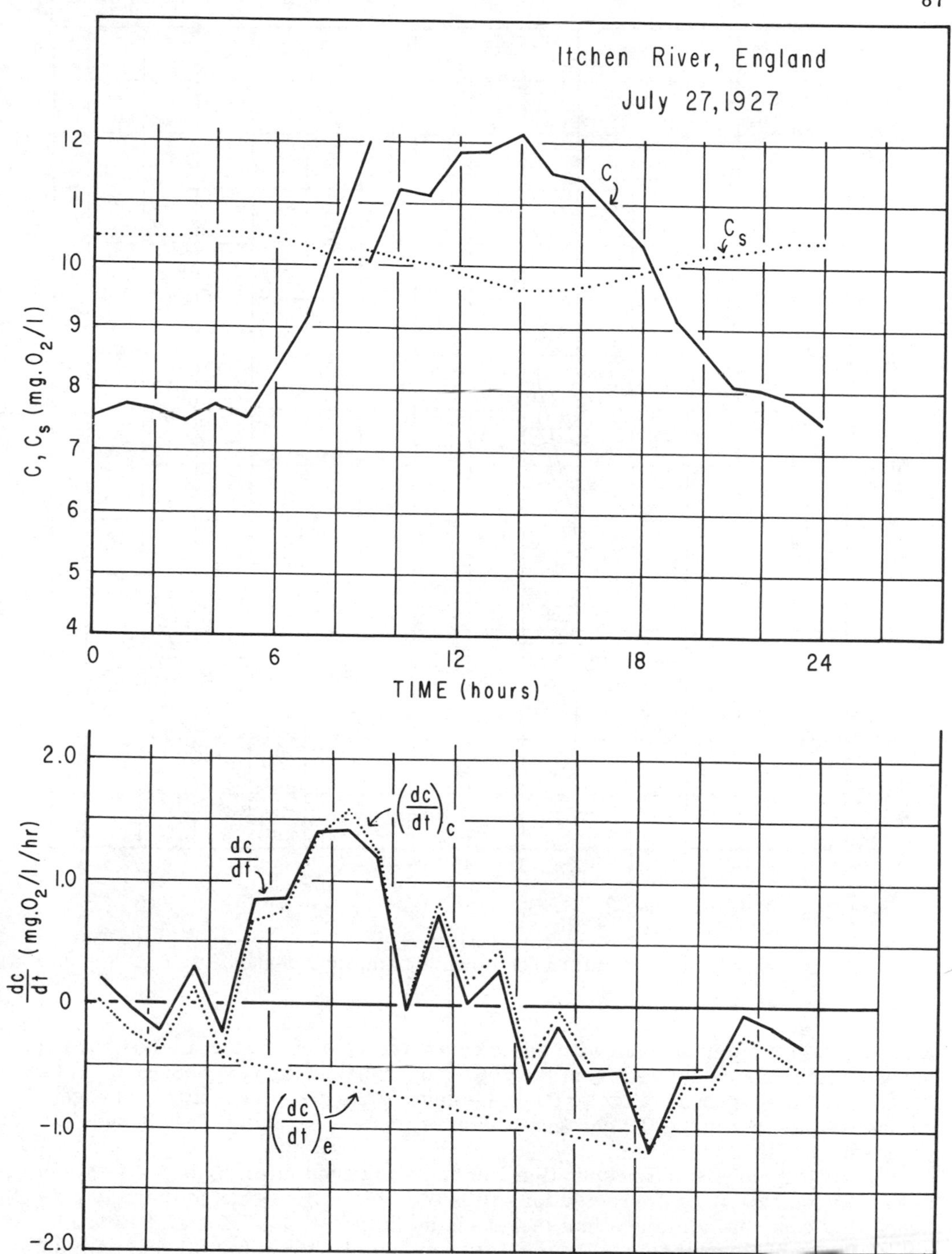

Figure 29. Diurnal and rate of change curves for Itchen River, England.

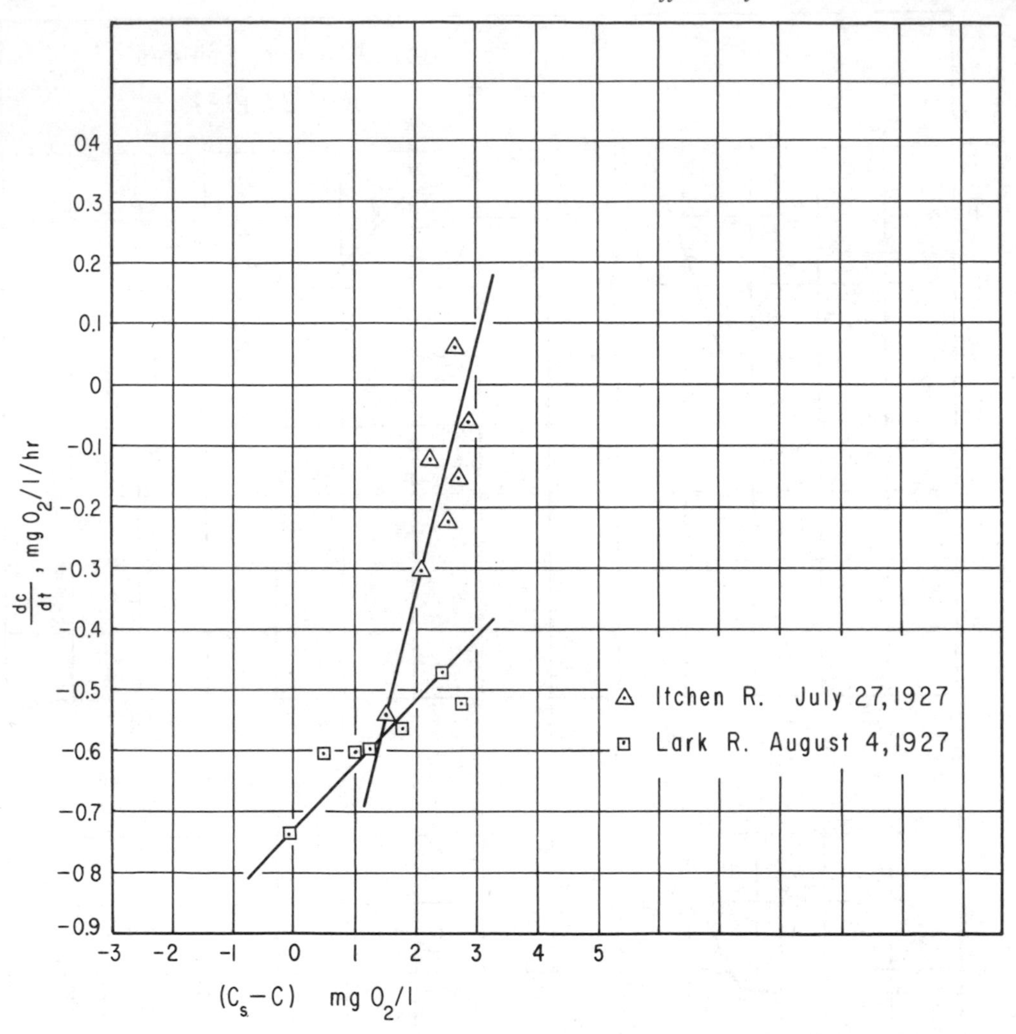

Figure 30. Determination of reaeration coefficient by graphical method.

Notably, values of K_2 derived with the uncorrected rate of change method have not agreed with those calculated from the O'Connor and Dobbins (13) equation. There appears to be a direct relation to the magnitude of the dissolved oxygen change during the day (for large DO changes it overestimates, for small DO changes it underestimates).

The photosynthesis and respiration can be determined after K_2 and the rate of change curve have been corrected for diffusion, (Fig. 29). Because there is evidence that community metabolism increases as labile organic material is produced during photosynthesis (14), an allowance must be made for increased respiration during the day. This increase becomes evident at the end of the day in the rate of change curve, which exhibits a large respiratory pulse (Fig. 29). One must estimate respiration during the day by drawing a line representing respiration, $(dC/dt)_c$, from the dawn hour to the maximum point of the postsunset respiration. It is thus assumed that respiration has increased during the day and reaches a maximum at a time just after sunset. By integrating under the respiration curve it is possible to obtain R.

$$R = \int_1^{SR}(dC/dt)_c\,dt + \int_{SR}^{SS}(dC/dt)_e\,dt + \int_{SS}^{24}(dC/dt)_c\,dt$$

or (11)

$$= \int_1^{SR}(-r)\,dt + \int_{SR}^{SS}(-r)_e\,dt + \int_{SS}^{24}(-r)dt$$

where SR and SS represent sunrise and sunset respectively.

Production is calculated in a similar way. Since for daytime hours it is necessary to estimate r_e, then p is the difference between the corrected rate of change curve in this region and r_e, and P_G, gross photosynthesis, is then the area between the two curves.

$$P_G = \int_1^{SR}[p - (-r)]\,dt = \int_{SR}^{SS}(p + r)dt \qquad (12)$$

The two values, P_G and R, are multiplied by the depth of water to obtain units of gms oxygen/square meter/day.

Certain problems arise in deep waters where stratification may exist, since the above method necessarily assumes complete mixing of the water. McFarland and Prescott (15) computed the diurnal change of oxygen for various depths off the California coast in kelp beds, corrected the rate of change graph by estimating diffusion from upper and lower water layers, then summed their values of P and R for a column of water. Of course here again the transfer coefficients are critical, but the method may be applied. Sugiura (16) gives a formula for oxygen rate of change which corrects for diffusion from the atmosphere and from lower layers of water, but does not investigate ways of measuring the diffusion coefficients between layers of water.

Carbon dioxide production may also be used to measure production of biomass. This method, which was developed by Beyers and Odum (17) and is explained in detail by Beyers, Larimer, Odum, Parker, and Armstrong (18), makes use of a pH-CO_2 titration curve to convert pH values from the natural water to carbon dioxide values. For example, after a sample of the natural water is relieved of its CO_2 content by bubbling nitrogen gas through it, it is titrated with distilled water saturated with known amounts of carbon dioxide. From these data a diurnal curve of carbon dioxide may be drawn, and P and R in units of gms carbon/square meter/day determined. The diurnal carbon dioxide method is a valuable supplement to the oxygen method when anaerobic conditions occur. Since correction for diffusion of CO_2 between water and the atmosphere is not necessary, the pH-CO_2 method may be more accurate than the oxygen curve method.

APPLICATION OF DIURNAL CURVE

The diurnal curve analysis may be used to study two problems. First, for a river or lake the uptake of oxygen by the organisms, the plants, the bottom sediments, and the decomposing waste may be estimated by the total respiration, R. If the uptake of oxygen by the decomposing waste were subtracted from R, one would have the term D_B of the Dobbins (12) equation. Second, for the same river or lake the total production of oxygen during the daytime is obtained, rather than just that by plankton as is measured in light and dark bottle experiments.

The light and dark bottle method of determining oxygen production and consumption by phyto- and zooplankton was first used by Gaarder and Gran in 1927 (19), but has been questioned by Ryther (20) on the grounds of the effects of enclosure on plankton, and by Odum and Hoskins (10) on the grounds of correct estimation of the total production and respiration of an ecosystem. The latter authors found a large underestimation of productivity where bottom plants and sediments were present.

CLASSIFICATION OF ECOSYSTEMS

Ecosystems may be classified according to production and respiration values and their ratio, P/R. For example, when $P/R > 1$, a state of autotrophy exists and more food is produced then is consumed. When $P/R < 1$, a state of heterotrophy exists and more food is consumed then is produced. Oligotrophic lakes and barren streams have low production and respiration values, while eutrophic rivers and lakes have high production and respiration values, with intermediate types existing between these extremes. For waters just below sewage outfalls, respiration will be high and production low, giving $P/R \ll 1$, while for recovering waters, which are among the most productive, P is very high, R is low (compared to P) and $P/R > 1$. The degradation of sewage as it passes down a river will cause large variations in P/R values (Fig. 31). Odum (7) computed P and R for the White River below the Indianapolis, Indiana, sewage outfall from data given by Denham (21). Just below the sewage outfall, R was very high, while P was low ($P/R < 1$). Downstream, as nutrients were released and plant life bloomed, P rose sharply as R decreased ($P/R \gg 1$). Further downstream a very eutrophic ecosystem was evident with large fluctuations in diurnal oxygen concentrations, high P and R values, and $P/R > 1$. At about 170 miles from the outfall, stabilization of the ecosystem had occurred, P and R values had decreased, and $P/R = 1$.

Copeland and Dorris (22, 23) have reported similar types of curves for oil refinery holding ponds where the abscissa was time instead of distance. This type of relationship for P and R casts doubt on the validity of any equation which assumes a steady diurnal pulse below a sewage outfall. The magnitude of the diurnal variation of oxygen will vary considerably below a sewage outfall.

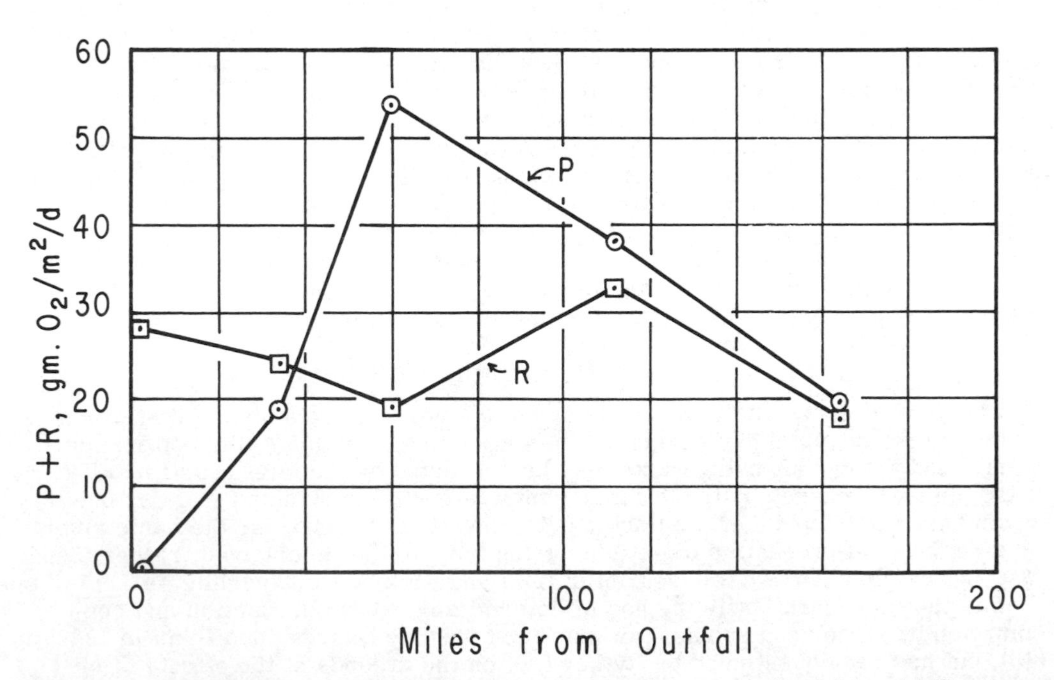

Figure 31. Stabilization of pollution in White River, Indiana, as indicated by stabilization of ecological system.

From the data on the White River in Indiana (21) and the holding ponds in Oklahoma (23), it appears that predictive curves could be drawn below sewage outfalls or in holding ponds for P and R, given some waste parameter.

ENERGY—P/R RELATIONSHIPS

To relate the energy stabilization concepts expressed earlier to the diurnal curve method, consider a diagram such as Figure 32 where P is plotted versus R. Not only may the magnitudes of P and R be easily ascertained but also their state of stability may be determined by the P/R ratio. For the White River study, where municipal sewage was involved, the progression of P, R, and P/R shows a definite trend from an unstable ecosystem to a stable ecosystem. Note the overshoot at the 60-mile station. This was caused by an algal bloom. That the values for oil refinery holding ponds exhibit the same trends indicates a similar behavior of ecosystems with different wastes. The winter curve shows that natural environmental stress coupled with waste may cause a very unstable system for long periods of time. However, the summer curve, which follows a course similar to that of the White River, again shows the overshoot beyond a stable condition and a return to stability. The constant influx of refinery waste caused the stable condition to be at $P/R < 1$.

Seasonal environmental stress on unpolluted systems is shown by a condition exhibited by Baffin Bay, Texas. A progression from an autotrophic to a heterotrophic community during change in seasons is noted. The planktonic production of this bay, determined by the light and dark bottle method, exhibited a similar response and in December accounted for the total production, while at other times the contribution was much less. Stress due to high salinities (24) also causes low production and respiration values because of the few organisms which can tolerate such conditions.

Stability, as depicted by energy balances, thus depends first on the natural environmental conditions and second on the amount of waste imports introduced into the ecosystem. The stabilization of the waste by the ecosystem is concurrent with the stabilization of the ecosystem itself. These results may be used conversely to detect unstable systems caused by environmental stress. That is, given values of P and R of an ecosystem, the state of eutrophication may be assessed, as well as its stability.

MODEL RESULTS

A study is underway at The University of Texas to attempt to develop predictive curves for P and R against various waste parameters. A 200-foot model is fitted with DO probes, *p*H meters, temperature probes, and pyrheliometers, from which data are taken continuously through a digital voltmeter and punched onto paper tape. Computer programs are used to translate the tape and compute the values of P and R by the diurnal curve method and by the *p*H-CO_2 method, compute efficiencies of photosynthesis, and compute respiratory and photosynthetic quotients. These data are used at present for correlation of uptake and release of radionuclides in the ecosystem, but can be used for pollutant effects.

Preliminary data from the model river are presented in Figures 33 and 34 (25). Community metabolism data for an 80-day period are shown in Figure 33. It should be noted that the large discrepancy between photosynthetic rates and community respiration rates as measured by oxygen methods was not present when carbon dioxide methods were used. A possible explanation was the long period of anaerobic conditions during the night and early morning (1/3 day in some cases). This results in some of the oxygen normally measured as photosynthesis being used during the early part of daylight to repay the oxygen debt incurred by the community during the time it was void of oxygen.

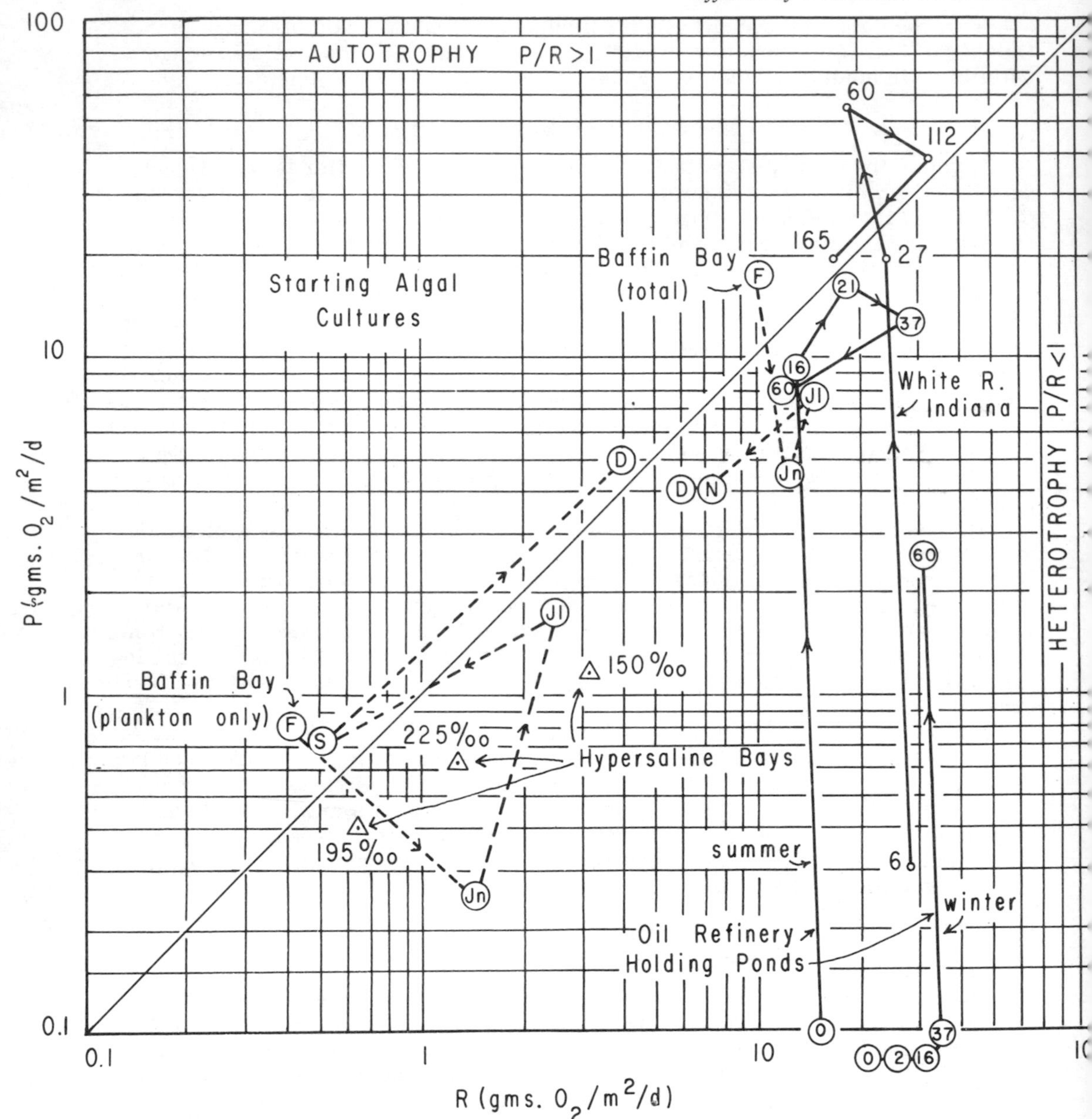

Figure 32. P/R diagram showing stabilization of polluted waters, unpolluted waters, and hypersaline bays.

The possibility that the transport of radionuclides in the model river was connected to community metabolism is shown in Figure 34. The P/R ratio of carbon dioxide metabolism was used in the comparison analysis because the period of anaerobic conditions casts some doubt on the oxygen data. The expected relationship is, therefore, that as the P/R ratio exceeds 1, the concentration of radionuclides in plant biomass should increase (uptake of nutrients; growth exceeds

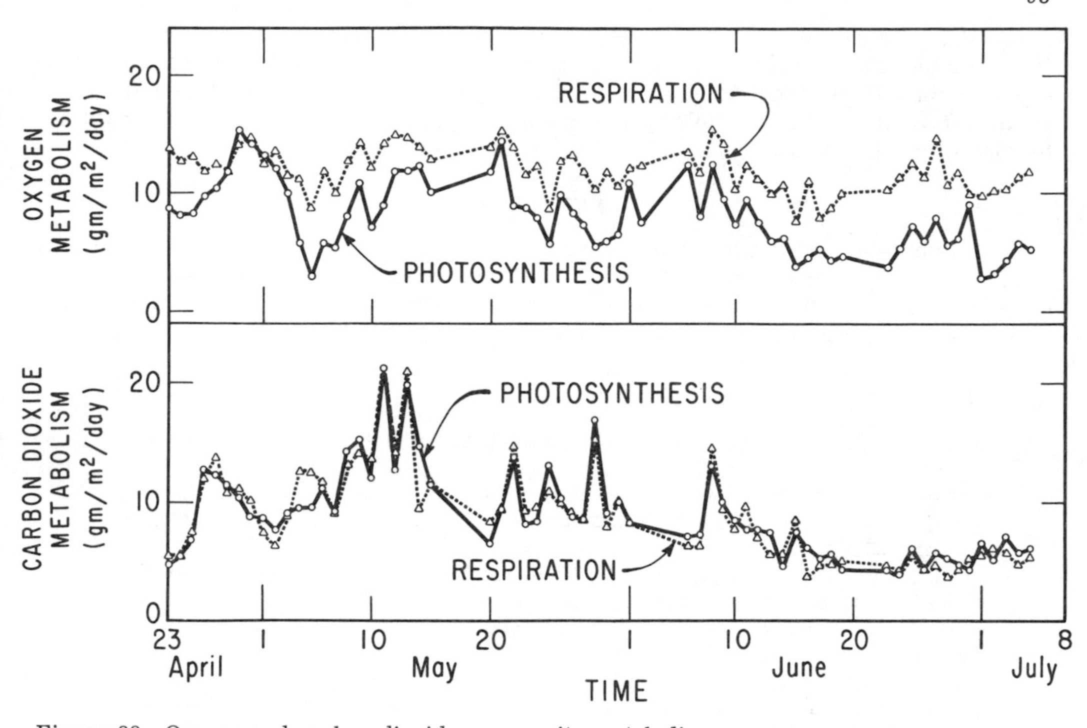

Figure 33. Oxygen and carbon dioxide community metabolism.

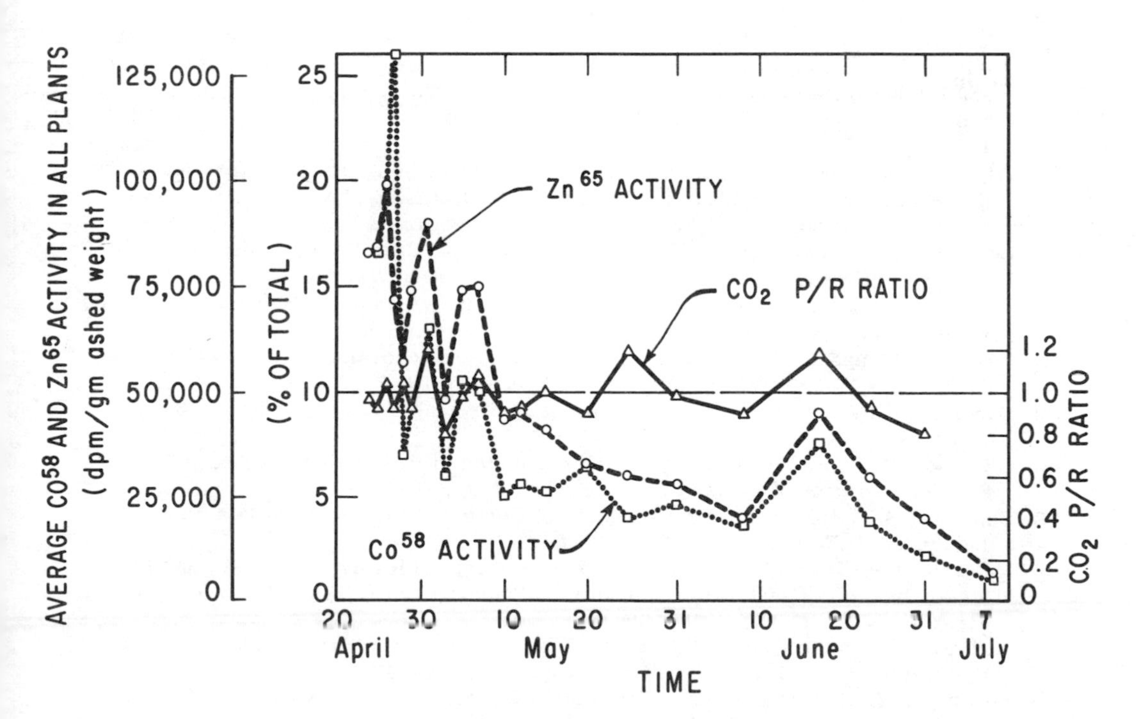

Figure 34. Average Co^{58} and Zn^{65} activity in all plants and the *P*/*R* ratio of Co_2 metabolism.

demands), and as the P/R ratio falls below 1, the concentration of radionuclides in the plants should decrease (release of nutrients; demands exceed growth). For the June data the expected relationship was apparent. The earlier data were ignored, since the radionuclide concentration was great and normal uptake could not be distinguished from surface adsorption phenomena.

SUMMARY

In conclusion, two methods to evaluate the effects of pollution on the ecological system have been presented. These methods can furnish valuable information to the engineer regarding the condition and the stability of ecological systems in receiving waters, and may ultimately become design criteria.

REFERENCES

(1) Odum, E. P. *Fundamentals of Ecology*. 2nd Ed. Philadelphia: W. B. Saunders Co. (1959).

(2) Patrick, R., M. H. Hohn, and J. H. Wallace. "A New Method of Determining the Pattern of the Diatom Flora," *Notula Naturae*, Acad. Nat. Sc., Phila., *259*, 1–12 (1954).

(3) Odum, H. T., J. E. Cantlon, and L. S. Kornicker. "An Organizational Hierarchy Postulate for the Interpretation of Species-Individual Distributions, Species Entropy, Ecosystem Evolution, and the Meaning of a Species-Variety Index," *Ecology, 41*, 395–399 (1960).

(4) Hohn, M. H. "The Use of Diatom Pupulations as a Measure of Water Quality in Selected Areas of Galveston and Chocolate Bay, Texas," *Publ. Inst. Mar. Sci. Univ. Tex., 6*, 206–212 (1959).

(5) Copeland, B. J. "Effects of Industrial Waste on the Marine Environment,' *J. Water Poll. Cont. Fed., 38*, 1000–1010 (1966).

(6) Odum, H. T., R. P. Cuzon du Rest, R. J. Beyers, and C. Allbaugh, "Diurnal Metabolism, Total Phosphorus, Ohle Anomaly, and Zooplankton Diversity of Abnormal Marine Ecosystems of Texas," *Publ. Inst. Mar. Sci., 9*, 404–453 (1963).

(7) Odum, H. T. "Primary Production in Flowing Waters," *Limnol. Oceanog., 1*, 102–117 (1956).

(8) Odum, H. T. "Analysis of Diurnal Oxygen Curves for the Assay of Reaeration Rates and Metabolism in Polluted Marine Bays," *Waste Disposal in the Marine Environment*, edited by E. Pearson. New York: Pergamon Press (1960).

(9) Copeland, B. J., and W. R. Duffer. "Use of a Clear Plastic Dome to Measure Gaseous Diffusion Rates in Natural Waters," *Limnol. Oceanog., 9*, 494–499 (1964).

(10) Odum, H. T., and C. M. Hoskins. "Comparative Studies on the Metabolism of Marine Waters," *Publ. Inst. Mar. Sci. Univ. Tex., 5*, 16–46 (1958).

(11) Odum, H. T., and R. F. Wilson. "Further Studies on Reaeration and Metabolism of Texas Bays, 1958–1960," *Publ. Inst. Mar. Sci., 8*, 23–55 (1962).

(12) Dobbins, W. E. "BOD and Oxygen Relations in Streams," *ASCE, 90*(SA3), 53–78 (June 1964).

(13) O'Connor, D. J., and W. E. Dobbins. "Mechanisms of Reaeration in Natural Streams," *Trans. Amer. Soc. Civil Engrs., 123*, 641 (1958).

(14) Copeland, B. J. "Evidence for Regulation of Community Metabolism in a Marine Ecosystem," *Ecology, 46*, 563–564 (1965).

(15) McFarland, W. N., and J. Prescott. "Standing Crop, Chlorophyll Content, and *in situ* Metabolism of a Giant Kelp Community in Southern California," *Publ. Inst. Mar. Sci. Univ. Tex., 6*, 109–132 (1959).

(16) Sugiura, Y. "On the Diurnal Variation of Oxygen Content in Surface Layers of the Hydrosphere," *Pap. Met. Geophys.*, Tokyo, *4*, 79–89 (1953).

(17) Beyers, R. J., and H. T. Odum. "The Use of Carbon Dioxide to Construct *p*H Curves for the Measurement of Productivity," *Limnol. Oceanog., 5*, 229–230 (1959).

(18) Beyers, R. J., J. L. Larimer, H. T. Odum, R. B. Parker, and N. E. Armstrong. "Directions for the Determination of Changes in Carbon Dioxide Concentration from Changes in *p*H," *Publ. Inst. Mar. Sci. Univ. Tex., 9,* 454–489 (1963).

(19) Gaarder, T., and H. H. Gran. "Investigations of the Production of Plankton in the Oslo Fjord," *Rapp. et Proc. - Verb., Cons. Int. Explor. Mer., 42,* 1–48 (1927).

(20) Ryther, J. H. "The Measurement of Primary Productivity," *Limnol. Oceanog., 1,* 72–84 (1956).

(21) Denham, S. C. "A Limnological Investigation of the West Fork and Common Branch of White River," *Invest. Indiana Lakes and Streams, 1,* 17–72 (1938).

(22) Copeland, B. J., and T. C. Dorris. "Photosynthetic Productivity in Oil Refinery Effluent Holding Ponds," *J. Water Poll. Cont. Fed., 34,* 1104–1111 (1962).

(23) Copeland, B. J., and T. C. Dorris. "Community Metabolism in Ecosystems Receiving Oil Refinery Effluents," *Limnol. Oceanog., 9,* 431–447 (1964).

(24) Copeland, B. J., and R. S. Jones. "Community Metabolism in Some Hypersaline Waters," *Texas J. Sci., 17,* 188–205 (1965).

(25) Copeland, B. J., and E. F. Gloyna. "Radioactivity Transport in Water-Structure and Metabolism of a Lotic Community, Part I (April–July 1964)," Environmental Health Engineering Research Laboratory and Institute of Marine Science, U.S. Atomic Energy Commission, *Tech. Report 8* (1965).

ANALYSIS OF THE DISSOLVED OXYGEN VARIATION IN A FLOWING STREAM

Donald J. O'Connor and Dominic M. DiToro
Manhattan College, New York, New York

The distribution of dissolved oxygen in a natural stream may be defined by the equation of continuity or mass balance in differential form:

$$\frac{\partial c}{\partial t} = U(x,t)\frac{\partial c}{\partial x} \pm \sum S(c,x,t) \tag{1}$$

in which

c = concentration of dissolved oxygen
U = velocity of flow in the x-direction
S = sources and sinks of oxygen

Equation 1 describes the temporal variation of oxygen in a stream in which there is a spatial distribution along the axis of flow. The equation applies to those cases in which the concentration is or may be assumed to be uniform over the cross-sectional area of the stream. Both the flow and the cross-sectional area from which the velocity is determined may be functions of space and time. The various sources and sinks may also be functions of time, space, and the concentration itself or the concentration of a different material. The concentration, c, may apply to any substance; however, it will be used specifically to refer to the concentration of dissolved oxygen, while the term L will describe the concentration of the biochemical oxygen demand. Since the development of the Streeter Phelps equation (1), many engineers and scientists have contributed much to the understanding of oxygen relationships in natural waters. No attempt will be made to review the significant contributions; reference will be limited to those which bear directly on the analysis in this work.

The sources of oxygen are the amount in the incoming or tributary flow--that due to natural or artificial aeration, and that due to the photosynthetic activity of the green plants. The first source is taken into account as the flux term of Equation 1, or an initial condition, and the second and third enter as source terms in Equation 1. The rate of reaeration is proportional to the dissolved oxygen deficit, and its coefficient is designated as

$$K_a(c_s - c) \tag{2}$$

The photosynthetic source depends upon many factors, such as sunlight, temperature, mass of algae, and nutrients. The effect of these factors will be included in the term P, representing the overall rate at which oxygen is released by photosynthesis, as first presented by Odum (2). If the photosynthetic rate is assumed to vary as the sunlight intensity during the day and to be zero at night, then this source may be defined by periodic function:

$$P_{(x,t)} = P_m \left\{\frac{2p}{\pi} + 2\sum_{n=1}^{\infty} a_n \cos[2\pi n(t - p/2)]\right\} \tag{3}$$

where

$$a_n = \frac{2\pi/p}{(\pi/p)^2 - (2n\pi)^2} \cos[(n\pi p)]$$

for $x \geqslant 0$; in which p = period of sunlight, and t and p are given in days. This is the Fourier series expansion of the function illustrated in Figure 35.

The sinks of dissolved oxygen include the utilization by the biochemical oxidation of organic matter, by the benthal deposits, and by the respiration of aquatic plants. The first factor may be divided into two distinct phases: carbonaceous and nitrogenous. The rate of oxygen consumption is usually assumed to be first order. The distribution of each component may then be defined as follows:

$$L = L_0 \, e^{\frac{-K_r x}{U}} \tag{4}$$

$$N = N_0 \, e^{\frac{-K_n x}{U}} \tag{5}$$

in which

L, N = concentration of the carbonaceous and nitrogenous components of BOD

K_r, K_n = coefficients defining the rate of removal in stream.

Equation 4 defines the longitudinal profile of carbonaceous BOD due to a discharge of wastewater at $x = 0$, which produces concentration, L_0 and N_0 at that location in the stream. The coefficient, K_r, incorporates all the factors which are effective in removing the carbonaceous BOD, such as sedimentation and volatilization. This rate of removal is not necessarily equal to the rate at which oxygen is utilized. The coefficient describing this reaction may be identified as K_d (3).

Much of the nitrogenous demand is found in the dissolved state and is therefore removed or changed only by oxidation. The analysis of the nitrogen stream data is therefore usually simpler than that of the carbon component, since the additional factors, such as sedimentation, are not present. The rate at which the nitrogenous BOD or ammonia decays directly reflects the rate at which oxygen is consumed. The coefficient, K_n, therefore reflects both the removal of ammonia and the utilization of oxygen.

In addition to the dissolved oxygen utilized by the reactions described above, it also may be consumed by benthal deposits and the respiration of plants. If river water contains dissolved oxygen, aerobic conditions will exist at the surface layer of the deposit. The rate of oxygen utilization is usually expressed in terms of mass per unit of stream bed area. If this term is multiplied by the ratio of river volume to bottom area, the volumetric rate is obtained, S, whose dimensions are consistent with the other factors in the oxygen equation (Eq. 1). The respiration of both microscopic and macroscopic plants may be a significant sink of dissolved oxygen. This factor depends on temperature, mass, nutrients, and areal distribution. It is convenient to express it in units similar to the sludge deposits, a volumetric rate, R.

As an example, an analysis of the oxygen distribution in the Grand River (4)

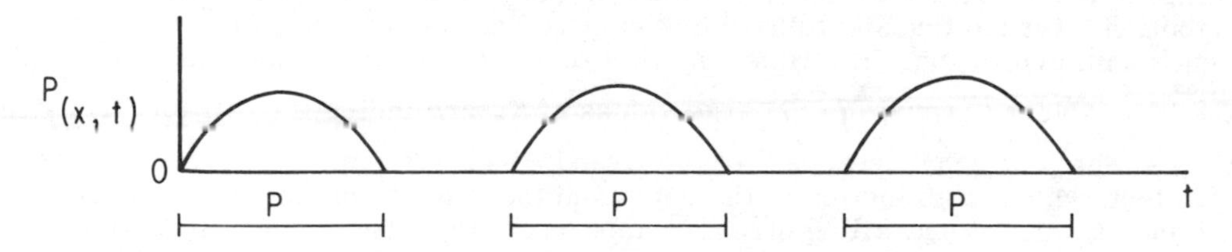

Figure 35. Assumed form of photosynthetic production of oxygen.

below Lansing, Michigan, is presented. The effluent of an activated sludge treatment plant is the one significant source of pollution in this area. The suspended solids concentration in the effluent is low. It is therefore assumed that the settling or organic matter in the stream is minimal. Flow velocities and field observations confirm this assumption. The effluent BOD is comprised of both carbonaceous and nitrogenous components, which are primarily in the dissolved or colloidal state. Thus the rate of decrease of both components directly reflects oxidation and deaeration. There are marked diurnal fluctuations of dissolved oxygen which are attributable to the photosynthetic activity of aquatic plants. In view of the above, benthal demands were assumed to be insignificant and the remaining factors are introduced into Equation 1 to describe the oxygen balance of the Grand River:

$$\frac{\partial c}{\partial t} = -\frac{Q}{A_x}\frac{\partial c}{\partial x} + K_a(c_s - c) + P_{(x,t)} - K_d L_{x'} - K_n N_x - R_{(x,t)} \qquad (6)$$

where $c_{(x,o)} = c_s - D_o$.

Expressing Equation 6 in terms of the dissolved oxygen deficit ($D = c_s - c$), replacing L and N by their appropriate spatial functions (Eqs. 4 and 5), P by the series of Equation 3 yields, after integration:

$$D_{(x,t)} = D_o\, e^{-\frac{K_a x}{U}} \qquad (7a)$$

$$+ \frac{K_d L_o}{K_a - K_r}\left[e^{-\frac{K_r x}{U}} - e^{-\frac{K_a x}{U}}\right] \qquad (7b)$$

$$+ \frac{K_n N_o}{K_a - K_r}\left[e^{-\frac{K_n x}{U}} - e^{-\frac{K_a x}{U}}\right] \qquad (7c)$$

$$+ \frac{R}{K_a}\left[1 - e^{-\frac{K_a x}{U}}\right] \qquad (7d)$$

$$- P_m \left\{ \frac{2p}{K_a}\left(1 - e^{-\frac{K_a x}{U}}\right) \right.$$

$$+ 2\sum_{n=1}^{\infty} \frac{a_n}{\sqrt{(K_a)^2 + (2\pi n)^2}} \cos\left[2\pi n(t - p/2) - tg^{-1}\left(\frac{2\pi n}{K_a}\right)\right]$$

$$\left. - 2e^{-\frac{K_a x}{U}} \sum_{n=1}^{\infty} \frac{a_n}{\sqrt{(K_a)^2 + (2\pi n)^2}} \cos\left[2\pi n\left(t - p/2 - \frac{x}{U}\right) - tg^{-1}\left(\frac{2\pi n}{K_a}\right)\right] \right\}$$

The subscript o refers to $x = 0$. For reasonable parameter values, three terms of the infinite series suffice. Equation 7 is the resulting temporal and spatial distribution after the transient phase has elapsed and the system has come to an equilibrium condition. The time required to achieve equilibrium is a function of the parameters $K_a t$ and $\frac{K_a x}{U}$. Large values of K_a are indicative of rapid transient times, which are characteristic of the Grand River system. The reaeration coefficient, which is a function of the depth and the velocity of flow, has a value of 5.5 per day at the prevailing stream temperature (5). The values of K_r and K_n are calculated by Equations 4 and 5, respectively, as follows: The logarithms of the observed data are plotted against an arithmetic scale of distance. The slope of the line drawn through these is divided by the flow velocity to determine the coefficient. By this procedure K_r is 0.8 per day and K_n is 1.9 per day. Since there is assumedly no settling or volatilization, $K_r = K_d$. The velocity, U, is calculated from the average freshwater flow and mean cross-sectional area. The values of L_o and N_o are taken directly from the observed data. The values P_m and R are assigned as 22 mg/liter day and 20 mg/liter day, which are reasonable values for this type of stream (2). Typical diurnal variations of dissolved oxygen calculated by Equation 7 are shown in Figure 36 for Stations 8 and 9, which are 4.1 and 8.3 miles from the outfall, respectively. The observed data are those

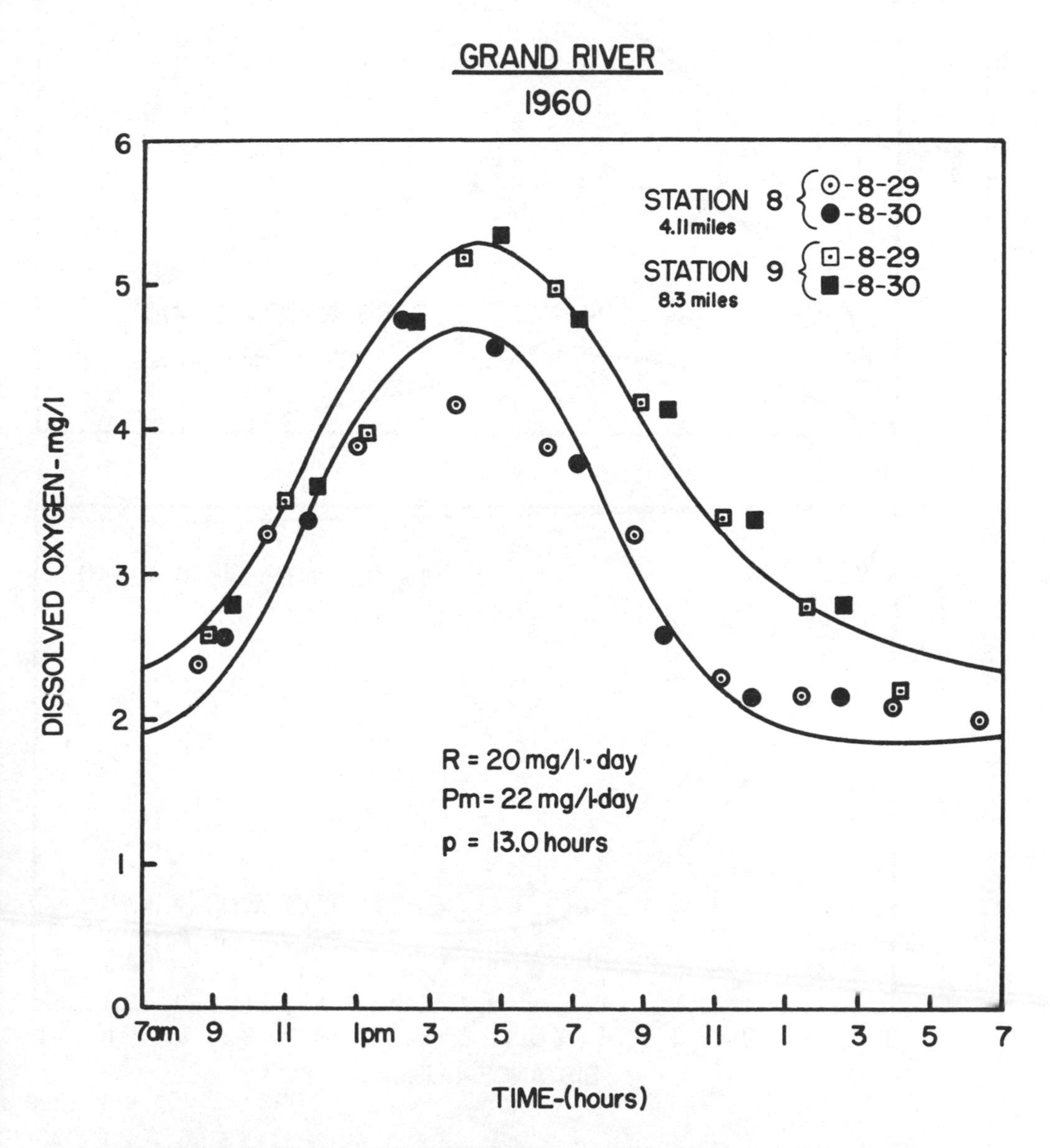

Figure 36. Diurnal variation of dissolved oxygen at two locations.

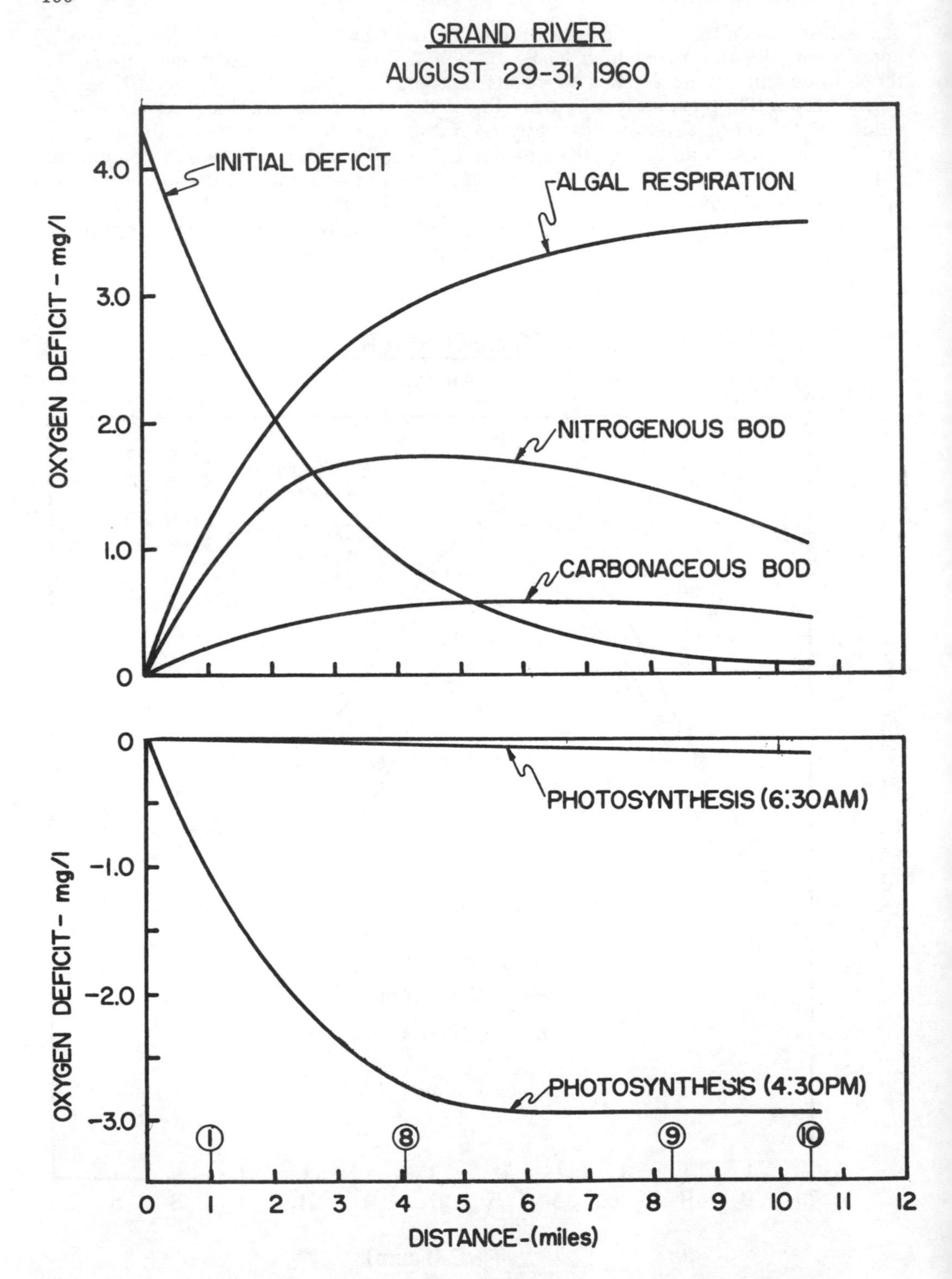

Figure 37. Components of the longitudinal distribution of dissolved oxygen deficit.

taken over two consecutive days, as indicated. The agreement between the calculated profile and the observations is reasonably good, indicating that a representative and realistic set of coefficients was employed in the analysis. Comparisons at other stations were comparable. The deficits due to each component of Equation 7 are computed and presented in Figure 37. Since components *a*, *b*, *c*, and *d* are independent of time, the distributions shown apply to any hour of the day or night. The photosynthetic contribution, however, is time dependent, and the maximum (4:30 p.m.) and the minimum (6:30 a.m.) profiles are shown, as well as an intermediate period between 11:00 a.m. and 1:00 p.m. The total dissolved oxygen distribution is the sum of the individual profiles. These are shown in Figure 38.

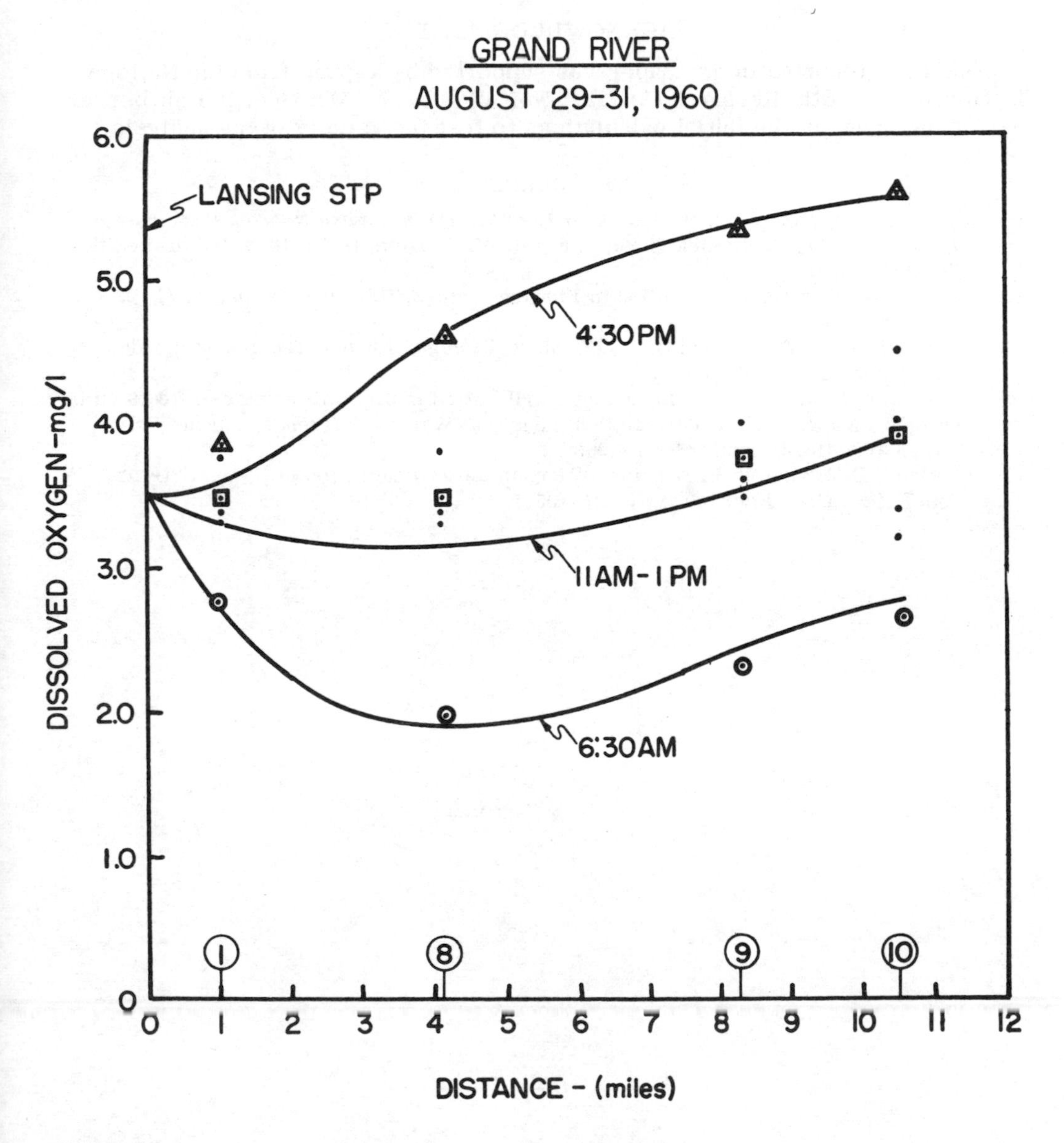

Figure 38. Dissolved oxygen profile at various times of the day.

It is important to note the significance of the various factors, particularly the relative magnitude of the carbonaceous and nitrogenous components. Effluents from biological treatment plants, particularly the high-rate type, should be evaluated in this regard. The response from the effluent BOD to stream BOD and stream DO deficit is direct and easily calculated, relatively speaking. The response of the DO deficit to the algae function also appears to be susceptible to analysis, but the relation between stream conditions and effluent concentration is presently lacking. More attention must be directed to this area of study. In any case, the analysis and the example presented in this paper will hopefully provide some insight into the complex relationship which governs the oxygen balance in streams.

ACKNOWLEDGMENT

The work reported in this paper was supported by a grant from the National Institutes of Health, Research Contract No. WP-00677. Mr. George Kehrberger performed many of the initial calculations to test the validity of the analysis.

REFERENCES

(1) Streeter, H. W., and E. B. Phelps. *A Study of the Pollution and Natural Purification of the Ohio River*. Public Health Bulletin 146. Washington, D.C.: U. S. Public Health Service (1925).

(2) Odum, H. T. "Primary Production in Flowing Waters," *Limnol. Oceanog., 1,* 102–117 (January 1956).

(3) Eckenfelder, W. W., Jr., and D. J. O'Connor. *Biological Waste Treatment*. London: Pergamon Press Ltd. (1961).

(4) Courchaine, R. J. "The Significance of Nitrification in Stream Analysis—Effects on the Oxygen Balance," *Proceedings*. 18th Industrial Waste Conference, Purdue University, Lafayette, Indiana, 38–51 (1963).

(5) O'Connor, D. J., and W. E. Dobbins. "Mechanism of Reaeration in Natural Streams," *Amer. Soc. Civil Engr. Trans., 123* (1958).

RELATIONSHIP BETWEEN THE PHYSICAL AND BIOLOGICAL ENVIRONMENTS—PHYSICAL EXCHANGE

Frank D. Masch
The University of Texas, Austin, Texas
Joe R. Wilson
Louisiana Polytechnic Institute, Ruston, Louisiana

Many water pollution problems involve diffusion processes. Removal of all pollutants from waste effluents at the point of outfall is hindered by cost factors, while economy demands maximum utilization of the assimilative capacity of the receiving waters. Efficient use of these natural disposal systems requires knowledge of the processes by which the contaminants are mixed and dispersed throughout the receiving waters.

Of the many factors which influence the quality of receiving waters, mixing and exchange are among the most important. These factors effect the ecology of the waters, and the net result is reflected in benefits which may be expressed in terms of the economic value derivable from the waters. The determination of the dispersion and exchange characteristics of a receiving water is also one of the more basic requirements for the development of any multivariable concept useful for determining the assimilative capacity, extent of dilution, or freshwater requirements of a receiving water. Quality, biological, ecological, and economic analyses can be considered only as partially complete until integrated with the mixing and transport characteristics of the receiving waters.

GENERAL CONSIDERATIONS

Dispersion occurs as a result of molecular and turbulent diffusion and as a result of shear flow mixing due to velocity gradients which may exist within the receiving water. An interchange of fluid between two zones in a turbulent field results in the simultaneous interchange of every characteristic of the fluid masses involved. Envision a fluid mass labeled with a tracer and separated by an imaginary boundary from a fluid mass containing no tracer. A small portion of the marked fluid moved across the boundary must, to satisfy continuity, be replaced by an equal volume of unmarked fluid. This results in a decrease in concentration of tracer in the mass on one side of the boundary and an increase in concentration of tracer in the mass on the other. If this process is repeated indefinitely, a uniform concentration of the tracer throughout both zones will eventually result. The masses involved in turbulent exchange are ill-defined lumps of fluid called "eddies" and the process is known as eddy diffusion.

Eddy diffusion is similar to molecular diffusion, the process by which properties migrate through fluids and solids due to Brownian motion of the molecules. The eddies and their random motion are considered analogous to the molecules and their random Brownian motion. The carrying capacity of turbulent eddies called "eddy diffusivity" or the "coefficient of eddy diffusion" is a characteristic of particular interest. In the field, dispersion results from processes other than simple diffusion. The term "coefficient of dispersion" is normally used to describe the apparent diffusivity resulting from all mixing and exchange processes which might be acting.

THEORETICAL BACKGROUND

Diffusion is the movement of a substance within another (the diffusing phase being in solution or suspension within the dispersing phase) or the migration of some property of the substance, such as its temperature.

Diffusion takes place whenever these is a gradient of the concentration of the dispersed phase or the intensity of the property which migrates. If the dispersing phase is in the solid state, the diffusion takes place as a result of molecular motion; if it is in the fluid state, the diffusion takes place as a result of either the molecular movements alone or the combined effect of molecular motion and the movements of macroscopic masses of the fluid.

The rate of transfer of properties depends fundamentally upon two independent variables: the extent of the difference of the characteristic in question between two adjacent zones (the gradient of concentration or intensity) and the carrying capacity of the flow. The basic equations of diffusion were first given by the physiologist Fick, and have become known as Fick's Laws of Diffusion. Fick's first law is given by the equation

$$M = -D\frac{\partial c}{\partial s} \qquad (1)$$

in which M represents the rate of transport of the characteristic of intensity or concentration c by diffusion in the direction of s across a unit area normal to s. The negative sign indicates that the transport is in the direction of decreasing concentration. D is a proportionality constant called the diffusion coefficient or diffusivity, and corresponds to the carrying capacity of the flow.

Combining Equation 1 with the law of conservation of mass leads to Fick's Second Law of Diffusion:

$$\frac{\partial c}{\partial t} = D\frac{\partial^2 c}{\partial s^2} \qquad (2)$$

The coefficient of diffusion, D, represents both physically and dimensionally the combination of a length and a velocity which together characterize the nature of the diffusion process. Einstein, in a theory of Brownian motion, defined the diffusion coefficient by the differential equation

$$D = \frac{1}{2}\frac{d(\sigma^2)}{dt} \qquad (3)$$

This equation assumes that random molecular motion causes normal distribution of the diffused substance. In Equation 3, σ is the standard deviation. The equation is not restricted to those cases in which the diffusion coefficient is constant.

In a turbulent flow regime the diffusion that results from the macroscopic turbulent movements of the fluid is known as turbulent or eddy diffusion. While the process is not truly one of diffusion in the classical sense, a strong analogy exists between the behavior of fluid masses and the nature of molecular motion. In other words, the eddies which are characteristic of turbulent flow are assumed to exhibit a random type of motion which is similar to molecular motion, and the differential equations which describe the two motions are assumed to be similar. Thus Equations 1 and 2 are applied to both molecular and eddy diffusion by use of appropriate values of D.

The values of the coefficient of molecular diffusion vary with the substances involved and with the temperature. Under most conditions molecular diffusion is isotropic and the diffusion coefficient is constant. A simple constant, D, cannot be established to define turbulent diffusion, however, because the turbulent diffusion process depends upon the turbulent structure of the flow. Since the turbulence is usually nonisotropic, the turbulent diffusion coefficient may be a function of space. It varies with the scale of the turbulence and is normally many orders of magnitude larger than the molecular diffusion coefficient.

Equation 2 is for the case of one-dimensional diffusion with a constant value of D. For the more general three-dimensional case with variable and nonisotropic diffusivity, the equation becomes

$$\frac{\partial c}{\partial t} = \frac{\partial}{\partial x}\left[D_x \frac{\partial c}{\partial x}\right] + \frac{\partial}{\partial y}\left[D_y \frac{\partial c}{\partial y}\right] + \frac{\partial}{\partial z}\left[D_z \frac{\partial c}{\partial z}\right] \tag{4}$$

By analogy with the kinetic theory of gases, Prandtl postulated that as the masses of fluid migrated laterally they carried with them the mean velocity (and hence the momentum concentration) of their point of origin. Thus if the flow is two dimensional with a velocity $\bar{u}(z)$ in the direction of x, a typical velocity fluctuation, u', due to a migration can be characterized as

$$u' = \ell \frac{\partial \bar{u}}{\partial z} \tag{5}$$

where ℓ, the mixing length, is the distance over which a migration takes place. The mixing length is related to the mean free path of lumps of fluid and is analogous to the mean free path of molecules within the system.

The advantage of Prandtl's approach is that the variable involved is simply a length, so that a plausible assumption can be made more easily than for D, which is the product of a length and a velocity. In fact, the mixing length concept can be considered as an assumption regarding the make-up of D:

$$D = \ell^2 \frac{\partial \bar{u}}{\partial z} \tag{6}$$

This concept relates the turbulent structure at a point to the mean velocity structure at the same point instead of to an area of influence. Thus it is an oversimplification of the process.

Richardson (1) developed another type of diffusion equation by relating the average separation of pairs of particles projected on an arbitrary axis, ℓ'. He assumed that the important independent variable in turbulent diffusion was separation of the particles of the diffusant rather than the actual particle position. His equation is

$$\frac{\partial q}{\partial t} = \frac{\partial}{\partial \ell}\left[F(\ell) \frac{\partial q}{\partial \ell}\right] \tag{7}$$

where $F(\ell)$, the neighbor diffusivity, is analogous to the diffusion coefficient and is a function of the particle separation, ℓ. Since ℓ is in effect a measure of the areal extent of the diffused substance, $F(\ell)$ is dependent on the scale of the diffusion phenomenon. Richardson concluded from some measurements on smoke plumes that

$$F(\ell) \sim \ell^{\frac{4}{3}} \tag{8}$$

It is to be noted that if the diffusion is Frickian (i.e., if $F(\ell) = D$ and is constant) Richardson's equation is identical to Equation 2

$$\frac{\partial q}{\partial t} = D \frac{\partial^2 q}{\partial \ell^2} \tag{9}$$

where q is the neighbor concentration.

Kolmogoroff (2) theorized that for large Reynold's numbers, the rate of diffusion should be a function of the 4/3 power of the scale of the turbulence times the 1/3 power of the rate of energy dissipation per unit mass of fluid. He reasoned that for flows with large Reynold's numbers, energy from the larger eddies is transferred down through the spectrum to the smaller eddies, where it is finally dissipated through viscous action. In the larger eddies a relatively small proportion of the energy is dissipated by viscosity and virtually all is transferred to the smaller eddies. As the eddy size decreases, a larger portion of the energy is dissipated by viscous action until viscosity becomes very significant. Kolmogoroff hypothesized that there is a subrange in the spectrum in which the eddies are isotropic and where the statistical characteristics of the turbulence are governed by both the viscosity and the rate of energy transfer. Assuming that an analogy exists between molecular and turbulent diffusion so that the viscosity can be replaced by a turbulent diffusion coefficient, dimensional analysis gives the relation

$$D \sim \ell^{\frac{4}{3}} E^{\frac{1}{3}} \tag{10}$$

Where E is constant, this equation is of the same form as Richardson's equation of a "four-thirds law," Equation 8.

Many investigations, including a theoretical study by Batchelor (3), an empirical model study by Orlob (4), and an empirical study in the field by Parker (5), have provided some support of Richardson's law that the coefficient of eddy diffusivity is proportional to the 4/3 power of the scale near the source. It is possible, however, that the coefficient becomes constant after some distance of travel. If turbulence is considered to be a superposition of eddies of all sizes, then it would seem likely that the diffusion coefficient would increase with the size of the patch until the patch reached the size of the largest eddy, and thereafter remain constant. The effect of the eddies larger than the patch is obviously convection, which would move the whole patch with no effect on its shape or size. The diffusion within the patch is influenced by those eddies of the scale equal to or less than the size of the patch. In the ocean, of course, the eddies can be very large, and for engineering purposes the mixing can perhaps be assumed to follow the 4/3 law.

G. I. Taylor (6) applied statistical concepts to turbulence theory. His theory was built around statistical correlation of fluid particle velocities in the fluid stream separated by a time interval. A corresponding Eulerian correlation coefficient is more easily obtained by substituting distance for time. Ippen and Raichlen (7) have measured the Eulerian function in open channels. Orlob's experiments indicate that the Eulerian correlation function gives a reasonable estimate of the Langrangian function. For small values of time, ξ:

$$R(\xi) = 1$$

$$\int_o^t d\,\xi = t$$

$$x = \bar{u}t$$

The pattern of diffusion immediately after release is wedge-shaped. For times greater than t_o, the time required for zero correlation, the value of the integral is constant:

$$D = \bar{u}^2 \int_0^{t \geq t_o} R(\xi)\, d\xi \tag{11}$$

Thus the pattern of diffusion is parabolic for $t \geq t_o$. Between these values, Ippen and Raichlen have found that the correlation coefficient can be approximated by the form $R(\xi) = e^{-N}$ given an easily integrated expression

$$\int_0^{t < t_o} R(\xi)\, d\xi = \frac{1 - e^{-Nt}}{N} \tag{12}$$

And the pattern of diffusion is

$$\sigma = 2\left(\frac{\bar{u}}{N}\right)^2 (Nt - 1 + e^{-Nt}) \tag{13}$$

Batchelor (3), with the aid of dimensional arguments and ergodic hypothesis, finds three regimes of relative diffusion. If the initial size of the cloud is small, these regimes are characterized by the following rates of growth:

(1) Initial

$$\frac{d\sigma_x^{\ 2}}{dt} = k_1 t\,(E\sigma_0)^{\frac{2}{3}} \tag{14a}$$

(2) Intermediate

$$\frac{d\sigma_x^{\ 2}}{dt} = k_2 E\,(t - t_1)^2 \tag{14b}$$

where

$$t_1 = k_3 \sigma_0^{\frac{2}{3}} E^{-\frac{1}{3}} \tag{14c}$$

(3) Asymptotic

$$\frac{d\sigma_x^{2}}{dt} = k_4 u''\ell \tag{14d}$$

where k_1 to k_4 are constants of order unity, σ_x is the standard deviation measured along x, t is time, σ_0 is the initial standard deviation of the cloud, and E is the rate of energy dissipation per unit mass through turbulence. For E the additional relationship may be noted:

$$E = \frac{(u'')^3}{\ell} \tag{15}$$

with u'' the root mean square turbulent velocity along the x axis, and ℓ the scale of turbulence. By analogy with molecular diffusion, an equivalent diffusivity may be introduced by the relationship expressed in Equation 3. From Equation 14 it is seen that the diffusivity is constant in the final phase, while it grows as the 4/3 power of cloud size in the intermediate phase, as noted in Richardson's law of relative diffusion. Relative diffusion is thus an accelerating process, the rate of growth increasing with the size of the cloud while the supply of eddies of requisite size lasts. When the cloud becomes large compared to the typical eddy in the diffusing field, its growth rate becomes constant and resembles molecular diffusion, except that the magnitude of diffusivity is of a higher order of magnitude.

The most complete and satisfactory analysis with respect to shear flow mixing has been made by Taylor (8) for pipe flow. In this analysis the universal velocity distribution law, credited to Von Karman, was combined with the Reynold's analogy. The universal velocity distribution law is

$$\frac{u_{\max} - u}{\sqrt{\frac{\tau_0}{\rho}}} = f\left(\frac{r}{r_0}\right) \tag{16}$$

where $u_{\max}$ is the maximum velocity (centerline), u is the velocity at any point of distance r from the center of the pipe of radius r_0. τ_0 is a wall shear and ρ is the mass density of the fluid. The Reynold's analogy is

$$\frac{\tau}{\rho\frac{\partial u}{\partial r}} = \frac{M}{\frac{\partial c}{\partial r}} \tag{17}$$

This relationship states that momentum transfer equals diffusant transfer where τ is the shear at any point in the fluid, $\frac{\partial u}{\partial r}$ is the velocity gradient at the point, M is the mass rate of transfer of diffusant at the point, and $\frac{\partial c}{\partial r}$ is the concentration gradient at the point.

Through a complicated analysis, Taylor derived the formula

$$D_x = 10.1\, r_0\, u_* \tag{18}$$

in which $u_* = \sqrt{\frac{\tau_0}{\rho}}$ is the friction velocity and D_x is the longitudinal dispersion coefficient. Taylor named D_x the virtual diffusion coefficient because it fits a solution of the diffusion equation. The constant 10.1 is made up of 10.05 from shear flow mixing and 0.05 from turbulent diffusion. The 0.05 from turbulent diffusion was obtained by assuming the longitudinal and transverse turbulent diffusion to be equal (isotropic turbulence). Taylor's equation has been modified for free surface flow and has been used in model studies of the Delaware Estuary with good results. Taylor's equation for free surface flow is

$$\frac{D}{\nu} = 77 \frac{n}{R^{\frac{1}{6}}} \text{Re} \tag{19}$$

where $n/R^{\frac{1}{6}}$ is a relative roughness ratio and Re is the Reynolds number. When used in estuaries, the Reynold's number in Equation 19 is written as

$$\text{Re} = \frac{2}{\pi} \frac{|u_{\max}|R}{\nu} \tag{20}$$

which assumes that the velocity variation is sinusoidal.

Fick's second law of diffusion, Equation 2, is the fundamental equation for dispersion of a fluid property. If the fluid is moving with some velocity, convective terms of the form $u\frac{\partial c}{\partial x}$, $v\frac{\partial c}{\partial y}$, and $w\frac{\partial c}{\partial z}$ must be included.

The solutions for the one-, two-, and three-dimensional diffusion equation are readily available in the literature and will not be repeated here; see for example, Diachishin (9). Diachishin also presents several interesting methods for finding values of the dispersion coefficient.

APPLICATION OF THEORETICAL METHODS

The dispersion coefficient is usually considered to be independent of time, particularly when the waste material is of a conservative nature. More often, though, this coefficient does vary with the spatial coordinates of the system. Hence, before any analytical solutions of the diffusion equation can be obtained, the dispersion coefficient must either be known, assumed, or measured in the field. Also, since velocity variations in streams and estuaries are often highly nonlinear, and cross-sectional areas are variable, analytical solutions of the basic equations which are useful in the field are not always easily obtained.

It is possible after making various simplifying generalizations to obtain solutions of the diffusion equation in rivers and estuaries. Such generalizations most often involve the assumption that the flow and the dispersion are one-dimensional.

STREAMS AND CHANNELS

Using an analysis similar to Taylor's, Elder (10) found the effective longitudinal dispersion coefficient, D_x, in a broad open channel to be

$$D_x = 5.9\, u_* h \tag{21}$$

where u_* is the frictional velocity based on the shear stress at the bottom of the channel of depth h. To adapt this equation to a wind-driven lake current, Csanady (11) formed the friction velocity from the shear stress on the surface. To obtain the surface shear stress, τ_s, he used the relationship of Deacon (12):

$$\tau_s = 0.0012\, \rho_A\, U_A^{\ 2} \tag{22}$$

where ρ_A is air density and U_A is the wind velocity at the 10-meter level. The friction velocity is then

$$u_* = \sqrt{\frac{\tau_s}{\rho}} = U_A \sqrt{0.0012\, \frac{\rho_A}{\rho}} \tag{23}$$

and the longitudinal dispersion coefficient is

$$D_x = 5.9\, h\, U_A \sqrt{0.0012\, \frac{\rho_A}{\rho}} \tag{24}$$

A very recent study by Fischer (13) has been carried out to study longitudinal dispersion in laboratory and natural streams. This study also involves an extension of Taylor's work to three-dimensional flow in wide channels. Equations and methodology are presented to predict the dispersion coefficients.

ESTUARIES

Again, by making numerous simplifying assumptions, solutions of the diffusion equation in estuaries have also been obtained. Some of the most notable of these solutions are those of Kent (14), O'Connor (15, 16), and Stommel (17). The solutions of these authors have been reported extensively in the literature and the reader is referred to the original publications for details.

The problem of waste movement in estuaries is often of such complexity that available solution methods are not readily applicable. This is particularly true with many of the bays along the Gulf Coast, where flows are two-dimensional. Once waste discharges enter an estuarine system they are subject to convective transport and to mixing and dispersion by tidal action, currents, wind action, and waves. The exchange of estuarine waters with Gulf or sea waters, as well as the interchange of waters between various segments of an estuary, all have significant effects on the disposition of waste material and the assimilative capacity of the estuary. Salinity and temperature gradients, when present, inhibit vertical dispersion and may have stabilizing influences which tend to restrict current movements. Numerous other factors, including physiographic features, density currents, Coriolis effects, and prolonged or unusual wind conditions, may affect the general circulation in an estuary and consequently its dispersion and exchange characteristics.

CONCLUSIONS

Methods for evaluating the assimilative capacity of a receiving water are quite complex because of the many variables involved and because the hydraulics of most receiving waters are those of nonuniform and often unsteady turbulent flows. The design of water quality sampling programs and the choice of methods for the analysis of data are decisions requiring a depth of understanding of dispersion and exchange characteristics.

The need for obtaining answers to the assimilative capacities of various receiving waters for administrative or planning purposes often requires a compromise in the choice of mathematical methods and the extensiveness of sampling programs. Such studies, though, should be considered as preliminary and should be followed up by more rigorous analyses. Well-planned sampling and measurement programs should be undertaken to collect data useful to the evaluation of transport phenomena. Such data would include, in part, velocities, stages, temporal and spatial variations of the velocity, density, salinity, and temperature. Data on indicators of pollution, such as BOD and DO, should be obtained so that evaluations of dispersion coefficients can be made from actual field data.

REFERENCES

(1) Richardson, L. F. "Atmospheric Diffusion Shown on a Distance-Neighbor Graph," *Proc. Royal Soc.*, *110*(Series A), 709–737 (1926).

(2) Kolmogoroff, A. N. "The Local Structure of Turbulence in Incompressible Viscous Fluids for Very Large Reynolds Numbers," *Comptes Rendus de l'Academies des Sciences de l'URSS*, *30*, 301–305 (1941).

(3) Batchelor, G. K. "Diffusion in a Field of Homogeneous Turbulence. II. Relative Motion of Particles," *Proc. Cambridge Philos. Soc.*, *48*, 345 (1952).

(4) Orlob, G. T. "Eddy Diffusion in Homogeneous Turbulence," *J. Hydra. Div. Proc. ASCE*, *85*(HY9), 75–101 (1959).

(5) Parker, F. L. "Eddy Diffusion in Reservoirs," *J. Hydra. Div. Proc. ASCE*, 87(HY3), 151–171 (1961).

(6) Taylor, G. I. "Diffusion by Continuous Movements," *Proc. London Math. Soc.*, *20*(Series 2), 196–212 (1921).

(7) Ippen, A. T., and F. Raichlen. "Turbulence in Civil Engineering: Measurements in Free Surface Streams," *J. Hydra. Div. Proc. ASCE*, *83*(HY5), 10 (1957).

(8) Taylor, G. I. "The Dispersion of Matter in Turbulent Flow through a Pipe," *Proc. Royal Soc. London*, *223A*, 446–468 (1954).

(9) Diachishin, A. N. "Dye Dispersion Studies," *J. Sanit. Engr. Div. Proc. ASCE*, *89*(SA1), 29–40 (1963).

(10) Elder, J. W. "The Dispersion of Marked Fluid in Turbulent Shear Flow," *J. Fluid Mech.*, *5*, 544–560 (1965).

(11) Csanady, G. T. "Turbulent Diffusion in Lake Huron," *J. Fluid Mech.*, *17*(3), 360–384 (1963).

(12) Deacon, E. L. "Aerodynamic Roughness of the Sea," *J. Geophys. Res.*, *67*(8), 3167–3172 (1962).

(13) Fischer, H. B. "Longitudinal Dispersion in Laboratory and Natural Streams," *Report No. KH-R-12*. W. M. Keck Laboratory of Hydraulics and Water Resources, California Institute of Technology, 250 (1960).

(14) Kent, R. E. "Turbulent Diffusion in a Sectionally Homogeneous Estuary," *J. Sanit. Engr. Div. Proc. ASCE*, *86*(SA3), 15–47 (1960).

(15) O'Connor, D. J. "Oxygen Balance of an Estuary," *J. Sanit. Engr. Div. Proc. ASCE*, *86*(SA3), 35–55 (1960).

(16) O'Connor, D. J. "Estuarine Distribution on Non-Conservative Substances," *J. Sanit. Engr. Div Proc. ASCE*, *91*(SA1), 23–42 (1965).

(17) Stommel, H. "Computation of Pollution in a Vertically Mixed Estuary," *Sewage Ind. Wastes*, *25*(9), 1065 (1953).

MATHEMATICAL MODELING OF MIXING PHENOMENA IN RIVERS

James R. Hays
Boeing Corporation, Huntsville, Alabama
Peter A. Krenkel
Vanderbilt University, Nashville, Tennessee

INTRODUCTION

Wastes originating from a wide diversity of establishments, and widely varying in characteristics, ultimately depend on the natural process of purification effected by our rivers, streams, lakes, and harbors. These natural processes can be efficiently utilized only if the dilution process is aided by adequate natural mixing and dispersion of the waste-waters immediately after their introduction into the receiving waters.

It is usually assumed that waste discharges will be completely and adequately mixed with the receiving waters subsequent to their introduction. Reality demonstrates, however, that ample time and distance must be available if complete mixing is to be realized.

Failure to obtain the assumed complete mixing may lead to localized pollution problems even though adequate water is available for waste assimilation. Factors that affect the time and the distance required for complete mixing have been outlined by Falk (1). In addition, the possible discharge of a "pulse" of toxic and/or objectionable waste material to a receiving water is always present. It is obvious that an effective means of predicting the dispersion characteristics of a receiving water would enable achievement of optimum usage of the natural purification factors inherent in receiving water systems.

THEORETICAL BACKGROUND

Available field data usually indicate significant discrepancies when compared to the mathematical models successfully tested in laboratory flumes. Since the values measured in the field are always higher than those predicted by the mathematical model, it is perplexing that an explanation has not been proposed. It will be subsequently demonstrated that the discrepancies cannot always be attributed to "experimental error," as stated by many investigators.

The Equation of Continuity for Turbulent Flow

The continuity equation for the transport of a conservative tracer in a river may be expressed as

$$\frac{\partial c}{\partial t} = \frac{\partial}{\partial x}\left(D^{mt}\frac{\partial c}{\partial x}\right) + \frac{\partial}{\partial y}\left(D^{mt}\frac{\partial c}{\partial y}\right) + \frac{\partial}{\partial z}\left(D^{mt}\frac{\partial c}{\partial z}\right) - \frac{\partial(v_x c)}{\partial x} - \frac{\partial(v_y c)}{\partial y} - \frac{\partial(v_z c)}{\partial z} \qquad (1)$$

where c equals the tracer concentration; x, y, and z are the coordinate directions with corresponding velocities v_x, v_y, and v_z; and D^{mt} includes the effects of both molecular and turbulent diffusivity and may be a function of x, y, and z (2). The first term represents the unsteady part of the conservation equation, the next three terms represent nonadvective turbulent diffusion, and the last three terms describe mass transfer by convective motion of the fluid.

The Continuity Equation for Pipe Flow

Equation 1 is formidable in application, and it is only natural that earlier investigators would select the simple geometry of the pipe on which to focus their efforts. For pipe flow, the transport equation can be written in cylindrical coordinates as

$$\frac{\partial c}{\partial t} = \frac{1}{r}\frac{\partial}{\partial r} rD^{mt}\frac{\partial c}{\partial r} + D^{mt}\frac{\partial^2 c}{\partial x^2} - v_x \frac{\partial c}{\partial x} \tag{2}$$

where r is the radial coordinate. This equation is restricted to zero velocity components in the radial and angular directions and no concentration gradients in the angular direction. The velocity, v_x, and the diffusivity, D^{mt}, are a function of r only.

G. I. Taylor (3) sought to circumvent the difficulties of solving Equation 2 by considering only the cross-sectional average concentration. He used empirical expressions for velocity and the Reynolds analogy to define the variation of v_x and D^m with r. Through heuristic arguments he concluded that the transport mechanisms described by Equation 2 could be represented by the following one-dimensional, dispersed flow model:

$$\frac{\partial c}{\partial t} = D_L \frac{\partial^2 c}{\partial x^2} - \overline{u}\frac{\partial c}{\partial x} \tag{3}$$

where D_L is the longitudinal mixing coefficient and $\overline{u}$ is the average velocity.

Calculation of the Longitudinal Mixing Coefficient from Experimental Data

Methods of determining the longitudinal mixing coefficient were elucidated in 1962 by Krenkel (4); however, several new approaches have been utilized since that time. Fischer (5) has proposed a method based on the change of variance of the concentration-time curve with time, as the tracer cloud moves downstream. The equation for D_L is

$$D_L = \frac{\overline{u}^2(\sigma_{t2}^2 - \sigma_{t1}^2)}{2\Delta t} \tag{4}$$

where σ_{t1}^2 and σ_{t2}^2 are the variances observed at two stations and Δt is the average residence time between the two stations. The variance is calculated from

$$\sigma_t^2 = \frac{\sum_i c_i t_i^2}{\sum_i c_i} - \left[\frac{\sum_i c_i t_i}{\sum_i c_i}\right]^2 \tag{5}$$

Harris (6) considered the mean travel time rather than the variance of the curve in calculating D_L.

$$\int_0^\infty \frac{1}{\sqrt{4\pi D_L t}} e^{-\frac{(x-\bar{u}t)^2}{4D_L t}} dt = \frac{1}{\overline{u}} \tag{6}$$

then

$$g(t) = \frac{\overline{u}}{\sqrt{4\pi D_L t}} e^{\frac{(x-\bar{u}t)^2}{4D_L t}} \tag{7}$$

satifies the requirements of a probability density function. Using the method of maximum likelihood, he arrived at the following estimation formulas:

$$\hat{u} = x\frac{1}{n}\sum_{i=1}^{n}\frac{1}{t_i} = x\left(\text{mean value of } \frac{1}{t}\right) \tag{8}$$

and

$$\hat{D}_L = \frac{\hat{\bar{u}}(\hat{\bar{u}}\bar{t} - x)}{2} \tag{9}$$

where $\bar{t}$ represents the mean value of t.

Thackston (7) used an algorithm proposed by Marquardt (8) for the least squares estimation of nonlinear parameters, implemented by a digital computer program by Baumeister and Marquardt (9). This program will handle any mathematical model in which a dependent variable can be expressed as a function of a number of independent variables and a number of arbitrary parameters, and will compute the least squares estimates of the parameters based on observed data. The program adjusts the parameters to minimize the residual squared error, ϕ, which is defined as

$$\phi = \sum_{i=1}^{n} (Y_i - \hat{Y}_i)^2 \tag{10}$$

where Y_i is the observed value of the dependent variable and $\hat{Y}_i$ is the value estimated by the function.

Either analytic derivatives or derivatives estimated by finite-difference methods may be utilized. Adjustment of any of the parameters may be omitted, their values being fixed or frozen to obtain a constrained minimization of ϕ. The observed and predicted values of Y are both printed and plotted along with nonlinear and support plane confidence limits for all estimated parameters. The program also computes and prints a matrix of correlations between the estimated parameters.

The solution to Equation 2 for a rapid introduction of a mass of tracer, M, is

$$\frac{C_i}{\frac{M}{A\bar{u}}} = \sqrt{\frac{Pe}{4\pi t_i T}}\; e^{\frac{-Pe\left(1 - \frac{t_i}{T}\right)^2}{4\frac{t_i}{T}}} \tag{11}$$

where $M/A\bar{u}$ is the area under the concentration-time curve, T is the mean residence time $(x/\bar{u})$, and Pe is the Peclet Number $(\bar{u}x/D_L)$. Using the observed values of C_i and t_i, the least squares estimates of T and Pe were computed. This form of the equation eliminates the need to use the distance, x, the cross-sectional area, A, or the weight of tracer injected, M, in each least squares fit. Given T and Pe, the values of D_L and $\bar{u}$ are easily computed from the observed distance, x.

Estimation of the Longitudinal Mixing Coefficient from Hydraulic Parameters

In the same article that Taylor (3) proposed the dispersed flow model, Equation 3, he derived the following relation between D_L and the stress at the wall τ_0;

$$D_L = 10.06R\left(\frac{\tau_0}{\rho}\right)^{\frac{1}{2}} \tag{12}$$

where R is the radius of the pipe and ρ the fluid density. In 1956 Aris (10) developed rigorously the relationship between Equations 2 and 3. He showed that Equation 12 is actually the result of equating the rate of change of the second moments of the distributions described by Equations 2 and 3.

A number of attempts have been made to apply the methods of Taylor and Aris to stream flow. Some investigators attempted to simply use Taylor's expression for D_L directly, calculating τ_0 from the rate of energy expenditure and using a hydraulic radius for R. Such applications are incorrect, since there is no relation between the geometry or velocity distributions in stream flow and those occuring in a pipe. Elder (11) assumed that only the vertical velocity gradient is important in stream flow, and developed an expression analogous to Taylor's Equation 12 but with the coefficient equal to 5.93. Other investigators have derived similar expressions for D_L based upon various assumptions (12, 13, 14).

Fischer (5) compared the predictions of some of the above expressions with the results of experimental laboratory and stream data. He found a large range in the values of the dispersion coefficient; in general the values were found to be many times greater than predicted. After a number of possible explanations were considered, he concluded that lateral nonuniformity was the most important. The application of Aris' method to assumed lateral velocity profiles showed that "lateral velocity gradients . . . can easily overwhelm all other effects in causing longitudinal dispersion." Fischer further showed that the dispersion coefficient is extremely sensitive to the form of the velocity profile, and suggested that successful predictions of D_L may have to be based upon detailed experimental knowledge of the velocity profiles.

Errors in the Estimation of the Longitudinal Mixing Coefficient

An example of the magnitude of the error in the estimation of D_L for natural streams is shown in Figure 39, taken from Thackston (7). The observed values of D_L were computed by Thackston by the least squares method from the data of Godfrey and Frederick (15), and are obviously many times larger than the estimated values as represented by the dashed line. The estimated values were based on Elder's (11) equation, with the constants evaluated in laboratory studies. This equation was tested and verified in field investigations on short, straight, uniform reaches in the Tennessee Valley. The marked disagreement between observed and predicted values of D_L in Figure 40 does not mean that the prediction equation is incorrect, but that it was not applicable to the data of Godfrey and Frederick (15). As previously noted, Fischer (5) has shown that even very slight lateral velocity profiles can cause much more mixing than the vertical velocity profiles, which is the assumed mixing mechanism in Elder's formulation. It is obvious that such a formulation as Elder's cannot be used to predict mixing coefficients in long reaches of natural streams where lateral velocity profiles and stagnant regions dominate the spread of tracer.

Kolmogoroff's Similarity Principle

The longitudinal mixing coefficient can also be estimated by using the similarity principle of Kolmogoroff, as shown by Krenkel (16), who obtained the following empirical equation from laboratory data:

$$D_L = 6.4h^{1.24}E^{0.30} \tag{13}$$

where E is the mean rate of energy dissipation per unit of fluid, which is found from

$$E = hS_e g \tag{14}$$

where S_e is the slope of the energy grade line and g is the acceleration due to gravity.

If the experimental data exactly followed the similarity principle, the exponent of h would be 4/3 and that of E, 1/3. Thackston (7) derived a form of Equation 13, which included a roughness correction and confirmed the functional relationship proposed by Krenkel on both laboratory tests and measurements in several Tennessee Valley Authority rivers under controlled discharge conditions.

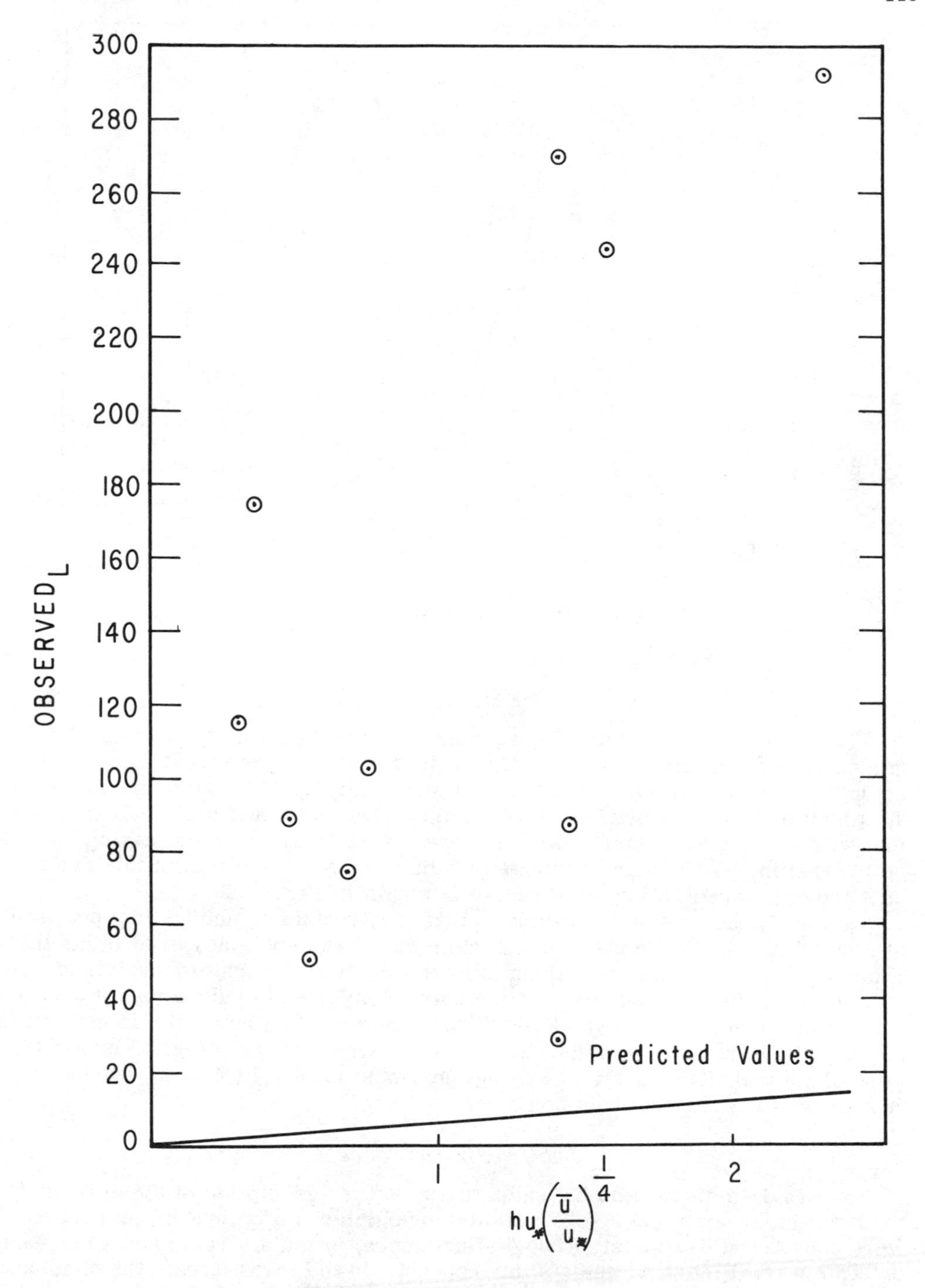

Figure 39. Values of D_L estimated by least-squares method from data of Godfrey and Frederick.

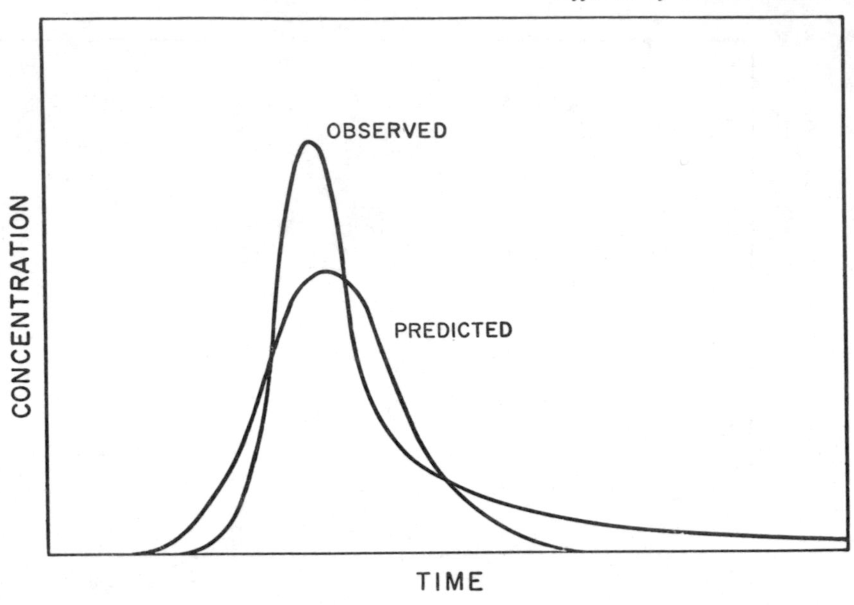

Figure 40. Typical dispersed flow predictions.

THE DEAD ZONE MODEL

The shortcomings of a one-dimensional representation of the mixing phenomena are not limited to an inability to predict D_L. Many investigators have noted that the dispersion model does not adequately explain experimental results. The deviations are always of the same form. The predicted distribution is normal with respect to distance, while observed results are skewed, having long tails on the trailing portions and truncated leading edges. The effect of this deviation on a typical concentration-time record is shown in Figure 40.

Taylor (3) observed this phenomenon at low Reynolds numbers in pipes, and attributed it to a significnat laminar layer which was not considered in his theory. Elder (11) observed the same thing in experiments in laboratory models of stream flow. He also postulated a laminar sublayer and made a quantitative attempt to describe this effect. Krenkel (4) commented on long tails in general and suggested that relatively stagnant regions contribute to the effect. Fischer (5) pointed out that "Stagnant areas along the banks, caused by debris, uneveness of the banks, etc., are also common . . . "

The Dead Zone Concept

The previous discussion indicates that a better description of the spread of material in streams and rivers could be formulated if a typical cross section were considered to consist of two distinct zones: a main stream and a stagnant or dead zone. Figure 41 depicts this concept. In the main stream the dominant mass transport mechanisms are longitudinal and lateral turbulent diffusion impressed upon a velocity profile with relatively weak gradients. Thus, many of the effects that cause deviation from the one-dimensional dispersed flow model have been isolated from this zone, and it should be adequately described by such a model. In the dead zone, longitudinal velocity is essentially zero, and lateral

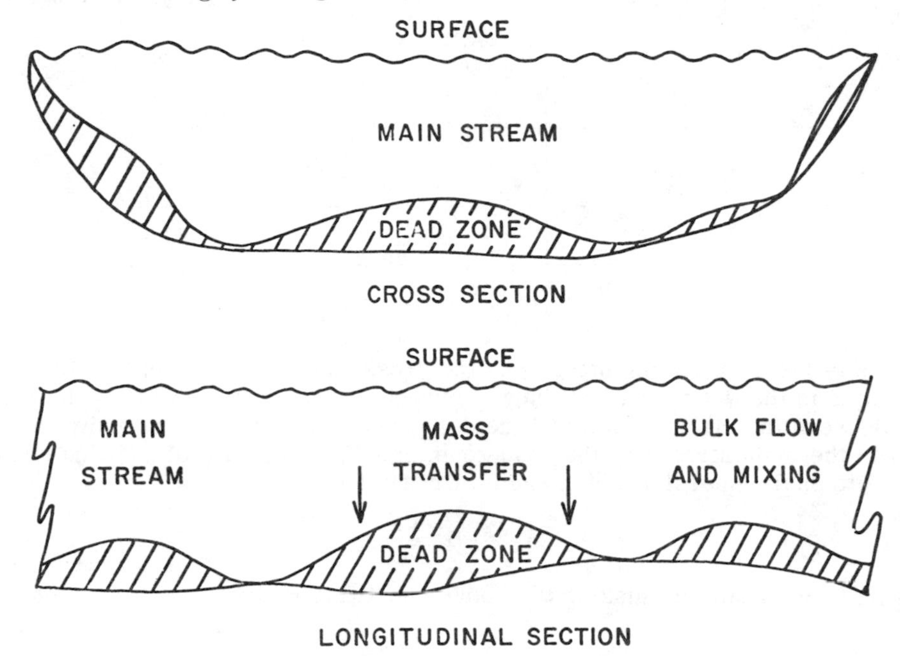

Figure 41. Dead-zone schematic.

mass transport is the only important mechanism. While some longitudinal transport may be present in the dead zone, it is negligible compared to such transport in the main stream. Also, note that the interface between the main stream and dead zone simulates the sharp velocity gradients characteristic of turbulent velocity profiles near the banks of streams and rivers.

It is not clear, at this point, what form the lateral mass transfer mechanism within the dead zone should take; however, it may be satisfactory to assume uniform concentration within a given dead zone cross section. This is tantamount to saying that any dead zone cross section is perfectly mixed. For this description it is appropriate to assume that mass transfer is proportional to the difference in the average concentration in the main stream and the concentration in the dead zone.

However, the perfectly mixed dead zone cross section may be too crude a description. A more sophisticated approach would be to consider that material must diffuse laterally in and out of the dead zone according to the time-varying concentration at the interface. In this case, the geometry of the dead zone must be specified in order to establish the rate at which material is exchanged between the main stream and the dead zone.

The Dead Zone Differential Equations

The differential equations describing the dead zone model are obtained by incorporating the physical description of the previous section into a mass balance. By referring to Table 21 the following mass balance can be made across the section x to $x + \Delta X$.

$$\frac{d(C_a A_a \Delta X)}{dt} = A_a N_a \big|_x - A_a N_a \big|_{x+\Delta X} + A_a U C_a \big|_x - A_a U C_a \big|_{x+\Delta X} + \Delta X P N_d \quad (15)$$

TABLE 21

	x	$x + \Delta x$
Main Stream	C_a Interface	$\longrightarrow u$
Dead Zone	C_d	No Flow

where x is longitudinal distance, A_a is the cross-sectional area of the main stream, P is the wetted contact length between the two zones, ΔXP is the contact area between the main stream and the dead zone, N_d is the rate of addition of mass to the main stream by the dead zone, and N_a is the rate of addition of mass by longitudinal dispersion which can be written as

$$N_a = -D_a \frac{\partial C_a}{\partial x} \tag{16}$$

Passing to the limit and making the above substitution gives

$$\frac{\partial C_a}{\partial t} = D_a \frac{\partial^2 C_a}{\partial x^2} - u \frac{\partial C_a}{\partial x} + \frac{P}{A} N_d \tag{17}$$

This equation is generally valid for any dead zone mechanism, which is defined by N_d.

As shown by Hays (2), several mechanisms can be proposed for the dead zone mechanism; however, space does not permit a discussion of these models here. As will be shown subsequently, the "perfectly mixed" model will adequately describe the mass transfer process and will be assumed to apply.

The Perfectly Mixed Dead Zone

If it is assumed that a dead zone cross section is perfectly mixed and mass transfer is porportional to the difference between the main stream and dead zone concentrations, then

$$N_d = K(C_d - C_a) \tag{18}$$

where C_d is the dead zone concentration and K is the mass transfer coefficient. The differential equation for the dead zone concentration is straightforward:

$$\frac{\partial (C_d A_d)}{\partial t} = -PN_d = -KP(C_d - C_a) \tag{19}$$

Thus, the simultaneous partial differential equations describing concentrations in both the main stream and dead zone can be written

$$\frac{\partial C_a}{\partial t} = D_a \frac{\partial^2 C_a}{\partial x^2} - u \frac{\partial C_a}{\partial x} + K \frac{P}{A_a} (C_d - C_a) \tag{20}$$

$$\frac{\partial C_d}{\partial t} = K \frac{P}{A_d} (C_a - C_d) \tag{21}$$

The conventional mass transfer group is usually written as Ka where a is the ratio of contact or wetted area to the volume of the main stream. It can be seen that

$$a = \frac{PL}{A_a L} = \frac{P}{A_a} \tag{22}$$

where L is the length of the section under consideration. In like manner

$$d = \frac{PL}{A_d L} = \frac{P}{A_d} \tag{23}$$

where d is the ratio of the contact area to the volume of the dead zone. Thus, Ka is the conventional mass transfer group based upon the volume of the main stream, and Kd is the mass transfer group based upon the volume of the dead zone. Equations 20 and 21 may be written

$$\frac{\partial C_a}{\partial t} = D_a \frac{\partial^2 C_a}{\partial x^2} - u \frac{\partial C_a}{\partial x} + Ka(C_d - C_a) \tag{24}$$

$$\frac{\partial C_d}{\partial t} = Kd(C_a - C_d) \tag{25}$$

Interpretation of the Concentration-Time Curves

Solutions of the dead zone model equations for commonly encountered boundary conditions can be found elsewhere (2). Figure 42 illustrates typical concentration-time curves resulting from the rapid injection solution for the perfectly mixed dead zone. For the calculation of these curves it was assumed that the injection and the measurement were made in the main stream. Table 22 defines the dimensionless groups that appear in the solution.

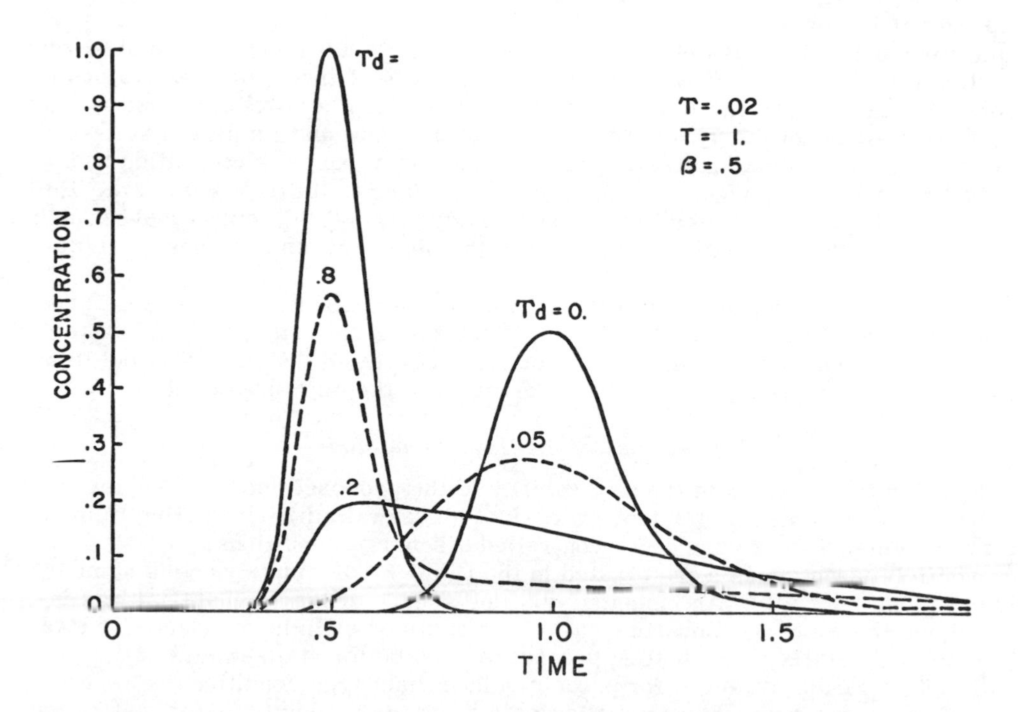

Figure 42. Rapid injection solution of perfectly mixed dead zone model.

TABLE 22

$$T = \frac{\text{Average Dispersion Transport Residence Time in Main Stream}}{\text{Average Velocity Transport Residence Time in Main Stream}}$$

$$T_d = \frac{\text{Average Dead Zone Residence Time}}{\text{Average Residence Time of Entire Section}}$$

α = Main Stream Fraction of Cross Section

β = Dead Zone Fraction of Cross Section

τ = Average Residence Time of Entire Section

The solutions are plotted as T_d varies from zero to infinity. As was previously demonstrated, when $T_d = 0$, representing an infinite mass transfer rate, the solution is given by the dispersed flow model. The result is a slightly skewed Gaussian curve. As the average residence time of the dead zone is increased the dead zone begins to pick up and retain material, resulting in attenuation of the curve peak and an increase in the tail as material is redeposited in the main stream. When $T_d = 0.2$, the dead zone mechanism completely dominates the spread of tracer, resulting in a long, highly skewed curve with linear decay. When the average residence time reaches $T_d = 0.8$, the mass transfer rate is so low that much of the tracer cloud flows by without being transferred to the dead zone. As a result, the initial portion of the curve is similar to the dispersed flow solution, but the material re-enters the main stream so slowly that a very long, slowly decaying tail is produced. As T_d approaches infinity the solution again reduces to the dispersed flow solution, but now the dead zone has been isolated from the main stream and the average residence time it $\tau = 0.5$. Thus, the first moment or average residence time changes discontinuously from $\tau = 1.0$ to $\tau = 0.5$ as T_d approaches infinity.

In Figure 42 the values of the relative dispersion coefficient and the dead zone fraction were $T = 0.02$ and $\beta = 0.5$. The shapes of the curves for other values of these parameters are easily imagined. For example, when β is decreased toward zero, the position of the $T_d = \infty$ curve shifts to the right and its peak decreases. The shapes of the other curves are of the same form, but peak truncation and spread are reduced. When $\beta = 0.0$, all curves reduce to the $T_d = 0.0$ curve. If β is increased, just the opposite effect takes place. The $T_d = \infty$ curve moves further to the left and the attenuation and spread of the other curves becomes more severe.

The effect of variation in the relative dispersion coefficient, T, is more pronounced on the $T_d = 0$ and $T_d = \infty$ curves. Decreasing the value of T will make these curves more peaked and will affect other curves in the same way but to a lesser degree. Increasing the value of T will have the opposite effect.

Applications of the Dead Zone Model

In order to demonstrate the applicability of the proposed model, a series of tests were undertaken in a 2-foot-by-60-foot glass-walled recirculating flume and in selected TVA rivers under controlled discharge conditions.

Artificial dead zones were created in the flume by placing a varying number of bricks along the walls. An instantaneous line source of tracer material was injected and the concentration-time curve was obtained utilizing conductivity measurements. Details of the testing procedures can be found elsewhere (2).

The TVA kindly arranged for predetermined discharge conditions below several of their impoundments, thus allowing almost ideal conditions for testing the proposed mathematical model in the field. The testing procedure consisted of injecting a line source of Rhodamine B and measuring the time-concentration curve at downstream stations, using fluorometric procedures. The methodology utilized in the field and in the laboratory will be discussed in detail in a subsequent paper.

Figure 43 shows a typical time-concentration experimental curve as well as the least squares best-fit prediction for the dispersed flow and the dead zone models. It is obvious that the dispersed flow model does not adequately describe the observed data. The applicability of the dead zone model is also worthy of note, inasmuch as the observed data fit the proposed mathematical model within the limits of experimental error.

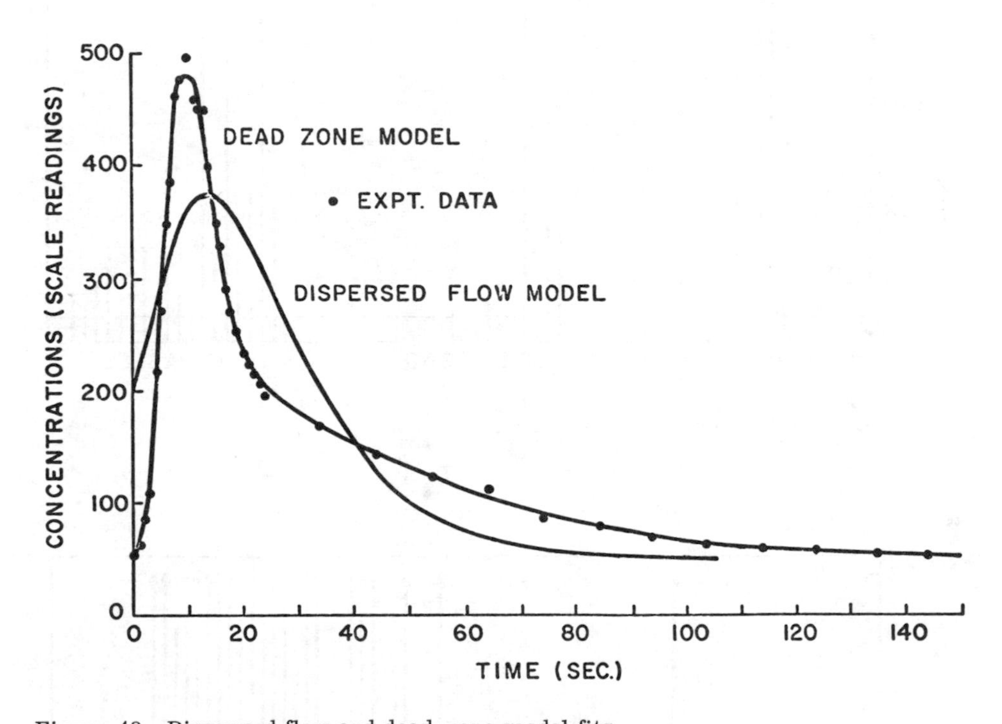

Figure 43. Dispersed flow and dead zone model fits.

In all of the tests with significant dead zones, a marked difference in the prediction ability of the dispersed flow and the dead zone models was observed. Figures 44 and 45 show typical results of both the river and the flume experiments plotted as the ratio of the squared deviation of the dead zone model, or the F statistic.

Confidence limits of 95 percent were used to indicate that 95 percent of the values of F above 1.85 are due to the superior predictive ability of the dead zone model and 5 percent are due to chance. All values above 1.85 indicate a superior predictive ability for the dead zone model.

SUMMARY AND CONCLUSIONS

Existing mathematical models and empirical equations for the determination of the mixing characteristics in rivers have been presented and discussed. It has been demonstrated that erroneous applications of these concepts are prevalent in the literature.

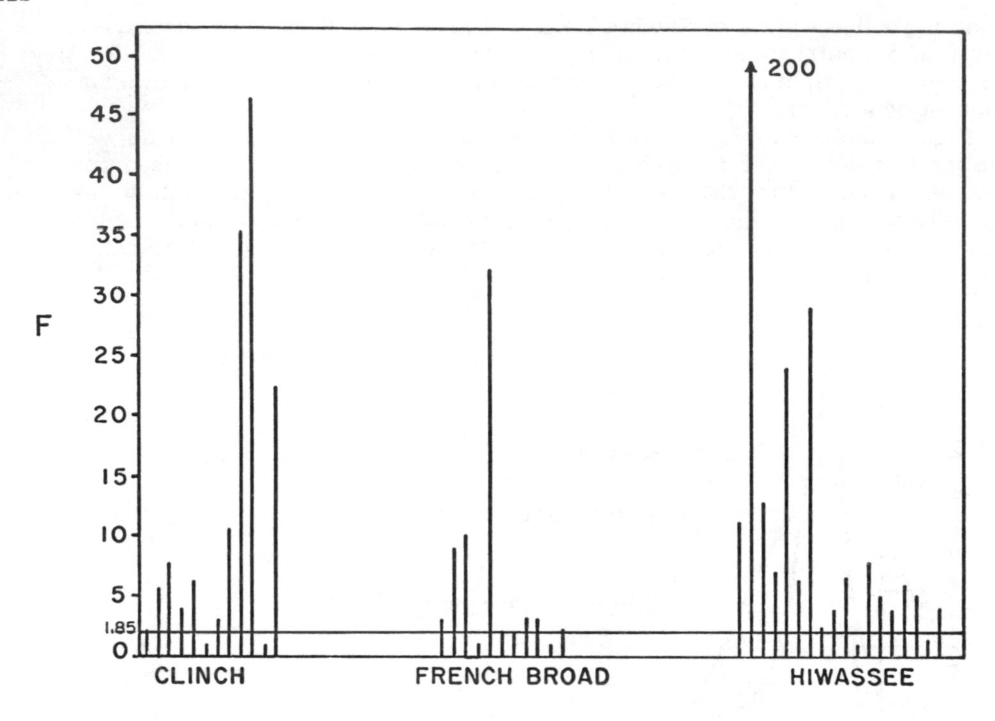

Figure 44. F statistic for channel tests.

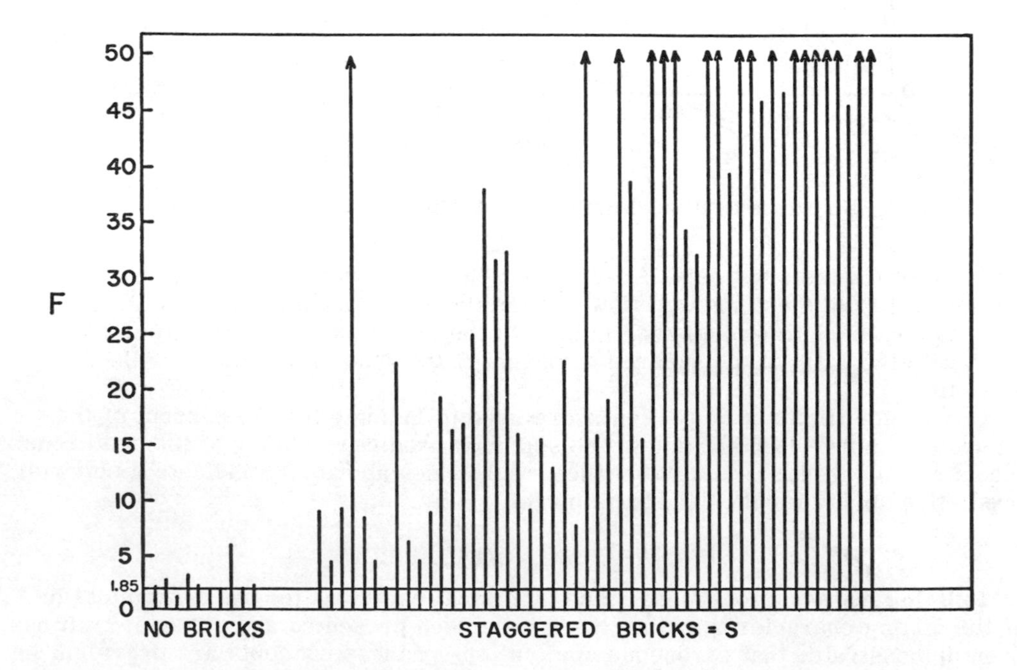

Figure 45. F statistic for channel tests.

In order to explain the discrepancies noted, a new mathematical model, denoted the dead zone model, was proposed. This model assumes that part of the tracer material injected into a river system finds its way into nonflowing portions of the river and is released slowly, causing the long tails observed.

The proposed model was tested both in a laboratory flume and in several TVA rivers under controlled conditions. The observed time-concentration curves were found to follow those predicted by the dead zone model quite closely, thus lending validity to this description of mixing phenomenon in rivers.

ACKNOWLEDGMENTS

The work reported herein was partly supported by Federal Water Supply and Pollution Research Grant Number WP-00328. The cooperation of the Tennessee Valley Authority is also gratefully acknowledged, as is the able assistance of Mr. Edward L. Thackston.

REFERENCES

(1) Falk, L. L. "Waste Dispersion in Receiving Waters," *J. Water Poll. Cont. Fed., 35,* 1464–1473 (November 1963).

(2) Hays, James, R. "Mass Transport Mechanisms in Open Channel Flow." Ph.D. Thesis, Vanderbilt University (1966).

(3) Taylor, G. I. "The Dispersion of Matter in Turbulent Flow through a Pipe," *Proc. Royal Soc. London, 234A,* 67 (1954).

(4) Krenkel, Peter A. "Waste Dispersion Characteristics of Streams Using Turbulent Diffusion Phenomenon," *J. Water Poll. Cont. Fed. 34,* 1203–1212 (December 1962).

(5) Fischer, H. B. Discussion to "Time of Travel of Soluble Contaminants in Streams," by T. J. Buchanan, *Proc. Sanit. Engr. Div. ASCE, 90*(SA6), 129–130 (December 1964).

(6) Harris, E. K. "A New Statistical Approach to the One-dimensional Diffusion Model," *Inter. J. Air Water Poll., 7,* 799–812 (1963).

(7) Thackston, E. L. "Longitudinal Mixing and Reaeration in Natural Streams," Ph.D. Thesis, Vanderbilt University (1966).

(8) Marquardt, Donald W. "An Algorithm for Least-Squares Estimation of Non-Linear Parameters," *J. Soc. Ind. Appl. Math.* (June 1963).

(9) Baumeister, T., III, and Donald W. Marquardt. "Least-Squares Estimation of Non-Linear Parameters," *Share General Program Library.* Share Distribution Number 1428 DFE 2134 (PA) (December 1962).

(10) Aris, R. "On the Dispersion of a Solute in a Fluid Flowing through a Tube," *Proc. Royal Soc. London, 234A,* 67 (1956).

(11) Elder, J. W. "The Dispersion of Marked Fluid in Turbulent Shear Flow," *J. Fluid Mech., 5,* 544–560 (1959).

(12) Thomas, I. E. "Dispersion in Open Channel Flow." Ph.D. Thesis, Northwestern University (1958).

(13) Parker, F. L. "Eddy Diffusion in Reservoirs and Pipelines," *J. Hydra. Div. ASCE, 87*(HY3), 151–171 (1961).

(14) Yotsukura, N., and M. B. Fiering. "Numerical Solution to a Dispersion Solution," *J. Hydra. Div. ASCE, 90*(HYS), 83–104 (September 1964).

(15) Godfrey, R. G., and B. J. Frederick. "Dispersion in Natural Streams," *Open File Report,* Washington, D.C.: United States Department of the Interior, Geological Survey (1963).

(16) Krenkel, Peter A. Discussion to "The Significance of Longitudinal Dispersion in the Analysis of Estuaries," *Advances in Water Pollution Research.* Vol. I. New York: Pergamon Press (1965).

A DISCUSSION OF "MATHEMATICAL MODELING OF MIXING PHENOMENA IN RIVERS"

Calvin C. Patterson
West Virginia University, Morgantown, West Virginia

The authors of the preceding paper are to be congratulated on making a significant advance in the knowledge of the mechanics of river mixing. The dead volume theory appears to be conclusively proven by the series of experiments using bricks in the flume to provide the dead volumes.

The writer, confronted by the same problem, proceeded on a different tack and obtained a direct solution of the differential equation. Two basic assumptions were required to obtain the solution, namely (a) the holdup and release of the dispersing tracer in the river is due to phenomena similar to ion exchange, and (b) the rate of holdup and release is controlled by lateral and vertical diffusion in the river.

The first assumption substitutes for the authors' dead volumes any volumes and materials in the river which act as stationary ion exchange materials. The second assumption obviates the need for a solution of simultaneous partial differential equations. Whether or not these assumptions are valid awaits additional work on the writer's model, the derivation of which is given below.

The differential equation for the transport of a tracer which is uniformly mixed over the channel cross section is

$$C_t(x,t) = D\,C_{xx}(x,t) - VC_x(x,t) - K\,[C(x,t) - C_i]\ ,$$

where

$C(x,t)$ = the concentration of the tracer, a function of x and t
x = the longitudinal distance from the release point to any point along the stream
t = time after release of the tracer
$C_t(x,t) = \dfrac{\partial C}{\partial t}$
$C_x(x,t) = \dfrac{\partial C}{\partial x}$
$C_{xx}(x,t) = \dfrac{\partial^2 C}{\partial x^2}$
A = the cross-sectional area of the stream
C_i = an equilibrium concentration
D = longitudinal dispersion coefficient
K = a constant which reflects the activity of the materials and volumes in the river that act as ion exchange materials for the particular tracer in use
M = mass of tracer released
V = mean velocity of the flow

The third term on the right hand side of the equation,

$$-K[C(x,t) - C_i]\ ,$$

accounts for the holdup and release of the tracer, which is assumed to be similar to ion exchange. When $C(x,t)$ is greater than the equilibrium concentration C_i, the tracer is going out of solution and into temporary storage. When $C(x,t)$ is less than C_i, the tracer is coming out of storage and into solution.

The differential equation was solved for the following set of boundary conditions:

$$C(x,0) = 0,$$
$$\lim_{t \to \infty} C(x,t) = 0,$$
$$C(0,0) = \frac{M}{A}\,\delta(t-0),$$

where $\delta(t-0)$ is the Dirac delta function. The solution obtained was

$$C(x,t) = \frac{M(x-Vt)\,e^{-Kt}}{A\sqrt{4\pi Dt^3}}\; e^{\frac{-(x-Vt)^2}{4Dt}} + KC_i \int_0^t e^{-Kt} \operatorname{erf} \frac{x-Vt}{\sqrt{4Dt}}\, dt \quad .$$

The use of the model to obtain numbers for $C(x,t)$, under a given set of conditions for X, M, A, D, K, and C_i, requires some fairly formidable calculations. In addition, the M/A term must have units of concentration per unit time, and uncertainties attend solutions which use the Dirac delta function. However, the model does yield curves which are similar to those obtained by the authors and others. For these reasons additional study of the model is desirable.

The same phenomenological events, a concentration-time curve which resembles a skew-frequency curve, were predicted by both mathematical models. These curves have been observed in field studies for instantaneous injection of tracers. Krenkel and Hays have demonstrated conclusively that dead volumes can create the phenomena in research flumes. The writer has obtained a model, but has yet to demonstrate that holdup and release are similar to ion exchange.

Regardless of which model proves to be the most useful, we seem to be closer to understanding basic mixing and transport phenomena in rivers.

BIOLOGICAL AND PHYSICAL RESPONSES IN A FRESHWATER DISSOLVED OXYGEN MODEL

Richard J. Frankel
Resources for the Future, Inc., Washington, D. C.
William W. Hansen
University of California, Berkeley, California

INTRODUCTION

To evaluate the effects of waste discharge on stream quality, it is necessary to understand the relationship between pollutants and stream environment. Pollutants not only lower stream quality but also alter environmental influences which provide for assimilation of waste discharges. Methods to analyze resulting conditions are an important part of water quality management, and a comprehensive stream study cannot bypass the need for encompassing all biological and physical responses which relate to stream pollution.

By far the most common criterion of water quality applied to a flowing stream by regulatory agencies is its oxygen resources in terms of dissolved oxygen (DO). It is the purpose of this study to: (a) set up a mathematical model expressing the dynamic relationships between the oxygen-demanding fractions of a wastewater and the responses of a living stream; (b) apply computer techniques to the model to determine the magnitude and the location of maxima and minima in the oxygen resources of the stream; and (c) verify the mathematical model by applying it to data observed in the field. Sensitivity of the mathematical model and accuracy of its predictions to actual conditions have been an important part of the study.

REVIEW OF PREVIOUS INVESTIGATIONS

The classical equations of Streeter and Phelps (1), which describe the concentrations of oxygen-demanding organic matter and of dissolved oxygen in a body of water, have frequently been applied to give the concentration profiles along a particular stream reach. The usual integrated form of these equations is

$$L_t = L_0 \cdot e^{-K_1 t} \tag{1}$$

and

$$D_t = \frac{K_1 L_0}{K_2 - K_1} \left(e^{-K_1 t} - e^{-K_2 t}\right) + D_0 \cdot e^{-K_2 t} \tag{2}$$

in which L_0 is the initial BOD at $t = 0$ (mg/l), D_0 is the initial DO saturation deficiency (mg/l), L_t and D_t are their values after t days, K_1 is the rate of BOD satisfaction or deoxygenation (day^{-1}), and K_2 is the rate of reaeration (day^{-1}).

Although Equations 1 and 2 are appealing in their simplicity, numerous physical and biological processes are taking place in natural streams which severely limit their usefulness. Dobbins (2) has listed a few of these processes, including:

1. The removal of BOD by sedimentation or adsorption.
2. The addition of BOD along the stretch by the scour of bottom deposits or by the diffusion of partly decomposed organic products from the benthal layer into the water above.
3. The addition of BOD along the stretch by local runoff.

4. The removal of oxygen from the water by diffusion into the benthal layer to satisfy the oxygen demand in the aerobic zone of this layer.
5. The removal of oxygen from the water by the purging action of gases rising from the benthal layer.
6. The addition of oxygen by the photosynthetic action of plankton and fixed plants.
7. The removal of oxygen by the respiration of plankton and fixed plants.
8. The continuous redistribution of both the BOD and the oxygen by the effect of longitudinal dispersion.

Dobbins' list is not intended to include all the factors which may alter the DO profile described by Equation 2. Furthermore, for computational purposes several of the factors would cancel or compensate for others in any particular reach, since they cannot all occur simultaneously; this is not, of course, to deny that all these processes take place. In addition, the following factors could be enumerated:

9. The variation of K_1, particularly at the onset of the nitrification stage; this variation precludes assuming K_1 constant over any extended period of time.
10. Changes in channel configuration which alter the characteristics of surface turbulence and consequently of the rate of transfer of oxygen from the atmosphere.
11. The effects of suspended and dissolved substances on the rate of diffusion of oxygen from the surface into the main body of the stream.
12. Diurnal variation in oxygen content, BOD, temperature, and flow-rate of influent discharges, whether wastes or natural tributaries.

The above is still not necessarily a complete list, but the list does include the more significant variables to be considered if reasonable accuracy in predicting DO concentrations is to be achieved. In many instances, it is impossible to obtain accurate estimates of the quantities involved, either because the interrelationships between certain quantities are not well understood or because of a lack of sufficient data. A number of techniques have been suggested by which some or all of the above factors can be taken into account in determining the DO profile (2–6).

DEVELOPMENT OF OXYGEN PROFILE EQUATIONS

In order to account for the various processes itemized in the preceding section, several distinct rate constants need to be identified:

1. The laboratory rate of deoxygenation K_1, which would be determined by analysis of bottle samples from a single section in the stream. This rate is a characteristic of the suspended and dissolved organic matter, is temperature dependent, and is independent of the oxidation activity of the local aquatic growths.
2. The "river rate" of deoxygenation K_r, which accounts for what might be called the "trickling filter effect." K_r is the difference between the gross stream rate of oxygen consumption by the remaining BOD and the rate K_1 characteristic of the stream's organic load, and is due to the activity of attached aquatic growths and slimes in converting oxygen-demanding organic matter into stable end products. It is temperature dependent and is substantially independent of the character of the organic load insofar as it is assumed that the suspension is nontoxic to the organisms and that the organisms are adapted to the local conditions.
3. The rate K_3 of BOD removal by sedimentation and/or adsorption. K_3 is a purely physical characteristic of the organic suspension and is affected by temperature only insofar as the viscosity of the water is temperature dependent, and for practical purposes this dependence is negligible. The magnitude of K_3 will, however, be dependent upon the stream velocity. A small positive value indicates

a rapidly moving ($V > 1$ ft/sec) stream which is on the verge of scouring benthal deposits; a large positive value indicates a more sluggish stream ($V < 0.6$ ft/sec) in which sludge deposition is taking place. It has been suggested that a negative value of K_3 would indicate scour of bottom sediments; this assumption appears difficult to justify, since it implies that the rate at which BOD is scoured is proportional to the total stream BOD load. For the purposes of this paper K_3 will take on only nonnegative values.

In any stream analysis, these three rates must be considered as specific quantities quasi-independent of each other. Previous usage of Equations 1 and 2 has interpreted K_1 to describe both the rate of removal of oxygen-demanding organic matter and the rate of oxygen consumption by the remaining BOD. That these are very different processes which take place at substantially different rates in natural watercourses has been demonstrated conclusively (7).

The addition of BOD along a stretch, and its effect on the oxygen resources of the stream, have been treated in several ways. Using the notation of Camp (3), let p designate the rate of addition of BOD to the overlying water from the benthal layer [mg/(l)(day)]; the rate of change of BOD in solution and suspension (L_s) is then given completely by

$$\frac{dL_s}{dt} = -(K_1 + K_r + K_3)L_s + p \tag{3}$$

and integrating between the upstream section at $t = 0$, $L_s = L_{s_0}$ and the downstream section of a reach,

$$L_{s_t} = (L_{s_0} - \frac{p}{K})e^{-Kt} + \frac{p}{K} \tag{4}$$

in which K is $K_1 + K_r + K_3$, as defined above, and t is the time of travel through the reach in days. In any particular reach we would have, on the average, either K_3, p, or both, equal to zero.

The rate p of addition of BOD to the overlying water due to resuspension of deposited solids can continue only as long as there is, in fact, a sludge deposit available to contribute BOD through scour; it is necessary therefore that a separate accounting of the BOD of the benthal layer be kept.

Although Camp (3) has used p in the same manner as it is used herein, that is, the rate of addition of BOD from the deposits to the overlying stream, he considers it to be only the rate at which unoxidized anaerobic decomposition products filter upward into the stream, and describes it mathematically in terms of the rate of change of the BOD of the benthal deposits,

$$Hp = \frac{dL_d}{dt} = -K_4 L_d \tag{5}$$

in which H is the depth of the stream (meters), Hp is the equivalent areal rate of addition of BOD to the overlying water [g/(sq m)(day)], L_d is the total areal BOD of the benthos (g/sq m), and K_4 is the rate constant of the anaerobic fermentation process. Hansen and Frankel (8) define p to represent the rate of addition due only to physical mechanisms; consequently, the interpretation of p given by Equation 5 is inconsistent with the concept of the processes represented by p and dL_d/dt, and the correct combination of the terms in Equation 5 would be given by

$$\frac{1}{H}\frac{dL_d}{dt} = -K_4\frac{L_d}{H} - p \tag{6}$$

which when integrated results in

$$\frac{L_{d_t}}{H} = \left[\frac{L_{d_0}}{H} + \frac{p}{K_4}\right] \cdot e^{-K_4 t} - \frac{p}{K_4} \quad . \tag{7}$$

The first term of the right-hand member of Equation 6 is the change in the benthal oxygen demand resulting from anaerobic fermentation in the layer, and the second term is the reduction resulting from resuspension into the overlying stream. The total BOD at any time t downstream from the initial point $t = 0$ is then given by the sum of Equations 4 and 7,

$$L_t = \left[L_{s_0} - \frac{p}{K}\right] e^{-Kt} + \left[\frac{L_{d_0}}{H} + \frac{p}{K_4}\right] e^{-K_4 t} + p\left[\frac{1}{K} - \frac{1}{K_4}\right] \tag{8}$$

where the terms are as defined previously. Equation 8 is of academic interest only, since two components must be accounted for separately; their demands upon the oxygen of the stream are independent, and in addition we must know the amount of benthal BOD present at any time in order to insure that the term involving scour does not exceed the amount that is physically available to be resuspended. Once this occurs we set $L_d = 0$ and Equation 8 reduces to Equation 4 with $p = 0$. Furthermore, it is only L_s that will be verified by analysis of bottle samples; an average value of L_d would require analysis of the bottom sediments.

In the case where we have sedimentation rather than scour, it can be assumed that there has been a period of steady flow of sufficient duration that the equilibrium conditions described by Velz (9) have been established, namely, that the BOD exerted by the deposits in a day is just equal to the BOD deposited. Since K_3/K is the fractional change in the suspended BOD that is due to sedimentation, we have

$$\frac{1}{H}\frac{dL_d}{dt} = \left(\frac{-K_3}{K}\right)\left(\frac{dL_s}{dt}\right) \tag{9}$$

and combined with Equation 3 where $p = 0$ integrates to

$$L_t = L_{s_0}\left(1 + \frac{K_3}{K}\right) \cdot e^{-Kt} \quad . \tag{10}$$

In this situation the rate of biochemical oxidation is the same $(K_1 + K_r)$ whether the organic material is still suspended or has just been deposited, so that no separation of the components (suspended and deposited) is necessary in order to determine the BOD influence on the oxygen budget.

Photosynthesis and Respiration

Two modifications of the Streeter-Phelps (1) equations which have thus far included explicitly the effects on the oxygen budget of photosynthesis and respiration by the stream biota are those of Camp (3) and Dobbins (2), and in both cases this effect has been taken into account by the addition of a constant term. Again using the notation of Camp, let a be the rate of production (consumption) of oxygen resulting from photosynthesis (respiration) in mg/(l) (day) (a factor which is included in Dobbins' term D_b); neglecting factors involving BOD (which do not affect the discussion or conclusions), we can write

$$\frac{dD}{dt} = -K_2 D + a \tag{11}$$

and its integral

$$D_t = \left[D_0 - \frac{a}{K_2}\right] e^{-K_2 t} + \frac{a}{K_2} \quad . \tag{12}$$

One criticism of Equation 12 is that for $t \to \infty$, $D_t \to$ "constant," and it is noted by writers mentioned above that a is not really constant but is dependent upon the time of day, biological conditions in the stream, and other factors. Any attempt to use Equation 12 in an actual stream study would necessitate, therefore, the evaluation of a at all points t days downstream required for the profile, as well as specifying its value at the particular time of day at which the data are collected at each point t.

Frankel (10) indicated that a similarity existed in the configuration of diurnal oxygen curves as reported in various river studies, in terms of hourly variations around the arithmetic mean daily concentration, and that in general the configuration was in agreement with the classical pattern. Consequently he incorporated a photosynthetic effect by utilizing a time-dependent factor, $F(\xi)$, obtained from field data; such that

$$D_t = \left\{ D_0 \, F(\xi) + c_s \, [1 - F(\xi)] \right\} e^{-K_2 t} \tag{13}$$

in which c_s is the saturation concentration of DO at stream temperature (mg/l), $F(\xi)$ is the time-dependent photosynthetic factor defined as the cyclic ratio of the hourly level of dissolved oxygen in the stream to the mean daily concentration of DO, and other terms as defined above. Equation 13 satisfies the criterion mentioned above but is mathematically awkward.

Hansen and Frankel (8) showed that if it is assumed that the classical pattern of diurnal DO variations in a stream can be represented by a periodic function, then Equation 11 can be written

$$\frac{dD}{dt} = -K_2 D + a \cos(\omega t + \phi) \tag{14}$$

in which a is the maximum rate of oxygen production (consumption) by photosynthesis (respiration) in mg/(l)(day). The integrated form of Equation 14 is

$$D_t = [D_0 - A\,(K_2 \cos\phi + \omega \sin\phi)]\, e^{-K_2 t} + A\,[K_2 \cos(\omega t + \phi) + \sin(\omega t + \phi)] \tag{15a}$$

in which $A = a/(\omega^2 + K_2^2)$, mg/(l)(day). The interpretation of Equation 15a (for t sufficiently large that the exponential terms may be neglected) is that the DO concentration is due to two factors: (a) oxygen transfer from the atmosphere, the rate of which is dependent upon the instantaneous concentration of DO as a result of photosynthesis and/or respiration; and (b) the oxygen produced (consumed) by these processes. Furthermore, for $K_2 \rightarrow 0$, we have $D_t \rightarrow D_0 + (a/\omega)\,[\sin(\omega t + \phi) - \sin\phi]$, such that in the absence of reaeration the oxygen concentration is a periodic function dependent upon the biological activity.

It is the purpose of the frequency ω and the phase ϕ to adjust the total travel time t (hours) so that the function $\cos(\omega t + \phi)$ in Equation 14, which has limits ± 1.0, becomes the appropriate fractional multiplier of the constant a at the point t hours downstream. For computational purposes the time of day t_0 at which the analysis begins at the initial point, and the time of day τ at which the oxygen consumption by biological respiration is a maximum, are brought into the analysis as

$$\phi = -\omega(36 - t_0 + \tau) \tag{15b}$$

in which t_0, the time of start, is constant throughout the run, and where the 36 is introduced in order to avoid getting the wrong sign in the cosine function. As a result of the above, it should be clear that t in Equation 14 is travel time downstream and may be treated as such mathematically.

Neglecting the decay terms, the maximum and minimum values of Equation 15a are

$$D_m = \left(\frac{a}{\omega}\right) \sin \alpha = \left(\frac{a}{K_2}\right) \cos \alpha \tag{16}$$

where

$$\alpha = \omega t_m + \phi = \tan^{-1}\left(\frac{\omega}{K_2}\right) \tag{17}$$

and D_m is the maximum or minimum deficit, depending upon the sign of the function. It can be seen from Equation 17 that the magnitude and the location of the maxima and the minima are determined both by the periodic production of oxygen by photosynthesis and by the reaeration "response" to the deficit at time t.

If, as Dobbins (2) and Lynch (11) have shown, we can assume first-order reactions and that the effect of longitudinal diffusion is negligible, then by combining Equations 4, 7, 10, and 15a, we obtain the rate of change of the oxygen deficiency given by

$$\begin{aligned} D_t = & \frac{(K_1 + K_r)(1 + K_3/K)}{(K_2 - K)} \left(L_{s0} - \frac{p}{K}\right)\left(e^{-Kt} - e^{-K_2 t}\right) \\ & + \frac{K_4}{(K_2 - K_4)} \left(\frac{L_{d0}}{H} + \frac{p}{K_4}\right)\left(e^{-K_4 t} - e^{K_2 t}\right) \\ & + [D_0 - A\,(K_2 \cos \phi + \omega \sin \phi)]\, e^{-K_2 t} \\ & + A\,[K_2 \cos(\omega t + \phi) + \omega \sin(\omega t + \phi)] \ . \end{aligned} \tag{18}$$

The terms in Equation 18 are, respectively, oxygen consumption resulting from biological oxidation of the suspended and dissolved BOD load, oxygen consumption by anaerobic decomposition products of the benthos, "decay" of the initial oxygen deficit, and production/consumption of oxygen by photosynthesis/respiration.

CASE STUDY—FLINT RIVER NEAR FLINT, MICHIGAN

In order to verify the mathematical statements presented in the foregoing section, as well as to test the sensitivity of the predicted DO profile to variations in assumed and given input parameters, an analysis was made of data available for the Flint River below the Flint, Michigan, Sewage Treatment Plant. The measured values of DO and BOD for the study period, 28–29 July 1959, were published by the Water Resources Commission of the state of Michigan (12). Also in the Commission's report was a description of the river conditions during the critical period, and a study of the biological extraction rate K_r.

The Commission's data were particularly useful, since they permitted description of the diurnal DO variation at a number of different points along the critical reach. Cross-section notes from the Commission's survey of a 30-mile stretch of the river above and below the critical sections were made available, and additional treatment plant data were obtained (13,14), such that the daily fluctuations in effluent flowrate and BOD could be imposed upon the model.

The factors affecting the suspended and dissolved BOD, L_s, were determined in the following manner, with the results computed by the IBM 7094 system and plotted on the IBM 1401-driven Cal-Comp plotter, of which Figure 46 is a tracing:

1. The total oxidation rate $k_1 + k_r$ at 26 °C, was taken to be 0.35/day in Reach 1, immediately above the Flint treatment plant outfall, where neither sedimentation ($k_3 = 0$) nor scour ($p = 0$) take place (12). (In the subsequent discussion all lower-case rate constants referred to are in terms of base 10.)

2. It was assumed that the addition to the stream of the sewage treatment plant (STP) effluent, containing more easily oxidized organic material, increases

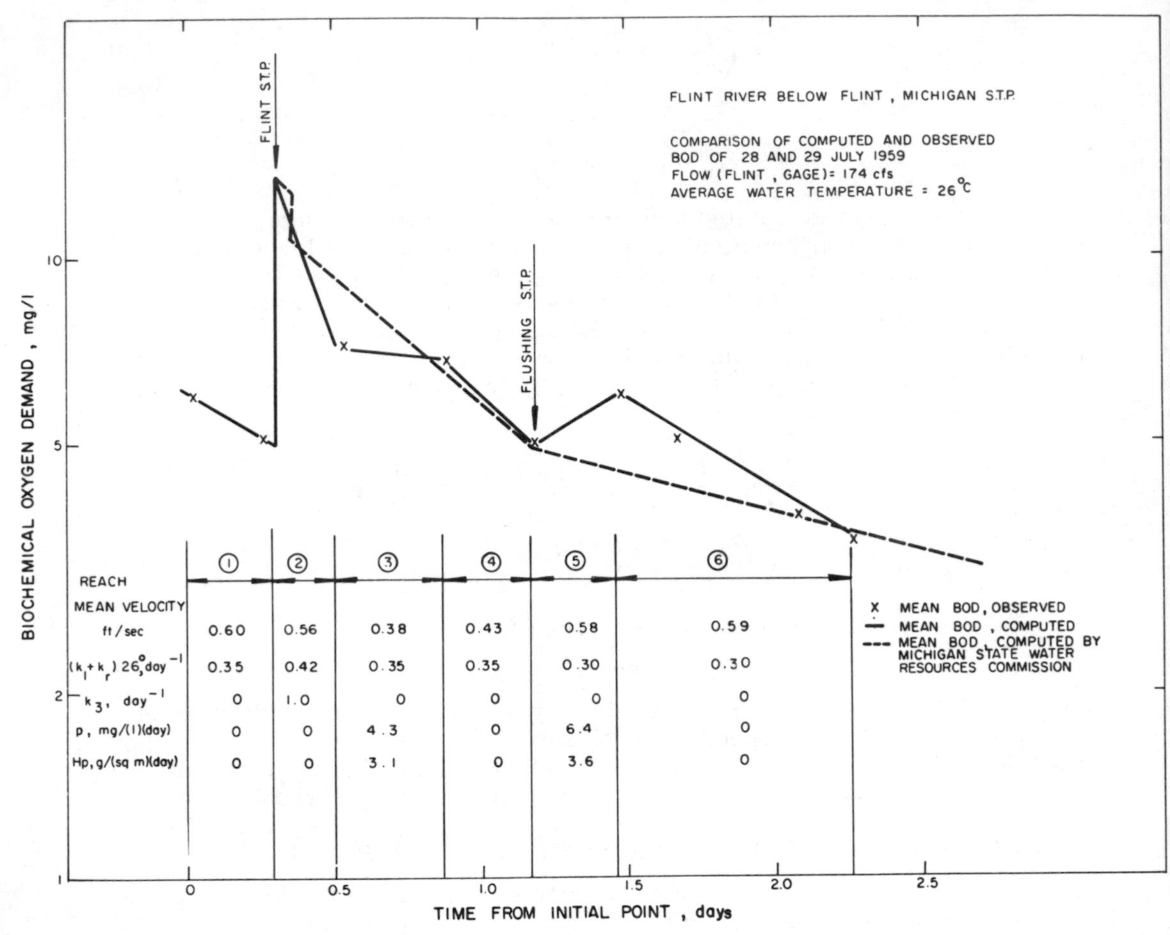

Figure 46. Graphical determination of BOD parameters.

the total oxidation rate in the stream to about 0.42/day, in effect increasing the oxidation rate of the suspended and dissolved organic matter from 0.17 to 0.24/day, while the biochemical extraction rate k_r of the stream organisms remains at 0.18/day.

3. Since a large fraction of the BOD load settles to the bottom immediately below the plant, it was assumed that the total oxidation rate returns to 0.35/day within about 2 miles below the point of discharge. This rate presumably persists for an additional 4.5 miles, after which distance the more easily oxidized fraction has been removed and the rate diminishes further to 0.30/day.

4. Deviations from these rates of BOD removal in the reaches below the plant were assumed to be due either to settling out of BOD to the bottom ($k_3 > 0$) or to resuspension into the stream of benthal deposits ($p > 0$) as tabulated in Figure 46.

It will not be suggested that the values arrived at in this fashion are necessarily precise or even that they closely approximate the true physical and biochemical environment, since verification of variables is not available generally, and particularly in this specific case. The values of the various input parameters determined in this manner are helpful, however, both as a guide to obtaining approximate orders of magnitude which their actual values would take and in determining the sensitivity of the mathematical model to major and minor changes in their assumed values.

A limitation of this particular set of data can be made by inspection of the fitted values tabulated on Figure 46. The scour rate of 4.30 mg/(l) (day) in Reach 3 would at first appear to be unreasonably high in view of the low velocity in this section. However, "scour" in this reach, as well as in Reach 5, is actually a direct result of these low velocities; organic matter is floated back into the stream from the benthos by adherence to rising bubbles of gases of anaerobic decomposition, a condition which occurs primarily in ponded and slack-water areas of the river. Furthermore, it must be noted that should both settling of suspended solids to the stream bottom and their concurrent resuspension by rising gases take place, the values of p or k_3 represent only the net effect of these two physical phenomena.

The atmospheric reaeration constant k_2 was estimated from the empirical expression developed by Owens, Edwards, and Gibbs (15), which was applicable for the conditions of this study; namely,

$$k_2\ (20\,^\circ\mathrm{C.}) = \frac{9.4\ V^{0.67}}{d^{1.85}} \qquad (19)$$

in which d is the average stream depth in feet, V is the velocity in ft/sec, and k_2 is in reciprocal days. The temperature correction was taken as 1.6 percent per °C.

Studies by M. C. Rand (16) indicated that a reduction in the rate of atmospheric reaeration would be expected as a result of organic pollution by domestic wastes. In the BOD range encountered, a linear reduction in k_2 of 0.3 percent per mg/l of suspended and dissolved BOD was read from Rand's curve, and a provision was included in the computer program for the sake of generality.

The effective oxygen demand L_d of the sludge deposits was evaluated by use of Equation 18 with $a = 0$ and with k_2 and the BOD constants as given by Equation 19 and Figure 46, respectively. It was further assumed that the mean daily DO conditions in the river could be determined by neglecting the daily variation in the treatment plant effluent BOD and flowrate and considering only their mean daily values, as is frequently done in studies of stream waste assimilation. Under these conditions the lower curve of Figure 47 was made to conform to the observed data by use of those values of L_{d_0} tabulated on the figure. The slack-water areas of Reach 6 were neglected in computation, since these areas did not cause the critical conditions for the entire reach considered. Clearly, Reach 6 would have been subdivided so as to generate a computed output conforming more closely to the measured mean DO. The resulting values for L_d behaved as would be expected, being largest immediately below the points of waste discharge and decreasing downstream thereafter. For sludge depths of 1–2 ft., as reported by the Commission (12), the magnitudes of L_d were consistent with the data given by Camp (3), where a rate of anaerobic decomposition $k_4 = 0.003$/day was assumed.

Applicability and Sensitivity of the Model

The expressions developed in this study must be programmed for digital computer processing if they are to be of any practical value in the analysis of a stream's oxygen balance. The program written for the IBM 7094 digital computer system is described in Hansen and Frankel (8); briefly the data required for each tributary or pollution source are as follows:

1. Distance below the initial point of the profiles (miles).
2. Mean daily flowrate (cfs) of tributary.
3. Mean daily temperature (°C.) of tributary.

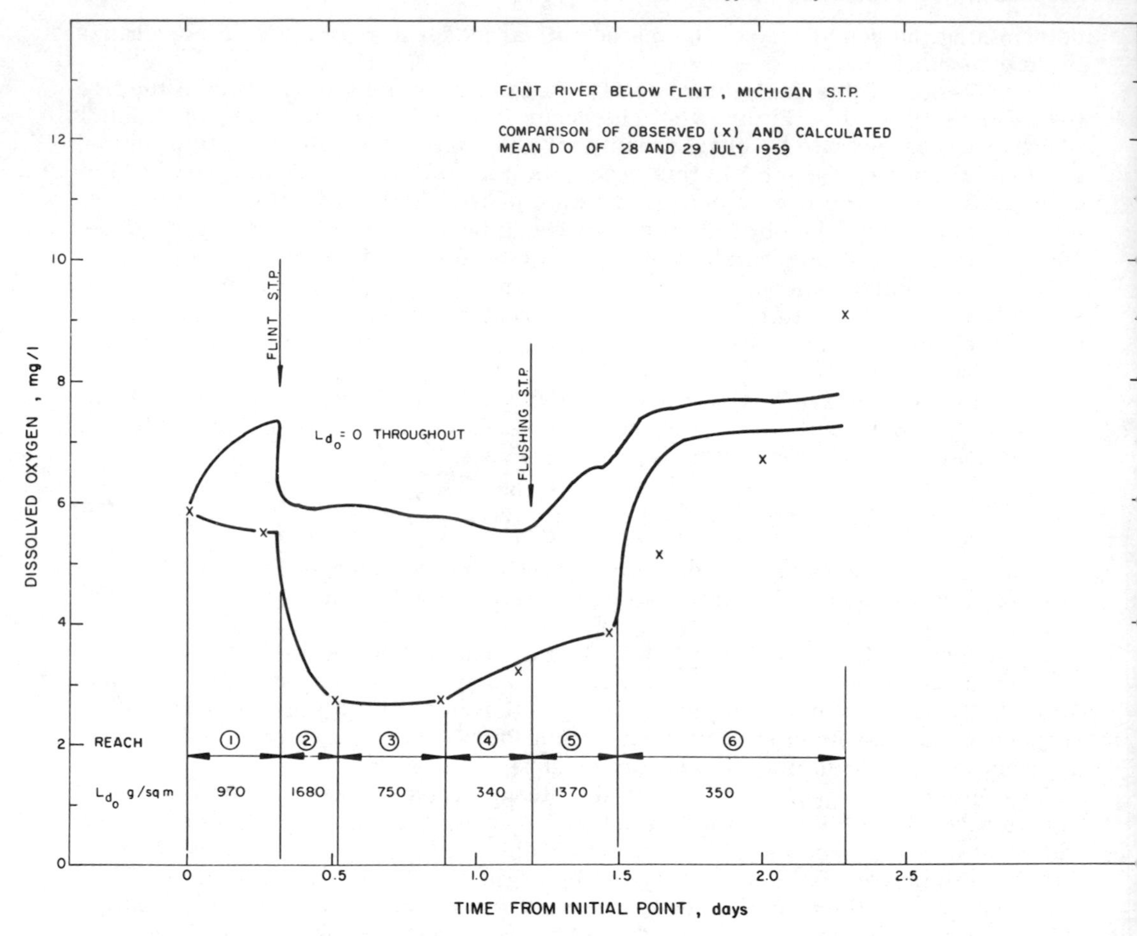

Figure 47. Evaluation of ultimate benthic oxygen demand.

4. Mean daily dissolved oxygen concentration (mg/l) of tributary.
5. Mean daily ultimate biochemical oxygen demand (mg/l) of tributary.
6. 20°C. deoxygenation rate k_1 of tributary BOD (day^{-1}, base 10).
7. 20°C. supplementary deoxygenation rate k_1', which may be used to account for any increase or decrease in the theoretical deoxygenation rate from nitrification, deposit of most easily oxidized material, or other factors.
8. Rate p of scour of bottom sediments [mg/(l) (day)] in stream below tributary.
9. Rate k_3 of sedimentation (day^{-1}, base 10) in stream below tributary.
10. Ultimate oxygen demand of sediments (mg/l) in stream below tributary.
11. Anaerobic decomposition rate k_4 of benthos (day^{-1}, base 10) in stream below tributary.
12. Maximum rate a of oxygen production (consumption) by photosynthesis (respiration) [mg/(l) (day)].
13. Phase lag time τ at which respiration of aquatic organisms below the tributary is a maximum; expressed on a 24-hour basis such that $\phi = \pi\tau/12$.
14. Biological oxidation rate k_r of attached organisms in stream below tributary (day^{-1}, base 10).

15. Series of twelve factors which represent the ratio of instantaneous hourly flow rate to the daily mean at 0200, 0400 . . . 1200 hr.

16. Series of twelve factors which represent the ratio of instantaneous hourly tributary BOD to the daily mean at 0200, 0400 . . . 1200 hr.

17. Series of twelve factors which represent the ratio of instantaneous hourly tributary DO to the daily mean at 0200, 0400 . . . 1200 hr.

18. Parameters A, B, C, D, which define the velocity-discharge and depth-discharge relations $V = A(Q^B)$ and $H = C(Q^D)$ in the stream below the tributary, and the flow rate Q_i, which defines the upper limit of the range of applicability of the set i of the parameters A_i, B_i, C_i, D_i.

Results of the application of the model to the Flint River data indicate how closely the oxygen resources can be accounted for in a stream. The variation in computed DO brought about by imposing upon the model the daily variation in initial conditions of stream DO and effluent strength and flow rate is demonstrated by Figure 48, in which, again, the rate of oxygen production by photosynthesis $a = 0$. This is essentially the procedure suggested by Li (4), and is as yet insuf-

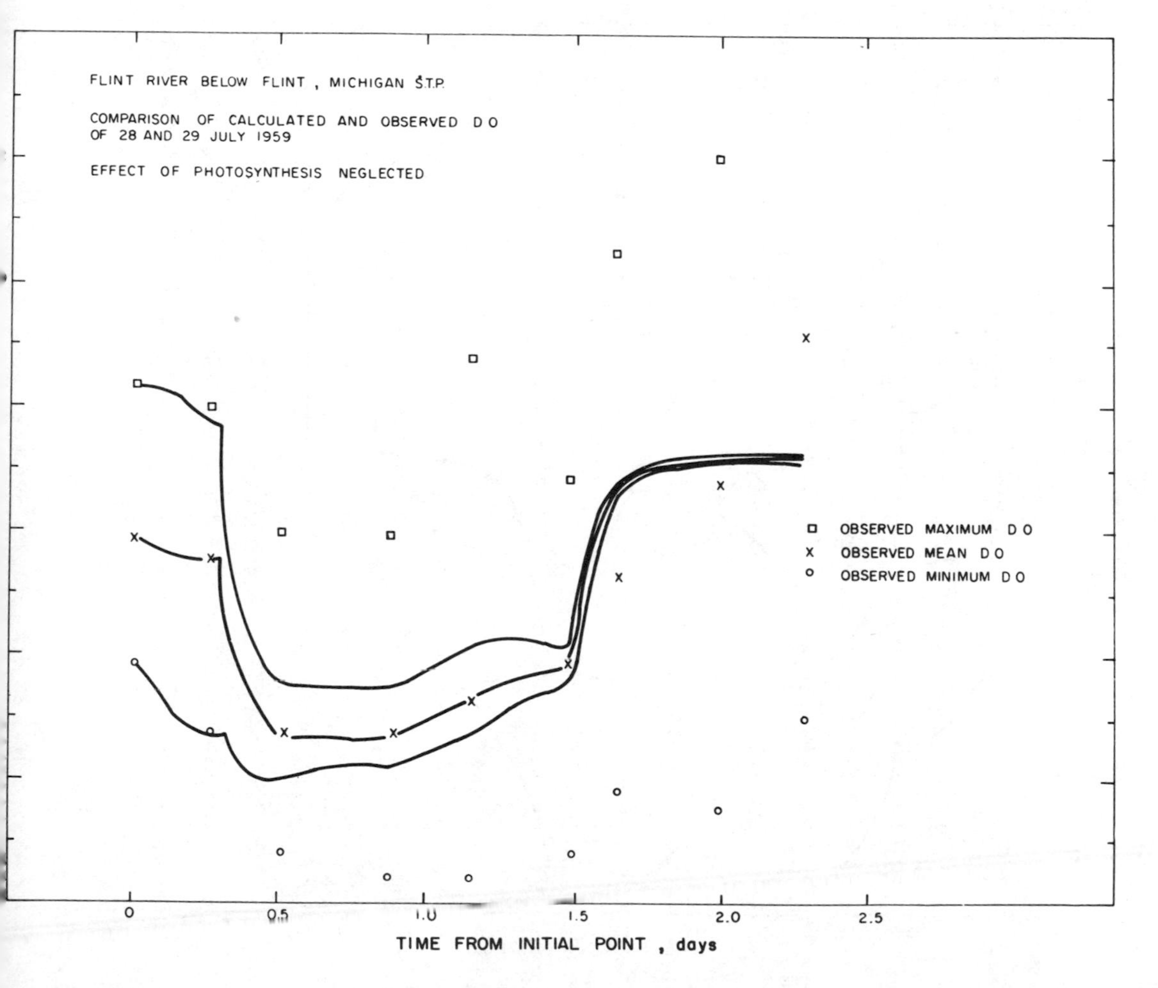

Figure 48. Variation in stream DO concentration resulting from cyclic treatment plant operation.

ficient; since the compound maximum and minimum oxygen concentrations do not even approximately represent the observed data. Moreover, in the absence of oxygen production and consumption by the stream biota, the computed maximum, mean, and minimum DO concentrations converge to a common value, as would be expected and as is confirmed by Li's example in his paper.

The error involved in neglecting benthal oxygen demand can be noted by inspection of the upper curve of Figure 47, in which the sludge demand L_d is taken to be zero throughout the entire reach studied.

The values of a introduced into Equation 18 were adjusted so as to produce a computed minimum DO profile conforming to the observed minima (8), since minimum DO concentrations are of much greater significance than are maximum concentrations. The required values for the equivalent areal distribution $a' = aH$, g/(sq m)(day), are shown on Figure 49, which is, as are the other profiles shown in this paper, a tracing of the computer-generated output plot.

It is perhaps surprising to note how closely the computed profile of maximum

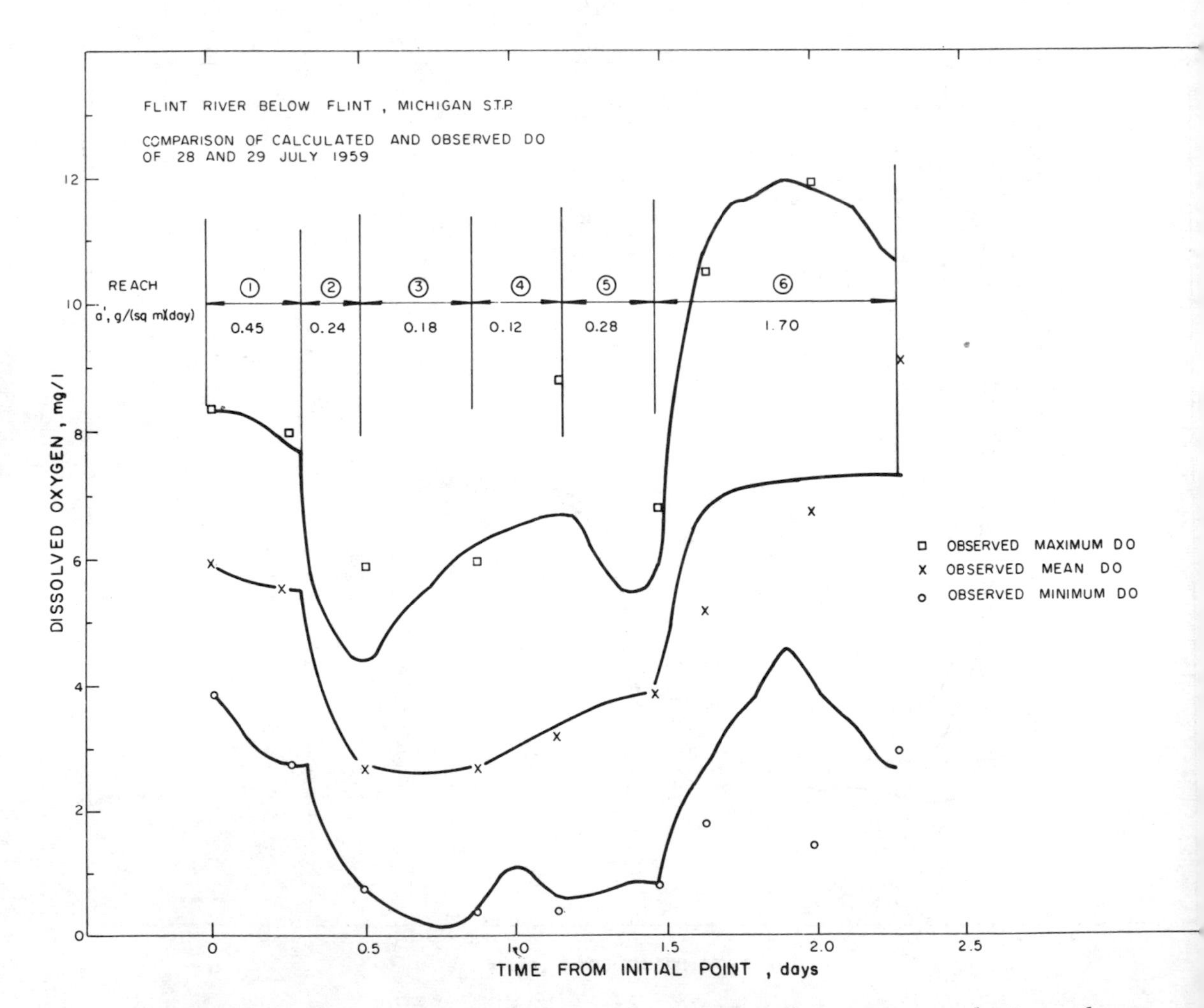

Figure 49. Graphical determination of rates of photosynthetic oxygen production and consumption.

DO describes the observed data, since values of a were chosen to reflect the minimum observed concentrations. At these particular points it appears that a second periodic term $b \cos(\omega t + a)$ in Equation 14, as perhaps indicated by the data of Gunnerson and Bailey (17), is not necessary to describe the rate of oxygen production by photosynthesis.

As in the case of the benthal oxygen demand, the rate constants a, determined by fitting the computer output to the data, appear to behave both in magnitude and in relative value as might be expected of a parameter purported to represent the rate of oxygen production (consumption) by photosynthesis (respiration). Hansen and Frankel (8) noted that the maximum areal rate ot production a' [g/(sq m)(day)], representing the density and variety of respiratory organisms, should be related to solar energy input E, mean depth H, and turbidity T by

$$a' \propto \frac{E}{HT} \tag{20}$$

since both depth and turbidity determine the effective rate of light input to the cells. If the geometric mean L_g of the suspended and dissolved BOD in each reach is considered to be a qualitative indication of the relative turbidity in each of the reaches, and if the solar energy input is assumed to be constant throughout, then the areal rate a' would be proportional to the reciprocal of the depth-mean BOD product. Hansen and Frankel (8) showed a remarkably good correlation between these parameters.

Table 23 is a summary of the sensitivity analysis of the model in which input variables were systematically eliminated in order to evaluate their effects on predicting downstream oxygen sources. The table shows the absolute differences in dissolved oxygen values obtained by subtracting the actual field data from the computed results for each change or elimination of the specified variables in the mathematical model. Table 23 indicates that if photosynthetic effects and daily fluctuations in waste loads are not taken into account, only average daily dissolved oxygen values can be estimated. For this particular case, photosynthetic effects showed a greater influence of the two on minimum dissolved oxygen values. Of equal magnitude was the importance of incorporating the oxygen demand of bottom deposits; the average daily dissolved oxygen figure was strongly influenced by its omission.

The rate of scour of bottom deposits and the rate of sedimentation had small effects on the overall oxygen profile but significant effects in specific reaches where either scour or sedimentation were important. The biological extraction rate of attached organisms in the stream showed a consistent though small effect on estimates of downstream average daily dissolved oxygen levels. Incorporation of the reaeration rate correction due to BOD appeared to be unnecessary for stream studies. The Streeter-Phelps formula was inadequate for prediction of even the average daily dissolved oxygen levels. Changes in stream cross-sectional area which affect evaluation of reaeration rates were of minor importance, since the stream exhibited both a low reaeration rate and a significant photosynthetic influence.

Discussion of Case Study

Table 23 shows that if fish and wildlife standards are to be evaluated in terms of a dissolved oxygen level, a clear distinction must be made between an average daily dissolved oxygen value and a minimum dissolved oxygen level. If only the average daily figure is important to fish preservation, a modified oxygen-sag model will suffice for river studies, but if the minimum dissolved oxygen value and/or the time period of exposure at a specific dissolved oxygen value are of

TABLE 23

SENSITIVITY OF MATHEMATICAL MODEL TO CHANGES IN INPUT VARIABLES

Model Conditions	Absolute Differences from Actual Field Data in Minimum and Average Daily Dissolved Oxygen Values, mg/l											
	Flint STP		Station 10		Station 11		Flushing STP		Station 13		Station 16	
	Min.	Ave.	Min.	Ave.	Min.	Ave.	Min.	Ave.	Min.	Ave.	Min.	Ave.
Flint River Field Data	2.8	5.5	0.8	2.7	0.4	2.7	0.4	3.2	0.8	3.8	3.0	9.1
Predicted oxygen profile from complete model	-0.1	0.0	-0.1	-0.1	0.0	+0.1	0.0	+0.3	-0.2	-0.1	-0.3	-2.0
Flint STP effluent assumed constant strength and flow	-0.1	0.0	-0.1	0.0	-0.1	+0.2	+0.2	+0.3	-0.2	-0.1	-0.3	-2.0
Rate of oxygen production by photosynthesis assumed zero	+2.2	0.0	+1.1	-0.1	+1.7	0.0	+2.4	+0.2	+2.6	-0.1	+4.1	-2.0
Oxygen demand of sediments in stream assumed zero	+1.6	+1.7	+2.9	+3.0	+2.7	+3.1	+2.5	+2.7	+3.1	+3.2	+0.3	-1.4
Rate of scour of bottom deposits assumed zero	-0.1	0.0	-0.1	-0.1	-0.4	+0.1	+0.3	+0.4	-0.1	+0.1	-0.2	-1.9
No reaeration rate correction due to high BOD	0.0	0.0	0.0	0.0	+0.1	+0.2	+0.3	+0.4	0.0	0.0	-0.2	-2.0
Photosynthesis and daily fluctuations in Flint STP effluent assumed zero,* oxygen demand bottom sediments neglected	—	+1.7	—	+3.0	—	+3.1	—	+2.8	—	+3.2	—	-1.4
Photosynthesis, daily fluctuations, rate of scour of bottom deposits and rate of sedimentation assumed zero	—	0.0	—	+2.7	—	+0.6	—	+0.4	—	0.0	—	-1.9
All above variables zero except biological oxidation rate of attached organisms in stream	—	+1.7	—	+3.4	—	+2.6	—	+2.0	—	+2.9	—	-1.4
Streeter-Phelps equation; all above variables zero	—	+1.9	—	+4.0	—	+3.6	—	+2.9	—	+3.3	—	-1.4

*By eliminating photosynthesis and daily fluctuations in waste loads, only average dissolved oxygen values can be computed.

importance, average daily figures are inappropriate and, consequently, most predictive models are unsatisfactory for estimating the effects of waste discharges on downstream dissolved oxygen values.

In the case studied, some of the necessary input data were determined by fitting the computer output to the observed DO concentrations. Although such an ex post facto examination is helpful in verifying the reliability of the model, in the usual case it is the output, and not the input, that is to be determined. Furthermore, it is recognized that the quantification of variables in the above fashion may lead to discrepancies attributable to what may be called the "lumper" effect. Nevertheless, the mathematical model presented herein appears to be much more realistic than the predictive models previously developed. The inherent ability of the digital computer to rapidly solve complex mathematical models allowed for all possible modifications to the oxygen-sag analysis to be incorporated where data were available. The model's applicability to a large range of stream and waste conditions is apparent, and its practicability is limited only by the lack of physical data.

Standard techniques are available for the identification of many of the parameters involved, for example, biochemical oxidation rates, settling rates, and areal benthal oxygen demand. Others may be more difficult to quantify, such as the rate p of addition of BOD from the benthos, and the rate a of biological oxygen production. It is evident that a specialist is required who, given the types and the density of aquatic plants and organisms, the rate of solar energy input, and stream depth, turbidity, and temperature, can predict the rate at which the local biota will produce and consume oxygen.

The data limitations mentioned above might at first appear to preclude any successful application of the analytical technique prescribed in this study. In view of these limitations, it is suggested that the most conclusive results would be obtained if the model were to be applied in a fashion similar to that described in the case study. The conditions existing in a stream below a point of waste discharge can be described mathematically by Equation 18, and the necessary data can be estimated by fitting to observed DO and BOD concentrations. The model can then be used most advantageously to determine what improvements in the stream environment would be made possible by greater dilution; additional storage which may provide either greater detention, more uniform effluent release, or both; and any other changes in plant operating or streamflow regulating practices.

SUMMARY AND CONCLUSIONS

An expression has been developed which will predict the spatial and temporal variations in the dissolved oxygen concentration in streams and rivers. A case study, assisted by digital computer techniques, demonstrates the efficacy of the equations, given the proper set of input conditions. As with any mathematical model of the physical environment, its limitations must be clearly understood, namely, input data specification, and application and interpretation of the model.

The input data required for complete utilization of the mathematical model indicate that current stream survey practices do not provide sufficient data to adequately describe biological and physical responses in a stream. New emphasis should be directed to collecting data along the lines indicated by the sensitivity analysis; namely, extent and oxygen demand of the sediments, the biological extraction rate of attached organisms in the stream, and the maximum rate of oxygen production (consumption) by photosynthesis (respiration). Diurnal fluctuations in waste loads, variations in reaction rates, and photosynthetic action in the stream have stronger effects on resulting conditions than many in the sanitary engineering profession have been led to believe. The study indicates the need for changing present predictive techniques used in evaluating pollution effects.

ACKNOWLEDGMENTS

The investigators are indebted to Dr. Clarence J. Velz of the University of Michigan, who furnished the data on the Flint River which made it possible to check the mathematical model against field observations. The study was conducted under a National Institutes of Health Grant (No. WP-00597) to the Sanitary Engineering Research Laboratory of the University of California at Berkeley.

REFERENCES

(1) Streeter, H. W., and E. B. Phelps. *A Study of the Pollution and Natural Purification of the Ohio River*. Public Health Bulletin 146. Washington, D.C.: U.S. Public Health Service (1925).

(2) Dobbins, W. E. "BOD and Oxygen Relationships in Streams," Proceeding Paper 3949, *J. Sanit. Engr. Div. ASCE, 90*(SA3), 53 (June 1964).

(3) Camp, T. R. *Water and Its Impurities*. New York: Reinhold Publication Corporation (1963).

(4) Li, W. "Unsteady Dissolved-Oxygen Sag in a Stream," Proceeding Paper 3129, *J. Sanit. Engr. Div. ASCE, 88*(SA3), 75 (May 1962).

(5) O'Connor, D. J. "The Effect of Stream Flow on Waste Assimilation Capacity," *Proceedings*, Seventeenth Purdue Industrial Waste Conference (May 1962).

(6) Thomann, R. V. "Mathematical Model for Dissolved Oxygen," Proceeding Paper 3680, *J. Sanit. Engr. Div. ASCE, 89*(SA5), 1 (October 1963).

(7) Velz, C. J., and J. J. Gannon. "Biological Extraction and Accumulation in Stream Self-Purification." Paper presented at International Conference on Water Pollution Research, London (1962).

(8) Hansen, W. W., and R. J. Frankel. *Economic Evaluation of Water Quality, A Mathematical Model of Dissolved Oxygen Concentration in Freshwater Streams*. Second Annual Report, Sanitary Engineering Research Laboratory Report Number 65-11. Berkeley: Sanitary Engineering Research Laboratory, University of California (August 1965).

(9) Velz, C. J. "Significance of Organic Sludge Deposits," *Oxygen Relationships in Streams*, Proceedings of Seminar, Water Supply and Water Pollution Program, Robert A. Taft Sanitary Engineering Center, 47 (March 1958).

(10) Frankel, R. J. *Economic Evaluation of Water Quality: An Engineering-Economic Model for Water Quality Management*. First Annual Report. Sanitary Engineering Research Laboratory Report Number 65-3. Berkeley: Sanitary Engineering Research Laboratory, University of California (January 1965).

(11) Lynch, W. O. Discussion of "BOD and Oxygen Relationships in Streams," by W. E. Dobbins, *J. Sanit. Engr. Div. ASCE, 91*(SA1), 82 (February 1965).

(12) Water Resources Commission, State of Michigan. *Report on Oxygen Relationships of Flint River: 1959 Survey, Flint to Montrose* (April 1960).

(13) Coventry, F. L., Plant Supervisor, Sewage Treatment Plant, Flint, Michigan. Private Communication (July 1964).

(14) Vallillo, A. L., Resident Engineering, Consoer, Townsend, and Associates, Chicago, Illinois. Private Communication (July 1964).

(15) Owens, M., R. Edwards, and J. W. Gibbs. "Some Reaeration Studies in Streams," *Inter. J. Air Water Poll., 8*, 469 (1964).

(16) Rand, M. C. "Laboratory Studies of Sewage Effects on Atmospheric Reaeration," *Sewage Ind. Wastes, 31*(10), 1197 (October 1959).

(17) Gunnerson, C. G., and T. E. Bailey. "Oxygen Relationships in the Sacramento River," Proceeding paper 3619, *J. Sanit. Engr. Div. ASCE, 89*(SA4), 95 (August 1964).

SECTION TWO

NEW CONCEPTS IN BIOLOGICAL WASTE TREATMENT

RESEARCH DEVELOPMENTS IN REGARD TO CONCEPT AND BASE VALUES OF THE ACTIVATED SLUDGE SYSTEM

Karl Wuhrmann
Swiss Federal Institute of Technology, Zurich, Switzerland

INTRODUCTION

Since any biological waste treatment system (aerobic and anaerobic) is in essence a continuous fermentation process, it can be completely described by algebraic means. Consequently, all causal relationships between plant operation parameters and plant performance needed by the design engineer should be strictly derivable. Mathematical description and numerical evaluation of continuous fermentations are possible, however, only with one-species fermentations and where flow conditions, composition and concentration of substrate, as well as other pertinent ecological conditions affecting bacterial growth, are strictly constant. None of these basic requirements is fulfilled in practical operation of treatment plants for the purification of domestic or industrial wastes. In view of the imperative need for exploiting the inherent possibilities of biological treatment processes to their very limits, an attempt has albeit to be made to apply the already established rules of continuous fermentations to the special case of waste purification. It is the author's conviction that further progress in this field will be possible only by research in line with theoretical considerations, and by use of existing purification plants for reference to a much higher extent. This implies however a reliable record of those few measurements indispensable to assessing plant performance in terms of the parameters requested and justified by theory. It is the purpose of this paper to demonstrate that the algebraic formulation used in fermentation is widely applicable in the practice of sewage purification even though some fundamental suppositions required by theory are not fulfilled. The basic assumptions which have to be made in shifting from pure culture fermentations to the field of waste treatment are (a) the entity of activated sludge in a plant is looked upon as if it would be a single species of organisms, and (b) entire groups of organic compounds in a waste may be regarded as "limiting substrate." The last assumption is reasonably valid for the total dissolved organic carbon compounds in domestic sewage; in industrial wastes a specific dominating pollutant may take this position.

Extensive use of the fermentation theory in the activated sludge field has already been made by Downing and his group (1–3) in view of nitrification in sewage purification. In industrial waste treatment, application on an experimental basis has been attempted by Evans and Kite (4) (gas liquors), Leibnitz and Schulze (5), and Behrens and Klappach (6) (soft coal pyrolysis wastes). In the United States, Schulze (7) has recently discussed the activated sludge process on the basis of fermentation theory.

THE INFLUENCE OF OPERATION PARAMETERS ON ACTIVATED SLUDGE TREATMENT PERFORMANCE: OBSERVATIONS AND INTERPRETATIONS

The experimental material used for this discussion has been extensively reviewed elsewhere (8); for detailed information on techniques and methods we refer to this paper. The respective experiments with the activated sludge process were executed in pilot plants on a technical scale (aerator volume 6–10 m^3, population equivalent of treated sewage up to about 800). Three dependant variables were tested at three levels, namely hydraulic load (ca. 9, 29, 59 $m^3/m^3/d$), mixed liquor suspended solids (ca. 600, 3,600, and 6,000 ppm) and oxygen concentration in the mixed liquor (ca. 1, 4, and 7 ppm). This set of 3^3 assays was repeated at a temperature range of 13–17°C. (mean = 16.3°) and 9–11°C. (mean = 10°), respectively. Within each temperature block, the twenty-seven experiments were completely randomized as far as their serial execution within a period of approximately five years is concerned. Three experiments could be done at one time (three identical plants were used). Each single assay was run for at least six to eight weeks, the first three to four weeks being used for achieving steady state operation with the parameters requested, and the second three to four weeks representing the observation period with intensive analytical investigations. Automatically collected 24-hour composite samples, which were deep frozen during the sampling period, served for analysis. In each assay nine samples were evaluated. All operation parameters, sludge measurements, and other factors were recorded daily. The experiment thus represents a complete block factorial design with fifty-four individual assays in two temperature blocks. With this arrangement the main action of each dependant variable is tested in nine parallels within one temperature block. The interactions of two variables are observed with three parallels respectively. There is only one experiment, however, for each set of interactions of three variables. This means that the result of one single assay within the entire experiment will have a considerable variance. Comparisons between single assays (for instance in Table 24) are therefore not recommended and should be made only after full consideration of the statistical error of their results. The experimental plan allowed a strictly statistical evaluation of the observations, and all figures presented in this paper are given with their variance or their confidence limits.

TABLE 24

PERCENT OF REMOVAL OF ORGANIC C IN THE FACTORIAL EXPERIMENT

Temperature > 13°C.						Temperature < 11°C.					
O_2 mg/l	Mixed Liq. Concentr. mg/l	Hydraul. Load $m^3/m^3/d$ 58	29	9	S*	O_2 mg/l	Mixed Liqu. Concentr. mg/l	Hydraul. Load $m^3/m^3/d$ 58	29	9	S*
1	600	49.0	63.5	64.0	176.5	1	600	30.4	46.2	57.7	134.3
	3,300	71.4	79.5	85.4	236.3		3,300	64.5	72.4	81.3	218.2
	6,000	74.5	71.0	85.0	230.5		6,000	67.0	71.7	78.5	217.2
	S	194.9	214.0	234.4	643.3		S	161.9	190.3	217.5	569.7
4	600	70.0	75.4	66.7	212.1	4	600	38.8	53.2	60.0	152.0
	3,300	70.0	81.5	80.4	231.9		3,300	59.5	70.0	79.1	208.6
	6,000	75.8	83.7	86.4	245.9		6,000	65.8	71.2	79.0	216.0
	S	215.8	240.6	233.5	689.9		S	164.1	194.4	218.1	576.6
7	600	61.8	65.4	70.4	197.6	7	600	36.1	48.6	63.6	148.3
	3,300	75.4	78.0	79.0	232.4		3,300	61.6	63.7	73.4	198.7
	6,000	78.9	79.8	83.6	242.3		6,000	72.2	67.7	78.6	218.5
	S	216.1	223.2	233.0	672.3		S	169.9	180.0	215.6	565.5
	S 600	180.8	204.3	201.1	586.2		S 600	105.3	148.0	181.3	434.6
	S 3,300	216.8	239.0	244.8	700.6		S 3,300	185.6	206.1	233.8	625.5
	S 6,000	229.2	234.5	255.0	718.7		S 6,000	205.0	210.6	236.1	651.7
	S total	626.8	677.8	700.9	2,005.5		S total	495.9	564.7	651.2	1,711.8

*S = sum.

In the following tables on the analysis of variance, the significance of results is judged conventionally for various probability levels as follows:

$$
\begin{aligned}
P &\leq 0.01 = \text{very high significance} \\
&\leq 0.05 = \text{highly significant} \\
&\leq 0.10 = \text{significant} \\
&< 0.10 = \text{insignificant}
\end{aligned}
$$

Summary of Observations

Removal of Organic C, Organic N, and BOD

In the following tables (see also Appendix) all values are assembled which will be used for further discussion. For additional information we refer to the earlier paper (8). Pertinent analytical measures for presedimented raw sewage and treated effluent comprised suspended solids (total and volatile), organic carbon, organic nitrogen, inorganic nitrogen compounds, total and phosphate phosphorus, and BOD. Sludge analysis comprised total and volatile solids, organic carbon, organic nitrogen, and total phosphorus. Since BOD values are meaningless for any metabolic consideration as well as for material balances (it is no parameter for substrate concentration or substrate amounts), most of the evaluations have been based exclusively on organic carbon, organic nitrogen, or dry solids.

As an example for the arrangement of the entire experimental series, Table 24 gives the complete set of the average percent removal of organic carbon in each assay. Indicated values for the operation parameters (dependant variables) correspond to the experimental plan, their actual magnitude differing only slightly from the design values.

The only reliable method for a comparative evaluation of such a large set of obsevations is the analysis of variance. Tables 25 and 26 represent this statistical treatment for the observations on organic carbon removal for the combined set of fifty-four assays as well as for each temperature block. The following conclusions are obvious from the two tables:

1. Even the small temperature difference (average 6.3°C.) between the two blocks exerts a highly significant influence on purification performance.

TABLE 25

ANALYSIS OF VARIANCE OF PERCENT OF REMOVAL OF ORGANIC C, CONSIDERING BOTH TEMPERATURE BLOCKS (54 ASSAYS)

Variance	DF	SSQ	MSQ	f	P
Temperature t	1	1,597.40	1,597.40	80.60	$\ll 0.001$
x_1'	2	4,025.75	2,012.87	101.60	$\ll 0.001$
R_h	2	1,462.75	731.37	36.90	$\ll 0.001$
O	2	79.64	39.82	2.01	> 0.100
$t \cdot x_1'$	2	242.13	121.06	6.11	0.005
$t \cdot R_h$	2	202.40	101.20	5.10	0.010
$t \cdot$ O	2	50.39	25.19	1.27	> 0.100
Residual	40	791.87	19.79		
Total	53	8,452.33	–		

DF = degrees of freedom
SSQ = sums of squares
MSQ = mean squares
f = variance ratio
P = probability of null hypothesis

TABLE 26

ANALYSIS OF VARIANCE OF PERCENT OF REMOVAL OF ORGANIC C, SPLITTING BETWEEN TEMPERATURE BLOCKS (2 × 27 ASSAYS)

Variance	DF	SSQ	MSQ	f	P
Summer ($\bar{t}$ = 16.3°C.)					
x_1'	2	1,147.08	573.54	28.30	$\ll$0.001
R_h	2	319.46	159.73	7.88	< 0.005
O	2	123.05	61.52	3.04	< 0.100
Residual*	20	404.88	20.24		
Total	26	1,994.47	—		
Winter ($\bar{t}$ = 10°C.)					
x_1	2	3,120.80	1,560.40	80.60	$\ll$0.001
R_h	2	1,345.69	672.84	34.70	$\ll$0.001
O	2	6.98	3.49	0.18	$\gg$0.100
Residual*	20	386.99	19.34		
Total	26	4,860.46	—		

*Interactions within temperature blocks not significant; their SSQ has been pooled with the residual variance.

2. Detention time and mixed liquor concentrations are determining factors for plant performance.

3. Mixed liquor oxygen concentration is of no significance within the limits of about 1–7 ppm at low temperatures. At high temperatures the plant efficiency is somewhat lower at 1 ppm than at 4 ppm.

4. It is of special interest that no significant interaction between the dependant variables exists, or in other words, that each of the four parameters is acting independently on plant performance. Although in full agreement with theory, this result is somewhat surprising in a complicated ecological system such as an activated sludge plant. It may be, however, that in this series of technical experiments certain interactions have been hidden by many additional and uncontrollable factors affecting the system.

We shall not discuss in detail the results concerning the removal of organic nitrogen and BOD. In essence the same fundamental observations as for organic C are valid and we restrain to reproduce a summary of percent removals in Table 27. All results of experiments at various oxygen levels but with equal load and mixed liquor concentrations have been averaged in this table, due to the fact that oxygen mostly exerted no statistically significant influence.

Sludge Production

Table 28 summarizes the total solids released from the plant as excess sludge plus suspended solids in the final effluent under the various operation conditions. The suspended solids represent an essential part of excess sludge production which has to be considered in any theoretical evaluation of plant performance. Unfortunately this parameter is frequently neglected in plant operation records. As a result no reliable material balance can be established, and hence some indispensable process constants can not be evaluated. The chemical composition of the excess sludges is found in Table 29. These figures are of great value for the interpretation of the mechanism of sludge production, as will be shown.

TABLE 27

MEAN VALUES OF PERCENT OF REMOVAL OF ORGANIC C, ORGANIC N, AND BOD*

(a) Organic C

Temp.	x_1'	Hydraul. Load 58	29	9	Confid. Limit (P = 0.1)
>13°C.	600	60.3	68.1	67.0	± 4.2
	3,300	72.3	79.7	81.6	
	6,000	76.4	78.2	85.0	
<11°C.	600	35.1	49.3	60.4	± 5.0
	3,300	61.9	68.7	77.9	
	6,000	68.3	70.2	78.7	

(b) Organic N

Temp.	x_1'	Hydraul. Load 58	29	9	Confid. Limit (P = 0.1)
>13°C.	600	50.3	55.7	63.2	± 7.8
	3,300	71.2	70.8	80.6	
	6,000	74.3	78.8	85.6	
<11°C.	600	36.8	43.8	60.1	± 9.4
	3,300	59.8	66.4	75.1	
	6,000	65.0	71.9	83.2	

(c) BOD

Temp.	x_1'	Hydraul. Load 58	29	9	Confid. Limit (P = 0.1)
>13°C.	600	68.4	79.3	85.9	± 5.5
	3,300	86.3	90.1	91.1	
	6,000	85.4	88.7	91.4	
<11°C.	600	50.3	57.1	79.3	
	3,300	82.3	84.9	92.7	± 4.4
	6,000	84.3	87.4	91.5	

*Each figure represents the average of N = 3 × 3 = 9 assays; values at the three oxygen levels have been pooled; x_1' = mixed liquor solids concentrations ppm.

Interpretation of Results

Although the theoretical basis of continuous fermentation systems which will be used for interpretation of the above results has been repeatedly published, a short abstract of the main assumptions and algebraic deductions may be useful.

Theory

Three assumptions form the basis of any algebraic description of a fermentation system. They may be formulated as follows:

I. The rate of multiplication of bacterial populations is proportional to the cells already present, that is, each cell is dividing at the same rate:

$$dx/dt = \mu x \tag{1}$$

II. The actual rate of multiplication is a fraction of the maximum rate that could occur when each indispensable nutrient would be in unlimited supply. When one indispensable substrate component is available in growth-limiting concentrations only, the multiplication rate depends on the concentration of this limiting factor in the following way:

TABLE 28

EXCESS SLUDGE PRODUCTION (g DRY SOLIDS/m^3 SEWAGE AND g ORGANIC C/m^3 SEWAGE AT HYDRAULIC LOADS OF 9–58 $m^3/m^3/d$ AND MIXED LIQUOR SUSPENDED SOLIDS OF 600–6000 PPM*

ppm O in Mix. Liqu.	Temperature <11°C. Without Effl. Ss.	Temperature <11°C. Total	Temperature >13°C. Without Effl. Ss.	Temperature >13°C. Total
	Dry Solids g/m^3			
1 mg O/l	69 ± 20**	118 ± 14	90 ± 16	101 ± 15
4	84 ± 20	121 ± 14	73 ± 16	99 ± 15
7	60 ± 20	105 ± 14	62 ± 16	95 ± 15
Mean	70 ± 12	115 ± 8	74.8 ± 9	102 ± 9
	Organic Carbon g/m^3			
1 mg O/l	24.0 ± 6.6	40.3 ± 4.9	30.2 ± 5.6	37.7 ± 6.0
4	29.1 ± 6.6	41.7 ± 4.9	27.1 ± 5.6	34.3 ± 6.0
7	19.9 ± 6.6	35.3 ± 4.9	22.1 ± 5.6	34.2 ± 6.0
Mean	24.2 ± 3.9	39.1 ± 2.9	26.5 ± 5.6	35.4 ± 3.4

*Excess sludge production not significantly different at the various levels of mixed liquor suspended solids and hydraulic loads.

**$\pm a$ = confidence limit at $P = 0.1$.

TABLE 29

ANALYSIS OF EXCESS SLUDGE

(a) Overall Average of Assays within Temperature Blocks.

	Temp. <11°C.	Temp. >13°C.	Difference between Temp. Blocks ($P = 0.1$)
Ash %	36.00	32.76	
Ignit. loss %	64.00 ± 2.72*	67.24 ± 2.72	highly significant
Org. C %	33.98 ± 1.84	34.43 ± 1.84	not significant
Total N %	4.97 ± 0.96	5.78 ± 0.96	highly significant**
Total P %	1.27 ± 0.52	1.48 ± 0.52	not significant
Total K %	0.40 ± 0.16	0.43 ± 0.16	not significant

*$\pm s$ = standard deviation of the mean values, calculated from all 54 assays.

**Highly significant dependency on operation parameters within temperature blocks, see Table 29b.

(b) Average Nitrogen Content of Excess Sludge at Hydraulic Loads of 9–58 $m^3/m/d$ and at Mixed Liquid Oxygen Concentrations of 1, 4, and 7 ppm.

Mix. Liqu. Susp. Sol. ppm	Temp. <11°C. %	Temp. >13°C. %
600	3.66	4.91
3,300	5.22	6.17
6,000	6.14	6.26

Confidence limits at $P = 0.1$: ± 0.22 percent.

$$\mu = \mu_m \frac{s}{K_s + s} \tag{2}$$

as postulated and experimentally sustained by Monod (9).

III. In each cell formed, the same amount of substrate is incorporated. This amount is a fraction of the total amount of substrate utilized, the other part being used for energy metabolism. Cell build-up and substrate utilization are then connected as follows:

$$x - x_0 = Y(s_r - s) \tag{3}$$

It has to be clearly understood that the postulates I–III represent nothing more than expressions reasonably fitting the experimental observations. The obvious similarity of Equation 2, for instance, with the Michaelis-Menten equation for the rate of enzymatic reactions, does not mean that growth rates and enzymatic reaction rates are identical. It is therefore nonsense and quite misleading when considerations of enzymatic reaction kinetics are introduced into our complex system of mixed biocenosis and more or less unknown substrate solutions. Equation 2 is just a convenient expression, incidentally more or less valid also with activated sludge in contact with wastes. The same precaution is necessary when using Equation 3 and the so-called yield factor. As will be explained later, this formula is convenient for expressing excess sludge production. It would be completely wrong, however, to assume that Y is a constant value and that it is only the incorporated fraction (in the true physiological sense) of the substrate disappeared from the medium. Y has to be considered as a proportional factor, the detailed meaning of which in an activated sludge system is variable and complex.

Summarizing this introduction, the author wishes to stress the opinion in behalf of the engineers that an algebraic expression, fitting biological observations satisfactorily and seemingly logically, very rarely represents the actual reactions or their rates which are suggested by the type of formulation. In the case of waste fermentations it is especially unsound to derive the type of reactions which might be involved from data correlating convincingly with a mathematical formulation. This does not discriminate against mathematical descriptions of the processes, however; the algebraic expressions are always to be considered as empirical.

With the above three fundamental assumptions any continuous fermentation system may be formulated (see for instance Herbert [10, 11]). For steady state conditions in a system with complete mixing in the areation basin and with sludge recirculation, the following derivations are found:

a) substrate (pollution) utilization:

$$s_r - s = x_1 \cdot \bar{t}(1 + a) \cdot \frac{\mu}{Y_S} \tag{4a}$$

or

$$s_r - s = x_1 \cdot \bar{t}(1 + a) \cdot \frac{s}{K_S + s} \tag{4b}$$

b) cell build-up ("excess sludge production"):

$$x_2 = Y_S(s_r - s) \tag{5}$$

Using Equations 1–5, the conventional terms of percent of substrate removal (purification efficiency), of sludge load, and of the relationship between these magnitudes can be rationally expressed as follows:

Percent substrate removal:

$$\eta = \frac{s_r - s}{s_r} = x_1 \cdot \bar{t}(1 + a) \cdot \frac{\mu}{s_r \cdot Y_S} \tag{6}$$

It must be kept in mind that this expression is valid exclusively for components in the substrate solution, which are biodegradable and hence are subject to the metabolic activity of the organisms in the purification system. Low removal percentages in a treatment plant may have two reasons therefore:

1. High proportions of nondegradable substances in the waste which nevertheless are included in the normally applied overall analytical parameters, or
2. Nonoptimal operation of the plant. Equation 6 shows that with a waste of constant average composition and concentration (i.e., the value of the fraction $\mu/s_r \cdot Y_S$ being roughly a constant), the percent removal is essentially related to the product of detention time and mixed liquor concentration. Since the growth rate and the yield factor are involved, both being strongly dependent on the physiological value of the polluting material, comparisons of percent removals between plants treating different kinds of wastes are normally not recommended.

The term "sludge load," introduced by Haseltine (12) as a convenient parameter for assessing the efficiency of an activated sludge system, is defined in terms of the above expressions as

$$S_b = \frac{s_r}{x_1 \cdot \bar{t}(1 + a)} \tag{7}$$

Percent removal as a function of sludge load is then

$$\eta = \frac{1}{S_b} \cdot \frac{\mu}{Y_S} \tag{8}$$

or in other words: the percent removal is in theory inversely proportional to sludge load, the quotient of actual growth rate and the yield factor being the proportional factor. Again the relationship is valid only for one and the same waste. In practice all dominantly domestic sewages are chemically close enough (irrespective of concentration differences) to provide for similar yield factors and growth rates. The use of the relationships in Equations 6 and 8 for dimensioning purposes is reasonable therefore, provided the "constant" μ/Y_S has been thoroughly established.

Observed Removal Efficiencies in Function of Plant Operation

In Figure 50 the observations in the factorial experiment for both temperature blocks and for the analytical values of organic C, organic N, and BOD are assembled. For practical purposes sludge load is plotted on a logarithmic scale, which leads to a distortion of the hyperbolic function indicated by Equation 8. It is seen that temperature affects removal percentages to a considerable extent at the higher sludge loads and that this influence disappears at very low loads. The reason is that metabolic rates cannot be affected by temperature in a situation where the amount of nutrients applied to the system is more effective as a limiting factor than temperature. The curves for the three analytical parameters are definitely different. This is understandable because the quotient μ/Y_S in terms of organic C, organic N, or BOD must be different. Finally we find from Figure 50 that the assays at various hydraulic loads (detention times) fit the curves well, as required by theory, due to the fact that the average composition of the sewage has been the same in the entire set of experiments. It is obvious that with a waste, allowing, for instance, higher growth rates than domestic sewage, the curves will be shifted to the right (to higher sludge loads). As an example, percent BOD removals from the treatment of paper mill wastes have been plotted in the same way, together with our results in Figure 51. Qualitatively, the hyperbolic relationship is again found.

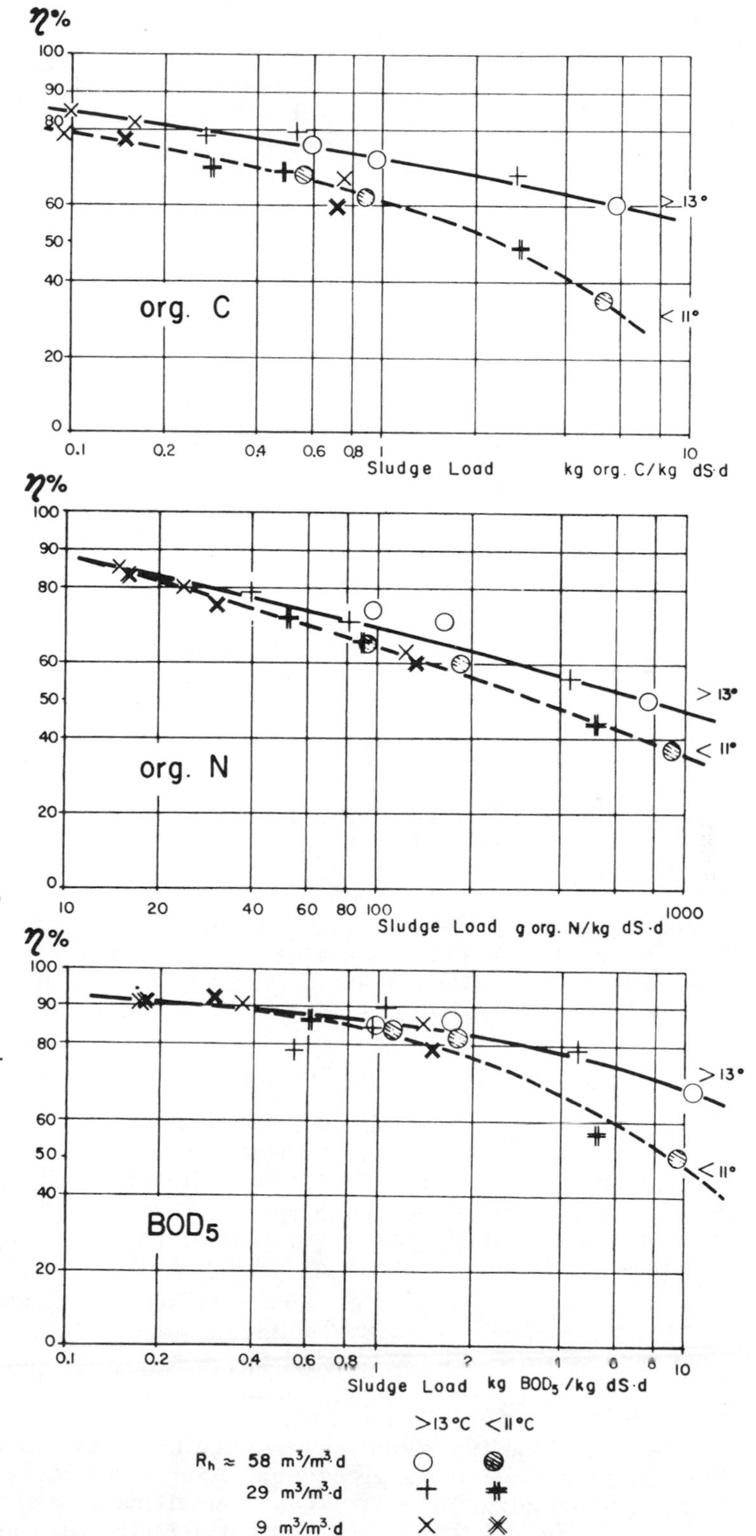

Figure 50. Percent removal of organic carbon, organic nitrogen, and BOD at two temperature levels in the factorial experiment. Indicated are the mean values of assays at the three oxygen levels investigated. From Wuhrmann (8).

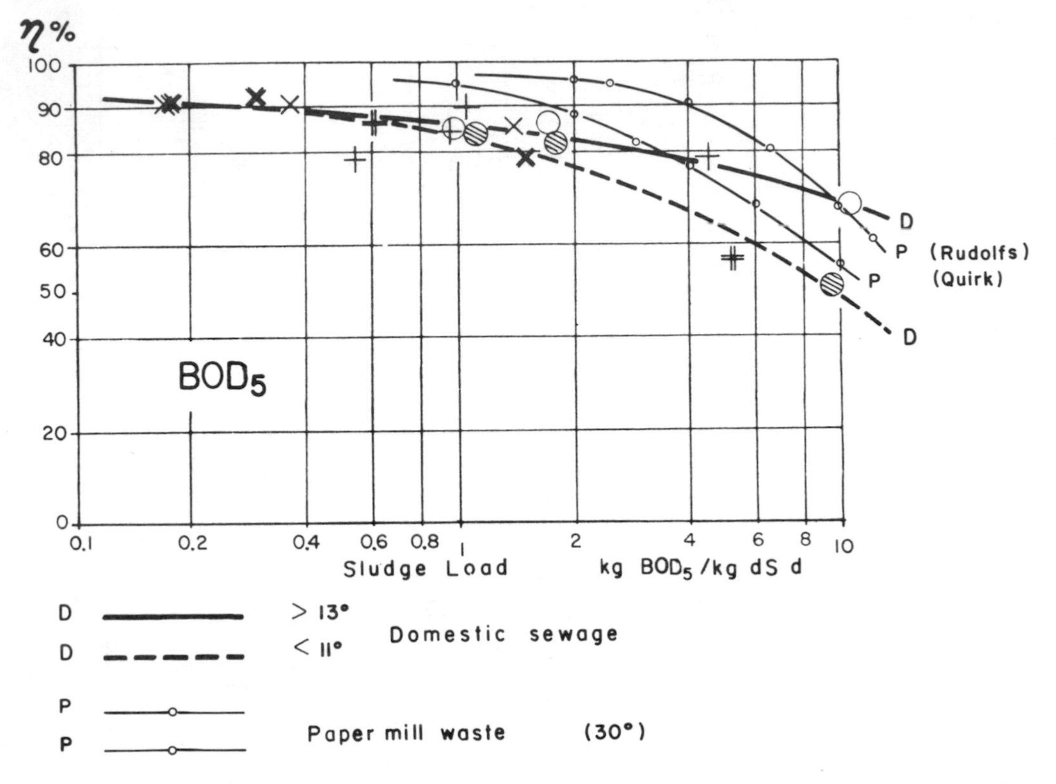

Figure 51. Percent removal of BOD, as in Figure 50. Similar relationships indicated for paper mill waste from investigations by Rudolfs *et al.* (21) and Quirk *et al.* (20).

The logical fitting of the experimental data to the function required by theory demonstrates that an activated sludge system is amenable to theoretical evaluation. Full use of this fact can be made, however, only on the basis of carefully collected numerical values of essential parameters, such as growth rates, and yield factors, for various wastes.

Excess Sludge Production in Function of Operation Parameters

Various relationships for the calculation of excess sludge production in the activated sludge system have been suggested. Equation 5, however, is the only rational expression which can be formulated. It has to be generalized for a system into which decomposable and undecomposable suspended solids are introduced and where growth effects may be partly compensated by autolysis of organisms or by predators. Equation 5 may therefore be rewritten as follows:

$$\begin{matrix}\text{gross sludge} \\ \text{increase}\end{matrix} = \begin{matrix}\text{organism} \\ \text{growth}\end{matrix} + \begin{matrix}\text{undecomp. susp.} \\ \text{solids from infl.}\end{matrix} - \begin{matrix}\text{loss by} \\ \text{autolysis} \\ +\text{ predators}\end{matrix}$$

$$x_2' = Y_S\,(s_r - s) - Y(s_r^* - s^*) + i_s - \lambda \cdot x_1 \qquad (9)$$

In essence this equation has already been proposed by Eckenfelder and O'Connor (13). Only the values of the gross yield factor Y_S are directly available from plant operation data. The respective observations in our experiments are given in Table 30. Since detention time exerted no statistically significant influence,

TABLE 30

MEAN VALUES OF THE GROSS YIELD FACTOR Y_S (g ORGANIC C IN TOTAL SOLIDS RELEASED/g ORGANIC C REMOVED) AT HYDRAULIC LOADS OF 9–58 $m^3/m^3/d$

	Temp. 11°C			Temp. 13°C.		
ppm O in ML						
ML susp. sol. ppm	1	4	7	1	4	7
600	0.86*	0.76	0.77	0.79	0.69	0.68
3300	0.82	0.80	0.77	0.77	0.67	0.57
6000	0.64	0.66	0.51	0.75	0.52	0.44
Mean		0.73**			0.66	

*Confidence limit for single values at P = 0.1:± 0.068.
**Confidence limit for means at P = 0.1:± 0.058.

the Y_S values of all assays with identical hydraulic loads were averaged. For practical needs the mean yield factor for sludge production in terms of organic carbon may be estimated to Y_S = 0.66 at temperatures of 13–17°C. and to Y_S = 0.73 at 9–11°C., respectively. Since the carbon content of excess sludge was normally around 35 percent, a conversion to dry solids production is easily possible.

Table 30 suggests a consistent decrease of the gross yield factor with increasing temperature and mixed liquor concentration. It decreases also to a slighter degree with increasing oxygen tension. None of these effects is to be expected from Equation 5, which means that the second and third terms of the generalized Expression 9 must be subject to variation in function of external factors. Temperature and the concentration of the mixed liquor are evidently significant factors affecting the amount of excess sludge. This is substantiated, for instance, by the nitrogen content of the excess sludges, produced at various operation conditions (Table 29b).

Assuming an average nitrogen content of 2 percent for the primary suspended solids carried into the aeration basin and of 7 percent for a pure bacterial mass (dry solids basis), values for the "true biological yield factor" Y and for undecomposed primary solids in the excess sludge i_s can be calculated (algebraic derivation see Wuhrmann [8]). Estimates of Y and their analysis of variance (Table 31) show immediately that the magnitude of Y is independent from the operation conditions in a plant, as is to be expected from physiological considerations and Equation 5. In accord with the above remarks it must be concluded, that the variance of the observed gross yield factors Y_S is obviously due to the terms i_s and $\lambda \cdot x_1$ in Equation 9. Calculation of the proportion of i_s as a percentage of dry weight of the excess sludge leads to the interesting result of Table 32. Although the numerical values in this table may be subject to a considerable error due to the somewhat arbitrary assumption underlying the calculation, they demonstrate conclusively the fundamental difference in sludge composition formed under various operation conditions. It is especially remarkable that the primary suspended solids in domestic sewage are extensively metabolized in an activated sludge system with low sludge loads.

The data gathered in our experiments unfortunately do not allow any reliable estimate of the important term for the sludge loss due to autolysis or predator action. It would be highly desirable to find a relationship between the magnitude

TABLE 31

ESTIMATES OF THE "TRUE BIOLOGICAL YIELD FACTOR" IN THE AERATION BASIN AT TEMPERATURES ABOVE 13°C.

(a) Analysis of Variance

Variance	DF	SSQ	MSQ	f	P
R_h	2	54,721	27,360	0.71	<0.5>0.3
x_1'	2	57,724	28,862	0.75	<0.5>0.3
O	2	148,726	74,363	1.92	<0.3>0.1
Residual	20	770,314	38,515		
Total	26	1,031,485	—		

(b) Mean Values Overall Levels of Hydraulic Loads and Mixed Liquor Suspended Solids

ppm O in Mix. Liqu.	Y_s	Confid. Limit at $P = 0.1$
1	0.685	
4	0.581	± 0.122
7	0.504	
Mean (27 Assays)	0.590	± 0.070

TABLE 32

ESTIMATES OF PERCENT PRIMARY SUSPENDED SOLIDS IN SLUDGE AT TEMPERATURES ABOVE 13°C.

(a) Analysis of Variance

Variance	DF	SSQ	MSQ	f	P
R_h	2	91.89	45.94	0.27	≫0.300
x_1	2	5,458.94	2,729.47	15.99	< 0.001
O	2	703.34	351.67	2.06	< 0.3 >0.1
Residual*	20	3,419.58	170.97		
Total	26	9,673.75	—		

*Interactions not significant.

(b) Mean Values at Hydraulic Loads of 9–58 $m^3/m^3/d$

ppm O in ML / ML Sol. ppm	1	4	7	Mean Overall O-Conc. (9 Assays)
600	54.2	34.5	44.8	44.5
3,300	25.3	22.6	9.5	19.1
6,000	16.6	9.8	6.6	6.6

Confidence limits at $P = 0.1$ for means of 3 assays = ± 14.14; of 9 assays = ± 8.18; of 27 assays = ± 4.70.

of $\lambda \cdot x_1'$ and the operation conditions, enabling much better predictions of excess sludge production than the presently available data.

BACTERIAL GROWTH RATES IN AN ACTIVATED SLUDGE PLANT

No estimate has ever been published on growth rates of the microbes in activated sludge under the conditions of actual plant operation. It is indeed very difficult to make measurements on any individual species occurring in the mixed population. Assuming all living bacteria in the sludge as a physiologically homogenous entity, however, we may get to an estimate of μ as an overall average figure. Equation 9 contains in its first term at the right side an expression for the net bacterial growth

$$R_h \cdot Y \cdot (s_R^* - s^*) = \mu \cdot x^* \quad (10)$$

when

$$x^* = x_1' - p \cdot x_2' \quad (11)$$

and p is the fraction of primary solids in the excess sludge (for estimates see Table 32). The equation may be rewritten and μ isolated to give

$$\mu = R_h \cdot \frac{x_2'(1 - p) + \lambda \cdot x_1'}{x_1' - p \cdot x_2'} \quad (12)$$

Again the unknown term $\lambda \cdot x_1'$ for sludge loss is hindering a numerical evaluation of Expression 12 in which all other values are observable. A rough estimate of an overall growth rate μ may be made, however, in the following way: at very high sludge loads (e.g., mixed liquor concentrations of 600 ppm dry solids or approximately 204 ppm organic C) and low oxygen tensions (for instance 1 ppm) the unknown term $\lambda \cdot x_1$ is presumably rather small. A value of 0.1 for λ will probably be adequate. At operation conditions with $x_1 = 600$ and $0 = 1$, we find from Table 33 a value for p of approximately 50 percent and from Table 29 a gross excess sludge production of approximately 37 g. organic C/m^3 treated sewage. Equation 12 yields, then,

$$\mu = 0.21 \cdot R_h [d^{-1}]$$

This estimate leads to an overall "mean generation time" of the sludge organisms of about 7.9 hours at $R_h = 10$ m^3/m^3/d, and of about 1.3 hours at a load of 59 m^3/m^3/d. These are only orders of magnitudes; they demonstrate, however, that domestic sewage of ordinary concentration represents an extremely poor growth medium in comparison to the nutrient solutions normally used for the cultivation of saprophytic bacteria, in which generation times around $t_D = 0.3–0.5$ hours may be observed under optimal conditions. We are coming to the conclusion, therefore, that the growth potential of the sludge organisms is used only to a very small extent in the conventional activated sludge process. This situation must necessarily be accepted, because the true limiting factor—which cannot be changed in practice—is the low nutrient concentration of the medium.

ESTIMATE OF THE OXYGEN CONSUMPTION RATE IN AN ACTIVATED SLUDGE PLANT

The preceding theoretical discussion finds a further, direct application in the estimation of the oxygen consumption in an aeration basin, and hence in the calculation of the necessary oxygen input to be required from an aeration device. A number of empirical rules have been published for this estimate but no causal approach to the problem is available. The presently used calculation method (see

TABLE 33

ENDOGENOUS RESPIRATION OF ACTIVATED SLUDGES FROM THE FACTORIAL EXPERIMENT

(a) Analysis of Variance of All Fifty-Four Assays

Variance	DF	SSQ	MSQ	f	P
Temperature t	1	77.04	77.04	17.60	< 0.001
R_h	2	12.43	6.22	1.42	$\gg 0.100$
x_1	2	429.20	214.60	94.00	< 0.001
O	2	2.46	1.23	0.28	$\gg 0.100$
$t \times R_h$	2	7.73	3.86	0.88	$\gg 0.100$
$t \times x_1$	2	8.62	4.31	0.98	$\gg 0.100$
$t \times O$	2	41.04	10.52	2.40	> 0.100
Residual	40	175.46	4.38		
Total	53	746.25	—		

(b) Mean Values of Endogenous Respiration at 25°C. and *p*H 7.5 in mg O/g Dry Solids per Hour. Pooled Values of Assays at Hydraulic Loads of 9–58 m^3/m^3/m/d and Oxygen in the Mixed Liquor of 1–7 ppm

Mixed Liquor Susp. Solids ppm	Temp. in Mixed Liquor		Proportion Summer/Winter
	<11°C.	>13°C	
600	19.2	16.9	0.88
3,300	16.1	13.0	0.87
6,000	12.0	10.2	0.85

Confidence limit at $P = 0.1$:± 1.28 mg O/g dS hr.

for instance Eckenfelder and O'Connor [13], or Emde [14]) introduced by Smith (15) is based on the assumption that the total amount of oxygen respired by a microbial population is the sum of the so-called endogenous respiration and the substrate respiration. It is rather doubtful whether this assumption is physiologically sound, and the controversy on this subject between microbiologists is still going on. It serves practical needs and available computation methods quite well, however, and may be adopted therefore for our purpose.

The necessary oxygen input W_c into an aeration basin must be equivalent to the total oxygen consumption q_g, and in addition it has to maintain the required oxygen concentration c in the mixed liquor

$$W_c = \frac{c_s}{c_s - c} \cdot q_g \qquad (13)$$

Assuming the total consumption to be

$$q_g = q_e + q_s \qquad (14)$$

adequate numerical values for q_e and q_s have to be found. In assessing q_s, two components have to be considered: (a) the respiration of organic compounds by the heterotrophic organisms in the sludge, and (b) the respiration of inorganic ions by certain autotrophic species. In practical operation only nitrification, that is, the microbial oxidation of ammonia and nitrite, will be important. The following discussion is based on an earlier publication of the author on this subject (16), in which additional material and literature may be found.

Endogenous Respiration of Activated Sludge in Function of Plant Operation Data

As will be seen below, an extensive discussion of endogenous respiration is necessary because it represents a pertinent item in the total oxygen utilization of the system. Numerical values on endogenous respiration rates of activated sludges have been published frequently. Consistent correlation of such data with plant operation is lacking, however, to a large extent. Orford, Heukelekian and Isenberg (17) found a linear relationship on plotting endogenous respiration rate Q_{O_e} versus log of sludge load (with BOD). The individual values showed a remarkable variance. These observations differ considerably from our data, which are partly summarized in the following tables and figures. It must be remembered that, according to the definition of endogenous respiration, reliable measurements can be made only (a) with carefully washed sludge, resuspended in adequate buffer solutions, (b) in relatively dilute suspensions (less than 2,000 ppm [18]), and (c) with an apparatus which guarantees the distribution equilibrium between water and gas phase at any time during the experiment. In the author's opinion these requirements are satisfied only by an adequate technique with micromanometers (Barcroft or Warburg type). The data discussed below have been gathered at standard conditions of *p*H 7.5 (phosphate buffer) and at the temperature of 25°C.

In each individual assay of the factorial experiment mentioned before, the endogenous respiration rate, as well as the respiration of the activated sludge fed with raw sewage, was measured at six different days in triplicate runs. A total of 972 results could be evaluated. Table 33 represents the analysis of variance of all estimations. It demonstrates conclusively that only the temperature and the solids concentration of the mixed liquor exert a significant influence on the endogenous respiration rate of the sludge. This conclusion allows a considerable consolidation of the data, in so far as they might be averaged over all hydraulic loads and oxygen levels. The resulting mean respiration rates Q_{O_e} at 25°C. are given in Table 33 with their confidence limits. The proportion of respiration rates of the "summer" and "winter" sludges is also indicated. Correlating the average respiration values with the respective sludge load (BOD) leads to Figure 52, which indicates a sharp fall of oxygen utilization rates when the sludge load is passing below the limit of about 1.5 kg BOD/kg dry solids/day. Very small loads of less than 0.5 kg BOD/kg dS/d are producing sludges consuming oxygen at rates less than about 5 mg O/g dS/hr at 25°C. Plotting these data on a logarithmic scale, as Orford *et al.* (17), results in an S-shape curve with asymptotic approximations of Q_{O_e} = 1.5 to 2.5 mg O/g dS/hr at sludge loads of less than 0.06 kg BOD/kg dS/d and of Q_{O_e} = c. 17 mg O/g dS/hr at loads of more than 1.3 kg BOD/kg dS/d (neglecting the influence of hydraulic load).

In plotting Q_{O_e}-values against sludge age we find Figure 53. Sludge age is defined as the theoretical detention time of a sludge particle in the entire system, that is, total sludge mass divided by the daily excess sludge release (suspended solids in the effluent included). Irrespective of the considerable scattering, the trend of an asymtotic decrease of respiration rate with increasing sludge age is obvious, and the higher oxygen consumption of winter sludges is again indicated.

The presently available data permit—at least for activated sludges developed with predominantly domestic sewage—a sufficiently precise determination of the endogenous respiration component in Equation 14. Since endogenous O_2-requirement is strictly proportional to the mixed liquor concentration we find

$$q_e = Q_{O_e} \cdot x_1 \quad \text{(g O/m}^3\text{ basin vol/hour)} \qquad (15)$$

Q_{O_e} at the temperature of t°C. is found from the standard values (determined at

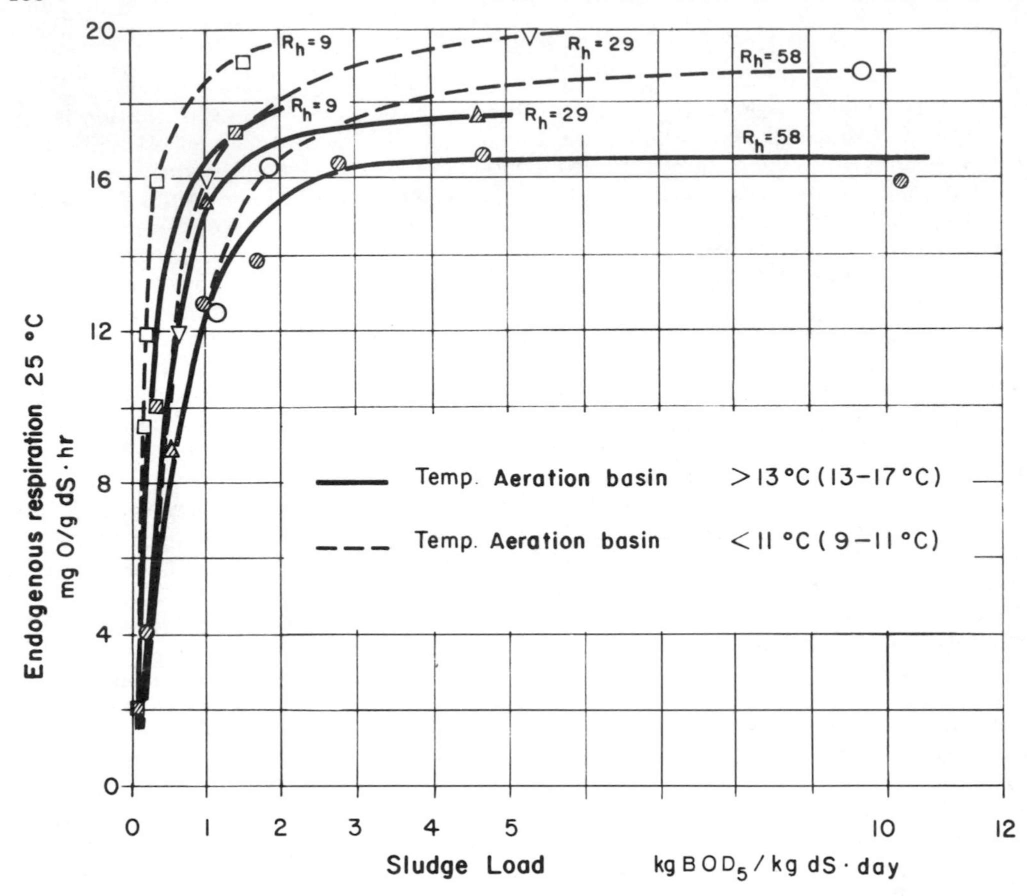

Figure 52. Endogenous respiration of activated sludge (standard conditions) in function of sludge load with BOD. Observations from the factorial experiment. Assays conducted under identical sludge loads but different oxygen tension in the mixed liquor have been averaged. From Wuhrmann (8).

25°C.) by calculation, using an average temperature factor of $\theta_{10°} = 2$. The large variation of Q_{Oe} with operation conditions of a plant definitely discourages the use of a fixed value for endogenous respiration in any calculation, as is proposed with the formula given by Smith (15), Eckenfelder (13), or Emde (14).

Substrate Respiration

O-Requirement for the Oxidation of Organic Compounds

For the time being there exists only one possibility for a strictly causal estimation of substrate respiration, namely the consideration of the general metabolic pathway of organic carbon compounds in the activated sludge system as a whole. In most general terms we might postulate the following pattern of carbon utilization:

total organic C resorbed by sludge $C_{tot.} = s_{rC} - s_C$

organic C incorporated in cells $C_s = Y(s_{rC} - s_C)$

hence organic C respired $C_r = (1 - Y)(s_{rC} - s_C)$

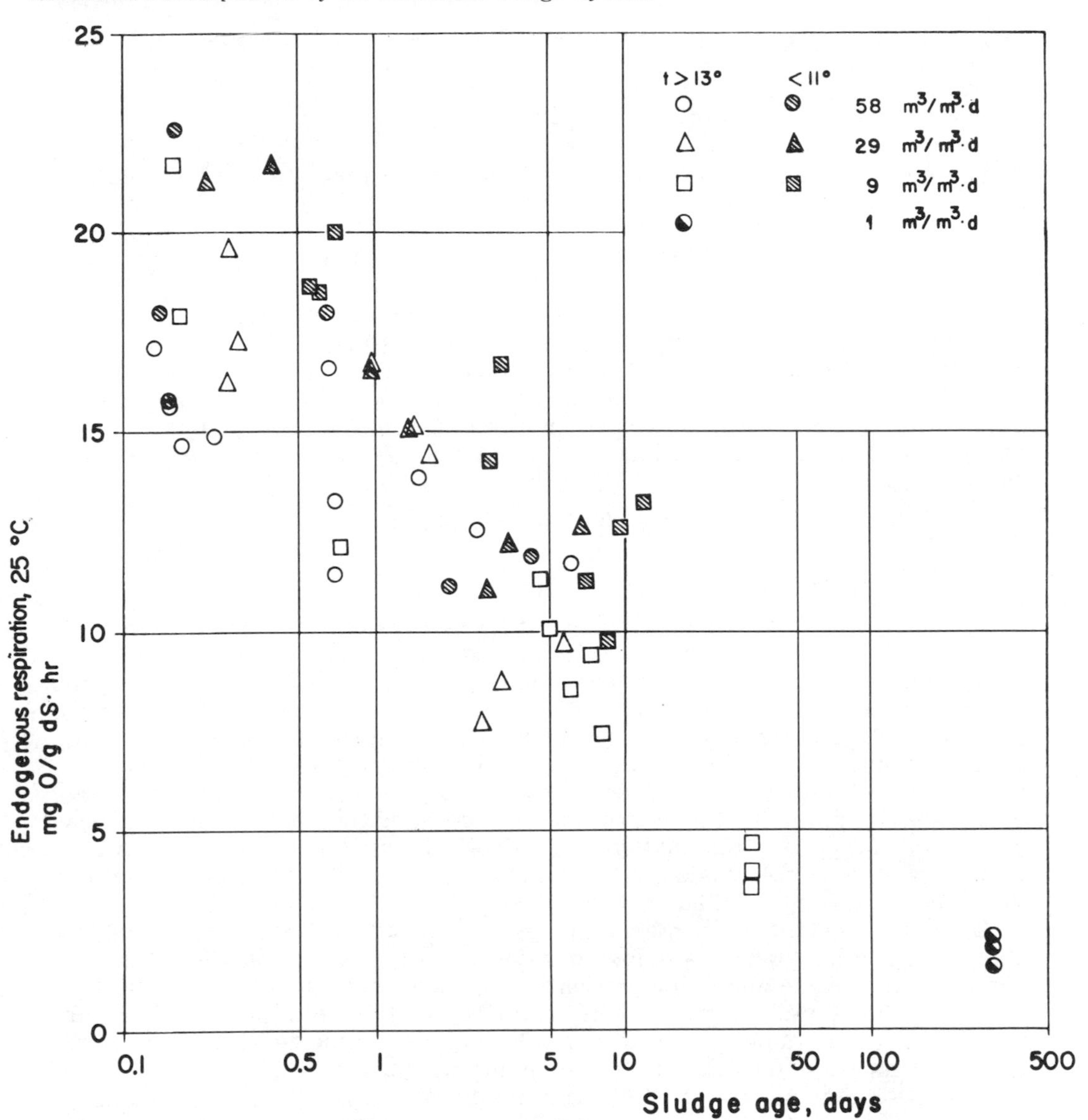

Figure 53. Endogenous respiration of activated sludges (standard conditions) of various sludge ages. Observations from the factorial experiment and additional assays conducted under comparable conditions in the experimental station. From Wuhrmann (16).

Since incorporated organic C can be measured in terms of excess sludge only, we have to replace the net biological yield factor Y by the gross yield factor Y_S (see Eq. 9). This operation also prevents the double accounting for the substrate used in endogenous respiration. To transfer the amount of organic C respired into amounts of oxygen used, we have to assume that all this C reappears in the form of CO_2 as the only end product. We may then use the respiration quotient

$$r_q = \frac{\text{mol } CO_2 \text{ evolved}}{\text{mol O used}}$$

as a factor for the estimation of the oxygen consumed. Substrate respiration rate is then

$$Q_{Os} = (1 - Y_S)(s_{r_C} - s_C)\frac{1}{r_q} \text{ mol O/mol C} \tag{16a}$$

Transferring to weight units, the oxygen consumption rate per volume aeration basin amounts to

$$q_S = 0.11 \cdot \frac{R_h}{r_q}(1 - Y_S^*)(s_{r_C} - s_C) \text{ g O/m}^3 \text{ basin/hour} \tag{16b}$$

Values for the respiration quotient have been determined at various occasions in our sludge respiration studies. A summary of the findings is compiled in Table 34. Emphasizing additionnal estimates with respiration substrates other than domestic sewage, it is proposed to use a value of $r_q = 0.65$ for the calculation of substrate respiration under normal conditions of municipal sewage purification. Since Y_S is found to be approximately 0,7, Equation 16b simplifies for average design purposes to

$$q_S = 0.051 \cdot R_h \cdot (s_{rC} - s_C) \tag{17}$$

Oxygen Requirement for Nitrification

All design formulae published in the literature neglect completely the oxygen consumption caused by the oxidation of ammonia and nitrite. This is a fundamental mistake, because it is not possible to prevent the growth of nitrifying organisms in a sewage plant, unless the treated waste carries some specific inhibitor for these bacteria. Most plant operators think that no nitrification is occurring in their plant when neither nitrite nor nitrate can be found in the effluent. Since these oxidation products are readly reduced to N_2 under the normal operation conditions of an activated sludge plant of conventional design, the concentration of nitrate in the final effluent is no criterion for the degree of nitrification. The only reliable basis for this judgment would be the change of the ammonia concentration from influent to effluent.

Some ammonia nitrogen entering the plant is used in cell synthesis. The observable amount of ammonia loss is rather small, however, in view of the quantities of organic nitrogen compounds which are decomposed and are partly liberating the nitrogen in the form of ammonia. Under operation conditions, preventing any measurable nitrification, the loss of NH_4^+ in the aerator amounts generally to much less than 20 percent of the inflowing quantity.

Designating the amount of ammonia N respired to NO_3 as $(s_{r_N} - s_N)$, and considering nitrate as the only end product of the oxidation, the quantity of oxygen consumed amounts to

$$Q_{O_N} = 4.6\,(s_{r_N} - s_N) \text{ g/m}^3 \text{ sewage}$$

and the consumption rate per unit basin volume is then

$$q_N = 0.19\, R_h\,(s_{r_N} - s_N) \text{ g O/m}^3 \text{ basin per hour} \tag{18}$$

where $(s_{r_N} - s_N)$ has to be measured as g NH_4 - N/m³ sewage.

Emphasis of nitrification in the calculation of total oxygen consumption presupposes some idea of whether nitrification will occur under the operation conditions considered. The fundamental investigations by the group of Downing (1–3) in England have deepened our prevailing knowledge on this subject to such an extent that prediction of nitrification is readily possible within certain limits. Assuming no inhibition of the nitrifying bacteria by components in the sewage, the

TABLE 34

RESPIRATION QUOTIENTS r_q OF ACTIVATED SLUDGES AT VARIOUS OPERATION CONDITIONS OF THE AERATION BASIN. TREATMENT OF MUNICIPAL SEWAGE.

Plant Operation Data						Q_{Oe}* mg O/g dS/hr	r_q** = $\frac{Mol\ CO_2}{Mol\ O}$	
Hydr. Load $m^3/m^3/d$	BOD Load $kg/m^3/d$	Mix. Liqu. Susp. Sol. ppm	Sludge Load kg BOD/kg dS/d	O in ML. ppm	Temp. in ML °C.		Endog.	With Raw Sewage***
90.0	10.80	2,280	4.720	4.0	15.0	16.70	0.62	0.62
60.0	7.20	2,600	2.770	4.0	15.0	16.50	0.63	0.68
10.6	1.30	6,950	0.190	3.5	13.4	4.05	0.63	0.58
10.6	1.30	7,080	0.180	3.5	16.4	3.74	0.55	*0.43*
10.6	1.30	7,100	0.180	3.0	16.8	4.72	0.63	0.61
1.0	0.12	6,570	0.018	6.0	16.0	1.62	0.60	0.65
1.0	0.12	7,500	0.016	6.0	16.0	1.98	0.61	0.65
1.0	0.12	7,740	0.016	6.0	16.0	2.30	0.56	*0.69*
Mean value							0.61	*0.63*

*Q_{Oe} = endogenous respiration of washed sludge resuspended in PO_4-buffer at 25°C.

**$\bar{r}_q$ = respiration quotient average value within the first two hours of observation.

***r_q with raw sewage = respiration quotient at substrate respiration after addition of 1 ml. double concentrated settled sewage to 2 ml. of sludge suspension.

fundamental parameter for the development of a sizeable population of these organisms in the activated sludge is the dilution rate of the sludge, that is, the proportion of the amount of sludge present in the system and the sludge released from the plant $x_1/R_h x_2$. This expression is identical with the definition of sludge age used previously. The English authors have also shown on a theoretical and experimental basis that nitrification goes almost to completion as soon as the conditions for the build-up of a population of nitrifiers are satisfied. Figure 54 demonstrates the amount of nitrification in terms of percent ammonia elimination in the high temperature block of our factorial design experiment. The graph indicates that by passing the critical limit of the sludge age of 1.5 to 2 days, more or less complete ammonia oxidation occurs under the conditions of the strength of our sewage. This limit is at the much higher sludge ages of around five days with lower temperatures (8–11°C.) of the mixed liquor.

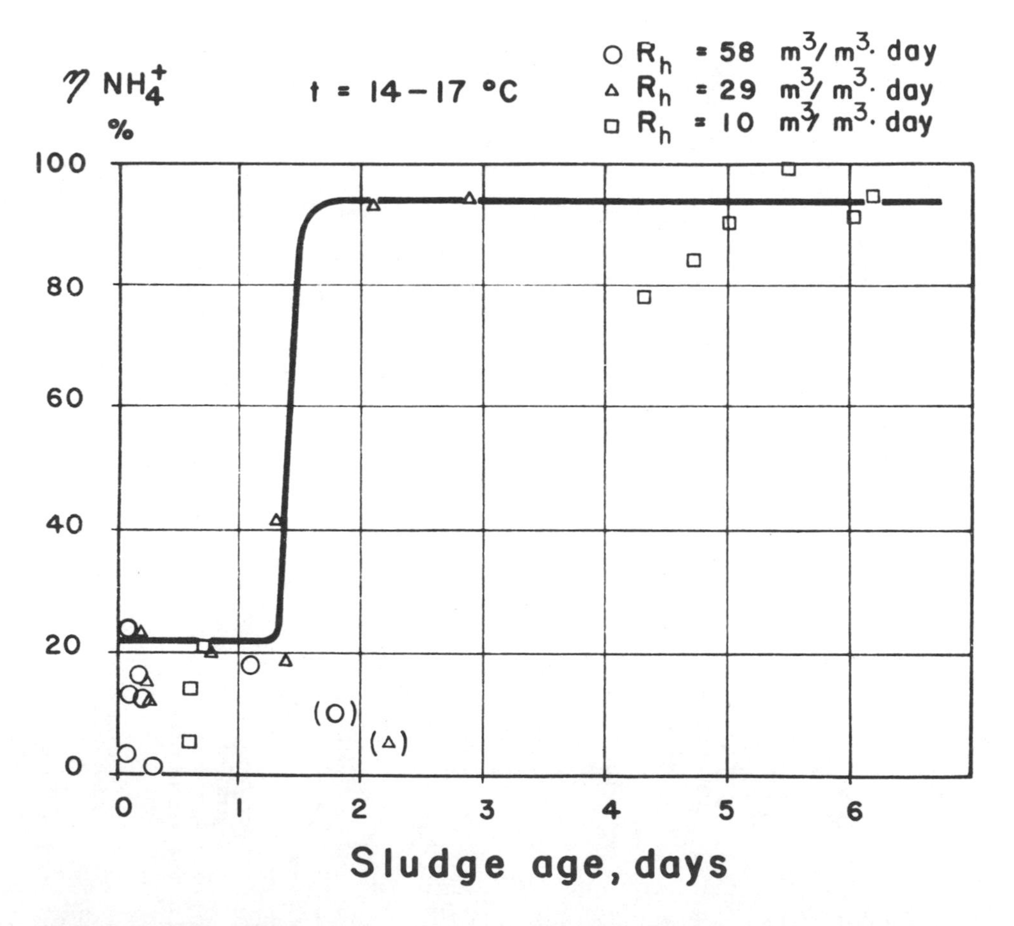

Figure 54. Removal of ammonia in activated sludge treatment of the sewage of the city of Zurich at temperatures between 14° and 17°C. in relationship to sludge age. Points in brackets are from assays in which full development of a nitrifying flora was not observed due to a too short operation period of the plant. From Wuhrmann (16).

Total Oxygen Consumption in the Aeration Basin

The necessary oxygen input into an aeration basin W_c, at an oxygen concentration of c ppm in the mixed liquor can now be explicitly indicated by introducing into Equation 13 the expressions of Equations 15, 16b, and 18:

$$W_c = \frac{c_s}{c_s - c}\left[Q_{Oe}\,x_1 + 0.11\,\frac{R_h}{r_q}(1 - Y_S)(s_{r_c} - s_c) + 0.19 \cdot R_h(s_{r_N} - s_N)\right] \text{[g O/m}^3\text{ basin volume/hr]} \quad (19a)$$

where Q_{Oe} and c_s have to be calculated for the temperature in the aeration basin. The highest mean temperatures to be expected in the mixed liquor should be considered for the evaluation of W_c because respiration rates are decreasing, and saturation values increase with decreasing temperature.

The general Equation 19a simplifies for plants treating dominantly domestic sewage by using Equation 17 to:

$$W_c = \frac{c_s}{c_s - c}\left[Q_{Oe}\,x_1 + 0.051\,R_h(s_{r_c} - s_c) + 0.19\,R_h(s_{r_N} - s_N)\right] \quad (19b)$$

It is rather difficult to compare the above equations with those indicated by earlier authors, who relied exclusively on BOD values. As far as settled raw city sewage is concerned, an approximate proportion between organic C content and BOD may be indicated. In our investigation we found a BOD/organic C relationship of about 1.8–1.9. In Cleveland, Schaffer *et al.* (19) found a proportion of 1.87. The two values correspond amazingly well. Regarding biologically treated sewage, however, we came to a nearly 1:1 or 1.2:1 proportion, whereas the investigation at Cleveland led to no difference between treated and untreated sewage. We have no explanation for this decrepancy; it indicates however that the introduction of BOD into Equations 19a or 19b will be dangerous and eventually rather misleading.

CONCLUSIONS

Although activated sludge plants or trickling filters are extremely complicated biological systems, as soon as we dig into the details their main features can be traced easily. The experimental data demonstrate that an evaluation on the basis of simple theories of continuous fermentation leads to relationships between operation parameters and operation results which are qualitatively consistent with theoretical requests. Concerning quantitative aspects, numerical values for the pertinent coefficients have been found for the treatment of municipal sewage of dominantly domestic origin. It is no problem to find the necessary data also for types of wastes by experimentation.

Reviewing the literature, one frequently gets the impression that too complicated thinking and sophisticated evaluation of nonessential data have produced unnecessary confusion for the design engineer, as well as for many experimental researchers. A more thorough emphasis of the basic concept of continuous operation is needed, especially in the research field of industrial waste treatment. Empery and intuition may be fruitful in many instances; they are, however, seldom the most economical approach to investigations of systems where numerous variables and —possibly their interactions are involved. In this respect the theoretical concepts—duly emphasizing the restrictions imposed by the variability of the practical conditions—offer at least a working hypothesis which permits an efficient experimental solution of practical problems. Some fundamental conditions have to be fulfilled however: (a) only true continuous systems disclose the necessary basic coefficients; it is hopeless to arrive at consistant results by means of draw and fill systems or other batch treatment methods; (b) analytical methods are required which indicate reliably the substrate concentrations. BOD is an unfit tool for this purpose. The best parameter presently available for the characterization of wastes and biological sludges is organic carbon. This measure also gives a quantitative figure for the amount of organic pollution not removed in a plant.

The present data have revealed two essential lacunae in our knowledge of the activated sludge system, namely (a) reliable figures for the growth rates of the bulk of the sludge organisms in function of waste characteristics and plant operation, and (b) the magnitude of the "sludge loss factor" under various conditions. A deeper insight into these two problems would make easier many predictions on plant behavior needed by the practician.

SUMMARY

The influence of hydraulic load, solids and oxygen concentration, and the temperature of the mixed liquor on the performance of the activated sludge process was investigated. A complete block factorial design experiment had been arranged, where the independent variables were tested at three levels (temperature at two levels). The set of 2×3^3 assays was evaluated on the basis of the theory of continuous fermentation in a completely mixed reactor.

The main actions and interactions of the independent variables on removal of organic carbon, organic nitrogen, and BOD, as well as on the production of excess sludge, were studied. Estimates of the gross yield factor in terms of organic carbon for the calculation of excess sludge quantities are given. The growth rate of the bulk of the sludge organisms is discussed. A causal formula is derived for the determination of oxygen consumption in an aerator, and the necessary numerical values for endogenous and substrate respiration in function of plant operation parameters are presented on the basis of experimental observations.

APPENDIX

SYMBOLS USED

a = proportion of recirculated sludge based on raw sewage flow
c = actual oxygen concentration in mixed liquor [ppm]
c_s = oxygen saturation concentration in mixed liquor [ppm]
η = fraction of substrate removed (purification effect)
i_s = primary suspended solids in the activated sludge [ppm]
K_s = concentration of limiting substrate for half maximum growth rate μ_m [ppm]
λ = fraction of activated sludge solids lost by autolysis or metabolism by predators
μ = growth rate [t^{-1}]
μ_m = maximum growth rate when all essential nutrients are in excess [t^{-1}]
p = fraction of primary suspended solids in the excess sludge
q_g = total oxygen consumption rate of mixed liquor per unit aeration basin volume [g O/m^3/h]
q_e = endogenous oxygen consumption rate [g O/m^3/h]
q_S = substrate oxygen consumption rate [g O/m^3/h]
q_N = oxygen consumption rate for ammonia oxidation [g O/m^3/h]
R_h = hydraulic load of aeration basin [m^3/m^3/d]
R_b = pollution load of aeration basin (organic carbon, organic nitrogen, BOD) [kg/m^3/d]
r_q = respiration quotient
S_b = sludge load (based on dry solids, dS) [kg/kg dS/d]

s = concentration of limiting substrate in effluent of an aeration basin [ppm]
s_r = concentration of limiting substrate in presedimented raw sewage [ppm]
t = time [h] or [d]
$\bar{t}$ = mean detention time in aeration basin based on sewage flow [h] or [d]
W_c = oxygen input into an aeration basin at an oxygen concentration of mixed liquor of c ppm [g O/m³/h]
x = organism concentration in general [ppm]
x_1 = organism concentration in a completely mixed fermentor [ppm]
x_1' = mixed liquor concentration in an activated sludge system [ppm]
x_2 = organism concentration in the liquid leaving a fermentation system [ppm]
x_2' = excess sludge concentration of an activated sludge system when all leaving solids are supposed to be suspended in the total effluent flow [ppm]
Y = yield coefficient (factor) of bacterial growths
Y_S = gross yield factor of an activated sludge system

Suffixes C, N, or B indicate organic carbon, organic nitrogen, or BOD, respectively.

TABLE 35

ORGANIC CARBON—PLANT LOAD, SLUDGE LOAD, AND PERCENT REMOVAL. MEAN VALUES FROM NINE COMPOSITE TWENTY-FOUR-HOUR SAMPLES PER ASSAY

	Mixed Liquor		Temp. >13°C.			Temp. <11°C.		
	ppm O	ppm Susp. Solids	Hydraul. Load m³/m³/d			Hydraul. Load m³/m³/d		
			58	29	9	58	29	9
Plant load kg/m³/d	1	600	3.69	1.48	0.43	3.72	1.59	0.58
		3,300	3.05	1.86	0.57	2.79	1.36	0.49
		6,000	3.43	1.54	0.58	4.43	1.59	0.44
	4	600	4.11	2.07	0.54	3.56	2.24	0.56
		3,300	3.06	1.83	0.55	2.69	—	0.57
		6,000	3.67	1.53	0.66	2.34	1.59	0.60
	7	600	3.05	2.12	0.49	3.77	1.79	0.37
		3,300	3.45	1.71	0.48	3.44	1.85	0.43
		6,000	3.45	1.72	0.66	3.12	1.74	0.70
Sludge load kg/kg dS/d	1	600	5.74	2.18	0.67	5.63	2.65	0.88
		3,300	0.94	0.55	0.17	0.82	0.41	0.15
		6,000	0.57	0.25	0.09	0.77	0.26	0.07
	4	600	5.86	3.09	0.84	5.07	3.28	0.83
		3,300	0.92	0.54	0.17	0.78	—	0.17
		6,000	0.61	0.26	0.11	0.38	0.26	0.10
	7	600	4.53	2.99	0.76	5.32	2.80	0.47
		3,300	1.01	0.51	0.14	1.03	0.56	0.13
		6,000	0.57	0.29	0.11	0.52	0.32	0.12
% removal	1	600	49.00	63.50	64.00	30.40	46.20	57.70
		3,300	71.40	79.50	85.40	64.50	72.40	81.30
		6,000	74.50	71.00	85.00	67.00	71.70	78.50
	4	600	70.00	75.40	66.70	38.80	53.20	60.00
		3,300	70.00	81.50	80.40	59.50	—	79.10
		6,000	75.80	83.70	86.40	65.80	71.20	79.00
	7	600	61.80	65.40	70.40	36.10	48.60	63.60
		3,300	75.40	78.00	79.00	61.60	63.70	73.40
		6,000	78.90	79.80	83.60	72.20	67.70	78.60

TABLE 36

ORGANIC NITROGEN—PLANT LOAD, SLUDGE LOAD, AND PERCENT REMOVAL. MEAN VALUES FROM NINE COMPOSITE SAMPLES PER ASSAY

	Mixed Liquor		Temp. >13°C. Hydraul. Load $m^3/m^3/d$			Temp. <11°C Hydraul. Load $m^3/m^3/d$		
	ppm O	ppm Susp. Solids	58	29	9	58	29	9
Plant load $g/m^3/d$	1	600	495.0	231.0	72.0	604.0	283.0	95.0
		3,300	474.0	291.0	80.0	652.0	302.0	88.0
		6,000	576.0	249.0	92.0	586.0	311.0	104.0
	4	600	611.0	308.0	92.0	762.0	296.0	104.0
		3,300	494.0	257.0	92.0	598.0	—	122.0
		6,000	575.0	227.0	98.0	539.0	310.0	83.0
	7	600	451.0	273.0	79.0	525.0	384.0	86.0
		3,300	488.0	288.0	72.0	640.0	301.0	96.0
		6,000	593.0	243.0	86.0	556.0	323.0	93.0
Sludge load g/kg dS/d	1	600	769.0	340.0	112.0	914.0	472.0	145.0
		3,300	146.0	85.8	23.5	192.0	90.7	26.7
		6,000	96.3	41.1	15.3	102.0	51.0	17.4
	4	600	870.0	460.0	143.0	1084.0	434.0	153.0
		3,300	149.0	76.4	28.0	175.0	3.0	36.0
		6,000	95.9	38.5	16.1	87.2	50.3	13.8
	7	600	670.0	485.0	123.0	741.0	600.0	110.0
		3,300	143.0	85.6	21.0	192.0	90.7	29.4
		6,000	98.8	41.6	14.3	92.7	59.3	15.8
% removal	1	600	42.4	54.6	55.5	46.7	45.1	61.3
		3,300	68.4	70.9	85.6	60.6	68.2	75.4
		6,000	73.0	71.0	87.0	58.4	70.3	88.2
	4	600	61.0	64.4	64.7	40.3	36.9	56.8
		3,300	65.1	75.6	75.5	54.4	—	75.6
		6,000	70.7	79.5	86.2	66.0	71.3	87.0
	7	600	47.5	48.1	69.4	23.4	49.4	62.1
		3,300	80.1	66.0	80.6	64.4	62.1	74.2
		6,000	79.3	86.0	83.5	70.6	74.2	74.5

REFERENCES

(1) Downing, A. L., H. A. Painter, and G. Knowles. "Nitrification in the Activated Sludge Process," *J. Proc. Inst. Sewage Purif.*, 2–25 (1963).

(2) Downing, A. L., and A. B. Wheatland. "Fundamental Considerations in Biological Treatment of Effluents," *Trans. Inst. Chem. Engr.*, *40*, 91–103 (1962).

(3) Downing. A. L., and A. P. Hopwood. "Some Observations on the Kinetics of Nitrifying Activated Sludge Plants," *Schweiz. A. Hydrol.*, *26*, 271–288 (1964).

(4) Evans, Ch. G. T., and S. Kite. "Further Experiments on the Treatment of Spent Liquors by Homogenous Continuous Culture," *Proceedings*, 3rd Symposium, Prague (1962), pp. 299–309, on continuous cultivation of microorganisms. Prague: Czechoslowak. Acad. Sci. (1964).

(5) Leibnitz, F., and R. Schulze. "Studies on Continuous Fermentation of Phenosolvan-extracted Industrial Effluents from Soft Coal Pyrolysis by a Strain of *Rhodotorula glutinis*," *Proceedings*., 3rd Symposium, Prague (1962), pp. 311–315. Prague: Czechoslowak. Acad. Sci. (1964).

TABLE 37

BOD—PLANT LOAD, SLUDGE LOAD, AND PERCENT REMOVAL. MEAN VALUES FROM NINE COMPOSITE SAMPLES PER ASSAY

	Mixed Liquor		Temp. >13°C.			Temp. <11°C.		
	ppm O	ppm Susp. Solids	Hydraul. Load $m^3/m^3/d$			Hydraul. Load $m^3/m^3/d$		
			58	29	9	58	29	9
Plant load $kg/m^3/d$	1	600	6.11	2.65	0.79	6.39	3.04	1.00
		3,300	5.44	2.71	1.35	5.25	3.30	0.95
		6,000	6.96	2.82	0.85	7.44	3.97	0.84
	4	600	6.66	3.35	1.07	6.65	3.76	1.06
		3,300	5.59	4:31	1.12	6.53	—	1.06
		6,000	5.35	3.95	1.07	6.68	3.96	1.10
	7	600	7.84	4.10	0.89	6.94	3.35	1.06
		3,300	5.75	3.48	1.25	6.51	3.18	1.05
		6,000	5.23	2.87	1.28	5.98	3.29	1.18
Sludge load kg/kg dS/d	1	600	9.49	3.90	1.23	9.68	5.06	1.52
		3,300	1.67	0.80	0.39	1.55	0.99	0.29
		6,000	1.17	0.46	0.14	1.29	0.65	0.14
	4	600	9.49	5.00	1.67	9.45	5.51	1.56
		3,300	1.80	1.31	0.35	1.92	—	0.31
		6,000	0.89	0.67	0.16	1.08	0.64	0.18
	7	600	11.60	5.78	1.40	9.80	5.23	1.36
		3,300	1.68	1.03	0.36	1.95	0.95	0.32
		6,000	0.87	0.49	0.21	0.99	0.60	0.20
% removal	1	600	56.20	79.00	80.00	40.90	50.50	82.70
		3,300	87.50	89.40	94.00	81.40	84.10	92.40
		6,000	85.40	84.00	90.50	82.00	91.10	92.30
	4	600	75.80	82.70	90.70	52.20	57.40	76.90
		3,300	80.50	92.60	91.00	86.00	—	93.90
		6,000	87.20	89.20	93.20	87.00	91.80	94.90
	7	600	73.20	76.20	87.00	57.90	63.50	78.20
		3,300	91.00	88.50	88.50	79.50	83.60	92.00
		6,000	83.70	93.00	90.50	83.80	80.30	86.80

(6) Behrens, U., and G. Klappach. "Prediction of Flow Rates for Continuous Fermentation of Phenosolvan-extracted Wastes from Soft Coal Pyrolysis by Activated Sludge," *Proceedings*, 3rd Symposium, Prague (1962), pp. 317–321, on continuous cultivation of microorganisms. Prague: Czechoslowak. Acad. Sci. (1964).

(7) Schulze, K. L. "A Mathematical Model of the Activated Sludge Process," *Devel. Ind. Microbiol.*, *5*, 258–266 (1964).

(8) Wuhrmann, K. "Hauptwirkungen und Wechselwirkungen einiger Betriebsparameter im Belebtschlammsystem. Ergebnisse mehrjähriger Grossversuche," *Schweiz. Z. Hydrol.*, *26*, 218–270 (1964).

(9) Monod, J. *Recherches sur la croissance des cultures bactériennes*. 2e édition. Paris: Hermann (1958).

(10) Herbert, D. "A Theoretical Analysis of Continuous Culture Systems," *S.C.I. Monogr. No. 12 on Continuous Culture of Microorganisms*, pp. 21–53. London: Soc. Chem. Ind. (1961).

(11) Herbert, D. "Multi-stage Continuous Culture," *Proceedings*, 3rd Symposium, Prague (1962), pp. 23–44. Prague: Czechoslowak. Acad. Sci. (1964).

TABLE 38

MEAN CONCENTRATIONS AND STANDARD DEVIATIONS OF ORGANIC CARBON, ORGANIC NITROGEN, AND BOD IN THE INFLUENT TO THE AERATION BASIN (I) AND IN THE FINAL EFFLUENT (E). ANALYSIS INCLUDING SUSPENDED SOLIDS. ALL VALUES AVERAGED FROM NINE COMPOSITE SAMPLES.

Mixed Liquor		Temp. > 13°C. Hydraul. Load, $m^3/m^3/d$						Temp. < 11°C. Hydraul. Load, $m^3/m^3/d$					
ppm O	Susp. Solids ppm	58		29		9		58		29		9	
		I	E	I	E	I	E	I	E	I	E	I	E
		ppm Organic Carbon											
1	600	63.4	32.4	53.0	19.4	48.9	17.6	64.0	39.5	54.7	29.1	64.0	27.1
		±5.7	±3.6	±7.2	±3.0	±6.1	±2.7	±12.4	±5.7	±10.3	±7.5	±12.4	±6.2
	3,300	53.0	15.2	64.6	13.2	63.4	9.2	48.4	17.2	46.6	12.9	54.7	10.3
		±7.2	±3.1	±11.3	±0.9	±8.3	±0.4	±9.0	±4.1	±9.1	±1.7	±10.3	±3.5
	6,000	60.1	15.4	53.2	15.4	64.6	9.7	76.7	24.6	54.2	15.3	48.4	10.4
		±12.9	±1.9	±6.0	±2.2	±11.3	±0.8	±13.5	±6.0	±8.2	±1.6	±9.0	±1.8
4	600	71.6	21.4	71.6	17.7	59.3	19.8	61.5	37.6	76.7	35.9	61.8	24.7
		±14.1	±2.2	±14.1	±2.0	±8.6	±3.7	±14.1	±14.1	±13.5	±10.9	±6.5	±2.4
	3,300	53.2	16.0	63.4	11.8	60.1	11.8	46.6	18.9			61.5	12.9
		±6.0	±2.6	±8.3	±1.7	±12.9	±3.4	±9.1	±4.6			±14.1	±6.4
	6,000	64.6	15.6	53.5	8.9	71.6	9.8	40.3	13.8	54.2	15.6	64.7	13.6
		±11.3	±1.3	±5.3	±0.8	±14.1	±2.9	±18.6	±3.6	±8.2	±1.9	±6.5	±2.2
7	600	53.5	20.4	74.0	25.6	53.2	15.8	64.7	41.4	61.5	31.6	40.3	14.7
		±5.3	±2.8	±6.9	±3.4	±6.0	±4.5	±6.5	±5.6	±14.1	±10.8	±18.6	±2.9
	3,300	60.5	15.0	60.1	13.2	53.5	11.1	61.8	23.7	64.0	23.2	46.6	12.4
		±10.0	±2.4	±12.9	±1.8	±5.3	±1.7	±6.5	±5.6	±12.4	±4.9	±9.1	±1.7
	6,000	72.0	15.1	60.5	12.2	74.0	12.1	54.7	15.2	61.8	20.0	76.7	16.4
		±12.8	±3.1	±10.0	±1.9	±6.9	±2.1	±10.3	±2.8	±6.5	±4.0	±13.5	±6.5

						ppm Organic Nitrogen							
1	600	8.5 ±1.7	4.9 ±0.4	8.2 ±1.1	3.7 ±0.6	8.3 ±1.4	3.7 ±0.9	10.4 ±1.9	5.5 ±0.6	9.7 ±1.6	5.3 ±1.2	10.4 ±1.9	4.0 ±0.3
	3,300	8.2 ±1.1	2.6 ±0.4	10.1 ±1.2	2.9 ±0.5	8.9 ±0.4	1.3 ±0.2	11.3 ±3.3	4.4 ±1.0	10.3 ±1.6	3.3 ±0.7	9.7 ±1.6	2.4 ±1.3
	6,000	10.1 ±1.5	2.7 ±0.5	8.6 ±1.2	2.5 ±0.5	10.1 ±1.2	1.3 ±0.3	10.2 ±3.3	4.2 ±1.2	10.6 ±1.5	3.1 ±1.2	11.3 ±3.3	1.3 ±0.4
4	600	10.6 ±0.7	4.2 ±0.4	10.6 ±0.7	3.8 ±0.6	10.2 ±1.5	3.6 ±0.5	13.2 ±1.7	7.8 ±1.9	10.1 ±3.3	6.4 ±1.3	11.5 ±1.1	4.9 ±0.5
	3,300	8.6 ±1.2	3.0 ±0.3	8.9 ±0.4	2.2 ±0.5	10.1 ±1.5	2.5 ±1.6	10.3 ±1.6	4.7 ±3.5			13.2 ±1.7	3.2 ±1.4
	6,000	10.1 ±1.2	2.9 ±0.3	7.9 ±0.8	1.6 ±0.9	10.6 ±0.7	1.5 ±0.8	9.3 ±1.8	3.1 ±1.4	10.6 ±1.5	3.0 ±1.6	9.0 ±1.0	1.2 ±0.3
7	600	7.9 ±0.8	4.1 ±0.07	9.5 ±0.9	4.9 ±1.1	8.6 ±1.2	2.6 ±0.4	9.0 ±1.0	6.9 ±1.8	13.2 ±1.7	6.6 ±2.2	9.3 ±1.8	3.5 ±1.3
	3,300	8.5 ±2.2	1.8 ±0.8	10.1 ±1.5	3.4 ±2.4	7.9 ±0.8	1.5 ±0.4	11.5 ±1.1	4.1 ±0.7	10.4 ±1.9	3.9 ±0.5	10.4 ±1.6	2.7 ±0.6
	6,000	10.4 ±4.2	2.1 ±0.9	8.5 ±2.2	1.2 ±0.5	9.5 ±0.9	1.5 ±0.7	9.7 ±1.6	2.8 ±0.3	11.5 ±1.1	2.9 ±0.4	10.2 ±3.3	2.6 ±1.0
						ppm BOD							
1	600	105 ±23	46 ±10	95 ±13	20 ±4	91 ±15	18 ±5	110 ±22	65 ±8	105 ±26	52 ±19	110 ±22	19 ±6
	3,300	95 ±13	12 ±3	94 ±18	10 ±3	149 ±25	9 ±3	91 ±34	17 ±7	113 ±58	18 ±6	105 ±26	8 ±2
	6,000	122 ±21	18 ±5	97 ±11	16 ±3	94 ±18	9 ±5	129 ±26	23 ±5	135 ±15	11 ±2	91 ±34	7 ±5
4	600	116 ±21	28 ±5	116 ±21	20 ±3	118 ±25	11 ±2	115 ±20	55 ±13	129 ±26	55 ±28	117 ±12	27 ±8
	3,300	97 ±11	19 ±5	149 ±25	11 ±2	122 ±21	11 ±5	113 ±58	16 ±9			115 ±20	7 ±2
	6,000	94 ±18	12 ±4	138 ±31	15 ±7	116 ±21	8 ±6	115 ±40	15 ±4	135 ±15	11 ±2	119 ±21	6 ±1
7	600	138 ±31	37 ±6	143 ±34	34 ±8	97 ±11	13 ±2	119 ±21	50 ±12	115 ±20	42 ±22	115 ±40	22 ±11
	3,300	101 ±17	9 ±1	122 ±21	14 ±3	138 ±31	16 ±8	117 ±12	24 ±10	110 ±22	18 ±1.7	113 ±58	9 ±2
	6,000	92 ±15	15 ±9	101 ±17	7 ±2	143 ±34	14 ±3	105 ±26	17 ±6	117 ±12	23 ±7	129 ±26	17 ±7

(12) Haseltine, T. R. "A Rational Approach to the Design of Activated Sludge Plants," *Biological Treatment of Sewage and Industrial Wastes*. Vol. 1, Aerobic Oxidation. New York: Reinhold Publ. Corp. (1955).

(13) Eckenfelder, W. W., and D. J. O'Connor. *Biological Waste Treatment*. Oxford: Pergamon Press (1961).

(14) Emde, W. Von der. *Beitrag zu Versuchen zur Abwasserreinigung mit belebtem Schlamm*. Veröff. Inst. F. Siedlungswasserwirtsch. TH Hannover, H. 1 (1957).

(15) Smith, D. B. "Measurements of the Respiratory Activity of Activated Sludge," *Sewage Ind. Wastes*, *25*, 767–792 (1953).

(16) Wuhrmann, K. "Grundlagen für die Dimensionierung der Belüftung bei Belebtschlammanlagen," *Schweiz. A. Hydrol.*, *26*, 310–337 (1964).

(17) Orford, H. E., H. Heukelekian, and E. Isenberg. "Effect of Sludge Loading and Dissolved Oxygen on the Performance of the Activated Sludge Process," *Advances in Biological Waste Treatment. Proceedings*. 3rd Conf. on Biological Waste Treatment, Manhattan College (1960). Oxford: Pergamon Press (1963).

(18) Wuhrmann, K. "Factors Affecting Efficiency and Solids Production in the Activated Sludge Process," *Biological Treatment of Sewage and Industrial Wastes*. New York: Reinhold Publ. Corp. (1956).

(19) Schaffer, R. B., C. E. van Hall, G. N. McDermott, D. Barth, V. A. Stenger, S. J. Sebesta, and S. H. Griggs. "Application of a Carbon Analyzer in Water Treatment," *J. Water Poll. Cont. Fed.*, *37*, 1545–1566 (1965).

(20) Quirk, T. P., R. C. Olson, and G. H. Richardson. "Bio-oxidation of Concentrated Board Machine Effluents," *Proceedings*, 18th Ind. Waste Conf., Purdue Univ., pp. 655–673 (1963).

(21) Rudolfs, W., and H. R. Amberg. "White Water Treatment. VI. The Activated Sludge Process," *Sewage Ind. Wastes*, *25*, 191–200 (1953).

CONCEPTIONS AND MISCONCEPTIONS IN BIOLOGICAL OXIDATION

A. W. Busch
Rice University, Houston, Texas

Two of the concepts derived from interdisciplinary activities are "systems theory" and "mathematical models." The intent of this paper is to show through the use of examples in biological oxidation that:

1. Systems knowledge is more basic and more powerful than systems theory, and

2. Mathematical model and thermodynamic analysis cannot substitute for common sense, which states that equations must be descriptive before they can be predictive, and that concepts must be applicable before they are applied.

FLUIDIZED CULTURE SYSTEMS

The obvious choice for the opening topic is the activated sludge system. Note that the word *system* is used in perference to *process*, for biological oxidation is the only process in the system comprised of aeration and subsequent solids separation. Biological oxidation is the conversion of soluble organics into bacteria with production of carbon dioxide and water as by-products. Somewhat unfortunately, bacteria will also slowly hydrolyze, and subsequently oxidize, organic matter present in particulate form. The fact remains that unless soluble organics are to be removed from aqueous solution, the biological oxidation process is not required. The process can be carried out in environments ranging from the BOD bottle to a pond or stream, with stoichiometry and kinetics varying only as a consequence, or reflection, of the environment.

When solids are separated and partially returned to, or fully retained in, the tankage, the name "activated sludge" is applied. Numerous modifications of the flowsheet have come into being and, curiously enough, most of these are reported to produce different "efficiencies" of organic removal. Now, because bacteria should cease working only when their energy (food) source is depleted, the inescapable conclusion is that the efficiency, or better, inefficiency, is designed into the plant. Thus, hydraulic *de*ficiency is often mistaken for process efficiency. Typical is the statement that a treatment facility converted from "conventional activated sludge" to "step aeration" can achieve an improvement in performance from 86 percent to 92.7 percent efficiency (1). System knowledge suggests that similar improvement may be attained by simply increasing the culture concentration (higher mixed liquor suspended solids)--a true process change, rather than a hydraulic change.

Another misconception in activated sludge systems is that the fluidized culture process is unduly sensitive to changes in feed. In fact, of course, the plant design determines the degree to which the process may be disrupted. While there are obvious and definable limits within which bacteria function most effectively, the plant design controls the maintenance of these limits, which are part of the process design criteria.

One of the most frequently used parameters in biological oxidation is hydraulic residence time. Often overlooked is the fact that the specified time was orginally established in conjunction with a concentration of biological culture. Thus, a unit rate of reaction is implied and is, of course, much more basic than residence time as a process parameter. Garrett (2) showed, a number of years ago, how simply a conventional activated sludge system can be controlled on a rate process basis. A completely mixed reactor is even more susceptible to precise and simple process control. However, the completely mixed reactor does not give rise to a "different" biological oxidation process, as has been postulated.

Oxygen and nitrogen requirements in biological oxidation bear an inverse relationship which process stoichiometry is useful in defining. However, process stoichiometry reflects the system environment and becomes absolute only in a growth system wherein maximum cellular yield is obtained from the available amount of carbon source (food). Because cell synthesis is a maximum, nitrogen requirement is also a maximum, and oxygen requirement is the minimum. An often encountered misconception in regard to oxygen and nitrogen is that there is a fixed requirement for each, both related to the 5-day BOD, and thus that the cell yield also bears a fixed proportionality to the 5-day BOD. Again, bacteria operate under a variety of conditions and, even if they are rate limited by a factor such as nitrogen availability, will ultimately convert the soluble carbon food source to cells, carbon dioxide, and water, if an exogenous hydrogen acceptor is available. The net stoichiometry is defined by the system environment and may vary rather widely. This is documented by the very fact that activated sludge is used in systems ranging from the high synthesis, "high-rate" configuration to the low synthesis, extended aeration flowsheet.

In short, system knowledge permits process design to achieve the desired effluent quality in a variety of configurations and thus provides a basis for system theory analysis.

THE NITRATE QUESTION

The nitrate ion is obviously well suited for use in a discussion of "radical" ideas. Nitrate has been proposed for uses ranging from a nitrogen source in the BOD test to a supply of "chemical oxygen" in the biological oxidation process.

Bacteria certainly can reduce nitrates to ammonia for use in cell synthesis, but the energy used in this reaction distorts the characteristic bottle stoichiometry, and the BOD value obtained is quantitatively lowered. The definition and experimental documentation of this phenomenon illustrates how important interdisciplinary knowledge can be. The theoretical prediction of the quantitative effect of nitrate reduction was based on established biochemical reactions and was subsequently experimentally verified (3).

The question of nitrates serving as a source of "chemical oxygen" involves a form of semantics. The fact that nitrate used as a hydrogen acceptor is reduced to nitrite shows that oxygen is indeed released, combining with hydrogen to form water in an ionic reaction. The oxygen thus released, however, does not serve as the hydrogen acceptor in the biochemical reaction; the nitrate ion meets this function. The enzyme involved in the use of nitrate as a hydrogen acceptor is specific, is not the enzyme in the oxygen sequence, and, most significantly, is in fact inhibited by the presence of dissolved oxygen. A thorough documentation of the nitrate system is currently in preparation (4).

ANAEROBIC SYSTEMS

The traditional concept of anaerobic systems assumes a two-stage sequence of biological reactions which excludes exogenous hydrogen acceptors and bears heavily on the existence of a specific group of organisms known as methane formers.

Quantitative relationships have not been as readily established for anaerobic systems compared to aerobic studies. At least two reasons may be postulated for the variability of reported data. One is that until relatively recently anaerobic studies were done only with "sludge" and the system was difficult to define or replicate. A second reason is that since the work involved "real" sludges of diverse nature, significant amounts of exogenous hydrogen acceptors may have been present in some systems.

Most of the reported studies also have been aimed at defining the effect of various constituents on the anaerobic reaction, always assuming that the two-stage "model" is valid. However, some work aimed at "optimizing" the system, again assuming the two-stage model to be valid, has disclosed some interesting anomalies.

One of the most significant anomalies is the difficulty that workers have had in isolating the ubiquitous methane formers for kinetic studies. Certainly methane production is widespread in nature and thousands of existing "digesters" produce methane continuously. Why then should isolation of the organisms responsible for this production be difficult? Could the fact be, as suggested by biochemistry and microbiology knowledge, that methane formation is not necessarily the exclusive province of a few species but rather is a capability of many species, exerted when the system environment so demands? This premise, and it is as yet only a premise, coupled with the exogenous hydrogen acceptor question, would explain much of the lack of repeatability and agreement of reported anaerobic studies.

THE FILM-FLOW BIOLOGICAL REACTOR

The film-flow biological reactor, commonly known as the trickling filter, carries an aura of mystic not really justified. The early study of the trickling filter compared its performance to that of conventional activated sludge systems. The latter are, of course, poorly constituted for handling waste flows of variable natures and in the comparison suffered accordingly. The recirculating, and hence diluting and equalizing, flow pattern of the trickling filter shows favorable characteristics of resistance to disruption of the biological process. However, the basic parameter of performance should be work done per unit volume of reactor, and here the case for the trickling filter begins to weaken. The microbial concentration represented by a one-micron, in thickness, film of bacteria on the surface of a bed of three-inch-diameter spheres is less than 1 mg. per liter of reactor volume. The fact that with such a low reactive capacity per unit volume the trickling filter is even considered on a practical basis is surprising and implies anew that fluidized cultures are grossly overdesigned (or underloaded) from a reaction rate viewpoint.

Research work has shown that for a given configuration and flow regime, process performance of the trickling filter is primarily a function of hydraulic loading, expressed as volume per unit time. This conclusion is entirely logical, since hydraulic residence time depends on liquid film thickness in the reactor. A recent experimentally verfied theoretical analysis has shown the process reaction to be diffusion controlled under laminar flow conditions (5). Thus the flow should be frequently intermixed, as is the case in rock media, or applied at sufficient rates to achieve turbulant flow, as is the recommended procedure for the new plastic packings. The evolution of small diameter towers of substantial depth for these plastic media appears to substantiate the concepts derived from knowledge of process and system characteristics. However, the "design" of a trickling filter is still primarily a sizing operation using empirical equations whose ancestry would be legally of questionable status. Once the trickling filter is built, little, if any, process control is available.

MATHEMATICAL MODELS

A popular item of interest today is mathematical modeling. The forcing of a set of experimental data to match the trace of a particular equation, by judicious selection of the scale of ordinate and abscissa, is "curve fitting," not mathematical modeling. The distinction between curve fitting and development of a mathematical model is often obscured by the fact that processes may sometimes be quite well described by an equation of a general nature and built-in flexibility. However, the essence of a model is that it not only "fits" a selected set of performance data but that it can also predict the response of the process to a perturbation of known characteristics. Thus a prerequisite of modeling is basic knowledge and analysis of the process, or system, in order to properly derive analytical data to support or, preferably, to disprove the model. A mathematical model may be considered an adjective, descriptive in a general sense but definitive only when properly applied to a specific problem.

A case in point is the reporting of an equation as of such-and-such order. Only when the order is specified as with respect to what variable(s), does it carry significance in process or system definition. A real pitfall is the danger of relating performance, or order, to the wrong parameter. Consider anaerobic digestion, magically converted from a 30-day to a 10-day process a few years ago. In one case activated carbon was the "catalyst" and in another recirculated gas did the trick. In actuality, as was found later, the mixing used in both "processes" was the significant parameter.

Concisely, a mathematical model is a description to work *from* rather than *toward.*

SYSTEM LIMITATIONS ON PROCESSES

Process limitation was touched upon in the discussion of the fluidized culture systems where hydraulic characteristics often determine process performance. The phenomenon may also be seen in research literature and has sometimes led to new "theories" or to the "disproval" of established theories. An example worth citing is the widely used Warburg apparatus. This fixed volume system has been subjected to a wide range of experimental loadings, some of which clearly, by simple calculation, exceed the resources of the experimental environment. Rather obviously the oxygen content of the gas atmosphere fixes the quantity of oxygen available, and the oxygen concentration influences the rate at which it becomes available in the liquid by transfer. Curious conclusions as to the effect of "this or that" additive on biological oxidation may be drawn from Warburg data if care is not taken in setting the experiment in tune with system capabilities.

SUMMARY AND CONCLUSION

The field of water technology, caught between a tradition of concepts based on stereotyped system design and the outpouring of new scientific knowledge, is filled with contradictions and misconceptions. In adjusting to the needs of today and tomorrow inadequate concepts must be discarded and new ideas generated. In the rush to exploit new information, however, an inadequate basis of knowledge may result in serious misconceptions drawn from poorly prepared experiment and system design.

REFERENCES

(1) *Planning Study to Year 2000.* Washington, D.C.: Board of Engineers, Department of Sanitary Engineering (August 1964).

(2) Garrett, M. T., Jr. "Hydraulic Control of Activated Sludge Growth Rate," *Sewage Ind. Wastes, 30*(3), 253 (1958).

(3) Lewis, J. W., and A. W. Busch. "BOD Progression in Soluble Substrates—VIII—The Quantitative Error Due to Nitrate as a Nitrogen Source," *Water Sewage Works, 106*(3–6), 106–109, 139–143, 185–187, 209–211 (March–June 1965).

(4) Schroeder, E. D. "Dissimilatory Nitrate Reduction by Mixed Bacterial Populations." Ph.D. Dissertation, Rice University (1966).

(5) Swilley, E. L., and B. Atkinson. "Film Flow Models for the Trickling Filter," *Proceedings*, 18th Annual Industrial Waste Conference, Purdue University (1963).

A DISCUSSION OF "CONCEPTIONS AND MISCONCEPTIONS IN BIOLOGICAL OXIDATION"

John F. Andrews
Clemson University, Clemson, South Carolina

Professor Busch has presented some thought-provoking ideas concerning future developments in biological processes for waste treatment. There is no doubt of the need for constant re-evaluation of these processes and application of new knowledge from the sciences and other branches of engineering. However, some of the ideas presented by Professor Busch may be misleading: These are his statements concerning the inefficiency of a fixed bed reactor (trickling filter) as compared to a fluidized culture reactor (activated sludge), and the possible non-existence of methane bacteria as separate species.

Professor Busch has calculated, using a one-micron film thickness and spheres three inches in diameter, that a trickling filter would contain less than 1 mg. of solids per liter of filter volume. When this is compared to the 2,000—4,000 mg/liter of solids commonly found in the conventional activated sludge aeration tank it would appear that the trickling filter process is more inefficient (per unit volume) than the activated sludge process by several orders of magnitude. Even if the film thickness were 100 microns, the activated sludge aeration tank would still contain a much larger quantity of solids per unit volume than the trickling filter. The actual picture, however, is not as black as that painted by Professor Busch. If one compares the two processes, as currently used, it will be found that there is not a great deal of difference in the volumetric loading rates (lbs. of $BOD_5/1,000\ ft^3$-day) of the two processes. This is illustrated in Table 39. Advances in solid-liquid separation devices and gas transfer devices will undoubtedly increase the allowable volumetric loading rates for the activated sludge process. Advances such as the controlled filtration process of Ingram's, however, should also increase the allowable volumetric loading rates for the trickling filter process.

Professor Busch has also hypothesized that methane production may be a result of the effect of environment on the more common bacteria and therefore the methane bacteria may not exist as separate species. However, he has offered no evidence to prove or disprove his hypothesis.

It should be pointed out that the bacteriological and biochemical literature contain little evidence to support this hypothesis. Dr. P. H. Smith (3), an authority on the methane bacteria, has recently conducted experiments, using pure cultures, which appear to disprove Professor Busch's hypothesis. A portion of this work will be presented by Dr. Smith at the ASM meeting in Los Angeles in May 1966.

TABLE 39

COMPARISON OF VOLUMETRIC LOADING RATES

Activated Sludge Process (1)	Vol. Load. Rate lb. BOD_5/1,000 - Ft^3-day	Trickling Filter Process (2)	Vol. Load. Rate lb. BOD_5/1,000 - Ft^3-day
Extended aeration	20	Low-rate	5–25
Conv. activated sludge	35	High-rate	25–300
Tapered aeration	35		
Step aeration	50+		
Activated aeration	50+		
Contact stabilization	70		
Hatfield process	70+		
Kraus process	100		
High rate	100		
Modified aeration	100		
Rapid bloc	150+		
Supra activation	400		

REFERENCES

(1) Stewart, M. J. "Activated Sludge Process Variations. The Complete Spectrum," *Water Sewage Works, 111* (April, May, June, 1964).

(2) American Society of Civil Engineers. *Manual of Practice No. 36. Sewage Treatment Plant Design.* New York: A.S.C.E. (1959).

(3) Smith, P. H., Department of Bacteriology, University of Florida, Gainesville. Private Communication.

REMOVAL OF NITROGEN BY BIOLOGICAL TREATMENT

Walter K. Johnson
University of Minnesota, Minneapolis, Minnesota

NEED FOR TREATMENT

The presence of profuse algal growths in receiving waters is one characteristic of eutrophication. Although both nitrogen and phosphorus are essential growth requirements for algae, the relative importance of each is still a subject of discussion. It is interesting to note that wastewaters have been analyzed specifically for the elements nitrogen and phosphorus for many years. In routine wastewater analysis the majority of the other elements, however, have been expressed simply as part of the total or suspended solids or as part of the biochemical or chemical oxygen demand. Nitrogen and phosphorus have been specifically identified for many reasons, not the least of which has been concern over the effect of these elements on eutrophication.

It has been shown in papers published in the Transactions of the 1961 Siminar on "Algae and Metropolitan Wastes" (1) by Sawyer and Ferullo and by Dugdale and Neess that nitrogen fixation occurs with blue-green algae. The result of this is that phosphorus appears as the key element. Mackenthun (2), however, states that of the two nutrient elements, nitrogen may be the most critical factor limiting algae production in natural waters, since phosphorus is stored in plankton as excess and may approach ten times the actual need. Gerloff and Skoog (3) stated that in their investigations with a particular algal species, neither nitrogen nor phosphorus was a limiting factor. Fitzgerald and Rohlich (4) found that the growth of algae in secondary sewage works effluents and lagoon water was more closely related to the amount of ammoniacal nitrogen present than the amount of phosphate-phosphorus. Consequently, from the information now known, it appears that the reduction of both nitrogen and phosphorus in wastewater plant effluents is important in controlling eutrophication. It also appears that other ecological factors may determine whether nitrogen or phosphorus limit algal growth in any one particular situation.

Because of these unknown and synergistic factors which apparently contribute to the growth of algae, the removal of solids and elements other than the nutrient elements should not be neglected. In fact, the ultimate solution to these disposal problems may require not only the removal of the nutrient elements but also the removal of all solids. Until such time as these high degrees of treatment are considered as necessary and economically feasible, much may be done in improving the nitrogen and phosphorus removal efficiencies of existing plants and processes. These improvements may be obtained through better operation and through modifications of existing treatment plant processes.

PHYSICAL METHODS OF REMOVAL

To gain the proper perspective of the role of biological methods of nitrogen removal it is necessary to review briefly the physical methods of removal. In conventional treatment processes, primary treatment by plain sedimentation is effective in the removal of organic forms of nitrogen. Data are presented in Table 40 of nitrogen removals obtained by plain sedimentation at the Minneapolis-St. Paul Sanitary District (MSSD) treatment plant.

TABLE 40

AVERAGE NITROGEN CONCENTRATIONS IN MSSD WASTEWATER

Year	No. of Tests	Nitrogen Concentrations—N						
		Raw Waste		Primary Effl.		Percent Rem.		
		NH_3	Org.	NH_3	Org.	NH_3	Org.	Total
1956	9	9.81	10.86	9.05	7.59	8.2	29.6	19.5
1957	10	9.10	10.70					
1958	19	10.85	12.07					
1964	26	—	—	10.90	9.10			
1965	7	17.60	13.60	16.90	9.40	4.0	30.9	15.7

The average total nitrogen removal shown in Table 40 is approximately 15–20 percent, most of which is in the organic form. In this primary treatment plant, the raw sludge is vacuum filtered and incinerated. In plants treating domestic wastes, sedimentation processes are usually the only physical processes contributing to the removal of nitrogen.

Specific supplementary physical methods of nitrogen removal have been reviewed by Rohlich (5). The effectiveness of plain sedimentation in removing nitrogen containing suspended and colloidal solids may be increased through the use of chemical coagulants. Ion exchange has been used to remove ammonia, nitrite, and nitrate ions. Ammonia may also be stripped from solution by aeration at high *p*H conditions.

BIOPRECIPITATION PROCESSES

Conventional methods of biological wastewater treatment, such as the activated sludge and trickling filter processes, usually remove only 30–50 percent of the incoming nitrogen concentrations. The removal of nitrogen is through the normal process of sludge growth where nitrogen is assimilated into biological cells. From work by Hoover (6) and others, the general formula for biological cell material has been expressed as $C_5H_7NO_2$, of which 12.4 percent is nitrogen. Consequently the removal of excess biological sludge solids results in the removal of the proportionate amount of nitrogen. Sawyer *et al.* (7–10) studied the nutritional requirements of activated sludge with industrial wastes, and expressed the assimilation of nitrogen in terms of a BOD removed to nitrogen removed (BOD:N) ratio. Since the nitrogen available in domestic wastes is usually in excess of that required by the sludge, maximum BOD:N ratios of 17-20 are usually observed. These ratios are in general agreement with the expected nitrogen uptake based on the biological cell formulation expressed above. Since the usual concentration of nitrogen in raw domestic wastes is 20–30 mg/l, these figures also agree with the observed removals of 30–50 percent.

STABILIZATION PONDS

Biological treatment of wastewaters in stabilization ponds involves several different concepts with respect to nitrogen removal. Biological oxidation mechanisms in ponds are basically similar to those found in the activated sludge and trickling filter processes. However, the cell-growth nitrogen normally discharged as excess sludge from the other treatment systems either remains in the pond, to be released again to the liquid, or is discharged in the pond outflow.

The possible use of stabilization ponds to remove nitrogen by biological methods depends upon the growth of algae in the ponds and the subsequent harvesting of these algal cells. The disposition of nitrogen in a stabilization pond is shown in Figure 55. Loehr and Stephenson (11) have concluded from their tests that a normal oxidation pond such as they used was not effective as a tertiary device to control the nitrogen discharge. They did not harvest the algal growth.

Nitrogen removal through the harvesting of algae has been the subject of a number of investigations. Herman and Gloyna (12) studied the nutritional requirements of algae with respect to nitrogen, and Oswald *et al.* (13) found that regardless of the method of separating the algae from the liquid, approximately two thirds of the total nitrogen was removed. In studies by Gates and Borchardt (14) nitrogen removals of 50 percent were obtained by harvesting the algal cultures grown in experimental ponds. They also presented data to indicate that similar operation with two-stage ponds would produce 98-percent removals of nitrogen. Methods of harvesting algae have been investigated and reported by Oswald *et al.* (13), Golueke and Oswald (15), and Van Vuuren and Van Duuren (16). The costs of harvesting the algae are one of the chief deterrents to the general use of this process for nitrogen removal. These costs, however, could in part be offset by the development of a suitable market for the recovered algal cells.

The stabilization pond is effective in the removal of nitrogen in other ways too, as indicated in Figure 40. In ponds such as those in Minnesota where the loadings are limited to 20 lbs of BOD/acre/day, considerable seepage is found. The seepage of nitrate-bearing pond waters through anaerobic deposits in the bottom of the pond results in microbial denitrification and the release of nitrogen gas. Also, ammonia nitrogen is adsorbed on the soil beneath the pond, as reported by Preul (17), and remains on the soil as long as anaerobic conditions exist. Under these conditions significant amounts of nitrogen are prevented from leaving with the pond effluent, and also are not carried into the groundwaters below the pond.

NITROGEN REMOVAL BY DENITRIFICATION

History

Nitrogen removal by the process of microbial denitrification has been a topic of research for a number of years. The fact that the processes of nitrification and denitrification have been quite commonly observed in wastewater treatment plants encourages the use of this process for nitrogen removal. One of the early and extensive studies of nitrification and denitrification was by Sawyer and Bradney (18) while they were investigating a rising sludge problem.

The denitrification process results in nitrogen removal through the reduction of nitrates and the release of nitrogen gas. Of the several types of nitrate reductions defined by Verhoeven (19), "true dissimilatory nitrate reduction" results in the release of nitrogen gas. The nitrates are reduced as a result of their use as hydrogen acceptors in a biological oxidation process.

In the 1950's a number of investigators began seriously to consider the denitrification process as a means of removing nitrogen from wastewaters. Christianson *et al.* (20) reported on experimental work with the denitrification of an industrial waste. There have been reports of pilot plant work conducted in South Africa (21) for the denitrification of sewage effluents. Wuhrmann (22–24) has described extensive work with the denitrification process, and Bringmann *et al.* (25–29) have reported on pilot plant studies for the removal of nitrogen by denitrification from supernatant liquors and wastewaters. Ludzack and Ettinger (30)

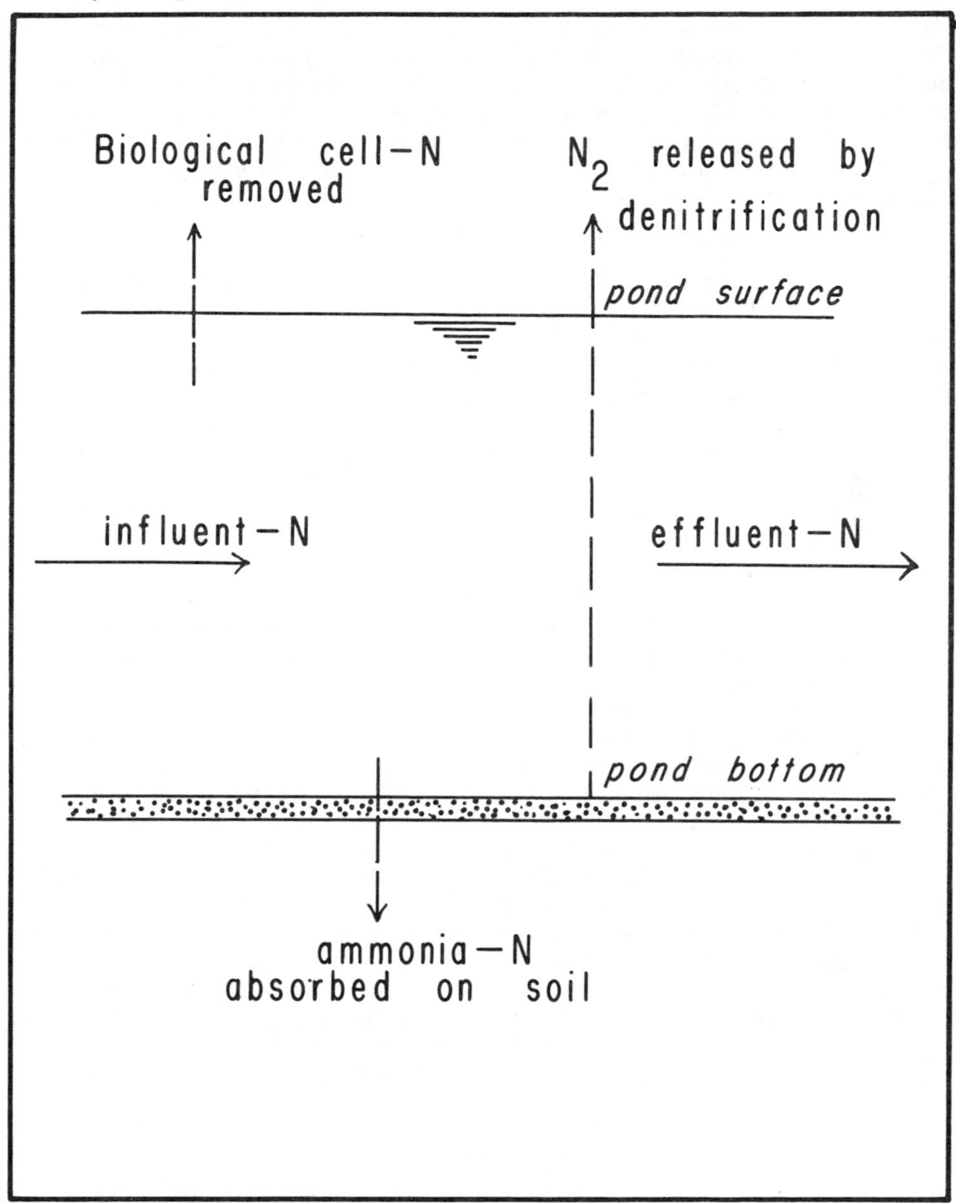

Figure 55. Disposition of nitrogen in stabilization ponds.

have reported on work with a semiaerobic activated sludge process utilizing denitrification for the elimination of nitrogen from a wastewater. Johnson and Schroepfer (31) also have reported on work with the denitrification process.

Nitrification

The existence of nitrates in a wastewater is, of course, essential for using a denitrification process. Certain nitrate-bearing trade wastes present no problem. Domestic wastewaters, however, usually contain no nitrates, and as a preliminary process to denitrification, a treatment process must be operated to produce a nitrified effluent. Microbial nitrification occurs primarily because of the activity of a specific group of autotrophic bacteria, although Eylar and Schmidt (32) have reported on a number of heterotrophic nitrifying organisms. The oxygen requirements in the transformation of ammonia nitrogen to the nitrate form are as follows:

$$NH_4^+ + 2\ O_2 = NO_3^- + 2H^+ + H_2O$$

It is easily shown experimentally that the oxygen uptake due to nitrification is in accord with this equation. Nitrification in the activated sludge process has been investigated recently by Downing and Bayley (33), Downing and Wheatland (34), Wuhrmann (23, 24), Bringmann (26), Ludzak and Ettinger (30), and Johnson and Schroepfer (31). Recent studies of the kinetics of nitrification in the activated sludge process have resulted in the publication of papers by Downing, Painter, and Knowles (35) and Downing and Hopwood (36). Their conclusions are essentially based on the growth rate characteristics of the nitrifiers. They presented experimental data to support their kinetic theory that "to achieve nitrification consistently the period of aeration must exceed a minimum value which is a function of the concentration of activated sludge, temperature, and the strength of the sewage." It was also concluded that "the minimum period of aeration [to achieve nitrification] will also be roughly proportional to the 5-day BOD of the sewage applied and will decrease very roughly in inverse proportion to the concentration of sludge in the aeration units." A relationship between BOD, sludge concentration, and aeration time is often expressed as the ratio of the pounds of BOD applied per day per pound of mixed liquor solids under aeration. The relationship between this load ratio and nitrification was also observed by Johnson and Schroepfer (31) in pilot plant studies conducted at 20°C. and with a synthetic milk waste. Another conclusion reached by Downing and his associates, "that nitrification will be either virtually complete or will not occur at all," was also observed by Johnson and Schroepfer (31). One of the main obstacles to obtaining continuous nitrification is the reduced activity of the nitrifiers at low temperatures. At moderate temperatures, however, continuous and complete nitrification of an activated sludge effluent will be obtained within the general concept of the conventional mode of operation. It is estimated that with a normal domestic waste, complete nitrification will require approximately 50 percent more air than that required for BOD stabilization. A flow diagram for the conventional activated sludge process is shown in Figure 56, Diagram A, as the first step in the denitrification process.

Denitrification

The second step in this method of nitrogen removal is that of the actual denitrification. The denitrifiers are facultative anaerobes and generally will use the nitrates in environments only of zero or low dissolved oxygen concentrations. Recent work by Mechsner and Wuhrmann (37), however, has shown considerable variation in the ability of a number of strains of bacteria to cause denitrification under a range of dissolved oxygen concentrations. They found that for certain bacterial species, denitrification could proceed at high concentrations of dissolved oxygen.

Several alternate flow diagrams which have been used for the denitrification process are presented in Figure 56. The flow pattern shown in Diagram B was used by Wuhrmann (22) in removing 60–80 percent of the incoming nitrogen. Basically it is the conventional activated sludge process with a mechanically

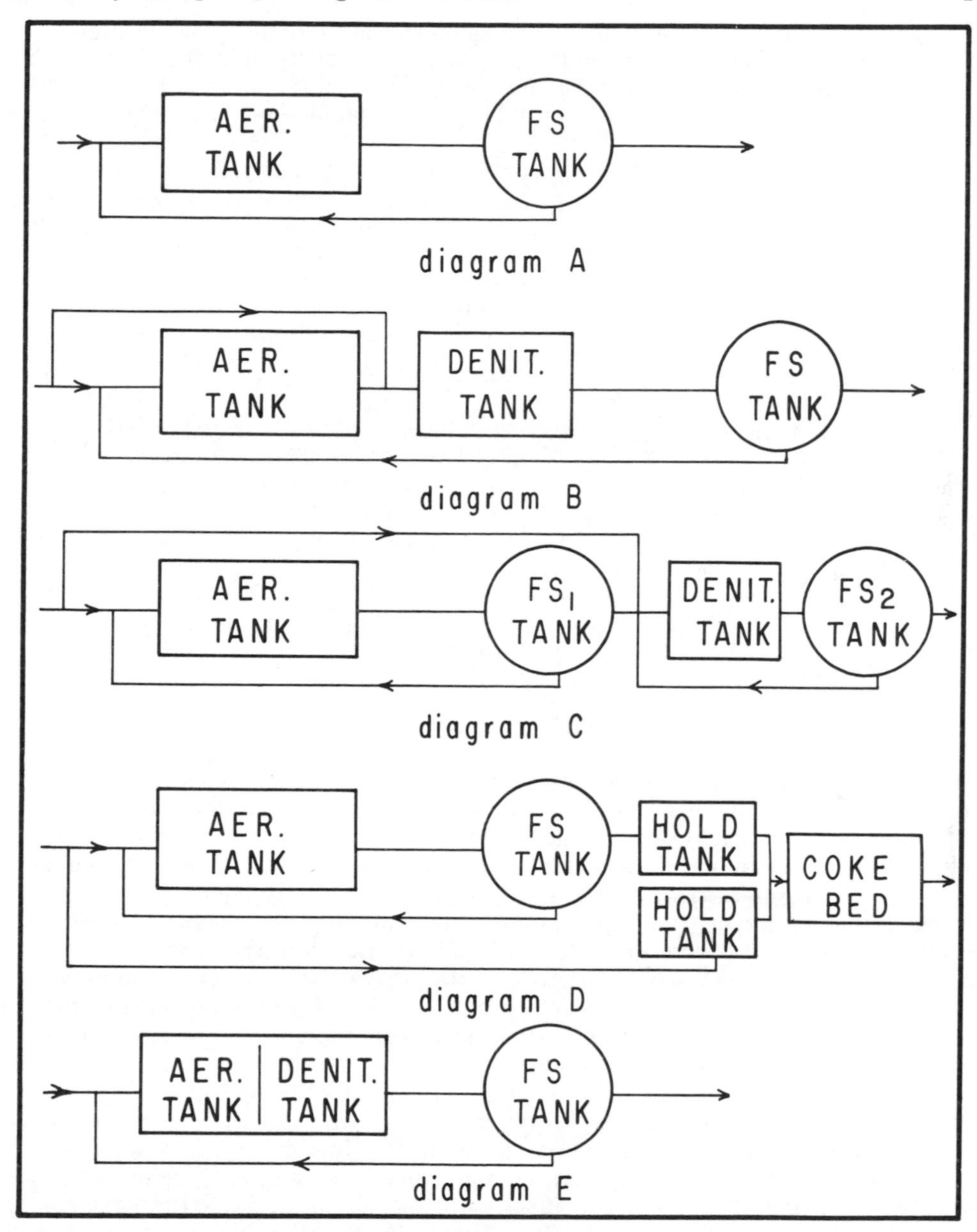

Figure 56. Alternate flow diagrams for denitrification.

mixed denitrifying tank placed between the aeration and the final settling tanks. The aeration tank is reduced in size as a result of bypassing a portion of the raw waste to the denitrification tank for use as the hydrogen donator.

Diagram C involves a denitrification process entirely separate from nitrification. This method of operation has the disadvantage of requiring two separation units, but it may be advantageous to have two separate microbial populations. In work by Johnson and Schroepfer (31) approximately two thirds of the flow was treated for BOD removal in the conventional activated sludge plant, and the remaining one third was stabilized in the unit utilizing nitrate oxygen. Overall nitrogen removals were approximately 60 percent. In these tests the nitrifying sludge showed a low sludge index, but the sludge in the denitrifying unit showed bulking tendencies.

Bringmann (25) originally concentrated on removing nitrogen from supernatant liquors, and in subsequent papers (29) has reported on work with domestic wastewaters. Pilot plant work was conducted with flow diagrams similar to those shown as Diagrams C and D in Figure 56, and in both cases the oxidation-reduction (O-R) potential was used to control the denitrification process. The use of holding tanks allowed the proportioning of the two flows in accordance with the O-R potential reading at the junction of the two streams. Satisfactory denitrification was achieved with readings of approximately -200 mv. Nitrogen removals of 60–70 percent were obtained. The use of the coke bed, as shown in Figure 56, may prove to be an extremely rapid method of denitrification.

One other rather unique method of operation is that used by Ludzak and Ettinger (30) as a semiaerobic activated sludge process as shown in Diagram E. The flow diagram is similar to that shown for Diagram B except that the aeration and denitrification portions of the process were contained in the same tank. A baffle separating the two compartments permitted recirculation of sludge from the aerator into the denitrification unit through a slot at the bottom, and back to the aerator over a weir at the top. Nitrogen removals under a range of operating conditions generally varied from 50 to 75 percent.

Process Control

One of the problems in the operation of the denitrification process is in the control procedures necessary for maintaining continuous nitrification and denitrification. The nitrification process is affected by variations in the wastewater characteristics, including temperature, nitrogen concentrations, and substances inhibiting the growth of the nitrifiers. Temperature and nitrogen concentration variations can in part be taken into account by controlling the aeration times and the mixed liquor solids concentrations. The inhibition of nitrification is not considered to be a serious problem with domestic wastes but could be a serious problem with specific industrial waste additives. There is the possibility that the effect of temperature on nitrification in the activated sludge process may be minimized by heating the return sludge.

The denitrifying bacteria do not appear to be quite as temperature dependent as the nitrifiers. The denitrification process requires that little or no dissolved oxygen be present for efficient operation. A denitrification unit is shown diagrammatically in Figure 57 to illustrate the control variables. The total demand and rate of demand for oxygen is a function of the wastewater characteristics. A stale raw wastewater with a low O-R potential will create a rapid rate of demand for dissolved oxygen and for the nitrate oxygen. However, a sufficient quantity of waste must be available to require the use of all dissolved and nitrate oxygen. The control problem lies, in part, in the continuous and rapid determination of the characteristics of the raw waste and of the nitrified effluent. Bringmann (29) has apparently found a solution to obtaining rapid denitrification, but the stability of the effluent (BOD) was not given in his paper. Raw-waste characteristics may be identified quite rapidly from continuous O-R potential and COD determinations, or through the use of a carbon analyzer. The nitrified effluent characteristics could be monitored by continuous dissolved oxygen and nitrate determinations. The significance in monitoring these constituents is in maintaining a

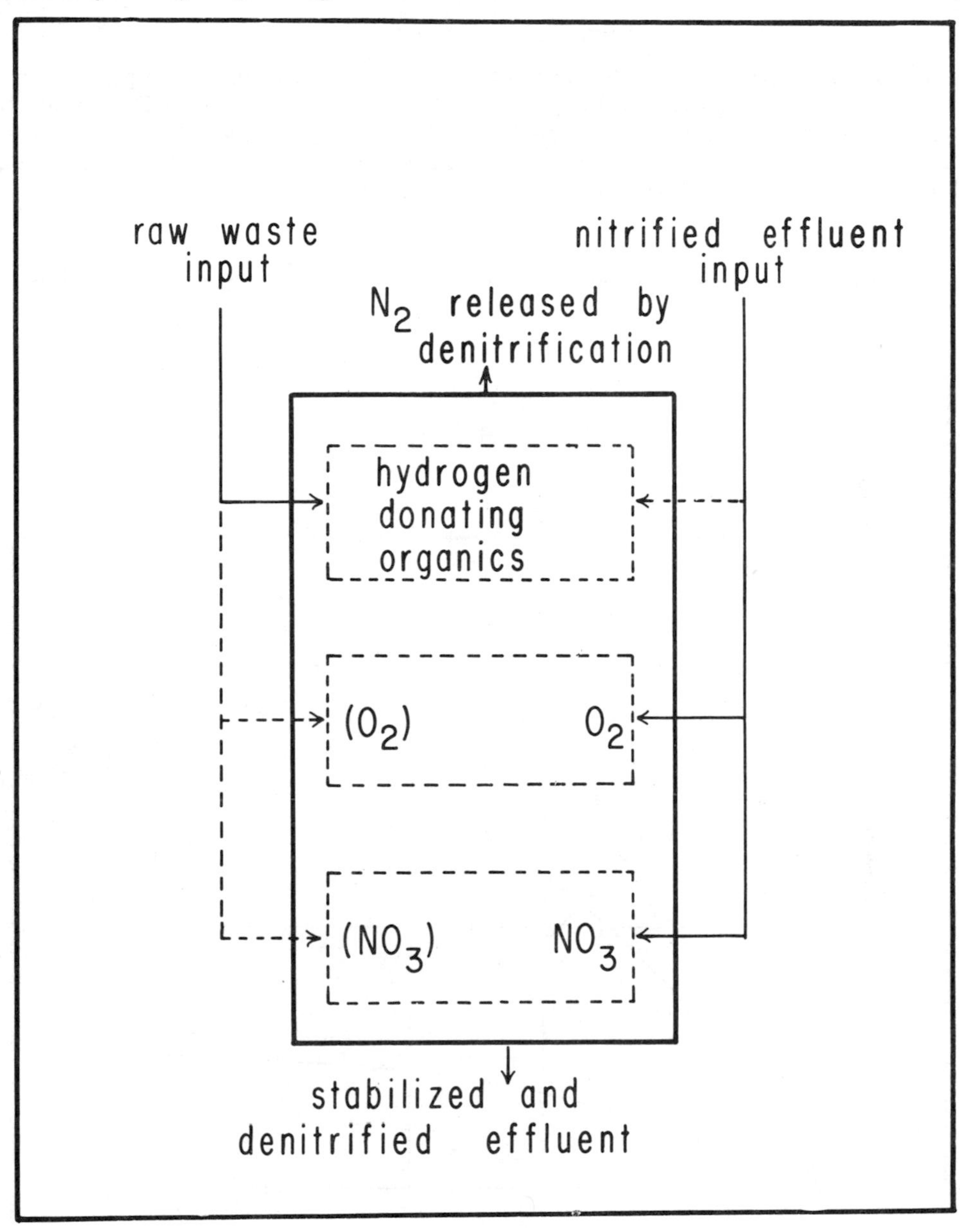

Figure 57. Control diagram for denitrification.

proper ratio between the oxygen demand and supply. Johnson and Schroepfer (31) found that a ratio of oxygen resources to 5-day BOD in the raw waste of approximately 0.8 resulted in both denitrification and stabilization of the wastes. Higher ratios did not yield complete denitrification, and appreciably lower ratios did not provide conditions for satisfactorily stabilizing the raw waste.

Limitations of the Process

One of the weaknesses of the process appears to be that of not being able to limit the process of assimilatory denitrification. As illustrated in Figure 58, the progressive denitrification of a wastewater yields nitrogen gas (N_2) due to dissimilatory denitrification, and ammonia nitrogen from the assimilatory process. Also, the addition of a portion of raw waste to serve as the hydrogen donator

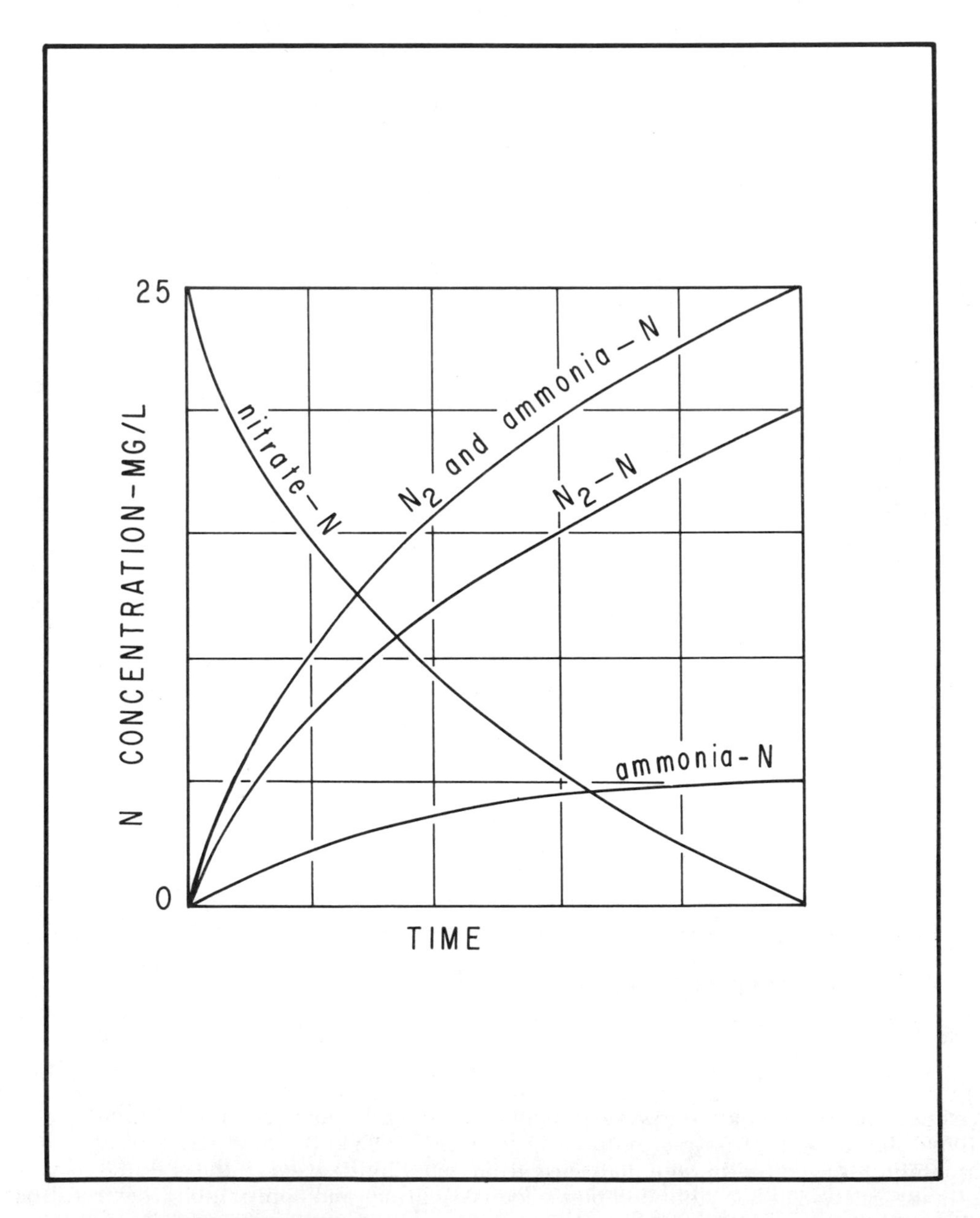

Figure 58. Batch denitrification.

results in the addition of some nonnitrified nitrogen. In tests by this writer, the denitrified effluent usually contained 5–6 mg/l of ammonia nitrogen. This usual yield of ammonia in the effluent helps to explain the fact that nitrogen removals by this process have usually been limited to 75 percent. Successive stages of nitrification and denitrification could conceivably result in considerably higher removals.

NITROGEN DISPOSAL

It must be emphasized that the entire realm of wastewater processing, inclusive of sludge disposal, must be considered when attempting to obtain increased removals. Plants using the anaerobic sludge digestion process invariably return supernatant to the process. In early work by Rawn *et al.* (38), nitrogen transformation in digestion was reported as shown in Table 41.

Both the digester supernatant and the liquor removed during the dewatering process are usually returned to the main flow of wastewater. Consequently, approximately 50 percent of the nitrogen originally removed in solid form is liquified and returned to the process to go out the effluent. Where nitrogen removal is of importance it certainly appears as if the conventional method of operating a sludge digestion process is undesirable, or that the supernatant liquors should be treated separately for nitrogen removal. The elimination of digester supernatant from the main plant flow and the treatment of such on sand beds would be a good first step toward reducing the quantity of nitrogen added to receiving waters.

The incineration of raw sludge has some particular advantages with respect to nitrogen removal. The ultimate disposal of nitrogen atoms is not to the ash but is removed from the plant site in the form of gaseous products, such as ammonia, nitric oxide, or nitrogen dioxide. Where nitrogen removal is of particular importance, there is no possibility of returning nitrogen to the flow, nor a need to treat supernatant separately as with the anaerobic digestion process.

TABLE 41

NITROGEN TRANSFORMATION DURING ANAEROBIC DIGESTION

Form	Raw Sludge	Digested Sludge	
		32 Days	55 Days
Percent in solid form	98.6	56.8	41.8
Percent in liquid form	1.4	43.2	58.2

REFERENCES

(1) "Algae and Metropolitan Wastes," *Trans.* 1961 Seminar, Robert A. Taft Sanitary Engineering Center, Cincinnati, Ohio, SEC. TR W 61-3 (1961).

(2) Mackenthun, Kenneth M. "A Review of Algae, Lake Weeds, and Nutrients," *J. Water Poll. Cont. Fed., 34*(10), 1077 (October 1962).

(3) Gerloff, Gerald C., and Folke Skoog. "Cell Contents of Nitrogen and Phosphorus as a Measure of Their Availability for Growth of Microceptis Aeruginosa," *Ecology, 35*(3), 348 (July 1954).

(4) Fitzgerald, G. P., and G. A. Rohlich. "Biological Removal of Nutrients from Treated Sewage: Laboratory Experiments," *Verh. int. Ver. Limnol., 15,* 597–608 (1965).

(5) Rohlich, Gerald A. "Methods for the Removal of Phosphorus and Nitrogen from Sewage Plant Effluents," *Proceedings, First International Conference, Advances in Water Pollution Research* (1962). New York: Pergamon Press (1964).

(6) Hoover, Sam R., and Nandor Porges. "Assimilation of Dairy Wastes by Activated Sludge. II. The Equation of Synthesis and Rate of Oxygen Utilization," *Sewage Ind. Wastes, 24*(3), 306 (March 1952).

(7) Helmers, E. N., E. J. Anderson, H. D. Kilgore, Jr., L. W. Weinberger, and C. N. Sawyer. "Nutritional Requirements in the Biological Stabilization of Industrial Wastes. I. Experimental Method," *Sewage Ind. Wastes, 22*(9), 1200 (September 1950).

(8) Helmers, E. N., J. D. Frame, A. E. Greenberg, and C. N. Sawyer. "Nutritional Requirements in the Biological Stabilization of Industrial Wastes. II. Treatment with Domestic Sewage," *Sewage Ind. Wastes, 24*(4), 496 (April 1952).

(9) Helmers, E. N., J. D. Frame, A. E. Greenberg, and C. N. Sawyer. "Nutritional Requirements in the Biological Stabilization of Industrial Wastes. III. Treatment with Supplementary Nutrients," *Sewage Ind. Wastes, 24*(4), 496 (April 1952).

(10) Kilgore, Harold D., Jr., and Clair N. Sawyer. "Nutritional Requirements in the Biological Stabilization of Industrial Wastes. IV. Treatment on High-Rate Filters," *Sewage Ind. Wastes, 25*(5), 596 (May 1953).

(11) Loehr, Raymond C., and Ralph L. Stephenson. "An Oxidation Pond as a Tertiary Treatment Device," *J. Sanit. Engr. Div. ASCE, 91*(SA3), 31 (June 1965).

(12) Herman, E. R., and E. F. Gloyna. "Waste Stabilization Ponds. I. Experimental Investigations," *J. Sewage Ind. Wastes Assoc., 30*(4), 511 (April 1958).

(13) Oswald, W. J., C. G. Golueke, R. C. Cooper, H. K. Gee, and J. C. Bronson. "Water Reclamation, Algal Production and Methane Fermentation in Waste Ponds," *Proceedings, First International Conference, Advances in Water Pollution Research* (1962). New York: Pergamon Press (1964).

(14) Gates, W. E., and J. A. Borchardt. "Nitrogen and Phosphorus Extraction from Domestic Wastewater Treatment Plant Effluents by Controlled Algal Culture," *J. Water Poll. Cont. Fed., 36*(4), 443 (April 1964).

(15) Golueke, C. G., and W. J. Oswald. "Harvesting and Processing Sewage-Grown Planktonic Algae," *J. Water Poll. Cont. Fed., 37*(4), 471 (April 1965).

(16) Van Vuuren, L. R. J., and F. A. Van Duuren. "Removal of Algae from Waste-Water Maturation Pond Effluent," *J. Water Poll. Cont. Fed., 37*(9), 1256 (September 1965).

(17) Preul, H. C. "Nitrogen Travel and Transportation in the Vicinity of Ponds," Paper presented at the Central States Water Pollution Control Association meeting, Urbana, Illinois (June 12, 1964).

(18) Sawyer, Clair N., and Leland Bradney, "Rising of Activated Sludge in Final Settling Tanks," *Sewage Works J., 17,* 1191 (November 1945).

(19) Verhoeven in McElroy, Wm. D., and Bentley Glass. *A Symposium on Inorganic Nitrogen Metabolism,* sponsored by the McCollum-Pratt Institute of Johns Hopkins University. Baltimore: The Johns Hopkins Press (1956).

(20) Christianson, C. W., E. H. Rex, W. M. Webster, and F. A. Vigil. "Reduction of Nitrate Nitrogen by Modified Activated Sludge." U. S. Atomic Energy Commission, Ti D-7517 (Pt. la), 264 (1956).

(21) South African Council for Scientific and Industrial Research. Thirteenth Annual Report, 286, (1957–1958). Abstr: *Water Poll. Abstr.,* 502 (1960).

(22) Wuhrmann, K. "Die dritte Reinigungsstufe: Wege and bisherige Erfolge in der Eliminierung eutrophierender Stoffe," *Schweiz. Z. Hydrol., XIX,* 409–427 (1957).

(23) Wuhrmann, K. "Effect of Oxygen Tension on Biochemical Reactions in Sewage Purification Plants." Conference on Biological Waste Treatment, Manhattan College (April 1960).

(24) Wuhrmann, K. "Nitrogen Removal in Sewage Treatment Processes." XVth International Congress of Limnology, Madison, Wisconsin, Plenary Session of Wednesday (August 22, 1962).

(25) Bringmann, G., R. Kuhn, and B. Wagner. "Model Experiments on the Biological Removal of Nitrogen as Gas From Treated Sewage," *Gesundheits-Ingenieur, 80,* 364–367 (1959).

(26) Bringmann, G. "Optimale Stickstoff-Abgasund furch Einsatz von nitrifizierendem Belebtschlamm und Redox-Steurung," *Gesundheits-Ingenieur, 81*(5), 140–142 (May 1960).
(27) Bringmann, G. "Complete Biological Elimination of Nitrogen from Clarified Sewage in Conjunction with a High-Efficiency Nitrification Process," *Gesundheits-Ingenieur, 82,* 233–235 (1961).
(28) Bringmann, G. "First Results of Operation of Semi-Technical Experimental Plant for the Biological Removal of Nitrogen from Waste Waters," *Gesundheits-Ingenieur, 83,* 106–108 (1962).
(29) Bringmann, G., and R. Kuhn. "Rapid Denitrification Process with Automatic Redox Control," *Gesundheits-Ingenieur, 83,* 333–334 (1962).
(30) Ludzack, F. J., and M. B. Ettinger. "Controlling Operation to Minimize Activated Sludge Effluent Nitrogen," *J. Water Poll. Cont. Fed., 34*(9), 920–931 (September 1962).
(31) Johnson, W. K., and G. J. Schroepfer. "Nitrogen Removal by Nitrification and Denitrification," *J. Water Poll. Cont. Fed., 36*(8), 1015 (August 1964).
(32) Eylar, O. K., Jr., and E. L. Schmidt. "A Survey of Heterotrophic Microorganisms from Soil for Ability to Form Nitrite and Nitrate," *J. Gen. Microbiol., 20,* 473–481 (1959).
(33) Downing, A. L., and R. W. Bayley. "Aeration Processes for the Biological Oxidation of Waste Waters," *Trans. Inst. Chem. Engr., 39*(5), A53–A59 (1961).
(34) Downing, A. L., and A. B. Wheatland. "Fundamental Considerations in Biological Treatment of Effluents," *Trans. Inst. of Chem. Engr., 40*(2), 91–103 (1962).
(35) Downing, A. L., H. A. Painter, and G. J. Knowles. "Nitrification in the Activated-Sludge Process," *J. Proc. Inst. Sewage Purif., Pt. 2,* 130–158 (1964).
(36) Downing, A. L., and A. P. Hopwood. "Some Observations on the Kinetics of Nitrifying Activated-Sludge Plants," *Schweiz. Z. Hydrol., XXVI,* 272–278 (1964).
(37) Mechsner, K. L., and K. Wuhrmann. "Beitrag zur Kenntnis der mikrobiellen Denitrifikation," *Path. Microbiol. 26.* 579–591 (1963).
(38) Rawn, A. M., A. Perry Banta, and Richard Pomeroy. "Multiple Stage Sewage Sludge Digestion," *Proc. ASCE, 63*(9, P 1), 673 (November 1937).

FACTORS TO BE CONSIDERED IN THE DESIGN OF ACTIVATED SLUDGE PLANTS

A. L. Downing
Water Pollution Research Laboratory, Stevenage, England

INTRODUCTION

In order to decide on the optimum design of an activated sludge plant for a given duty, more detailed information is required than is at present available on the inter-relationships between operating variables and performance. Recent studies in this laboratory have indicated ways in which the performance of plants can be improved by changes in design and method of operation, and have thrown into relief some of the more important problems which still require investigation.

EFFECTS OF RETENTION PERIOD AND LOADING

Production of Nitrified Effluents

Nitrifying bacteria in activated sludge plants are almost wholly confined to the activated sludge. They will thus be removed in any sludge withdrawn from the system or lost in the effluent, and under steady operating conditions the concentration of these organisms will increase above that of the small inoculum which enters in the incoming waste or from the air only if the percentage increase in their concentration due to growth during aeration exceeds the percentage increase in the concentration of activated sludge as a whole (1, 2).

In the case of *Nitrosomonas*, the organism responsible for oxidation of ammonia to nitrite, the condition for an increase in concentration can be expressed algebraically as

$$\frac{\Delta C_M}{C_M} > \frac{\Delta C_S}{C_S} \tag{1}$$

the symbols being defined at the end of the text.

For the case when the flow through the aeration units is piston-like, and the concentration of dissolved oxygen is nonlimiting, and taking into account that the concentration of ammonia in the sewage is much greater than the quite low concentration below which the rate of growth becomes concentration dependent, *Nitrosomonas* will grow logarithmically during passage of the sludge through the aeration unit. The magnitude of the growth constant, k, is such, however, that to a close approximation the increase in concentration of this organism will be given by

$$\Delta C_M = \frac{k C_M t_R}{1 + p} \tag{2}$$

The growth constant of *Nitrosomonas* in mixtures of domestic sewage and activated sludge roughly doubles for each increase in temperature of 7°C. in the range normally found in treatment plants; also k decreases with decreasing pH value below 7.2, though it remains reasonably constant in the range pH 7.2–8.0. The combined effects of these two variables in the temperature range 5–25°C. and the pH range 6–7.2 can be specified by the equation

$$k = [0.18 - 0.15\,(7.2 - p)]\,e^{0.12\,(T-15)} \tag{3}$$

in which 0.18 is the value of k in days^{-1} at 15°C. and a *p*H value of 7.2.

The increase in concentration of activated sludge cannot be deduced from first principles, but from experiments described elsewhere (3) it has been found empirically that ΔC_S varies with operating conditions approximately according to the equation

$$\Delta C_S = \frac{f_1 f_2 L\,(0.20 + 0.25 t_R^{-\frac{1}{2}})}{1 + p} \tag{4}$$

in which t_R is expressed in days and where f_1 and f_2 are numerical factors, the magnitudes of which depend respectively on the concentration of sludge maintained in the aeration units, and on the temperature of mixed liquor, in accordance with the approximate equations

$$f_1 = 1 - 0.00004\,(S - 3{,}000) \tag{5}$$

$$f_2 = 1 - 0.02\,(T - 16) \tag{6}$$

Equation 5 being valid in the range S = 1,000–10,000 mg/l and Equation 6 in the range T = 7–25°C.

If follows from the above considerations that for a nitrifying population to be built up there is a minimum period of retention, t_M, which must be exceeded, and that this is related to other operating variables by the following equation:

$$t_M = \frac{f_1 f_2 L\,(0.20 + 0.25 t_M^{-\frac{1}{2}})}{k C_S} \tag{7}$$

If t_R exceeds t_M the concentration of *Nitrosomonas* will build up under steady conditions to an equilibrium concentration, C_{ME}, such that

$$\frac{\Delta C_M}{C_{ME}} = \frac{\Delta C_S}{C_S} \tag{8}$$

This equilibrium concentration will be sufficient to oxidize virtually all the incoming ammonia, in a period approximately equal to $\frac{t_M}{1 + p}$ and it will be nearly proportional to the concentration of ammonia in the sewage and to C_S. The rate at which equilibrium is approached will however depend on the operating conditions, since these will determine by how much the rate of growth of *Nitrosomonas* exceeds its rate of removal in sludge withdrawn or lost from the plant.

Figure 59 shows examples of the predicted relations between the minimum period of retention of sewage and the operating conditions for the case when, as is common in practice, the flow of returned sludge is approximately equal to that of sewage. It may be seen that the minimum period of retention decreases with increasing temperature and increasing concentration of sludge carried, and with decreasing strength of the sewage applied. In practice the maximum concentration of sludge which can be carried depends on the operating conditions, but over a wide range of conditions is of the order of 6,000–7,000 mg/l. Thus for a plant treating settled sewage of the strength usually found in Britain, with a 5-day BOD of about 250 mg/l, the minimum period of retention under winter conditions at minimum temperatures of, say, 7°C., is about 9 hours. However the concentration of sludge in most full-scale plants is usually maintained at a much lower figure—3,000 mg/l would probably be a fair average—and in this case the minimum period of retention under the above conditions is about 20 hours, or much more than the period of 10–12 hours commonly provided. This is one of several reasons why many full-scale plants do not achieve nitrification in winter.

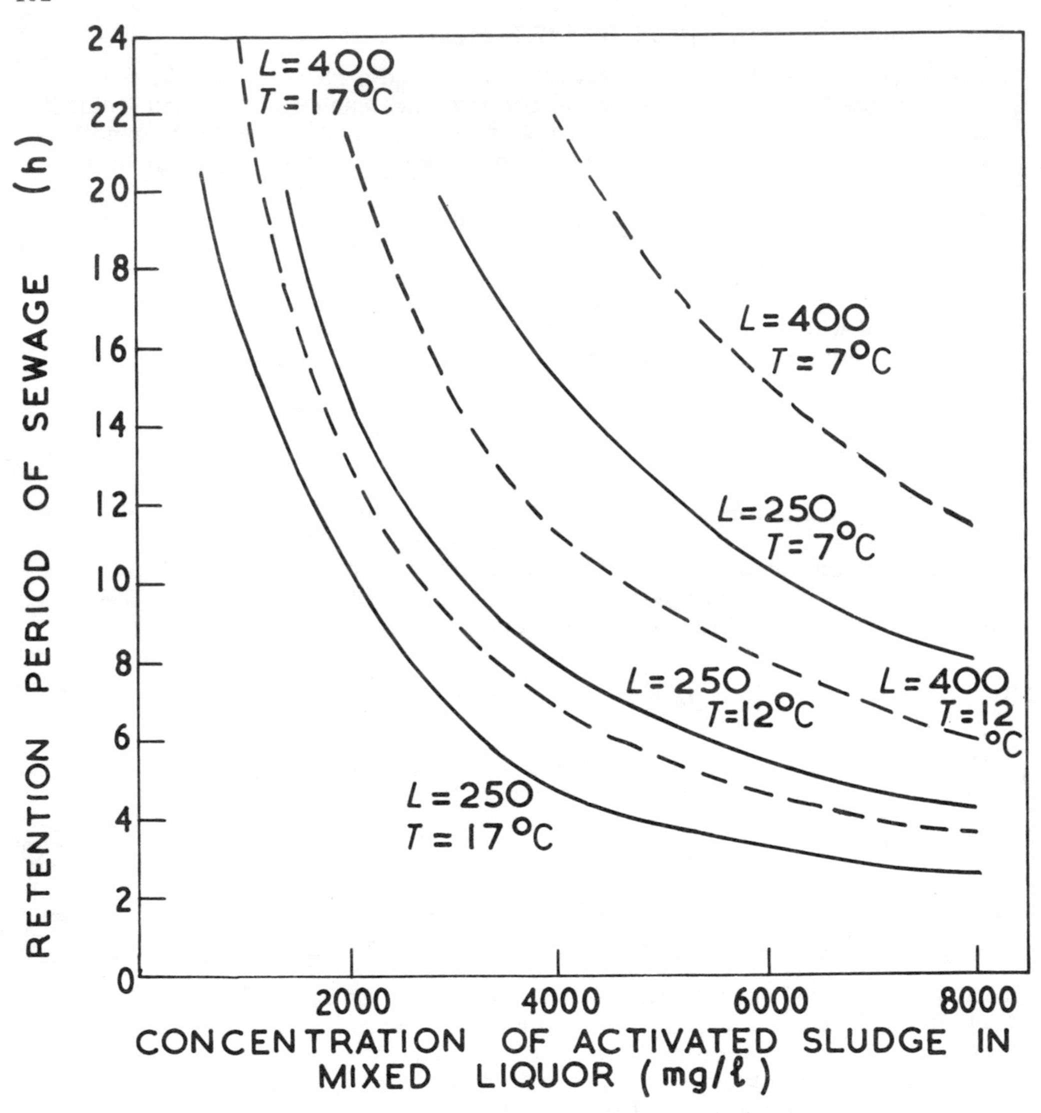

Figure 59. Predicted minimum period of retention of sewage for consistent nitrification in activated sludge plants for different operating conditions. L = 5-day BOD of settled sewage (mg/l); T = temperature of mixed liquor (°C.).

Evidence of the general qualitative validity of the present approach is afforded by data from experimental and pilot plants in the United States (4) and in Switzerland (5) and from pilot and full-scale plants in this country (1, 3, 6). Figure 60 shows some further examples of such data. In Figure 60(a) the concentrations of ammonia in the effluents from eight small uniformly mixed activated sludge plants at the end of six weeks of operation, during which sewage was applied to each plant at a different rate, giving periods of retention ranging from 2 to 36 hours, are compared with predicted variations in concentration of ammonia with period of retention for sewage of the average strength of that applied. It can be

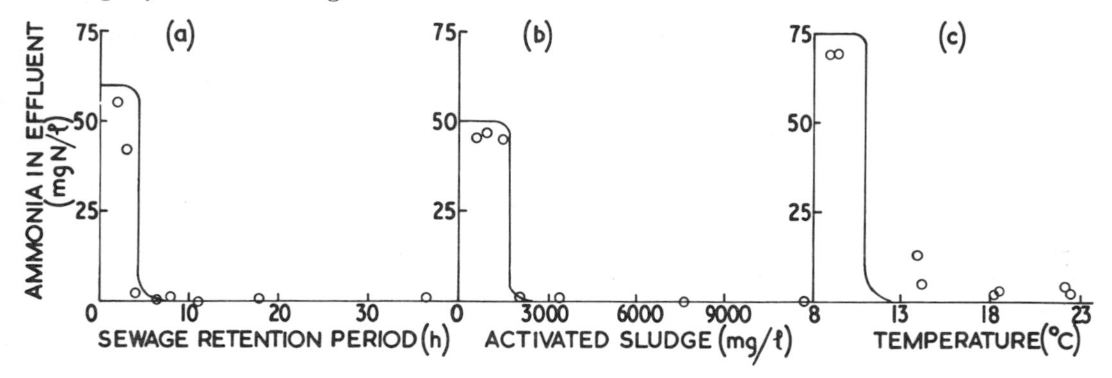

Figure 60. Observed (0) and predicted (———) effects of (a) retention period, (b) concentration of activated sludge, and (c) temperature, on the concentration of ammonia in the effluent from uniformly mixed plants.

seen that there is reasonably good agreement between observation and prediction. Figure 60(b) shows similar data for an experiment in which the period of retention was constant and the concentration of activated sludge was varied, and Figure 60(c) shows results obtained when the temperature of the mixed liquor was the factor varied. Here again there is reasonable agreement between observation and prediction, although in the case of Figure 60(c) the observations are rather too widely spaced to test prediction very precisely.

Removal of Carbonaceous Matter

As yet there is no general theory comparable with that for nitrification by which the effect of operating conditions on the removal of carbonaceous matter, or of the BOD due to this material, can be predicted. The relation between retention period or loading on the removal of BOD has, however, been examined experimentally. In recent studies percentage removal has been correlated empirically with the organic load on the plant, expressed as weight of BOD applied per unit weight of sludge in the aeration units per unit time (units commonly used being g/g/day); in terms of the symbols adopted here, loading = $L/C_S\ t_R$. In Figure 61 average results over periods of four or five months from pilot plants operated at this laboratory at temperatures in the range mainly from 14 to 20°C. are compared with data obtained by Wuhrmann (7) and with other data from various sources, as collated by Emde (8). The results of the recent studies with pilot plants in this laboratory are roughly consistent with the continuous trend proposed by Wuhrmann (7) for temperatures above 13°C. Such correlations, however, though useful as a general guide, should be interpreted with caution, since inevitably all the factors of importance are not revealed, as is indicated by the scatter in the data. The implication of the trends shown in Figure 61 is that if the concentration of sludge were maintained at a customary level of about 3,000 mg/l, effluent having a BOD of less than 20 mg/l could be produced from a sewage with a BOD of 250 mg/l with periods of retention of 10 hours, which is consistent with experience; if the concentration of sludge were increased to 6,000 mg/l the retention time could be reduced to 5 hours, or less than half that normally provided in conventional plants. Figure 59 shows, however, that operation under these conditions would inevitably entail loss of nitrification in cold weather. Where nitrification is not required, operation with shorter periods of retention than in conventional plants appears to be feasible, but is not without drawbacks that are discussed later.

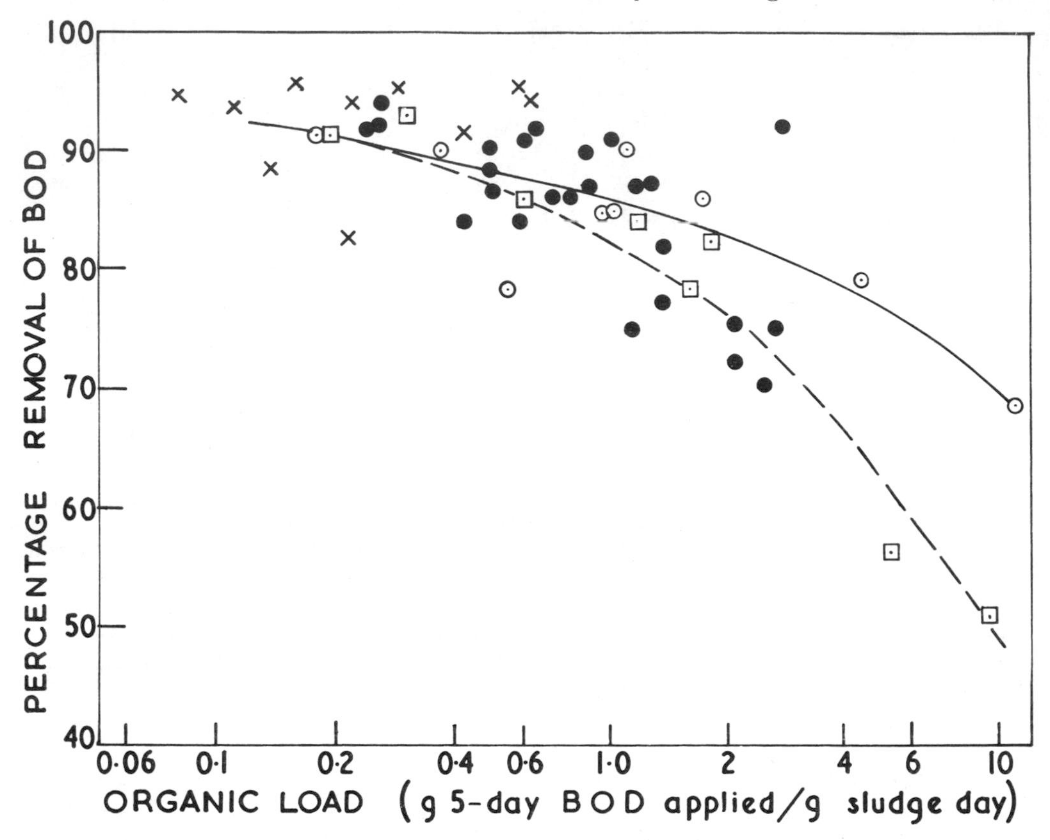

Figure 61. Relation between percentage removal of 5-day BOD in activated sludge plants and organic load applied: x = pilot plants, present work, 13–20°C.; 0 = full-scale and pilot plants (8); ⊙ = pilot plants, temperatures above 13°C. (7); ⊡ = pilot plants, temperatures below 11°C. (7); ——— = correlation proposed by Wuhrmann, > 13°C.; - - - = correlation proposed by Wuhrmann, < 11°C.

Sludge Production

Equations 4, 5, and 6 show respectively the dependence of sludge production on retention time, sludge concentration, and temperature. Having regard to the possible range of variation of these factors, the first, retention time, is perhaps the most important of the three. Allowing for a loss of solids in the effluent of 30 mg/l, the total rate of production of secondary sludge in a high-rate plant with a retention period of 2 hours, would be about twice that in a conventional plant with a period of retention of 10–12 hours; the increase in the total production of sludge (activated plus primary sludge) as compared with that in a conventional plant would be about 20 percent. It is not yet possible to assess accurately the effect this would have on the costs of sludge treatment and disposal, but it seems likely that these would increase at least in proportion to the increase in sludge production and possibly more.

Sludge Settleability and Dewaterability

Also affected by retention period (or by loading) is the rate of settling of the sludge. Figure 62(a) shows the relation between retention period and the average

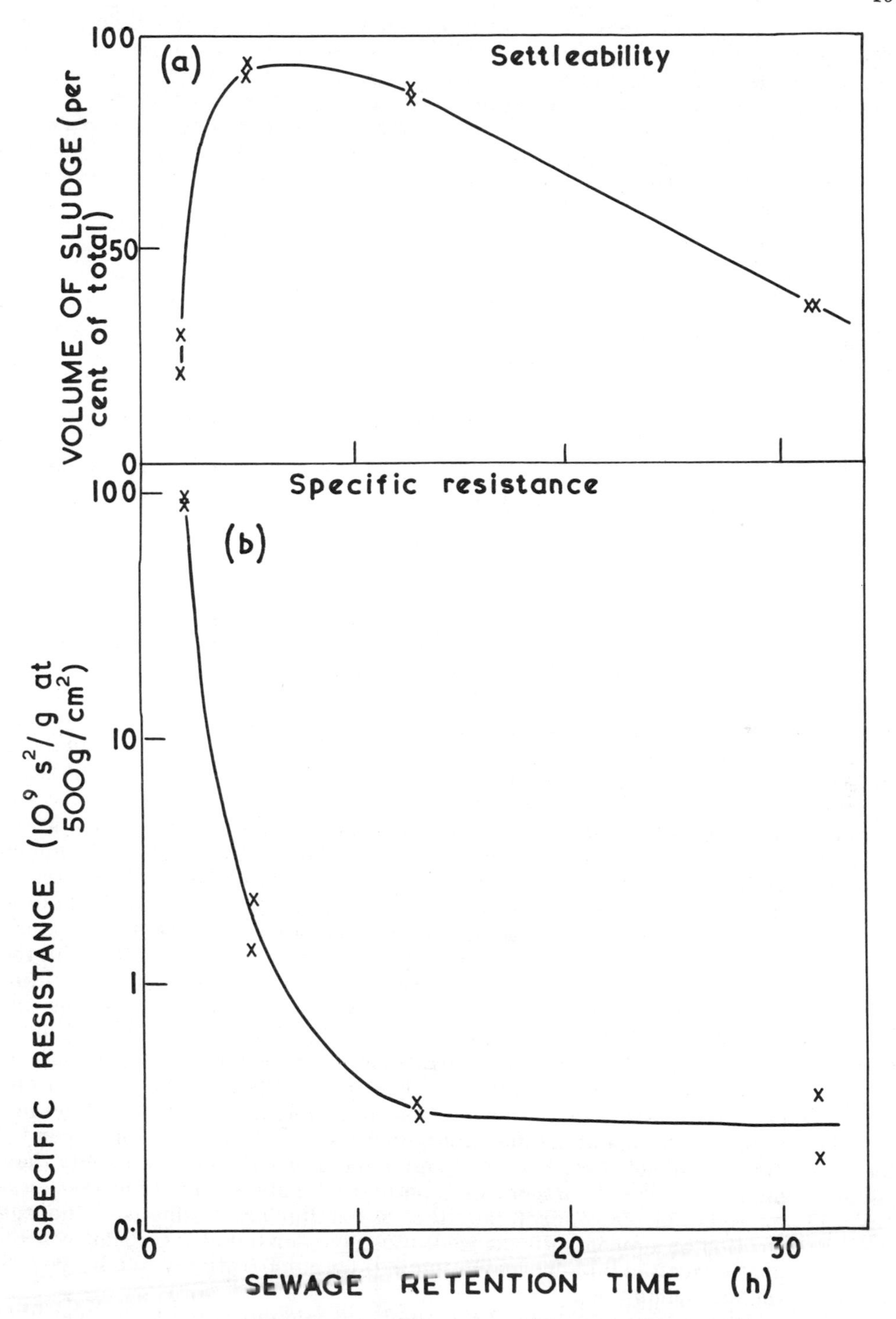

Figure 62. Relations between retention time for sewage in uniformly mixed activated sludge plants and the settled volume after 0.5 hour and specific resistance to filtration of the sludge.

percentage of the total volume of liquid occupied by sludge, after settling mixed liquor for 0.5 hour, during treatment of settled domestic sewage over a period of two months in small experimental plants in this laboratory in which the aeration units were uniformly mixed. It can be seen that the rate of settling was lowest at retention periods of the order of 5 hours, the average percentage settled volume after 0.5 hour being about 92. At very short or very long retention periods, however, the rate of settling was much faster. Similar effects have been reported in the literature (9).

Figure 62(b) shows that the specific resistance of the sludges to filtration (a measure of the degree of difficulty with which they could be dewatered by draining on open beds or by vacuum filters) increased rapidly with decreasing period of retention (10). Recent work has shown that the specific resistance of digested mixtures of primary and activated sludge also increases with decreasing periods of retention in the activated sludge plant.

EFFECTS OF LONGITUDINAL MIXING

The degree of longitudinal mixing in aeration units appears to have a number of important effects, some of which have received relatively little attention.

Effects on Biological Oxidation

The effects of mixing on the kinetics of the degradation of complex organic substrates have not yet been worked out in detail. The effects of mixing on nitrification are better understood. In interpreting and predicting these effects the procedure used is to assume that the actual aeration units consist of a number of uniformly mixed compartments in series, each of equal volume. The number of these hypothetical units is taken to be that for which the residence-time distribution of liquid flowing through the system is the same as the observed distribution for the actual aeration units. Then by applying already established kinetic equations for growth of nitrifying bacteria, the relation between the concentrations of ammonia and of nitrifying bacteria in each hypothetical unit and those in the next can be written down. These equations can be solved by iteration for steady state conditions, but this is very laborious if carried out by hand. However, it has been shown by Knowles (in preparation), that the required solution can be obtained very rapidly using an electronic digital computer. The actual variation in concentration of ammonia in the treatment plant is then taken to be that obtained by plotting the predicted concentration in each hypothetical unit against the distance from the inlet to the mid-point of the unit (expressed as a percentage of the total length) and drawing a smooth curve through the points. Figure 63(a) shows some examples of the calculated concentrations of ammonia for various numbers of hypothetical uniformly mixed units, and Figure 63 (b) shows the effect of concentration of sludge and of the degree of mixing on the predicted variations in concentration of ammonia along the length of the actual unit. It will be seen from the latter figure that the distribution of ammonia approaches quite closely that for perfect piston flow once the number of hypothetical units to which the system corresponds exceeds ten. In general the effect of longitudinal mixing is to increase the concentration of ammonia discharged, though under operating conditions favorable for nitrification this concentration will be comparatively small even in uniformly mixed plants.

One of the main practical uses of the above technique is for the estimation of the rate of consumption of oxygen due to nitrification at any given point in the aeration units.

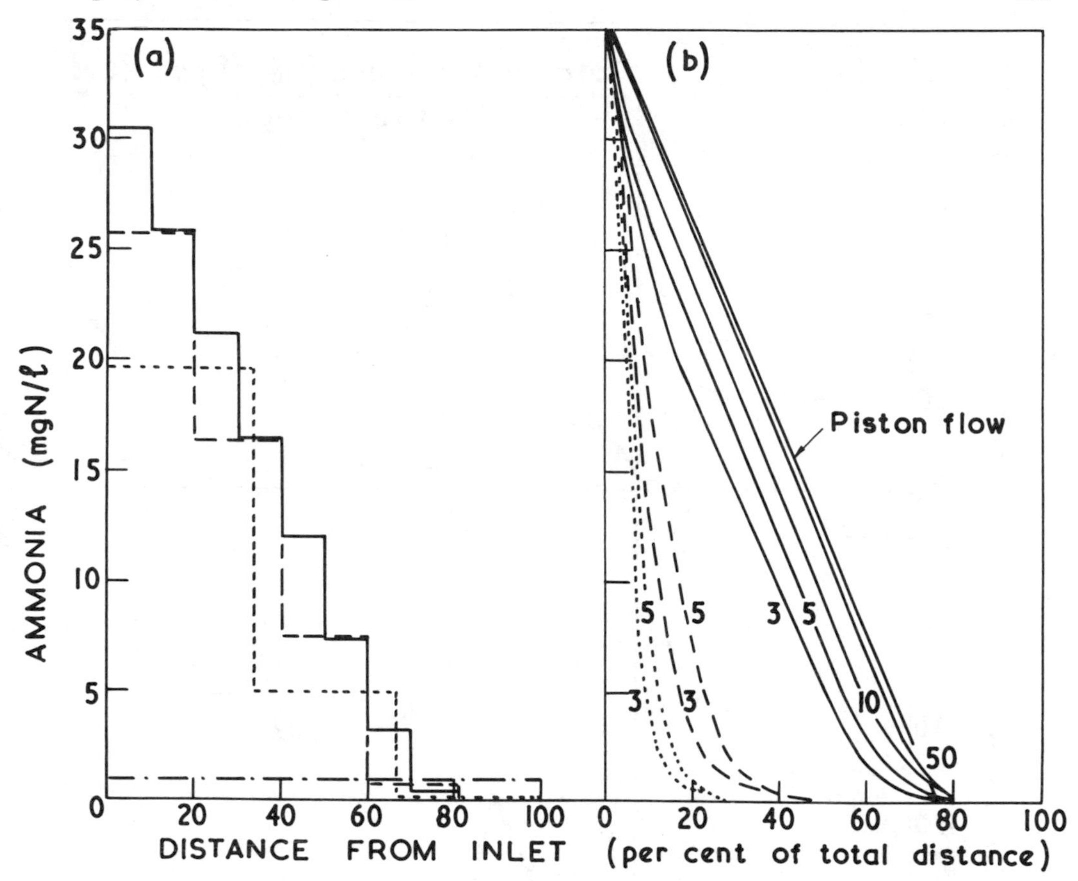

Figure 63. Effect of longitudinal mixing on the distribution of ammonia in aeration units of nitrifying activated sludge plants under steady conditions. Temperature, 14°C.; 5-day BOD of sewage, 200 mg/l; ammonia in sewage, 70 mg/l (as N); retention period of sewage, 10 hours; retention period of mixed liquor, 5 hours: (a) Calculated steady-state concentrations in hypothetical series of uniformly mixed aeration units. 2,000 mg/l activated sludge. Number of uniformly mixed units: ——— = 10; - - - = 5; . . . . = 3; -·-· = 1. (b) Expected distribution of ammonia in actual aeration units. Number of uniformly mixed units to which actual units correspond printed against each curve. Concentration of activated sludge (mg/l) ——— = 2,000; - - - = 4,000; . . . . = 6,000.

Effects on the Influence of Inhibitory Substances

When the incoming waste contains appreciable concentrations of materials which inhibit microbial activity, the degree of longitudinal mixing can have an important effect on plant performance; plants in which such mixing is high appear to be less sensitive to the effects of inhibitors than those in which the flow is more pistonlike. One illustration of this is given in Figure 64, in which are compared the effects of the addition of potassium cyanide (1 mg/l as HCN) on nitrification in, at one extreme, a uniformly mixed aeration unit and, at the other, a fill-and-draw plant; in the latter the conditions during aeration can be regarded as roughly representative of those in an aeration unit through which the liquid travels with perfect piston flow. Whereas nitrification was virtually eliminated

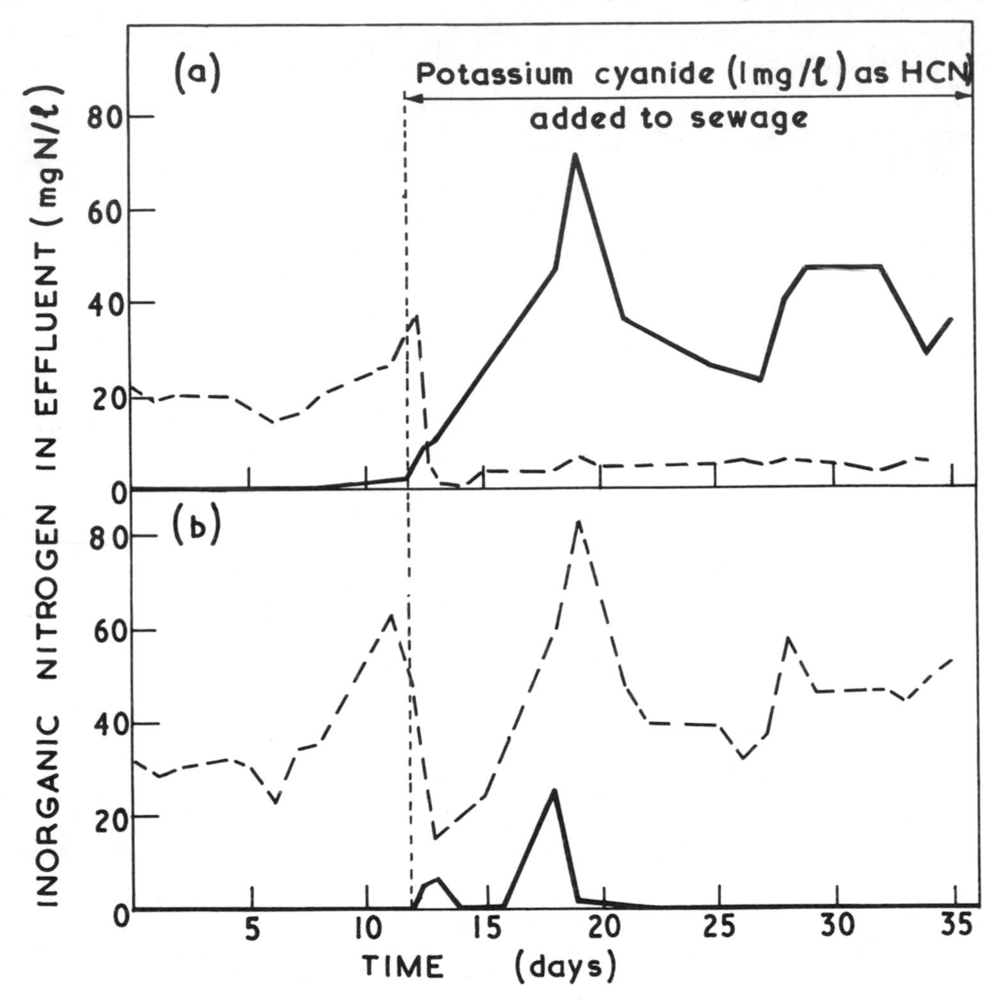

Figure 64. Comparison of the effects of the addition of cyanide to the sewage on nitrification in (a) fill-and-draw and (b) a uniformly mixed activated sludge plant. ——— = ammonia; - - - = total oxidized nitrogen.

in the fill-and-draw plant after addition of cyanide to the sewage and was not recovered in the following three weeks, there were only comparatively small increases in the concentration of ammonia in the effluent from the uniformly mixed plant during the first ten days after addition of cyanide, and subsequently ammonia was almost completely removed. This difference is largely the result of a difference in the fate of cyanide during aeration. In the uniformly mixed plant, because any element of liquid entering the aeration units became, as it were, diluted by the whole contents of the aeration unit, and because activated sludge rapidly developed an ability to metabolize cyanide, the concentration of cyanide in the aeration unit never exceeded 0.1 mg/l, and after a few days had fallen below the limit of detection by the method used. Cyanide was also completely metabolized during aeration in the fill-and-draw plant, and the rate at which this occurred increased as the sludge became adapted. However, appreciable time was required in each cycle before the concentration was reduced from the initial value of about 0.5 mg/l, which was shown in independent batch tests to produce severe inhibition

(11), to a concentration at which the inhibitory effect was no longer of great significance.

PATTERN OF AERATION

To make the best use of the tank capacity available it is essential to ensure that the rate of oxidation of polluting matter is not restricted by supply of oxygen. At the same time, since the rate of aeration, and thus the power required to maintain a given concentration of dissolved oxygen, is inversely proportional to the oxygen deficit, it is desirable in the interests of economy that the concentration is not maintained at a higher level than necessary. Where nitrification is required it would appear that the optimum concentration is around 2 mg/l or perhaps a little higher. For carbonaceous oxidation a concentration of 0.5 mg/l is probably adequate.

In order to assess accurately the intensity of aeration required to maintain the optimum concentration of dissolved oxygen it is necessary to know the rate of consumption of dissolved oxygen at all points in the aeration units. There is no doubt that in the past, lack of information on the variation in rate of consumption of oxygen with operating conditions has resulted in the adoption of designs that were far from ideal, especially for achieving nitrification.

In Figure 65 measurements by a respirometric method (12) of rates of consumption of dissolved oxygen due to nitrification in activated sludge plants (the residence-time distribution for which was the same as that for three uniformly mixed aeration units in series) are compared with those predicted. It can be seen that the observed and predicted demands for a given concentration of sludge, though by no means the same, are qualitatively similar. In fact precise agreement would not be expected, because it was not possible to maintain the perfectly steady conditions on which predictions were based. It will be evident that the rate of consumption of oxygen due to nitrification varies considerably with the concentration of sludge, a fact that has not generally been appreciated. Similarly, the oxygen demand due to nitrification varies, though again in an approximately predictable way, with other operating variables, such as temperature, concentration of ammonia, and the BOD of the sewage.

Rates of consumption of oxygen due to carbonaceous oxidation cannot yet be predicted from first principles. It is possible, however, to estimate these rates from empirical correlations based on measurements in pilot plants, results of which have already been reported (13).

Once the rate of oxygen consumption is known the number of aerators and the power requirements can be estimated from already published data on oxygenation capacities and aeration "efficiencies" (14). Estimates of the approximate total average rates of consumption of oxygen in the aeration units of a plant producing a fully nitrified effluent from settled sewage having a BOD of 250 mg/l and containing 40 mg/l ammonia are shown in Figure 66(a) (left-hand scale). The corresponding estimated flows of air (per unit plan area of the aeration tank) required to maintain a concentration of 2 mg/l dissolved oxygen in a fine-bubble diffused air unit of conventional type, 12 ft. deep, are shown by the right-hand scale. These rates of flow are considerably greater, especially in the first half of the aeration units, than the figure of 0.15 ft^3/ft^2 min (0.05 m^3/m^2) (uniformly distributed) commonly adopted as a basis for British design until recently.

It also seems clear that maintaining a constant rate of aeration from inlet to outlet, as is done in the majority of existing full-scale plants, is a far from ideal arrangement. The most efficient system seems likely to be one in which the rate of aeration is tapered from inlet to outlet and is controlled automatically so that it matches the oxygen demand. The possiblities of developing such a system using membrane electrodes to monitor concentrations of dissolved oxygen are now being studied in this Laboratory.

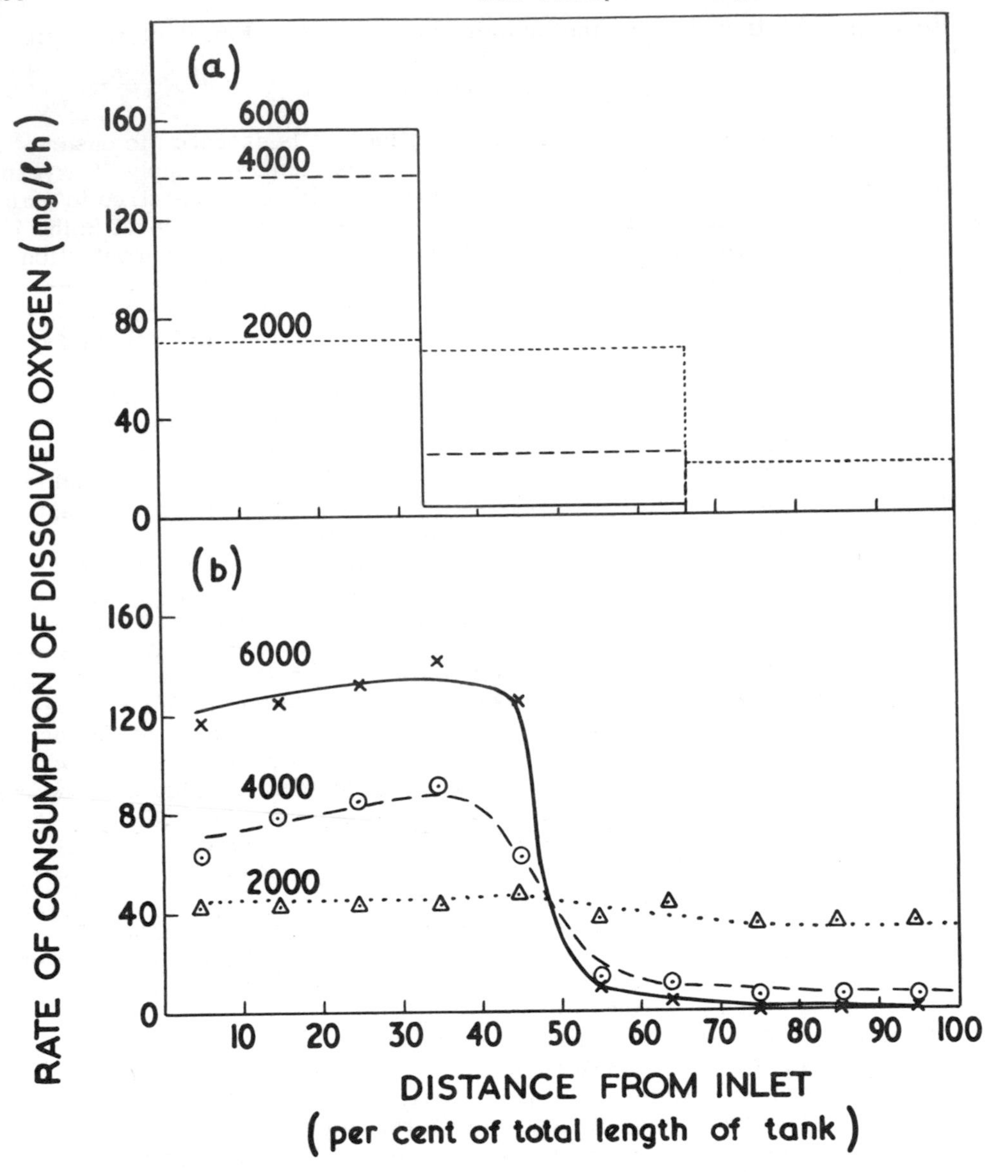

Figure 65. Rates of consumption of dissolved oxygen due to nitrification in activated sludge plants: (a) Predicted for steady conditions in three uniformly mixed aeration units in series; (b) Observed in hydraulically equivalent pilot plants under approximately steady conditions. Concentration of activated sludge printed against each curve. Concentration of ammonia in sewage, 70 mg/l; temperature 14°C.

Meanwhile it is thought that the arrangement indicated in Figure 66(b) would make a reasonably satisfactory basis for design for conventional plants (of the type employed in Britain) from which a fully nitrified effluent was required. The right-hand scale shows the approximate average flows of air required for a conventional fine-bubble aeration system, and the left-hand scale the approximate

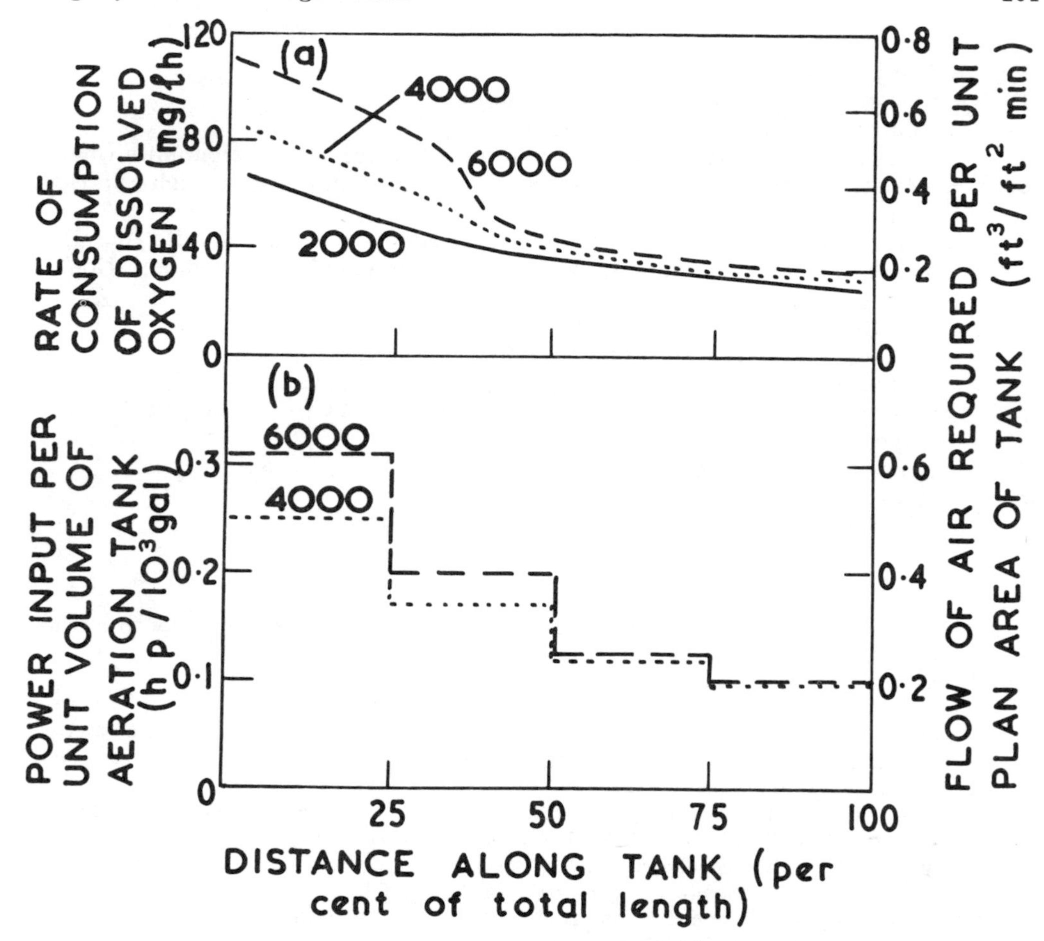

Figure 66. Approximate rates of consumption of dissolved oxygen to be expected and rates of aeration necessary to maintain aerobic conditions in long, baffled aeration units of activated sludge plants treating a typical settled domestic sewage having a 5-day BOD of 250 mg/l and containing 40 mg/l ammonia (as N): (a) Expected demand and equivalent rates of aeration needed to maintain 2 mg/l dissolved oxygen; (b) Basis for design of tapered aeration system to achieve consistent nitrification. Activated sludge concentration (mg/l): - - - = 6,000; . . . . = 4,000; ——— = 2,000.

power input needed per unit volume of tank for diffused air or mechanical aeration systems operating with aeration efficiencies of 2,000 g/kWh, about the order which appears to be obtained under favorable conditions in full-scale practice.

ACKNOWLEDGMENTS

The experiments on the effect of retention period on settleability of sludge were carried out by Mr. J. C. Merkens, and those on the effect of cyanide on nitrification by the late Mr. W. Mason. Mr. A. M. Bruce made the measurements of specific resistance of sludge. Thanks are due particularly to Mr. G. Knowles, who devised the computer program for calculating the effects of mixing on nitrification. Dr. H. A. Painter provided some of the data on the rates of respiration of activated sludge.

SYMBOLS USED

L = 5-day BOD of sewage (mg/l)
F = flow of sewage (volume per unit time)
V = volumetric capacity of aeration units
C_S = concentration of activated sludge in mixed liquor in aeration units (mg/l)
ΔC_S = increase in concentration of activated sludge in passing through aeration units (mg/l)
C_M = concentration of *Nitrosomonas* in mixed liquor in aeration units (mg/l)
ΔC_M = increase in concentration of *Nitrosomonas* in passing through aeration units (mg/l)
k = growth-rate constant for *Nitrosomonas* (days^{-1})
p = ratio of flow of returned sludge to that of sewage
t_R = period of retention of sewage in aeration units (days)
t_M = minimum period of retention of sewage necessary to achieve nitrification (days)
T = temperature of mixed liquor (°C.)
f_1, f_2 = numerical factors
P = pH value

REFERENCES

(1) Downing, A. L., and A. P. Hopwood. "Some Observations on the Kinetics of Nitrifying Activated-Sludge Plants," *Schweiz. Z. Hydrol., 26,* 271 (1964).
(2) Downing, A. L., H. A. Painter, and G. Knowles. "Nitrification in the Activated-Sludge Process," *J. Proc. Inst. Sewage Purif.*, 130 (1964).
(3) Hopwood, A. P., and A. L. Downing. "Factors Affecting the Rate of Production and Properties of Activated Sludge in Plants Treating Domestic Sewage," *J. Proc. Inst. Sewage Purif.*, 435 (1965).
(4) Johnson, W. K. and G. J. Schroepfer. "Nitrogen Removal by Nitrification and Denitrification," *J. Water Poll. Cont. Fed., 36,* 1015 (August 1964).
(5) Wuhrmann, K. "Die Grundlagen der Dimensionierung der Beluftung bei Belebtschlammanlagen," *Schweiz. Z. Hydrol., 26,* 310 (1964).
(6) Department of Scientific and Industrial Research. *Water Pollution Research 1963.* London: Her Majesty's Stationery Office (1964).
(7) Wuhrmann, K. "Hauptwirkungen und Wechselwirkungen einiger Betriebsparameter im Belebtschlammsystem," *Schweiz. Z. Hydrol., 26,* 218 (1964).
(8) Emde, W. Von der. "Aspects of the High-Rate Activated-Sludge Process," *Conference on Biological Waste Treatment.* New York: Manhattan College (1960).
(9) Simpson, J. R. "Extended Sludge Aeration Activated-Sludge Systems," *J. Proc. Inst. Sewage Purif.,* 328 (1964).
(10) Ministry of Technology. *Water Pollution Research 1965.* London: Her Majesty's Stationery Office (1966).
(11) Downing, A. L., T. G. Tomlinson, and G. A. Truesdale. "Effect of Inhibitors on Nitrification in the Activated-Sludge Process," *J. Proc. Inst. Sewage Purif.,* 537 (1964).
(12) Painter, H. A., and K. Jones. "The Use of the Wide-Bore Drooping-Mercury Electrode for the Determination of Rates of Oxygen Uptake and of Oxidation of Ammonia by Micro-Organisms," *J. Appl. Bacteriol., 26,* 471 (1963).
(13) Ministry of Technology. *Water Pollution Research 1964.* London: Her Majesty's Stationery Office (1965).
(14) Downing, A. L., and A. B. Wheatland. "Fundamental Consideration in Biological Treatment of Effluents," *Trans. Inst. Chem. Engr., 40,* 91 (1962).

DISCUSSION OF "FACTORS TO BE CONSIDERED IN THE DESIGN OF ACTIVATED SLUDGE PLANTS"

J. B. White
University of Manchester, England

Since World War II plant scale work has been carried out at the Manchester, England, treatment plant to guide the design of new works recently completed. The developments have been carried out in close collaboration with machinery manufacturers, resulting in a significant improvement in the design of "Simplex" surface aeration units. The Mark III E type installed at the new plant is undoubtedly a very efficient aerator and circulator. Its designed efficiency is 4 pounds oxygen for brake horse-power-hour, and it achieves intensive aeration without danger to the sludge floc. The aerator plant consists of 88 pockets, each 35 feet square and 10 feet deep. Each pocket has a Mark III E aerator rotating at 45 rpm and absorbing 20 bHP under maximum immersion conditions. The detention period is 2.82 hours. The sewage treated is very strong and contains a large fraction of industrial wastes. Detention periods three or four times longer would previously have been required. The horsepower per million gallons[1] treated is 33 for aeration alone. Recirculation of activated sludge requires a further 7 HP per million gallons.

I am indebted to Gerald Ainsworth, Manager, Manchester Corporation, River Department, for the details.

---

[1] Imperial gallons = $1\frac{1}{4} \times$ U. S. gallons.

DEVELOPMENTS IN BIOLOGICAL FILTRATION

Vaughn C. Behn and Parviz Monadjemi
Cornell University, Ithaca, New York

INTRODUCTION

A biological or trickling filter is a basic waste treatment process used for reducing the organic load present in municipal and industrial wastewater. It consists of a bed of stones or other natural or synthetic media upon which the wastewater is applied, with the subsequent growth of microbial slimes in the filter.

During the past few decades a number of empirical and mathematical models have been developed to define the action of trickling filter.

In an earlier paper (1) an attempt was made to summarize and relate the then existing formulations. Attention was given to the work by Phelps, Velz, Schulze, Howland, and Stack. In particular, the relationship between the equilibrium load contained in a saturated filter, as proposed by Phelps and Velz, and the applied load which would saturate a unit depth, as suggested by Stack, was demonstrated. The availability factor utilized in the National Research Council formulas was reviewed from the standpoint of its physical interpretation and its role in the Stack equation for a recirculating filter.

Since then, a number of new formulations have appeared in the literature, which will be reviewed in the first section of this paper along with certain of the older mathematical formulations.

The second part consists mainly of some new concepts concerning the factors which affect the performance of a biological system, such as trickling filter. The effect of flow pattern on the efficiency of a system undergoing a first-order reaction is described. Attention is called to the importance of concentration of bacteria in most biological systems, no matter what the pattern of flow is. Certain observations are made on the relationship of flow to the concentration of bacteria in determining the efficiency of a trickling filter system.

VARIOUS MATHEMATICAL FORMULATIONS

Single Stage Filter

Many workers have examined the mechanism of BOD removal in trickling filter.

Velz (2) proposed a "basic law" for the performance of trickling filter. He postulated that the amount of BOD removed per unit depth was proportional to the BOD remaining.

$$\frac{ds}{dH} = -K_H s \qquad (1)$$

or, upon integration

$$\frac{s_e}{s_0} = e^{-K_H H_0} \qquad (2)$$

where s_e is the removable BOD of the effluent, s_0 is the removable BOD of the influent, H_0 is the depth of the filter, and K_H is a rate constant.

Velz, and later Stack (3), assumed that there is a given loading above which the purification rate, $\frac{ds}{dH}$, remains constant. Phelps and Velz (4) stated that the limiting BOD load is a function of storage capacity of the bed. Assuming that s_f, the BOD load stored in the bed, is oxidized according to a first-order reaction, and that new BOD is being added at the rate s_a in the filter of depth H_0

$$\frac{ds_f}{dH} = -K_f s_f + s_a (1 - e^{-K_H H_0}) \tag{3}$$

At limiting BOD load $\frac{ds_f}{dH} = 0$ and maximum load to be applied is

$$(s_a)_{max} = \frac{K_f s_f}{(1 - e^{-K_H H_0})} \tag{4}$$

Stack (3) introduces a more refined concept, that of filter saturation at various depths in sequence.

Fair and Geyer (5) presented the rate of BOD removal in a filter as

$$\frac{ds}{dH} = -K_H S\left(\frac{s}{s_0}\right)^n \tag{5}$$

or alternatively

$$\frac{ds}{dt} = -K_t S\left(\frac{s}{s_0}\right)^n \tag{6}$$

where s_0 is the initial removable BOD applied to the filter, and n is a coefficient which is a measure of the nonuniformity of the rate of purification. When $n = 0$, Equation 5 reduces to Velz's law, that is, first-order reaction.

Both Stack and Velz worked with depth as the parameter. W. E. Howland (6) proposed that the rate of BOD removal was a function of the time of contact, t:

ds

$$\frac{ds}{dt} = -K_t s \tag{7}$$

which integrates to

$$\frac{s_e}{s_0} = e^{-K_t t} \tag{8}$$

The contact time, t, in a column cubically packed with spheres is (7)

$$t = 1.3 H_0 \left(\frac{3\nu}{g}\right)^{\frac{1}{3}} \left(\frac{A_v}{Q}\right)^{\frac{2}{3}} \tag{9}$$

where

ν = kinematic viscosity
g = acceleration due to gravity
A_v = specific surface area
Q = volumetric rate of flow/unit area

Sinkoff, Porges, and McDermott (7), making use of experimental results, concluded that the contact time in general is given by

$$t = C_1 H_0 \left(\frac{A_v}{Q}\right)^{n'} \tag{10}$$

where C_1 is a constant and the exponent n' varies with the type of filter medium and the hydraulic characteristics of the system. For example, Sinkoff, Porges, and McDermott (7) found n' to range between 0.53 for porcelain spheres to 0.83 for glass spheres.

Studies by Schulze (8) on a screen filter gave a value of n' equal to 0.66. Schulze combined Equations 10 and 8 to obtain

$$\frac{S_e}{S_0} = e^{-K' \frac{H_0}{Q^{.66}}} \tag{11}$$

in which the effect of specific surface area is apparently assumed to be constant and is included in the value of K'.

Eckenfelder (9) modified Equation 11 and took into consideration that C_2, the amount of active surface film covering the filter medium, decreases with depth, that is,

$$C_2 \propto \frac{1}{H^m} \tag{12}$$

By making proper substitution, Eckenfelder obtained the following:

$$\frac{S_e}{S_0} = e^{-K'' \frac{H_0^{1-m}}{Q^{n'}}} \tag{13}$$

However, the constituents of domestic wastes are not removed at the same rate. The components which are more readily oxidizable are utilized with a faster rate. Because of this fact, Eckenfelder modified Equation 13 to a retardent form in order to describe the overall reduction of BOD. His final equation is as follows:

$$\frac{S_e}{S_0} = \frac{1}{1 + \frac{C_3 H^{1-m}}{Q^{n'}}} \tag{14}$$

Eckenfelder determined the following values for the constants of this equation for the treatment of domestic sewage on rock filters:

$$\frac{S_e}{S_0} = \frac{1}{1 + \frac{2.5 H^{.67}}{Q^{.5}}} \tag{15}$$

where the depth H is in feet and the hydraulic rate Q is in million gallons per acre per day.

Equation 14 is apparently obtained from Equation 13 by expanding the latter in the form of $\frac{1}{e^x}$ and ignoring all but the first two terms in the denominator which gives it the retardent form.

Ames, Behn, and Collings (10) developed a mathematical model for the mechanism of trickling filter. The development of this model was based on certain hypotheses resulting from theoretical considerations of filter operation that were similar in character to those that occur in chemical engineering treatment of packed columns. They described a component of the waste liquor, the BOD, being adsorbed into the biological slime and then undergoing a first-order biochemical reaction.

Through mass balance techniques, partial differential equations were set up and solved for the transfer of BOD. The resulting steady-state equation relating the fraction of BOD in the bulk stream at any depth H is

$$s = \beta + (s_0 - \beta) \exp \frac{-R}{(R+1)} \frac{kA_v}{\rho Q} H \tag{16}$$

where

$R = \frac{K}{\alpha k A_v}$ and

K = first-order reaction constant
k = mass transfer coefficient
A_v = specific surface area
α = equilibrium constant
β = nontransmissible fraction of BOD
ρ = liquid density

Amado (11) wrote out the complete expression for the exponent as

$$\frac{-R}{R+1} \frac{kA_v}{\rho} = \frac{-\frac{1}{\rho}}{\frac{\alpha}{K} + \frac{1}{kA_v}} \tag{17}$$

This last form shows the constants in the exponent to be in the familiar form of the overall mass transfer coefficient, which is here called K_m.

$$\frac{1}{K_m} = \frac{1}{kA_v} + \frac{\alpha}{K} \tag{18}$$

The overall mass transfer coefficient consists of two individual resistances: one to adsorption, $\frac{1}{kA_v}$, and the other to reaction, $\frac{\alpha}{K}$. In a manner similar to Eckenfelder's mean active film concept, the overall mass transfer coefficient was assumed to be inversely proportional to some power of depth, and also by analogy to gas adsorption processes it was assumed to be proportional to the volumetric flow rate per unit area raised to some power. Using these two assumptions, the following final equation was obtained:

$$s = \beta + (s_0 - \beta) \exp - K_1 \frac{H^{m'}}{Q^{n'}} \tag{19}$$

where K_1, n', and m' are constant for a specific waste.

The constants in Equation 19 were determined by Amado, through experimental studies run on an eight-foot-high laboratory trickling filter model, to be

$$\frac{s}{s_0} = 0.1 + 0.9 \exp \frac{-0.61 H^{0.628}}{Q^{0.440}} \tag{20}$$

where H is in feet and Q is in cubic feet per square foot per hour. This equation checks closely with the one proposed by Eckenfelder.

Atkinson, Busch, and Dawkins (12) considered the trickling filter as a "complex system of mass transport and reaction kinetics." They based their analysis on a steady-state filter. This equilibrium condition is attained after a certain period of time which is dependent upon the applied organic load, the hydraulic loading, and the "dimensions of the flow path." Furthermore, for the sake of simplicity, they assumed a first-order process. Through a mass balance about an element of volume dV for a single-stage filter, the following expression resulted

$$\frac{ds}{dH} = -KLQhW \tag{21}$$

where

h = film thickness
W = film width

which integrates to

$$s = s_0 e^{-K \frac{hWH}{Q}} \tag{22}$$

if $\frac{hWH}{Q}$ is considered as an equivalent detention time t, the above expression is the same as Formula 8.

More recently, Galler and Gotaas (13) proposed a mathematical model for trickling filter using a large number of data and multiple regression analysis. They included recirculation, temperature, hydraulic rate, depth, and organic loading as the important factors whose effects were to be determined. They obtained the following formula:

$$s_e' = \frac{0.31\, s_0'^{1.19} (1+N)^{0.28}}{(1+H_0)^{0.67}\, T^{0.15} \left[(1+N)Q_2\right]^{0.06}} \tag{23}$$

s_e' = BOD load of effluent, pounds/acre/day
s_0' = BOD load of influent, pounds/acre/day
T = temperature in degrees Centigrade
N = ratio of recirculation to inflow rate
Q_2 = hydraulic rate, million gallons/acre/day, undiluted

Note that the exponent of the flow into the filter is close to zero, which means that the hydraulic rate, as shown by Equation 23, is not an important factor, a result which is at variance with the finding of others.

Recirculating Filters

The first attempt to quantitatively define the effect of recirculation was in the NRC formula (14). The average number of passes through the filter, F', was given as

$$F' = 1 + \frac{R}{I} \tag{24}$$

where R is the rate of recirculation and I is the rate of incoming flow.

However, it is a fact that on each pass the difficulty with which the organic matter is removed will increase. Correspondingly, a removability factor f is introduced and the average number of "effective" passes, F_1 is obtained as follows:

$$F_1 = \frac{1 + \frac{R}{I}}{\left[1 + (1-f)\frac{R}{I}\right]^2} \tag{25}$$

The average number of "effective" passes is maximized when

$$\frac{R}{I} = \frac{2f-1}{1-f} \tag{26}$$

Equations 24 and 25 do not relate recirculation with reaction kinetics. Velz (2) did this, assuming that in Equation 2 the value of H_0 would be increased directly by the right-hand side of Equation 24. For more discussion and other derivations, see the reference by Behn (1).

With recirculation ratio $\frac{R}{I} = N$, Eckenfelder (9) presented the following formulas for sewage:

$$\frac{S_e}{S_0} = \frac{1}{(1+N)\left(1+2.5\frac{H^{.67}}{Q_1^{.5}}\right) - N} \qquad (27)$$

where S_0 is the BOD of undiluted waste and Q_1 is the diluted hydraulic rate in million gallons per acre per day on the filter.

The diluted influent BOD is given by a simple mass balance as

$$S_i = \frac{S_0 + NL_e}{1+N} \qquad (28)$$

The application of recirculation to the equation given by Amado (11), that is, the combination of Equation 28 and Equation 20, results in

$$\frac{S_e}{S_0} = \frac{0.1 + 0.9\exp\left\{-0.61\frac{H^{0.628}}{[(1+N)\,Q_2]^{0.44}}\right\}}{0.1 + 0.9N\left\{1 - \exp\frac{-0.61H^{0.628}}{[(1+N)\,Q_2]^{0.44}}\right\}} \qquad (29)$$

where here Q_2 is the undiluted hydraulic rate in cubic feet per square foot per hour, and the depth H is in feet.

The removability factor which appears as a result of recirculation has not been taken into account in Equations 27 and 29.

In practice, recirculation is an established fact with the operation of high-rate trickling filters. It contributes to the uniformity and the equalization of applied load, and the flexibility of plant operation through the adjustment of the rate of recirculation. It is also recognized that recirculation has a beneficial seeding effect on plant influent. The optimum equalization rate of recirculation is dependent on economic considerations, and, in general, very high rates of recirculation become uneconomical.

NEW CONCEPTS

A continuous flow system generally consists of some form of reactor, such as activated sludge, trickling filter, or sedimentation basin, the purpose of which is to reduce some undesirable property, for example, BOD, or solids associated with the flow. The degree of success of the operation, that is, the efficiency of the system, depends mainly on the following two factors (15):

1. The flow pattern—the way in which material passes through the system, which depends on the physical design of the system.
2. The kinetics of the reaction taking place—the mechanism by which, for example, BOD is removed.

Flow Pattern

The flow pattern can be characterized by the distribution of residence times of flow particles passing through the system (16). The two extreme cases of flow pattern are plug flow and completely mixed flow. In the majority of real cases, however, the flow type falls in between the two.

Completely Mixed Case

The age distribution of the particles in the effluent of this type of flow ranges from zero to infinity. If we denote the percentage of particles having residence times, that is, ages, between o and t by F, then F is given by

$$F = 1 - e^{\frac{-q}{V}t} \tag{30}$$

where V is the volume of the reactor and q is the flow rate. See Figure 67.

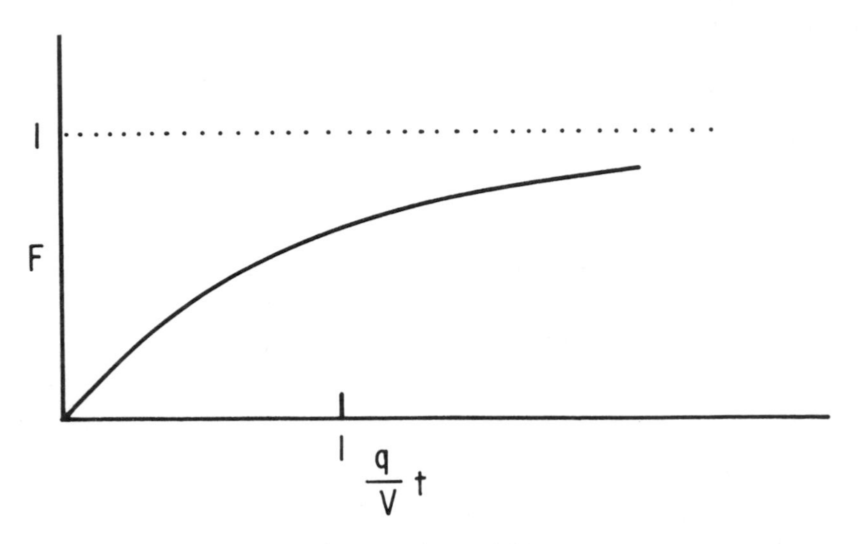

Figure 67. Flow pattern for complete mixing.

Plug Flow Case

Here all the fluid particles in the effluent have stayed in the tank an equal amount of time, that is, they all have the same age which is equal to $\frac{V}{q}$. In this case F is shown in Figure 68.

Mixed Flow

In general flow cases there occurs longitudinal mixing and short-circuiting which renders a mathematically undefined flow pattern looking like Figure 69, the shape of which can be determined through tracer techniques.

To demonstrate the importance of the flow pattern, suppose we have a system in which a first-order reaction, for example, that of the decay of radioactivity, is occurring. The performance, P, of this system or the fraction of the concentration remaining in the effluent is given by

$$P = \int_{t=0}^{\infty} e^{-kt} \frac{dF}{dt}\, dt \tag{31}$$

where K is the first-order reaction rate constant. If the flow is completely mixed, then

$$F = \left(1 - e^{\frac{-q}{V}t}\right) \tag{32}$$

and

$$P = \int_{t=0}^{\infty} e^{-kt} \frac{d}{dt}\left(1 - e^{\frac{-q}{V}t}\right) = \frac{1}{1 + \bar{t}K} \tag{33}$$

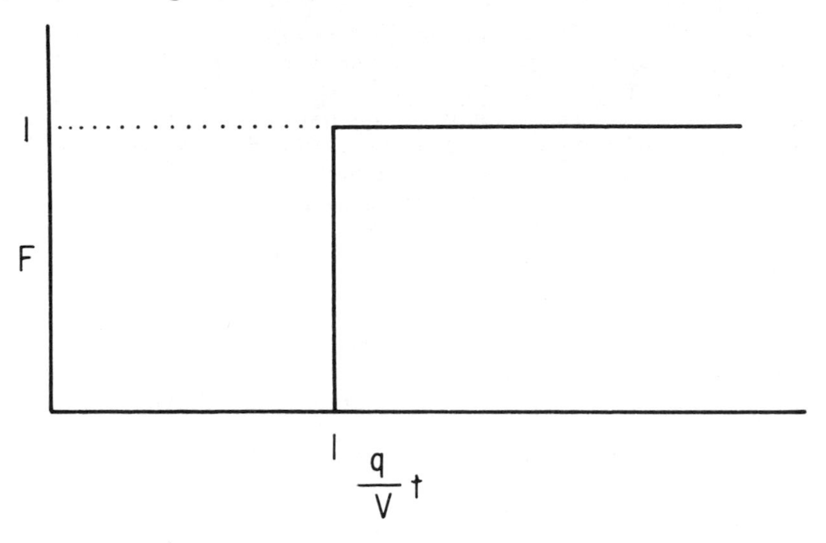

Figure 68. Flow pattern for plug flow.

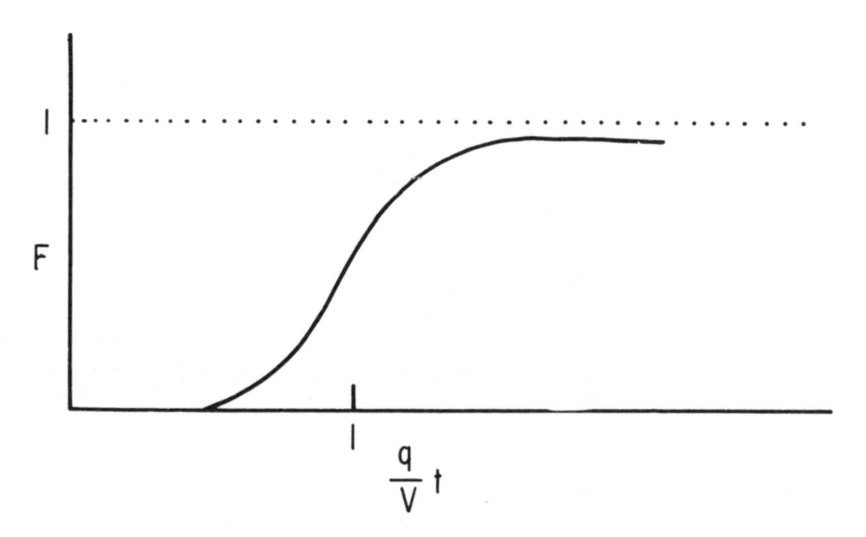

Figure 69. Flow pattern for mixed flow.

where $\bar{t} = \frac{V}{q}$.

In the case of plug flow, we have $\frac{dF}{dt} = 0$ for $t \neq \bar{t}$, and $\frac{dF}{dt} = \infty$ for $t = \bar{t}$, and the performance is given by

$$P = \int_{t=0}^{\infty} e^{-Kt} \frac{dF}{dt} dt = e^{-K\bar{t}} \tag{34}$$

These two results, Equations 33 and 34, we are all familiar with. For the case of Figure 69, graphical method is used to determine the efficiency.

Usually the calculations for the performance of a system are based on either plug flow or completely mixed flow, and then on the basis of these calculations some conclusions are drawn concerning the reaction kinetics of the system. These calculations are not exactly correct when dealing with real flow patterns which occur in the system deviating from the assumed ideal case.

The attainment of plug flow in practice is very difficult. However, it is usually assumed that the flow of liquid through a packed column approximates that of a plug flow, with the following factors affecting the degree of approximation: the viscosity, density, and velocity of the liquid, and the size and shape of the packing material.

Another way of approximating this type of flow is by a series of small vessels with complete mixing in each arranged in a long chain (17). To attain a true plug flow, we increase the number of vessels without limit, while their volume approaches zero in such a way that the total volume of the chain remains constant.

Reaction Kinetics

It is often assumed that the kinetics of biological oxidization of organic material follows a first-order reaction. The reasoning is based more on convenience and empirical results than on theory.

A direct consequence of biological utilization of organic material is the formation of new cells, which in turn utilize the available nutrient. So it is important that consideration be given not only to BOD concentration, but also to the concentration of bacteria. A simple and practical rate formulation which considers both these factors is that proposed by Keshevan, Behn, and Ames (18):

$$\frac{ds}{dt} = -KsN \tag{35}$$

where N is bacterial concentration. If we assume that the increase in the concentration of bacteria is proportional to the amount of BOD removed,

$$\frac{dN}{ds} = -a \tag{36}$$

then the combination of Formulas 35 and 36 results in a logistic type of rate equation used for population forecasting. This fact, and the fact that population dynamics of different species have inherently basic similarities, could be considered as an indirect support for the soundness and applicability of Equation 35.

Applications to Trickling Filters

In the field of chemical engineering it is usually assumed that flow through a packed column could be approximated as plug flow, that is, the flow pattern corresponds to Figure 68. If we consider that this is true of our trickling filter, and that BOD removal rate occurs by first-order reaction, the correct formula to use would be

$$\frac{s}{s_0} = e^{-kt} \tag{37}$$

This, of course, formed the starting point for analysis such as that by Schulze (8) and Eckenfelder (9). This is tantamount to assuming, in the case of the analysis by Ames, Behn, and Collings (10) that the resistance to adsorption is very small compared to resistance to reaction, that is, kA_v is very large compared to $\frac{K}{\alpha}$ in the equation

$$\frac{1}{K_m} = \frac{1}{kA_v} + \frac{\alpha}{K} \tag{18}$$

If we prefer to use an equation with the concentration of bacteria expressed in it, we should use the basic differential form:

$$\frac{ds}{dt} = -KLN \tag{35}$$

The integration of Equation 35 is not a straightforward matter, because of the limits one would place on the bacteria from an initial value of N_0 to N will not have its physical counterpart.

We could resort to Equation 35, writing down by analogy:

$$\frac{1}{K_m} = \frac{1}{kA_v} + \frac{\alpha}{KN} \tag{38}$$

This leads to another difficulty in that as $\frac{KN}{\alpha}$ increases and approaches the value of kA_v, they both have to be taken into account. While there has been ample work done on trickling filters, we cannot say with any degree of assurance just what the parameters are in value in Equation 38.

While waiting for basic research to improve the understanding of the mechanism of the trickling filter, the design engineer may apply the equation credited to Echenfelder or that to Amado with confidence that it will lead in the correct direction.

ACKNOWLEDGMENTS

Grateful acknowledgment is given that this work was made possible by PHS Grant No. WP-00234-05 by the Division of Water Supply and Pollution Control, Department of Health, Education, and Welfare.

REFERENCES

(1) Behn, V. C. "Trickling Filter Formulations," *Air Water Poll., 5,* 2–4 (May 1963).

(2) Velz, C. S. "A Basic Law for the Performance of the Trickling Filters," *Sewage Works J., 20,* 4 (July 1948).

(3) Stack. V. T., Jr. "Theoretical Performance of the Trickling Filter Process," *Sewage Ind. Wastes, 29,* 9 (September 1957).

(4) Phelps, E. B. (with C. J. Velz). *Public Health Engineering.* 1, 2. New York: John Wiley & Sons (1948).

(5) Fair, G. M., and J. C. Geyer. *Elements of Water Supply and Waste Water Disposal.* New York: John Wiley & Sons (1955).

(6) Howland, W. E. "Flow over Porous Media as in a Trickling Filter," *Proceedings,* Twelfth Industrial Waste Conference. Bulletin No. 94, Purdue Engineering Extension (1957).

(7) Sinkoff, M. D., R. Porges, and J. H. McDermott. "Mean Residence Time of a Liquid in a Trickling Filter," *Proc. ASCE, 85* (SA6) (1959).

(8) Schulze, K. C. "Trickling Filter Performance, ' *J. Water Poll. Cont. Fed., 32,* 3 (1960).

(9) Eckenfelder, W. W. "Trickling Filteration Design and Performance," *Proc. ASCE, 87*(SA4) (1961).

(10) Ames, W. F., V. C. Behn, and W. Z. Collings. "Transient Operation of the Trickling Filter," *Proc. ASCE, 88*(SA3) (May 1962).

(11) Amado, M. A. "Analysis of BOD Reduction in Trickling Filters." M. S. Thesis, Cornell University, 1964.

(12) Atkinson, B., A. W. Busch, and G. S. Dawkins. "Recirculation, Reaction Kinetics, and Effluent Quality in a Trickling Filter Flow Model," *J. Water Poll. Cont. Fed., 35,* 10 (1963).

(13) Galler, W. S., and H. B. Gotaas. "Analysis of Biological Filter Variables," *Proc. ASCE, 90*(SA6) (December 1964).

(14) NRC Subcommittee Report, "Sewage Treatment at Military Installations," *Sewage Works J., 18,* 5 (September (1946).

(15) Herbert, D., R. Elsworth, and R. C. Telling. "The Continuous Culture of Bacteria: A Theoretical and Experimental Study," *J. Gen. Microbiol., 14,* 3 (1956).

(16) Danckwerts, P. V. "Continuous Flow Systems," *Chem. Engr. Sci., 2,* 1 (February 1953).

(17) Powell, E. O., and J. R. Lowe. "Theory of Multi-Stage Continuous Cultures," in *Continuous Cultivation of Microorganisms,* edited by I. Malek, K. Beran, and S. Hospadka. New York: Academic Press, 1962.

(18) Keshevan, K., V. C. Behn, and W. F. Ames. "Kinetics of Aerobic Removal of Organic Wastes," *Proc. ASCE, 90*(SA1) (February 1964).

NEW CONCEPTS IN OXYGEN TRANSFER AND AERATION

W. Wesley Eckenfelder and Davis L. Ford
The University of Texas, Austin, Texas

The supply of oxygen to an aerobic biological system and the transfer mechanisms involved have been the subject of several investigations in recent years (1-4). The purpose of this paper is to review some of these more recent concepts of oxygen transfer and to summarize data on the design of aeration equipment.

THEORY AND GENERAL DEVELOPMENT

Oxygen, a sparingly soluble gas in pure water, disperses itself throughout a liquid body by the process of diffusion through an air-liquid interface. Lewis and Whitman (5) developed the two-film concept, which considers a thin film of gas and a film of liquid at the gas-liquid interface. Since a steady-state transfer across the film precludes a concentration build-up, the diffusional resistances on the gas and liquid sides can be considered to be in series, and the controlling rate will be that which offers the greatest resistance to diffusion. Assuming equilibrium conditions at the interface and liquid film control in oxygen transfer, the transfer rate can be expressed:

$$N = K_L A \ (C_s - C) \tag{1}$$

The principal limitation to the Lewis and Whitman concept is the assumption of steady-state transfer. Danckwerts (6), following the work of Higbee (7), approached the nonsteady-state problem by application of equations developed for transient molecular diffusion in a column of infinite depth. He defined the liquid film coefficient as the square root of the product of the diffusion coefficient and the rate of surface renewal:

$$K_L = \sqrt{D_L \cdot r} \tag{2}$$

Surface renewal, r, is the average frequency with which the film is replaced with liquid from the body of the solution.

The oxygen transfer process can be considered to occur in three phases. Oxygen molecules from the gas are initially transferred to the liquid surface, resulting in a saturation or equilibrium condition at the interface. This rate is very rapid. The liquid interface has a finite thickness with unique properties. This layer or film is composed of water molecules with their negative ends facing the gas phase and is estimated to be at least three molecules thick (8). During the second phase, the oxygen molecules must pass through this film by molecular diffusion. In the third phase, oxygen is mixed in the body of liquid by diffusion and convection. It is assumed that at low mixing levels (laminar flow conditions) the rate of oxygen absorption is controlled by the rate of molecular diffusion through the undisturbed liquid film (Phase 2). At increased turbulence levels the surface film is disrupted, and renewal of the film is responsible for the transfer of oxygen to the body of liquid. This surface renewal can be considered as the frequency with which fluid with a solute concentration C_L is replacing fluid from the interface with a concentration C_S. As depicted in Figure 70, the turbulent eddies from the liquid bulk move to the interface, undergo a short interval unsteady-state molecular diffusion, and are then displaced from the surface by subsequent eddies. It follows that the total mass transfer is a function of the eddy

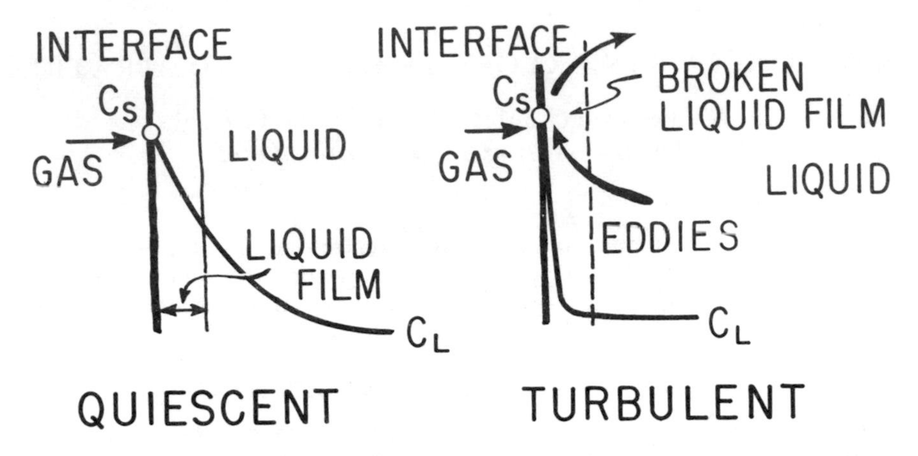

Figure 70. Mechanism of oxygen transfer.

exposure time and the molecular exchange during the time interval. Dobbins (9) has proposed a relationship which best describes the aforementioned transfer mechanism:

$$K_L = \sqrt{D_L r} \quad \coth \sqrt{\frac{r_L{}^2}{D_L}} \tag{3}$$

When the surface renewal rate is zero (Phase 1), K_L is equal to D_L/L, and the transfer is controlled by the molecular diffusion through the surface film. As r increases, K_L becomes equal to the $\sqrt{D_L \cdot r}$, and the transfer is a function of the rate of surface renewal.

Equation 1 can be re-expressed in concentration units:

$$\frac{dC}{dt} = K_L \frac{A}{V} (C_s - C) = K_L a \ (C_s - C) \tag{4}$$

$K_L a$ is an overall transfer coefficient and includes the effects of changes in the liquid film coefficient K_L and increases or decreases in interfacial area, A. Since in most aeration applications it is not possible to measure the interfacial area, the overall coefficient $K_L a$ is usually employed to characterize aeration performance.

Factors Affecting K_L and $K_L a$

There are several factors which influence K_L and/or $K_L a$. The most significant of these are temperature and surface active agents present in the liquid. The temperature effect can be defined by the relationship:

$$K_t = K_{20^\circ C} \cdot \Theta^{(T-20)} \tag{5}$$

The temperature effect of K_L, Θ, has been reported to vary from 1.016 to 1.037. A study of Eckenfelder and Barnhart (10) on bubble aeration found a value for Θ of 1.028, which is an approximate average of the values reported by other investigators. When considering $K_L a$ in bubble aeration systems, the effect of temperature on the bubble size and velocity must also be included, since this will effect $\frac{A}{V}$. An evaluation of available data showed Θ to be 1.02 for $K_L a$ in bubble aeration systems.

The presence of surface active agents will have a marked effect on the oxygen transfer rate, as they affect both the liquid film coefficient K_L and the A/V ratio and hence K_La (11, 12). This effect will be reflected by changes in concentration of surfactant and by changes in the nature of the aeration surface.

A surfactant will concentrate at an interface so that the interfacial concentration will be greater than that in the body of the liquid. As a result, a "film" of adsorbed surfactant molecules is concentrated at the interface, which provides a barrier to molecular diffusion. Under equilibrium conditions the excess surface concentration of surfactant molecules has been defined by the Gibbs equation (13):

$$\Gamma = \frac{c}{RT}\,\frac{d\gamma}{dc} \qquad (6)$$

Equation 6 indicates that the excess surface concentration of surface active molecules will increase with increasing solution concentration to a maximum. Further increase in solution concentration will yield no additional increase in surface concentration. The maximum level presumably results at complete surface coverage. This has been defined as the critical micelle concentration, above which increased concentration of surface active molecules will aggregate only in the bulk of solution. Under equilibrium conditions K_L will decrease with increasing surfactant concentration to the critical micelle concentration. Since at this level the interface is completely covered, increased concentration of surfactant will have no further effect on K_L.

The intensity of mixing also will influence the degree to which the surface active agents affect the oxygen transfer rate. Three regimes can be considered, as shown by the results of Mancy and Okun (14). Reference is made to Figure 71, in which:

$$\text{alpha } (\alpha) = \frac{K_La \text{ of the waste}}{K_La \text{ of pure tap water}}$$

and

$$\text{alpha}' \ (\alpha') = \frac{K_La \text{ of the waste}}{K_La \text{ of pure tap water}}$$

Under laminar conditions (approaching a stagnant film surface) there is substantially no effect on α or α', since the resistance in the bulk of solution to oxygen transport exceeds the combined interfacial resistance. This condition would rarely be encountered in aeration practice. Under moderately turbulent conditions a maximum depression in the K_L or α' relative to the concentration of surfactant present occurs, since the interfacial resistance to molecular diffusion by the absorbed surfactant molecules controls the transfer rate. The life of the interface would have to be sufficient to establish equilibrium with respect to absorption of the surfactant, as shown in Equation 3. At high degrees of turbulence α' approaches unity, due to the high surface renewal rates, resulting in an inability to establish an adsorption equilibrium at the interface. Unity is often exceeded by α as a result of the increased A/V values associated with turbulent conditions at the surface. These ranges were shown by Mancy and Okun (14), and further confirmed by studies on a pharmaceutical waste effluent, as shown in Figure 72.

The effect of surfactant concentration on α and α' for diffused and surface aeration is shown in Figure 73. In surface aeration units operating at high mixing intensities, there may be no depression in α' due to the high surface renewal rate generated. Values greater than 1.0 for α may result from an increased interfacial area, because of surface turbulence and entrained air bubbles at and around aerator contact surfaces. In diffused air systems α' will decrease with increasing surface concentration, becoming a constant above the critical micelle

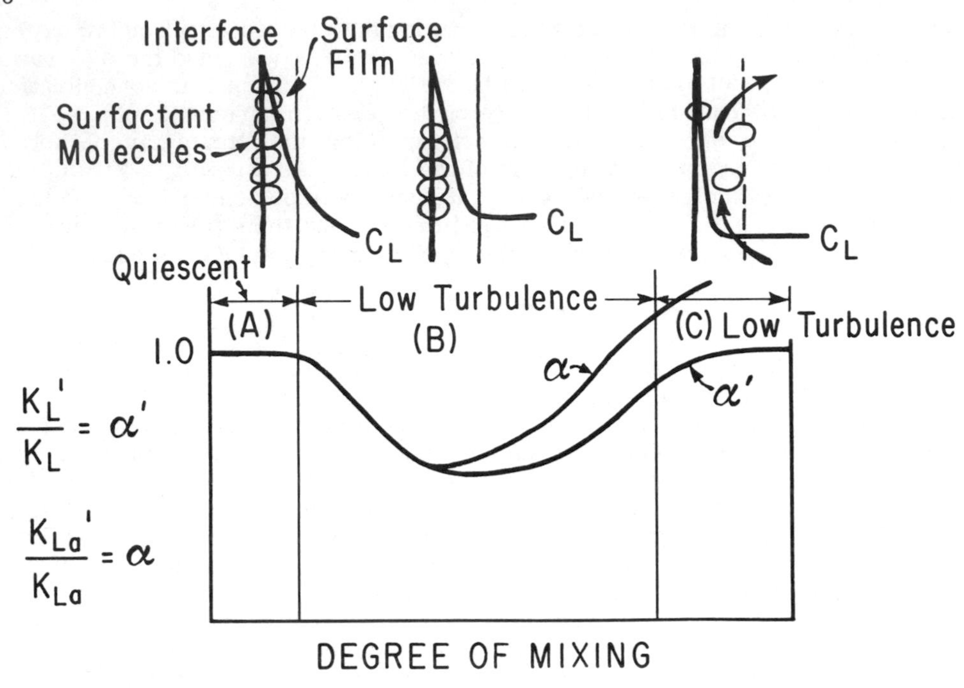

Figure 71. Effect of surfactants on oxygen transfer.

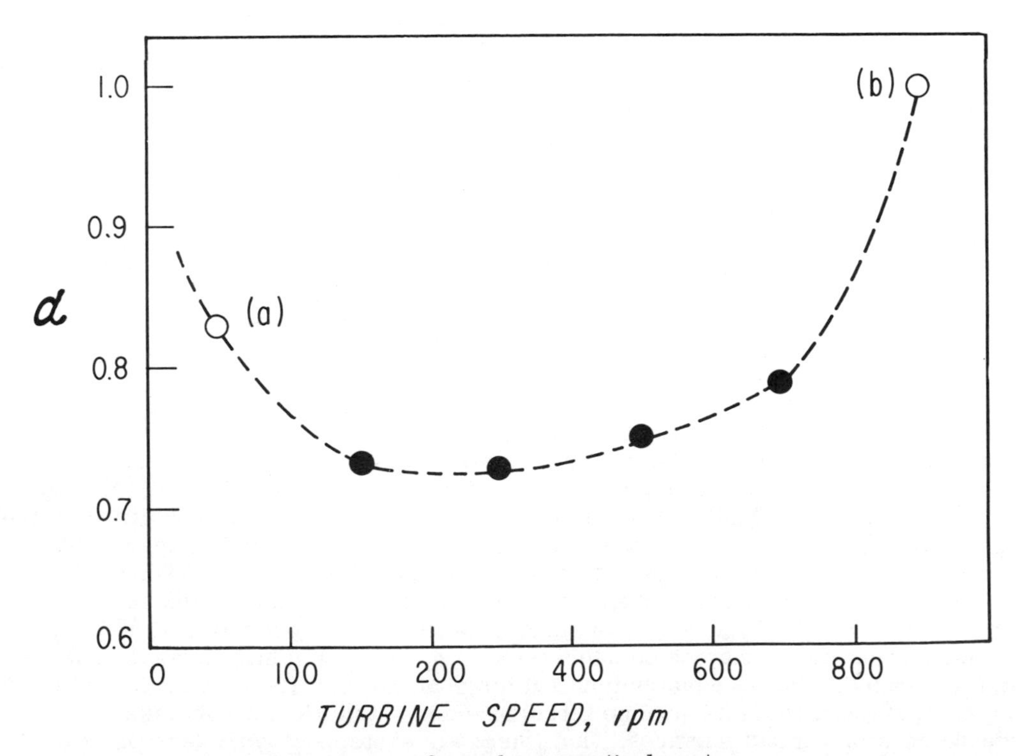

Figure 72. Effect of mixing on α for a pharmaceutical waste.

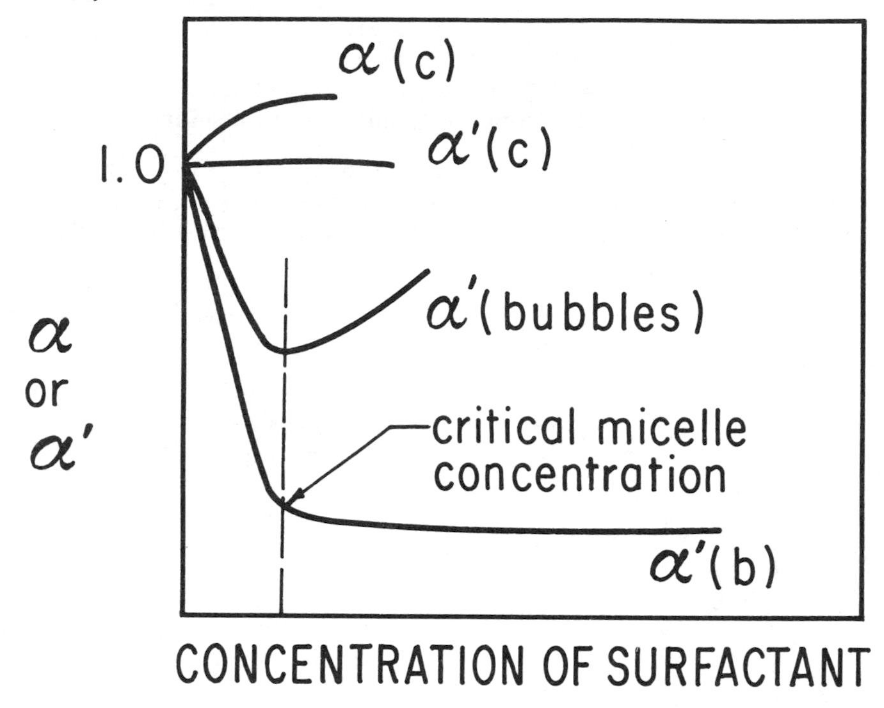

Figure 73. Effect of surfactant concentration on α and α' for various aeration systems.

concentration, as has been shown by Mancy and Okun (11) and Eckenfelder and O'Connor (15). At higher surfactant concentrations, the increase in interfacial area due to smaller bubble size may exceed the decrease in K_L causing an increase in α. It should be pointed out that some surfactants might have no effect on α' in a given diffused air system. If the migration of the surfactant molecules toward the surface is not completed during the bubble contact period, little influence on K_L would be apparent (16).

Given values of alpha as determined by various investigators are summarized in Table 42. Evaluation of these effects requires measurements under mixing intensities and surfactant levels which will be encountered in practice.

DETERMINATION OF MASS TRANSFER COEFFICIENTS

Three of the most commonly accepted techniques used to determine aeration equipment performance are (a) the nonsteady-state aeration of a deoxygenated water, (b) the steady-state and nonsteady-state aeration of activated sludge, and (c) the steady-state aeration of tap water.

Nonsteady-State Aeration of a Deoxygenated Water

The most common method of determining aeration equipment performance has generally been adopted as a standard. It involves reaeration of tap water from which the dissolved oxygen has been previously removed by the addition of sodium sulfite and a cobalt catalyst. Equation 4 describes the nonsteady-state transfer of oxygen which applies during reaeration:

$$\frac{dC}{dt} = K_L a\ (C_s - C_L)$$

The use of this equation is based on the following assumptions:

1. The entire liquid content is completely mixed and therefore of uniform composition at any time (t).
2. $K_L a$ is constant and therefore is independent of time.

$K_L a$ is determined from the slope of a semilogarithmic plot of the concentration deficit ($C_s - C_L$) versus time of aeration. This is illustrated in Example 1.

Example 1—$K_L a$ Determination

The aeration of deoxygenated tap water in a given tank gives the following oxygen deficit values at various times:

Time	Oxygen Deficit $C_s - C_1$
0	10.6
6	8.4
12	7.2
18	6.2
24	5.3
30	4.6
36	4.0
42	3.4
48	2.9
54	2.5
60	2.2

$K_L a$ is equal to the slope shown in Figure 74.

$$K_L a = \frac{\log(C_s - C_1)_{t_1} - \log(C_s - C_1)_{t_2}}{t_2 - t_1} \qquad 2.3 \cdot 60$$

$$K_L a = 1.52\ hr.^{-1}$$

Multiple sampling points should be selected in the tank and an average value employed in the determination of $K_L a$.

Steady-State Aeration of Tap Water (17)

Steady-state aeration provides an independent check of the nonsteady-state tap water procedure. Deoxygenated or low-oxygen-content water is continuously fed at a constant flow rate to the aeration tank. $K_L a$ is computed from the relationship

$$\frac{dc}{dt} = K_L a\ (C_s - C_L) = Q\ (C_L - C_i) \tag{7}$$

where C_i is the dissolved oxygen content of the influent water. When the condition of (Oxygen transfer rate) + (feed stream dissolved oxygen addition) = (effluent stream removal rate), the steady-state equation is

$$K_L a = \frac{Q(C_L - C_i)}{(C_s - C_L)} \tag{8}$$

Steady-State and Nonsteady-State Aeration of Activated Sludge

The performance of aeration equipment can be determined from operating data from an activated sludge system. In the aeration of activated sludge, Equation 4 must be modified to account for the effect of the oxygen utilization rate of the mixed liquor:

TABLE 42

Unit	Waste	Alpha (α)	Conditions	Reference
Sparjers	Activated sludge effluent	1.320	10–25 scfm/unit 15' depth, 25' width	(20)
Plate tubes	Activated sludge effluent	0.860	6–14 scfm/unit 15' depth, 25' width	(20)
INKA System	Kraft Black Liquor			
	20 ppm	0.875	6' depth, 6.8'width 2.6' submergence	(21)
	100 ppm	0.750	6' depth, 6.8' width 2.6' submergence	(21)
	200 ppm	0.625	6' depth, 6.8' width 2.6' submergence	(21)
Small bubble diffuser	20 ppm	0.880	100 liter volume 3' depth; 10 × 10 cm bubble air diffuser	(21)
	100 ppm	0.813	100 liter volume 3' depth; 10 × 10 cm bubble air diffuser	(21)
	200 ppm	0.662	100 liter volume 3' depth; 10 × 10 cm bubble air diffuser	(21)
Aeration cone	Tap water + 5 ppm anionic detergent	1.330	12,500'³; 6' diameter 36 rpm	

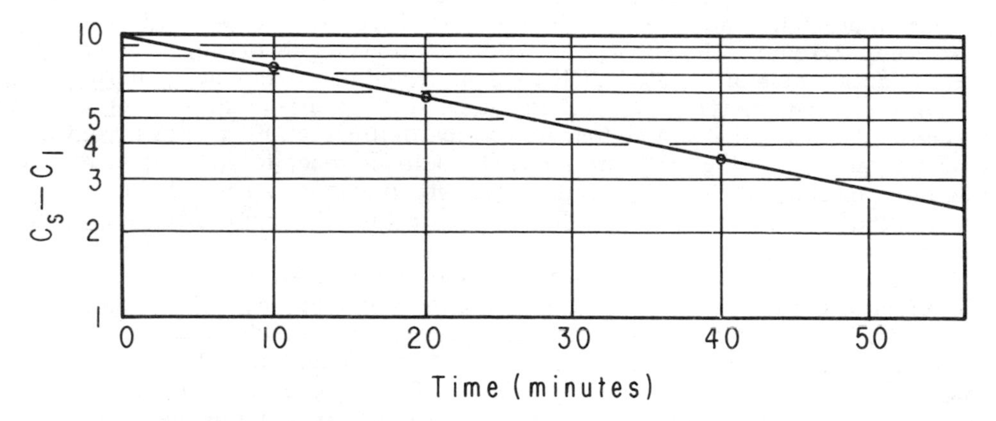

Figure 74. Determination of $K_L a$.

$$\frac{dc}{dt} = K_L a \; (C_s - C_L) - r_r \tag{9}$$

Under steady-state conditions $dc/dt = 0$ and $K_L a$ can be determined as follows:

$$K_L a = \frac{r_r}{(C_s - C_L)} \tag{10}$$

The oxygen uptake rate should be measured in the absence of immediate oxygen demand and when the mixed liquor has a dissolved oxygen level in excess of 1.0

mg/l. The K_La obtained includes the effects of α, temperature, and solids concentration, and is specific only to the particular waste being treated. The waste treatment system must be at steady-state conditions during the entire test period. This includes organic loading, dissolved oxygen concentrations, and feed composition.

In the nonsteady-state procedure, the dissolved oxygen is allowed to approach zero by microbial respiration. Aeration is then started and the dissolved oxygen build-up measured. K_La can be computed from the slope of a plot of dc/dt vs. C in accordance with a rearrangement of Equation 11:

$$\frac{dc}{dt} = (K_La\ C_s\ - r_r) - K_La\ C_L \tag{11}$$

$(K_La\ C_s - r_r)$ will be a constant for any specific operating condition. These methods are summarized in Table 43.

Aeration Equipment

The aeration equipment employed for sewage and industrial waste treatment consists of air diffusion units (producing small or coarse bubbles), turbine aeration systems in which air is released below the rotating blades of an impeller, and surface aeration units in which oxygen transfer is accomplished by high surface turbulence and liquid sprays.

Diffused Aeration

Diffused aeration devices are commercially available in several basic types. Small orifice devices are constructed of silicon dioxide or aluminum oxide held in a porous mass with a ceramic binder, or in tubes or bags wrapped with Saran or nylon material. The size of bubbles released from this type of diffuser ranges from 2.0 to 2.5 mm. The absorption efficiency (oxygen absorbed/oxygen supplied) depends on the size of the air bubbles released and the turbulence generated in the system. Another type of air diffuser uses a large orifice device, such as the sparjer. The sparjer contains four short tube orifices at 90° centers from which the air is emitted at high velocity. Tank turbulence tends to redivide large bubbles into smaller bubbles. The orifice diameters normally range from 1/5" to 1/4". Other commercial units include the hydraulic shear diffuser, the Venturi diffuser, and the INKA diffuser.

Several factors affect the transfer characteristics of diffused aeration units. The effect of the liquid depth above Saran tubes and sparjers (18) is shown in Figure 75. The oxygen transfer increased with increasing depth to an exponent of 0.88 for sparjers and to an exponent of 0.72 for Saran tubes (18). The deviation of these exponents from the 2/3 power in Equation 14 probably can be attributed to the difference in hydraulics in a spiral flow aeration tank as compared to an aeration column. The effect of tank width on oxygen transfer at various gas flows is shown in Figure 76.

Eckenfelder (19) showed that oxygen transfer from air bubbles could be correlated to the dimensionless Sherwood and Reynolds numbers and the liquid submergence depth. The correlation developed reduces to

$$K_L = CV_B/H^{1/3} \tag{12}$$

Equation 12 shows that the liquid film coefficient K_L is proportional to the velocity of the bubble, relative to the liquid, which in turn is related to surface turbulence and shear and, hence, surface renewal. The interfacial area in the aeration tank will be

TABLE 43

Method	Assumption	Advantages	Limitations
1. Nonsteady-state aeration of tap water	1. Complete mixing 2. Constant temperature	1. Simple and rapid method 2. Good control of variables 3. Lab-scale applications	1. Independent alpha determination—all conditions must be reproducible
2. Steady-state aeration of tap water	1. Complete mixing 2. Constant temperature	1. Perfect mixing readily achieved 2. Smaller volume of water can be used, as $K_L a$ evaluation accuracy is independent of volume 3. No transient methods are required 4. Good variable control	1. Evaluation of small aerators only because of high flow rates which are required to obtain good accuracy 2. Impractical for evaluation of large-scale units
3. Activated sludge; steady-state field conditions	1. Complete mixing 2. No significant microbial change during test period 3. Substrate composition, loading factor, and tank DO does not change during test period	1. $K_L a$ rating is made under actual field conditions—most accurate evaluation if good test procedure is used	1. Difficult to control variable during test period 2. Respiration factor sometimes difficult to correctly evaluate
4. Activated sludge; nonsteady-state field conditions	Same as above	Same as above	Same as above
5. Steady-state sulfite oxidation method	Sulfite reaction rate is independent of sulfite concentration, and the rate of reaction is not the limiting factor	1. Simple test procedure	1. Involves gas absorption plus a chemical reaction; exact kinetics are unknown 2. Catalyst concentration affects reaction rate 3. Biological oxidation rates are much slower than sulfite oxidation rates

$$A = \frac{6\, G_s H}{d_B V_B} \tag{13}$$

Equation 12 neglects the interfacial area of the tank liquid surface. The overall film coefficient $K_L a$ is therefore equal to

$$K_L a = \frac{C G_s H^{\frac{2}{3}}}{d_B V} \tag{14}$$

Since d_B is proportional to G_s over the range of air flows normally encountered

$$K_L a = \frac{C' G_s^{(l-n)} H^{\frac{2}{3}}}{V} \tag{15}$$

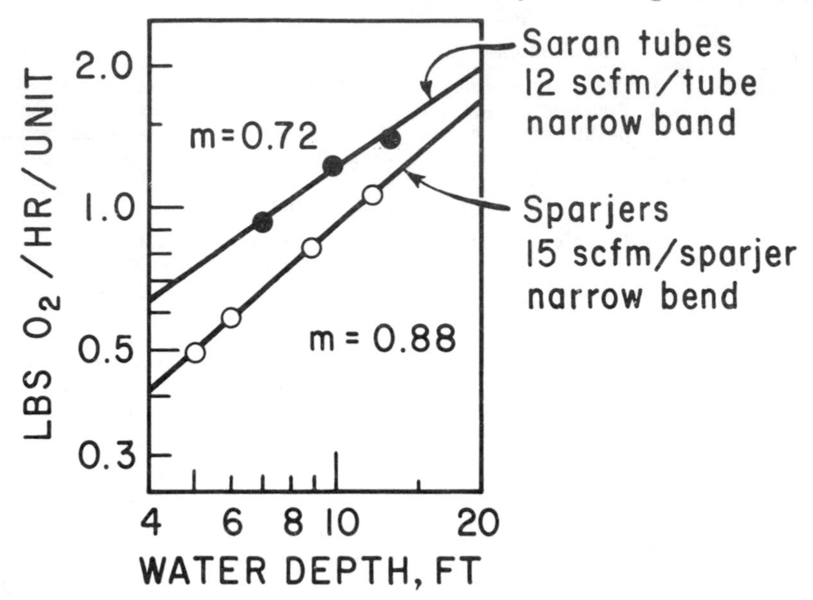

Figure 75. Effect of liquid depth on oxygen transfer in bubble aeration systems (18).

A modification of Equation 15 is used to characterize oxygen transfer from diffused aeration equipment in water:

$$N = C'' G_s^{(l-n)} H^{\frac{2}{3}} \tag{16}$$

The performance of Saran tubes in water in a liquid depth of 14.4 ft., correlated according to Equation 16, is shown in Figure 77. Improved performance at high air rates is observed with a wide band diffusion system. This is probably due to a better distribution of air bubbles and a higher velocity, yielding a higher liquid film coefficient, K_L.

The transfer characteristics of sparjers in water (18, 20) (14.5 ft. depth) are shown in Figure 78. The transfer rate is only slightly improved by employing wide band arrangements and by using the smaller orifice units.

The performance of INKA type aeration units, in which large volumes of air are released at low submergence heads, is shown in Figure 79. The location of the aeration unit has little effect on the oxygen transfer characteristics.

The performance characteristics in accordance with Equation 16 and Figures 7, 8, and 9 are summarized in Table 44.

As would be expected, reducing the tank width at the same air flow per unit increases the oxygen transfer efficiency while the interfacial area remains substantially constant; the higher resulting liquid velocities increase K_L and hence $K_L a$ and N. An exponential factor for tank width based on the data of Bewtra (18), $(W_{24}/W)^{0.36}$ can be used, as shown in Figure 76, as a correction to Equation 16.

The transfer rate of oxygen per diffuser is independent of diffuser spacing, provided the spacing is sufficient to minimize interfering bubble patterns.

Equation 16 can be modified to adjust for actual work operating conditions (Eq. 19). Correction must be made for the saturation value in the waste, the operating dissolved oxygen level, the transfer rate, α, and temperature.

$$N = C G_s^{(l-n)} \frac{H^m}{W^p} (C_{sw} - C_L)\, 1.02^{(T-20)}\, \alpha \tag{17}$$

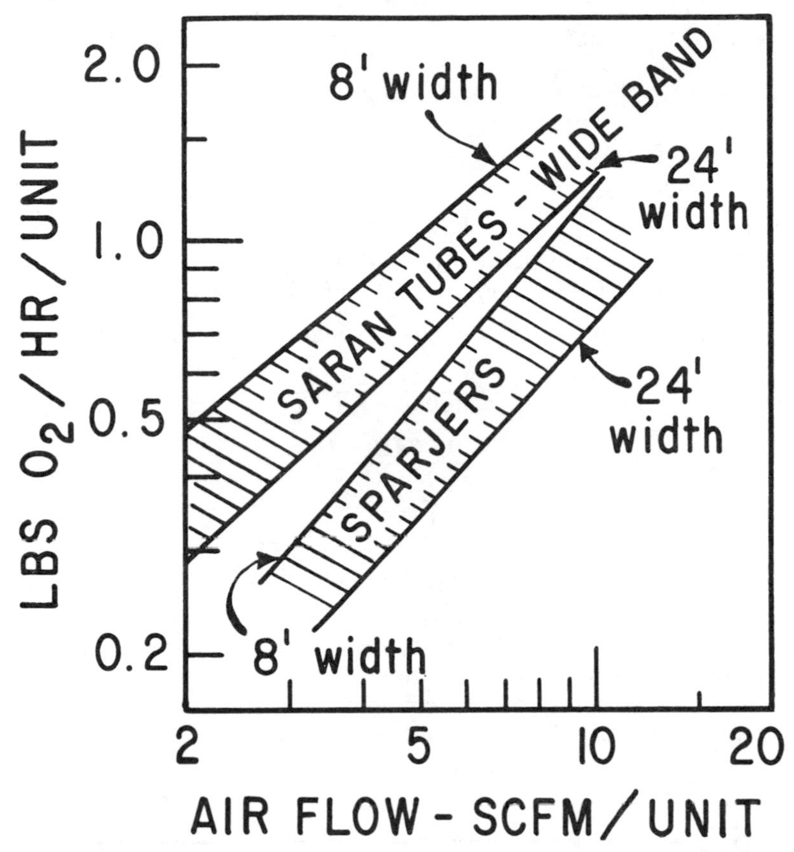

Figure 76. Effect of tank width on oxygen transfer in bubble aeration systems (18).

The application of this relationship to aeration design is shown in Example 2.

Example 2—Diffused Aeration Design

The aeration data defined for design conditions are as follows

lbs oz/hr = 320
Temperature = 30°C.
α = 0.85
C_{SM} = 8.6 mg/l (computed as saturation at the aeration tank mid-depth)

The performance of the selected air diffuser is

$$N = C\, G_s{}^n \left(\frac{H}{H_{14.4}}\right) \left(\frac{W_{24}}{W}\right) \left(\frac{C_{SW} - C_L}{C_s}\right) (1.02)^{T-20}\, (\alpha)$$

$$N = \left[\frac{C\, W_{24}{}^m}{H_{14.4}{}^g C_{s\,20°}}\right] G_s{}^n \frac{H^g}{W^m} (C_{SW} - C_L)\, (1.02^{T-20})\, \alpha$$

$$= 0.0069\, G_s{}^{.92} \frac{H^{.72}}{W^{.36}} (C_{SW} - C_L) 1.02^{(T-20)} \cdot \alpha$$

The required aeration volume is 80,000 ft.^{3}; using a liquid submergence depth of 15 ft. and a tank width of 30 ft., required tank length is 180 ft.

For an air flow (G_s) of 8 scfm/diffuser unit and a submergence depth of 15 ft.

$$N = 0.0069\ (8)^{0.92}\ \frac{(15)^{0.72}}{(30)^{0.36}}\ (8.6 - 1.0) \cdot 1.02^{10} \cdot 0.85$$

$$= 0.75 \text{ lbs. } O_2/\text{hr/unit}$$

$$\text{No. of units} = \frac{320}{0.75} = 428$$

spacing = 180 ft/428 = 0.42 ft. or 5 inches or 10 inches wide band spacing
air flow = 428 units × 8 scfm/unit = 3,410 scfm

The required blower horsepower is computed (using 8 psi on the blower):

$$HP = \frac{\text{psi} \cdot \text{scfm} \cdot 144}{33{,}000 \cdot \text{Eff}}$$

$$= \frac{8.0 \cdot 3410 \cdot 144}{33{,}000 \cdot 0.7}$$

$$= 170 \text{ HP}$$

Turbine Aeration

In turbine aeration, air is discharged from a pipe or sparge ring beneath the rotating blades of an impeller. The air is broken into bubbles and dispersed throughout the tank contents. Present commercial units employ one or more submerged impellers, and may employ an additional impeller near the liquid surface for oxygenation from induced surface aeration.

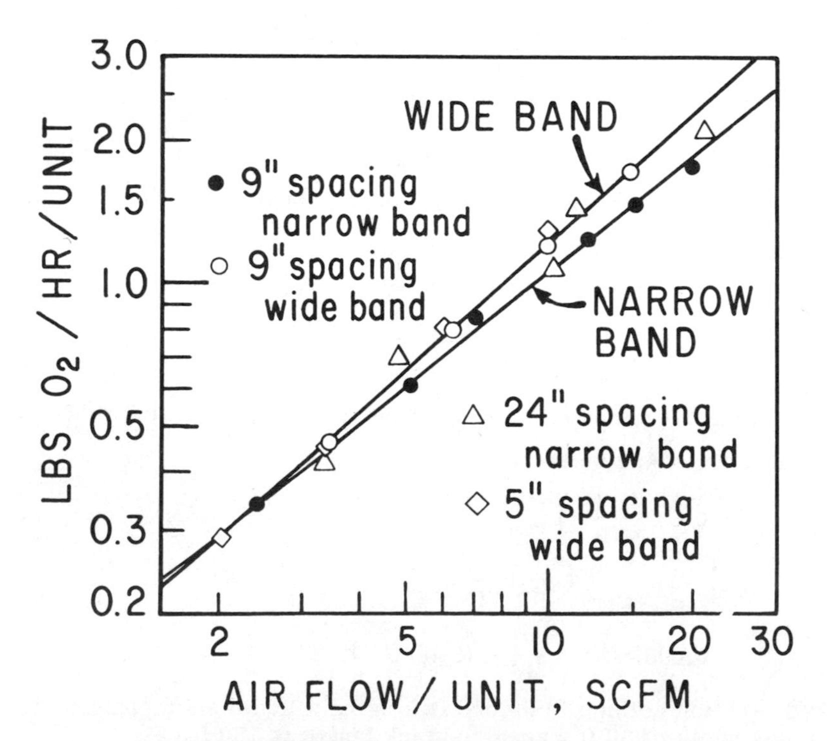

Figure 77. Oxygen transfer from Saran tubes in water (18).

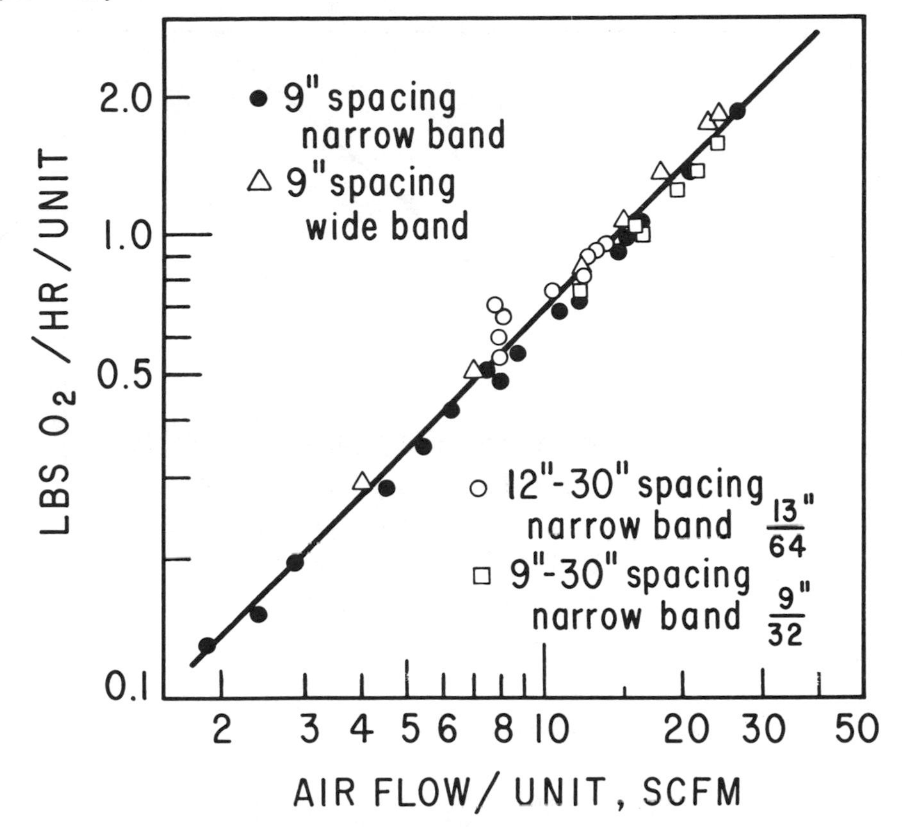

Figure 78. Oxygen transfer from sparjers in water (18, 20).

In addition to air flow, both the diameter and the speed of the impeller will affect the bubble size and velocity, thus influencing the overall transfer coefficient, $K_L a$. Equation 16 can be modified for turbine aeration:

$$N = CR^x G_s{}^n d_t^y (C_s - C_L) \qquad (18)$$

The power drawn by the turbine aerator can be computed from the relationship:

$$\text{HP} = Cd_t{}^n R^m \qquad (19)$$

When air is applied beneath the impeller, the actual power drawn is reduced, since a less dense mixture is being pumped by the turbine. This relationship has been shown by Eckenfelder (15) and others.

Quirk (22) developed two significant correlations between the oxygen transfer efficiency and the power supplied to the system from the rotor (HP_R) and the air flow (G_s): It can be shown that Equation 19 can be developed from the relationship, as shown in Figure 80.

$$\left(\frac{\text{O}_2 \text{ transfer efficiency}}{\Delta C}\right) = C^1 \left(\frac{\text{HP}_R}{G_s}\right)^n \qquad (20)$$

Equation 20 can be re-expressed:

$$\text{O}_2 \text{ transfer efficiency} = CP_d^n \quad \text{where } P_d = \frac{\text{HP}_R}{\text{HP}_c} \qquad (21)$$

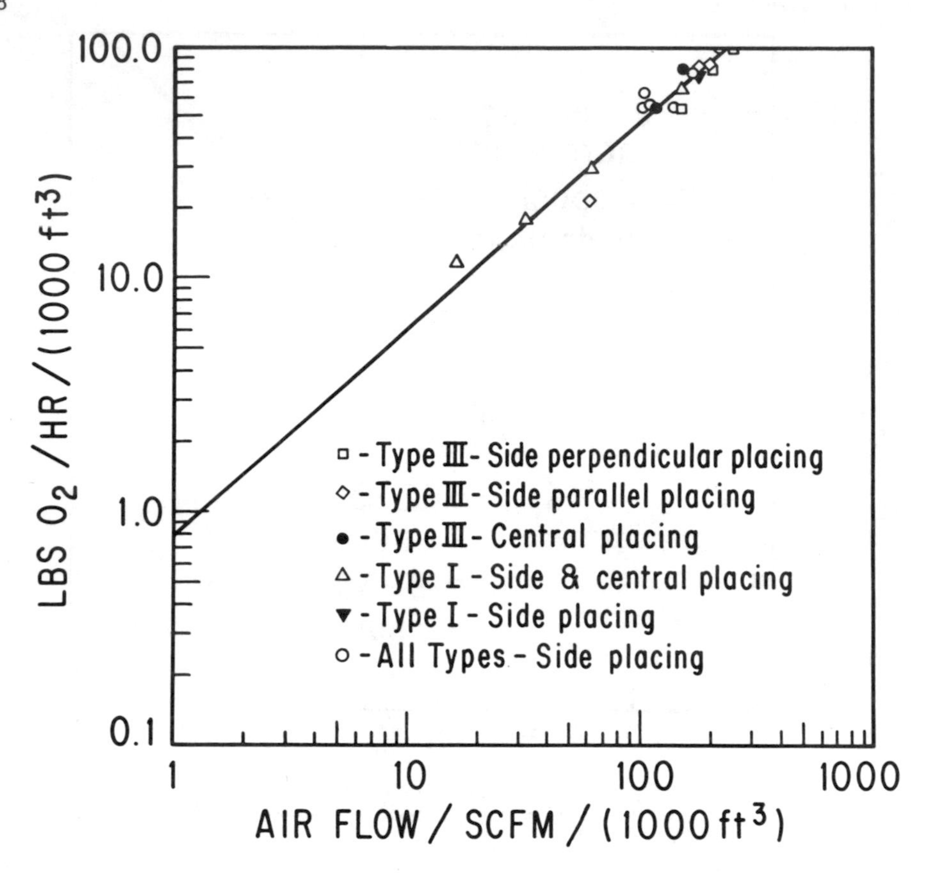

Figure 79. Oxygen transfer characteristics of the INKA aeration system (21).

TABLE 44

Unit	C	N	Conditions	Reference
Saran Tubes	0.160	0.90	9" spacing; wide band 14.4' depth, 24' width	(18)
Saran Tubes	0.170	0.81	9" spacing; narrow band 14.4' depth, 24' width	(18)
Saran Tubes	0.150	0.92	9" spacing; narrow band 14.4' depth, 24' width	(18)
Sparjers	0.081	1.02	24" spacing; wide band 14.8' depth, 24' width	(18)
Sparjers	0.062	1.02	9" spacing; narrow band 14.8' depth, 24' width	(18)
Sparjers	0.064	1.02	9/32" orifice; 25' width 15' depth	(20)
Sparjers	0.068	1.02	13/64" orifice; 25' width 15' depth	(20)
Plate Tubes	0.350	0.49	single row; 25' width, 15' depth	(20)
Plate Tubes	0.200	0.80	double row; 25' width, 15' depth	(20)
INKA System	0.036	0.95	6.8' width, 6' depth, 2.6' submergence	(21)

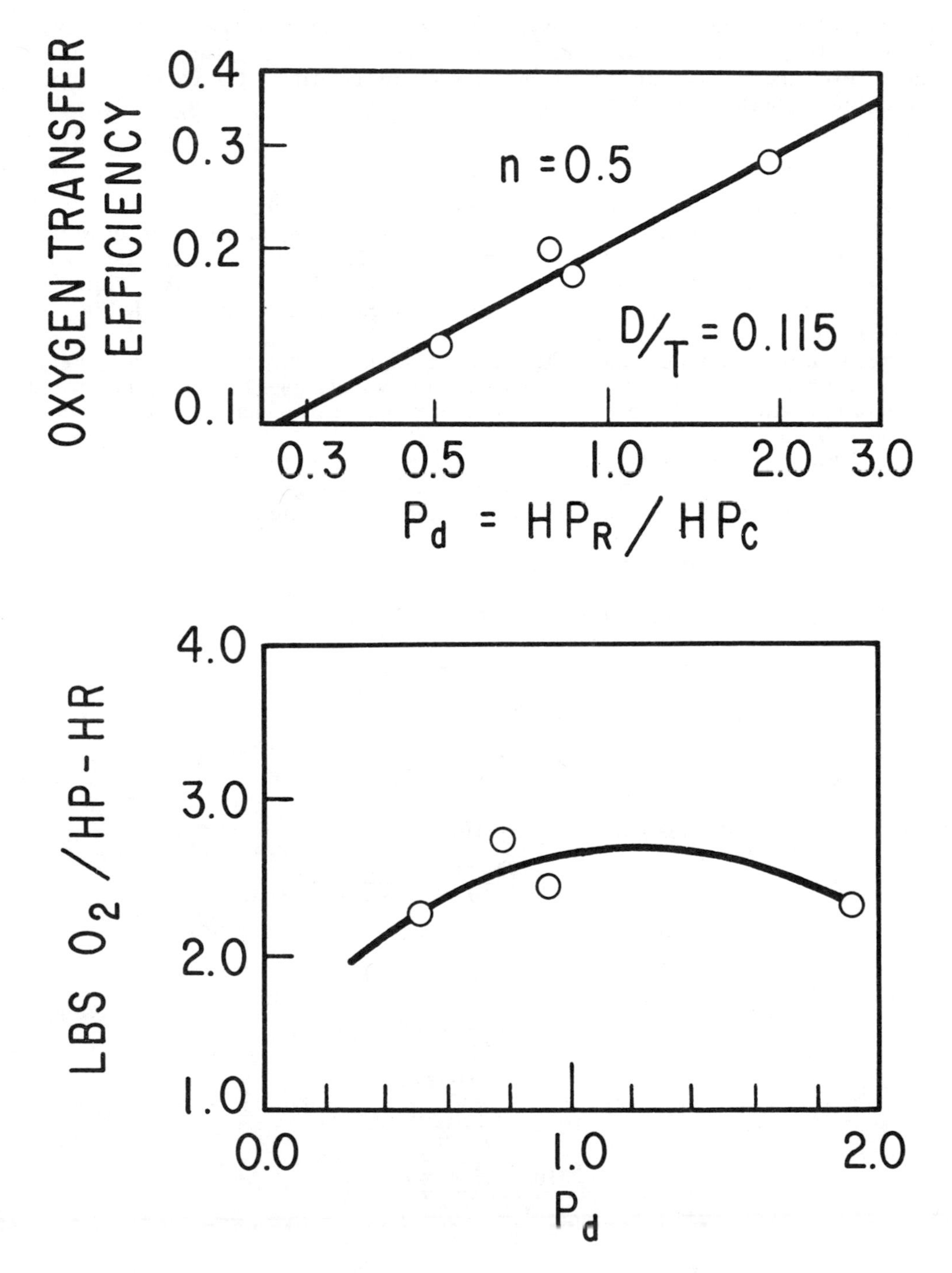

Figure 80. Oxygen transfer from turbine aeration system (22).

Quirk (22) further showed that oxygenation efficiency can be related to P_d by differentiating the oxygenation efficiency with respect to P_d, equating the differential to zero, and solving for the optimum power distribution. The value is a function of the exponent n in Equation 21.

$$P_d^* = \left(\frac{n}{1-n}\right) \tag{22}$$

in which P_d*is the power distribution for optimum oxygenation efficiency.

In most cases, P_d^* occurs near 1.0. (This implies an equal power expenditure by the turbine and the blower.) At extremely high air rates ($P_d \ll 1.0$) large bubbles and flooding of the impeller yield poor oxygenation efficiencies, while at very low rates ($P_d \gg 1.0$) too much turbine horsepower is being expended in fluid mixing.

Variation in oxygen demand in the system can most easily be adjusted by varying the air rate under the impeller. This in turn will change P_d. The anticipated range of operation should cover the maximum range of oxygenation efficiency as related to P_d.

Available data indicate that the oxygenation efficiency of turbine aerators in water should vary from 2.5 to 3.0 lbs O_2/HP-hr (including motor and reducer losses). A turbine aeration design is illustrated in Example 3.

Example 3—Turbine Aeration Design

$$\%O_2 \text{ transfer efficiency} = C\left(\frac{HP_r}{HP_c}\right)^{0.5}$$

The optimum operating range is:

$$\frac{n}{1-n} = O_e$$

$$\frac{0.5}{0.5} = 1.0 = O_e$$

lbs O_2/hr/rotor = 107

$$G_s = \frac{\text{lbs } O_2/\text{hr}}{(60 \times 0.232 \times 0.0746) \times \text{T.E.}}$$

(lbs O_2) = 0.232 (lbs of air)

1 lb air occupies 0.0746 ft^3

$$= \frac{107}{1.05 \times 0.20} = 510 \text{ scfm}$$

Compressor Horsepower

$$HP = \frac{G_s \times p \times 144}{33{,}000 \times E}$$

$$= \frac{510 \times 5.5 \times 144}{33{,}000 \times 0.7}$$

$$= 17 \text{ HP}$$

Correction for waste conditions

$$\frac{17 \text{ HP}}{\left(\frac{C_{SW} - C_L}{C_s}\right) \times \alpha \times 1.02^{(T-20)}}$$

$$\frac{17 \text{ HP}}{\frac{7.6}{10.0} \times 0.85 \times 1.22} = 21 \text{ HP}$$

Turbine Horsepower

$$HP_r = HP_c = 21$$

The operating horsepower under aeration will decrease due to the decreased density of the aerating mixture. The operating horsepower will be about 70 percent of the ungassed horsepower. The ungassed horsepower will be

$$\frac{21}{0.7} = 30 \text{ HP}$$

The aeration efficiency is:

$$\frac{107}{42} = 2.55 \text{ lbs } O_2/\text{HP-hr}$$

Surface Aerators

During the past five years, surface aerators have found increasing application in activated-sludge plants and aerated lagoons in the United States. This is largely due to improved design resulting in increased oxygen transfer capacity.

Several types of surface aerators are in use today. The brush aerator employs a rotating steel brush which sprays liquid from the rotating blades. Mixing is accomplished by an induced velocity below the rotating element. Oxygenation capacity is expressed per foot of rotor and is related to the submergence of the blades.

Bladed surface aerators pump liquid from beneath the blades and spray the liquid across the surface of the water. Some units employ a draft tube. The units may be permanently mounted or placed on pontoons or floats. A recently developed unit employs a submersible pump which delivers liquid against a plate, from which it is sprayed across the water surface. These units are float mounted on polyethylene "doughnuts."

Oxygen transfer in most types of surface aerators may be considered to occur in two ways: transfer to droplets and thin sheets of liquid sprayed from the blades of the unit, and transfer at the turbulent liquid surface and from entrained air bubbles where the spray strikes the surface of the liquid.

Reference is made to Figure 81 in which liquid with an oxygen concentration C_1 is drawn through the aerator and sprayed into the atmosphere. There is a rapid increase in oxygen content of the sprayed liquid to concentration of C_2. (The quantity of oxygen transferred in this phase is limited to the concentration gradient or driving force ($C_s - C_2$) and to the volume of liquid discharged from the blades.) When the liquid strikes the water surface, rapid mixing occurs, resulting in an oxygen concentration of near C_1. Oxygen transfer occurs from the turbulent liquid surface and from entrained air bubbles under a maximum driving force ($C_s - C_1$). Investigations conducted on a surface aeration unit showed that 40–60 percent of the total oxygen was transferred to the spray liquid and the remainder of the oxygen was transferred in the turbulent mixing zone.

The aforementioned discussion assumed substantially complete mixing in the basin (i.e., the dissolved oxygen is uniformly distributed throughout the tank). Increasing the surface area, such as placing the aerator in a large lagoon as compared to an aeration tank, will increase the total oxygen transferred. This will occur as a result of surface transfer from the waves and the turbulent motion of the liquid surface. Eckenfelder (23) showed an increased transfer of 9 percent

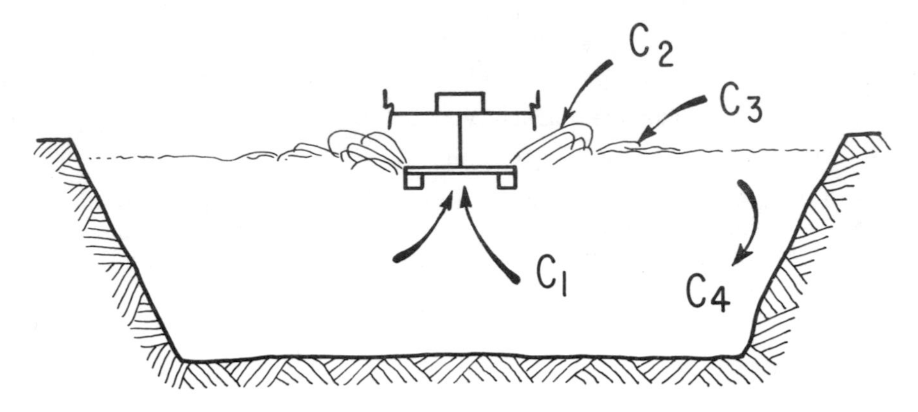

Figure 81. Mechanism of oxygen transfer in a surface aeration unit.

in the total oxygen transferred by a 7.5 HP Hi-Cone aerator by increasing the liquid surface area from 800 $ft.^2$ to 5,000 $ft.^2$

Recent use of surface aerators in large lagoons and streams has yielded conditions where complete mixing does not apply. A dissolved oxygen concentration gradient is therefore established through the liquid. In these cases, the concentration of dissolved oxygen in the immediate vicinity of the aerator will be greater than that in the remote part of the basin, and the previously described methods of performance evaluation do not apply. Kalinske (24) has described a mathematical relationship for this case, although caution must be used to insure consideration for the oxygen transfer at the turbulent water surfaces.

Since the total oxygen transfer is related primarily to the total surface generated and the quantity of liquid pumped, performance will be related to the submergence of the impeller in the liquid, and the speed and diameter of the rotating element, as shown in Figure 82. For most units the pounds of oxygen/HP-hr transferred remains substantially constant over a wide range of unit sizes at optimum submergence. This equipment can therefore be designed by adjusting the oxygenation capacity for anticipated operating conditions:

$$N = N_0 \frac{C_{SW} - C_L}{9.1} \alpha \cdot 1.028^{(T-20)} \tag{23}$$

This calculation is illustrated in Example 4:

Example 4—Surface Aeration Design

It has been found that a surface aerator will transfer 3.5 lbs. O_2/HP-hr in water at 20°C., zero dissolved oxygen. Using an aeration tank 35 ft. wide, 12 ft. deep and 200 ft. long, six units may be employed to transfer 320 lbs O_2/hr.

$$N = 3.5 \frac{(8.6 - 1.0)}{9.1} \cdot 0.85 \cdot 1.22$$

$$N = 3.0 \text{ lbs } O_2/\text{HP-hr.}$$

$$\frac{320 \text{ lbs } O_2/\text{hr}}{3.0 \text{ lbs } O_2/\text{HP-hr}} = 107 \text{ HP}$$

$$\text{Each unit} = \frac{107}{6} = 18 \text{ HP}$$

Use 20 HP units

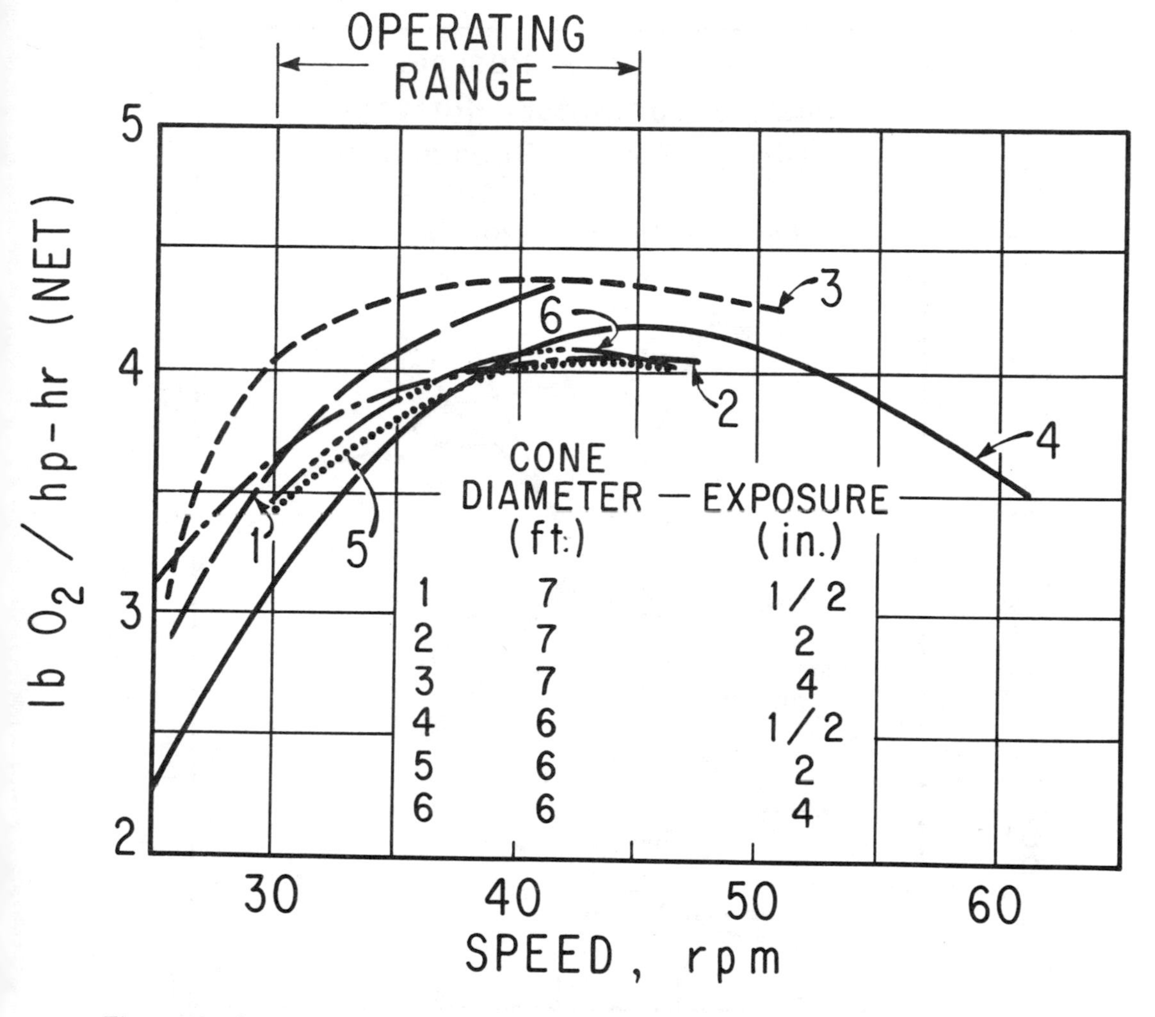

Figure 82. Oxygen transfer characteristics of a Simplex surface aerator.

The transfer capacities of the brush aerator using the angle-iron type rotors and the Kessner Brush are shown in Figure 83 (24–26). A wide range of efficiencies is observed, depending on the type of brush and the aeration conditions.

Most surface aeration units will transfer 3.2–3.8 lbs O_2/HP-hr depending on tank geometry, surface area, and unit construction.

Symbols Used

$$\frac{dC}{dt} = K_L a\,(C_s - C)$$

$$\alpha = \frac{K_L a \text{ waste}}{K_L a \text{ water}}$$

$$\alpha' = \frac{K_L \text{ waste}}{K_L \text{ water}}$$

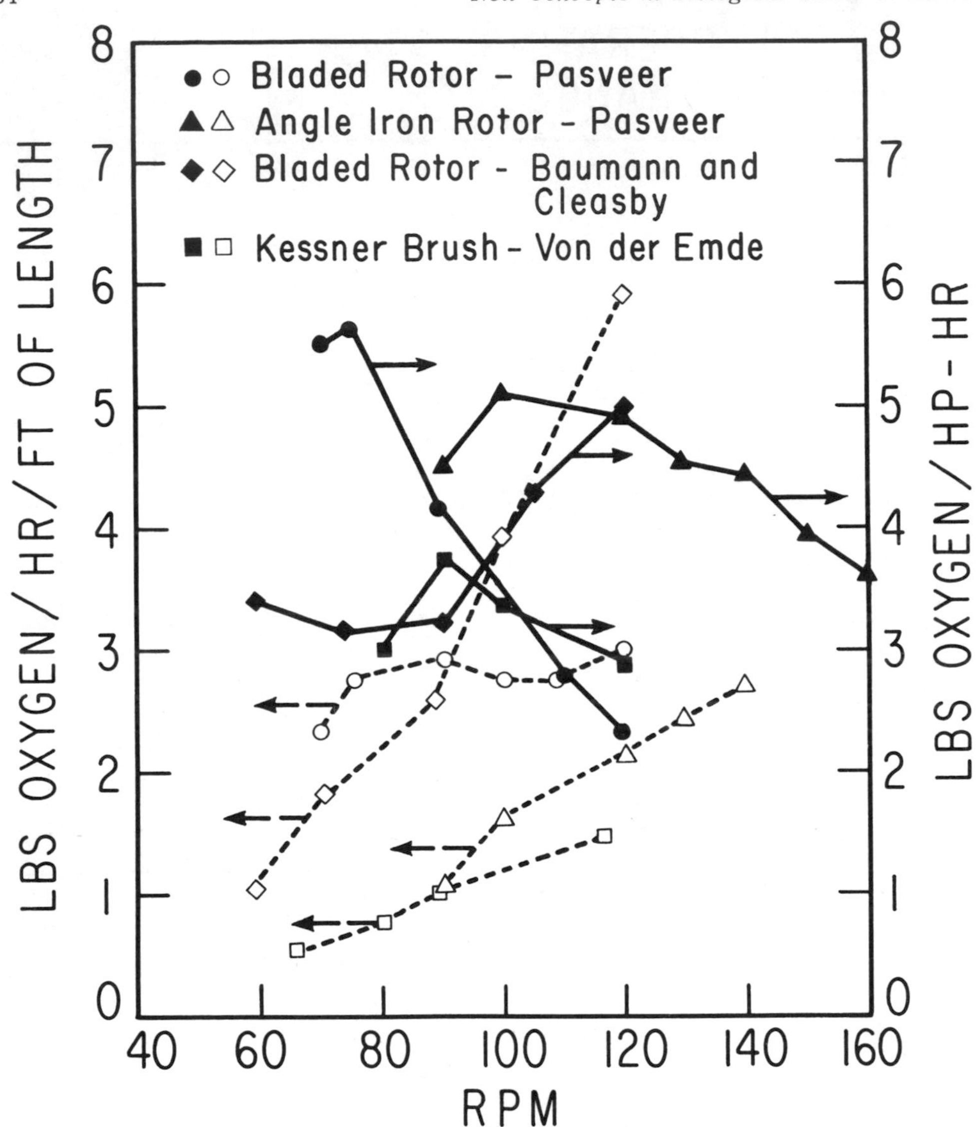

Figure 83. Oxygen transfer from brush aeration units.

A = interfacial area (ft.^{2})
C_L = dissolved oxygen concentration in liquid
C_s = saturation concentration of O_2 in water
C_{SM} = oxygen saturation concentration at tank mid-depth
C_{SW} = oxygen saturation concentration for waste
D_c = diffusivity coefficient of oxygen in water (ft^2/hr)
d_t = impeller diameter (ft.)
d_B = mean bubble diameter
G_S = air flow, scfm/aeration unit
H = liquid depth (ft.)
HP_r = drawn horsepower of turbine unit

HP_c = compressor horsepower
K_L = liquid film coefficient (ft/hr), as defined in text
K_La = overall transfer coefficient, (hr.$^{-1}$) $\left(K_L \frac{A}{V}\right)$
L = liquid film thickness
Γ = excess surface concentration on surfactant
γ = surface tension
N = lbs O_2/hr/aeration unit
Q = liquid flow rate
$\overline{R}$ = gas constant
R = impeller peripheral speed (ft/sec)
r = interface renewal rate
r_r = oxygen utilization rate mg/l/hr
t = time
T = temperature °C.
V = liquid volume
v_B = bubble velocity
W = aeration tank width (ft.)

REFERENCES

(1) Ippen, A. T., and C. E. Carver, Jr. "Basic Factors of Oxygen Transfer in Aeration Systems," *Sewage Ind. Wastes, 26*(7), 813 (July 1954).
(2) Eckenfelder, W. W. Jr. "Aeration Efficiency and Design," *Sewage Ind. Wastes, 24*(10), 1221 (October 1952).
(3) Gaden, E. L., Jr. "Aeration and Oxygen Transport in Biological Systems—Basic Consideration," *Biological Treatment of Sewage and Industrial Wastes*. Vol. 1, p. 172. New York: Reinhold Publishing Corporation (1956).
(4) Dobbins, W. E. "Mechanism of Gas Absorption by Turbulent Liquids," *Advances in Water Pollution Research, Proc.* 1st. Intl. Conf. Water Pollution Research. Vol. 2, p. 61. London: Pergamon Press Ltd. (1964).
(5) Lewis, W. K., and W. G. Whitman. "Principles of Gas Adsorption," *Ind. Engr. Chem., 16,* 1215 (1924).
(6) Danckwerts, P. V. "Significance of Liquid Film Coefficients in Gas Adsorption," *Ind. Engr. Chem., 43,* 1460 (1951).
(7) Higbee, Ralph. "The Rate of Adsorption of a Pure Gas into a Still Liquid during Short Periods of Exposure," *Trans. Amer. Inst. Chem. Engr., 31,* 365 (1935).
(8) Adamson, A. W. *Physical Chemistry of Surfaces.* New York: Interscience Publishers, Inc. (1960).
(9) Dobbins, W. E. "The Nature of the Oxygen Transfer Coefficient in Aeration Systems," *Biological Treatment of Sewage and Industrial Wastes,* edited by McCabe and Eckenfelder. New York: Reinhold Publishers (1956).
(10) Eckenfelder, W. W., and E. B. Barnhart. Paper presented Amer. Inst. of Chem. Engrs., Atlanta, Georgia (February 1960).
(11) Mancy, K. H., and D. A. Okun. "Effect of Surface Active Agents on the Rate of Oxygen Transfer," *Advances in Biological Waste Treatment,* edited by Eckenfelder and McCabe. New York: Pergamon Press (1960).
(12) Eckenfelder, W. W. "Design of Aerated Lagoons," *Proc.* 14th Industrial Waste Conference, Purdue University (1959).
(13) Gibbs, J. W. *The Collected Works of J. W. Gibbs.* New York: Longevers Green and Company (1931).
(14) Mancy, K. H., and D. A. Okun. "The Effects of Surface Active Agents on Aeration," *J. Water Poll. Cont. Fed., 37,* 212–225 (February 1965).
(15) Eckenfelder, W. W., and D. J. O'Connor. *Biological Waste Treatment.* New York: Pergamon Press (1964).

(16) McKeown, J. J., and D. A. Okun. "Effects of Surface Active Agents on Oxygen Bubble Characteristics," *Advances in Biological Waste Treatment,* edited by Eckenfelder and McCabe. New York: Pergamon Press (1960).

(17) McWhirter, J. R. "Fundamental Aspects of Surface Aerator Performance and Design," 20th Industrial Waste Treatment Conference, Purdue University (1965).

(18) Bewtra, J. K., and W. R. Nicholas. "Oxygenation from Diffused Air in Aeration Tanks," *J. Water Poll. Cont. Fed.,* (October 1964).

(19) Eckenfelder, W. W. "Absorption of Oxygen from Air Bubbles in Water," *J. Sanit. Engr. Div. ASCE,* 85 (July 1959).

(20) Eckenfelder, W. W., and E. B. Barnhart. Unpublished Thesis. Manhattan College (1965).

(21) Ganczarczyk, Jerzy. "Some Features of Low Pressure Aeration." 2nd International Conference on Water Pollution Research, Tokyo, Japan (1964).

(22) Quirk, T. P. "Optimization of Gas-Liquid Contacting Systems." Unpublished report (1962).

(23) Eckenfelder, W. W. "Design and Performance of Aerated Lagoons for Pulp and Paper Waste Treatment," *Proc.* 16th Industrial Waste Conference, Purdue University (1961).

(24) Kalinske, A. A. "Power Consumption for Oxygenation and Mixing," *Advances in Biological Waste Treatment,* edited by Eckenfelder and McCabe. New York: Pergamon Press (1960).

(25) Baumann, E. R., and J. L. Cleasby "Oxygenation Efficiency of a Bladed Rotor." Paper presented at the National Meeting of the American Institute of Chemical Engineers, Mineapolis, Minnesota (September 28, 1965).

(26) Pasveer, A. "Developments in Activated Sludge Treatment in the Netherlands." Manhattan Conference on Biological Waste Treatment (1960).

(27) Von der Emde, W. Discussion. *Advances in Water Pollution Research.* Vol. II. New York: Pergamon Press (1963).

AERATION DEVELOPMENTS IN EUROPE

Wilhelm von der Emde
Technische Hochschule Wien, Vienna, Austria

Prior to the construction of large sewage treatment plants, investigations were conducted on new aeration systems in large scale, and comparisons were made with known aeration processes in several plants, for example, Emschergenossenschaft in Essen, the city of Hamburg plant, and the Bayrische Biologische Versuchsanstalt in Munich. This paper describes some of these tests. Economic aspects and the behavior of these aeration systems under operational conditions are discussed.

DIFFUSED AIR

Emschergenossenschaft tested the following aeration systems in a steel tank 20 feet in length, 20 feet in width, and 13 feet in depth:

Saran-tube aerators (Chicago Pump Company)
Brandol-tube aerators (Schuhmacher'sche Fabrik)
Plastic-box aerators (Oswald Schulze, Gladbeck)

Brandol-tube aerators consist of ceramic material with the spheres linked together by synthetic resins. The width of the pores average 290 microns when using granulation Brandol 80. The plastic aeration boxes look like flat steel chests. The surface of the chest is covered with a thin leaf of polyethylene plastic.

In the course of the tests, the quantity of air and the arrangement of the aeration devices were varied. The following arrangements, as shown in Figure 84, were chosen:

Location
at one side,
at both sides, and
over the whole plane of the aeration tank.

The quantity of air supplied was in accordance with optimum conditions advised by the manufacturer.

The oxygenation capacity tests were run on tap water, on tap water with detergents added, and on final effluent. Nitrogen was used to remove oxygen before the investigation was started. The results are summarized in Figure 85. The results confirm the investigations of Morgan and Bewtra, in which a distribution of diffused air over several rows increases the oxygenation efficiency. The efficiency is higher if the devices are placed at both sides of the aeration tank rather than at one side. Distribution of the devices over the whole floor furnishes optimum results (three rows of aeration devices). The above-mentioned three systems had approximately the same oxygenation efficiency.

Application of an arrangement over the whole floor, with its better oxygenation efficiency, is related to the longer time of contact between air bubbles and water. Velocities near the floor were about 2 ft/s when the aerators had been set at one side only and 0.7 ft/s for the whole floor distribution of the aeration devices, as shown in Figure 86.

Tests were also conducted on medium bubble aeration (perforated tubes, diameter of the openings 2 mm., exit velocity 50–70 ft/s, Fig. 87) and on coarse bubble aeration. The coarse bubble aeration employs openings of two inches in

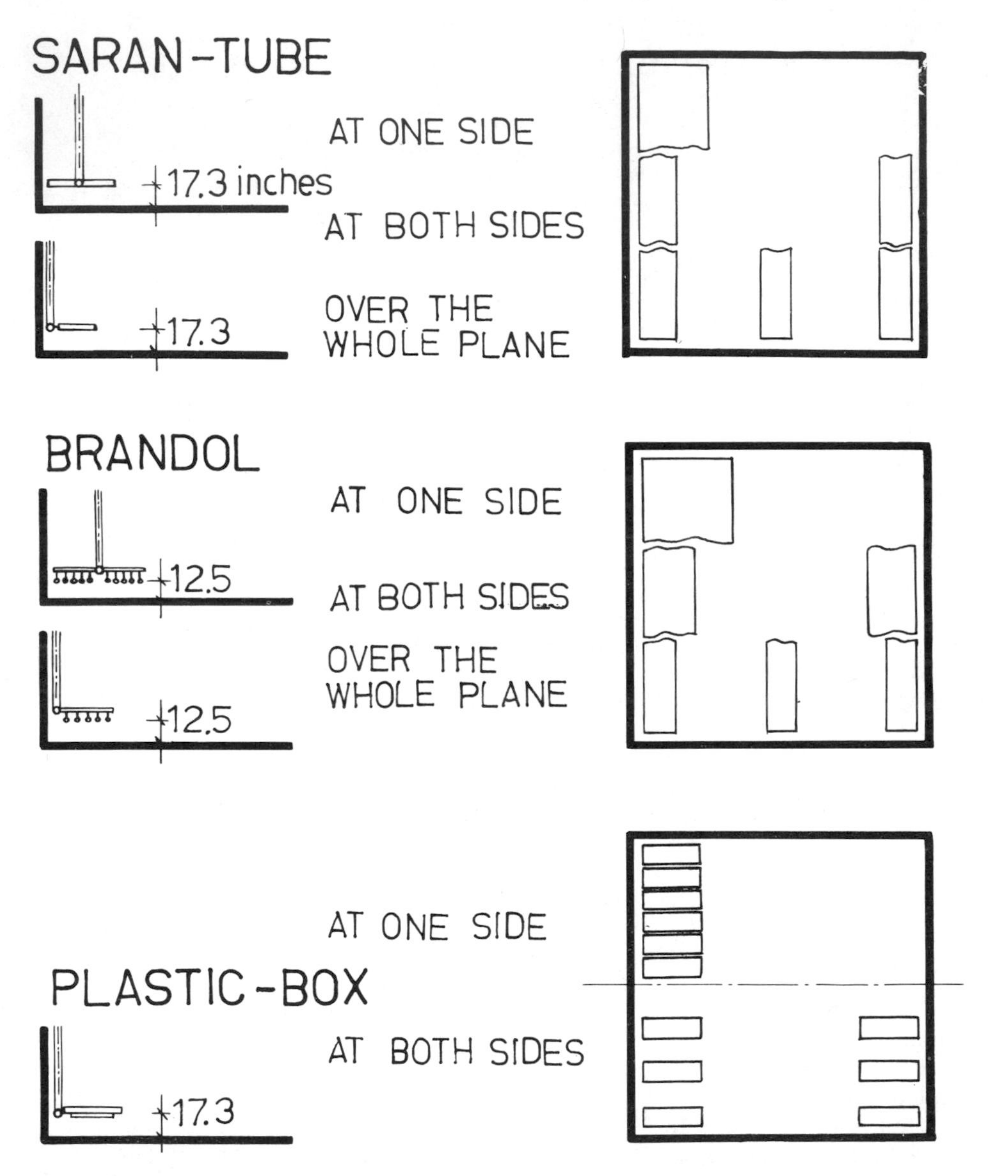

Figure 84. Diffused air—location of diffusers.

diameter. To raise the oxygenation efficiency, Emschergenossenschaft developed inclined steel plates equipped with welded rips to divide the bubbles (Fig. 88).

Tests show that these improved large bubble aeration devices are able to achieve the same oxygenation efficiency as the medium bubble aeration (Fig. 89).

The oxygenation tests employing tap water with detergents and biologically treated sewage (concentration of detergents 3–9 mg/l) showed values of 60 percent in the case of fine bubble aeration and 70–80 percent for medium and coarse bubble aeration compared to pure water. Comparing the results of coarse and medium bubble aeration, the former showed higher efficiencies.

AERATOR LOCATION	OXYGEN ABSORPTION in %		
	SARAN TUBES	BRANDOL TUBES	PLASTIC BOXES
ONE SIDE	13.4	16.1	13.0
BOTH SIDES	14.3	15.6	15.8
WHOLE PLANE	18.6	18.4	-

AERATOR DEPTH ~11 ft

AIR FLOW 3÷5 m^3AIR / m^3tank·h

Figure 85. Diffused air—oxygen absorption.

FINE BUBBLE AERATION—DANJES SYSTEM

To increase the travel of the bubbles, the Danjes system has the filter tube aerators adjusted to a moving bridge. Baffles in front of the tube aerators take care that the velocity of the water beyond the aerators will be 1.6 ft/s, the speed of the bridge being 0.8 ft/s. The air bubbles do not move straight upward, since they are carried away with the liquid flow (Fig. 90).

In the usual spiral flow tank, air bubbles moving upward affect a water movement and reduce the time of contact between air bubbles and water. The baffles adjusted to the bridge bring about an upward whirl of the sludge. The rising air bubbles create no spiral flow, giving an increase in the time of contact. The oxygenation efficiency was 13.9 percent for an immersion depth of 3.3 feet. An increase in the air input lowered the efficiency to 8 percent. These investigations were conducted in tap water. A pilot plant for complete oxidation (2,000 inhabitants) is now in operation in Munich. This system is primarily applicable to low-loaded sewage plants with a low oxygen consumption rate.

CONE AERATION

Simplex Cone

Many plants in Europe employ Simplex high-intensity cones 6 feet in diameter. At 51 rpm (16 ft/s peripheral speed), the oxygenation capacity of the cone

VELOCITIES IN ft/s

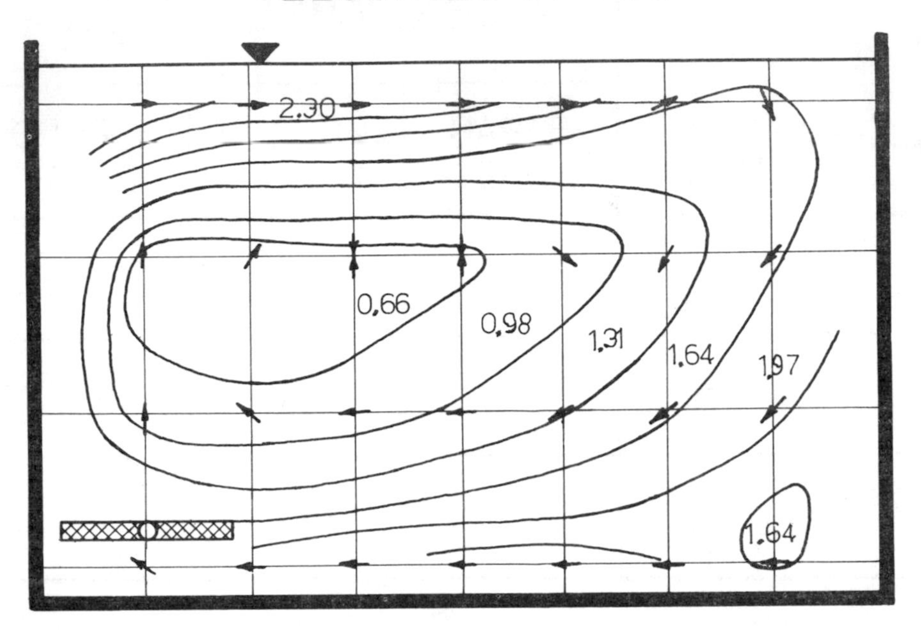

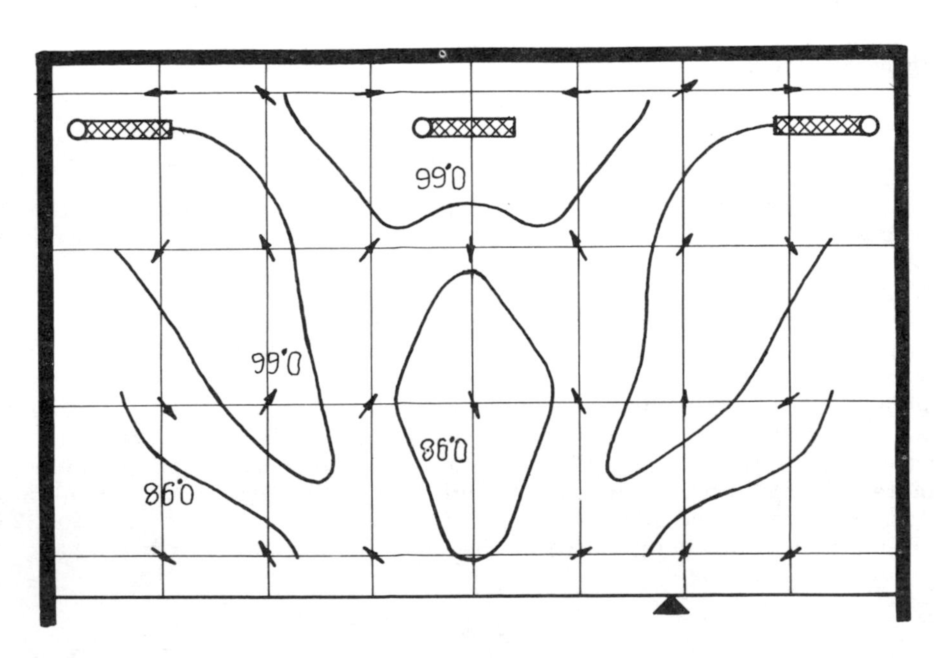

Figure 86. Diffused air—circulation velocity.

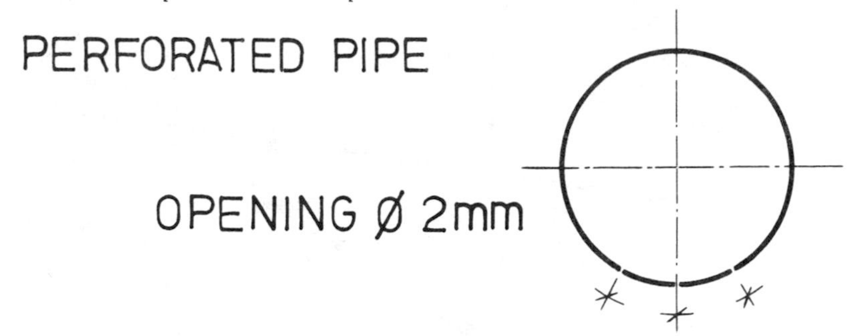

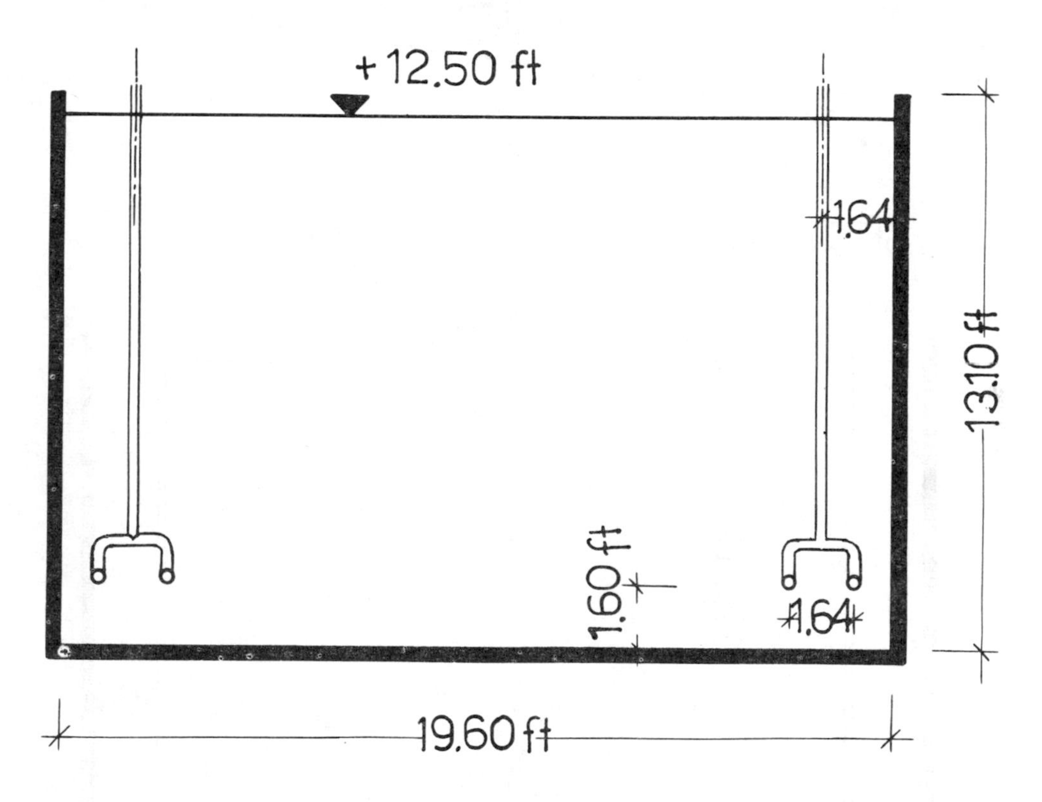

Figure 87. Medium bubble aeration—cross-section detail.

is 50 lb O_2/h. This peripheral speed disperses the moved water into small droplets, as can be seen in Plate 1. Increasing the peripheral speed to 58 rpm or 18 ft/s resulted in an increase in oxygenation capacity of only 15 percent. The distance of the thrown water was considerably larger, and wetting troubles were observed. Operational reasons indicate speeds less than 16 ft/s if the surface of the aeration tank is smaller than 33 feet by 33 feet.

The oxygenation capacity decreases to 22 lb/h at 51 rpm and 6 inches of freeboard (Fig. 91). The quantity of water pumped was reduced from 14 to 5 mgd. By

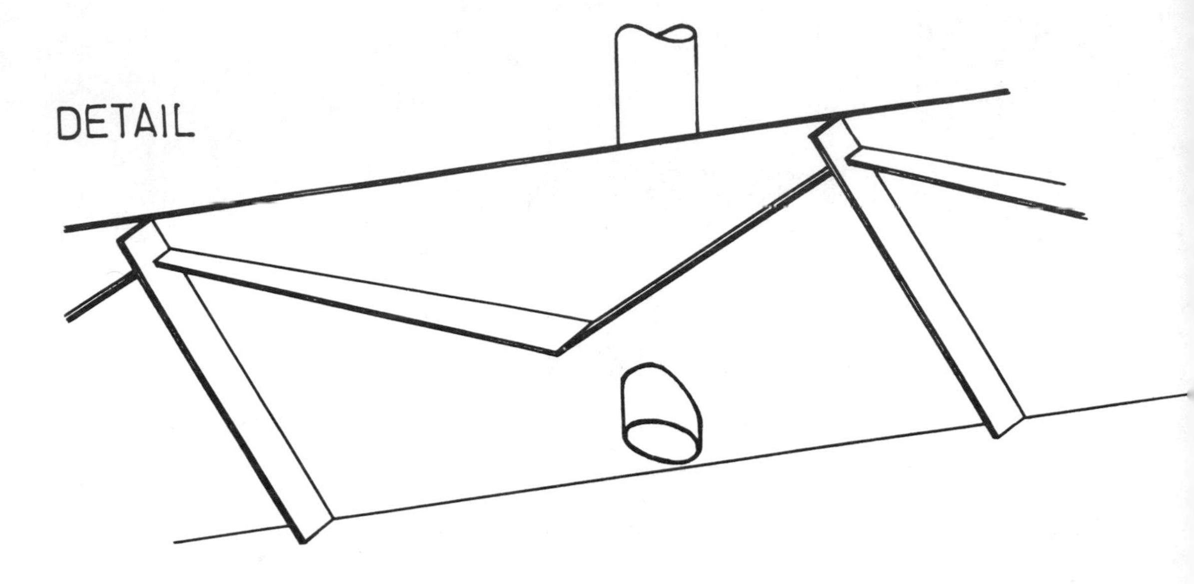

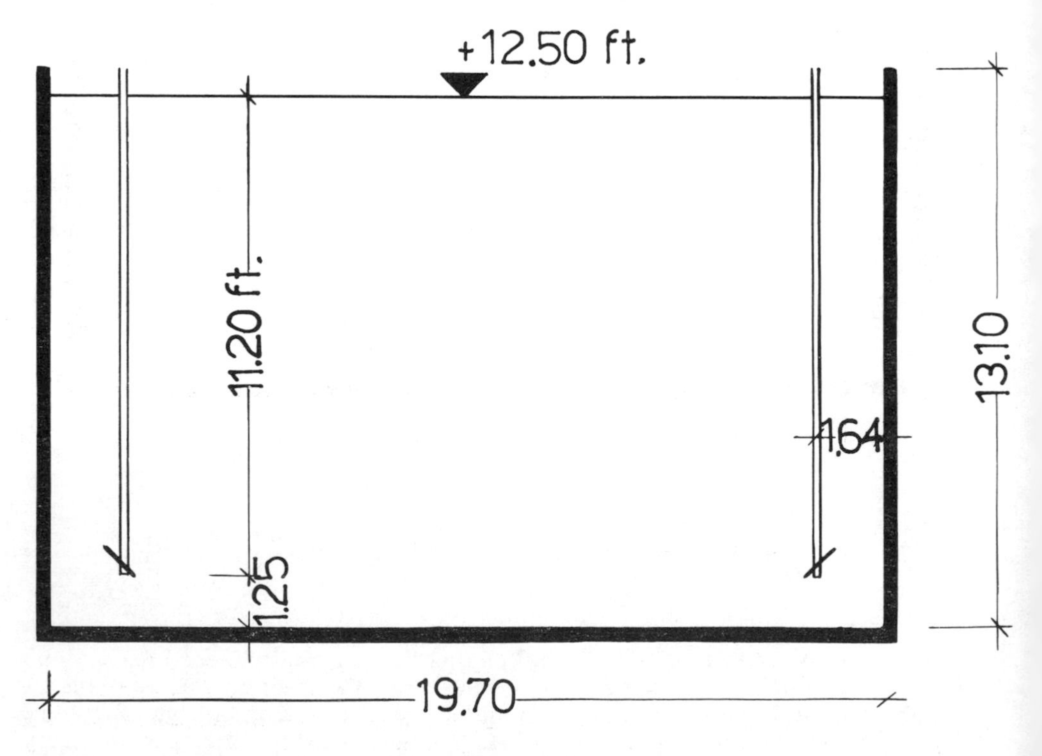

Figure 88. Coarse bubble aeration—cross-section detail.

AIR FLOW m^3/m^3h	OXYGEN ABSORPTION	
	MEDIUM PERFORATED PIPES	COARSE OPEN PIPES ×
3	9.8	9.5
4	9.0	8.8
5	8.4	8.4

AERATOR DEPTH 11 ft.
AERATORS ON BOTH SIDES
× OPEN PIPES AND DISTRIBUT. PLATES

Figure 89. Medium coarse bubble aeration—oxygen absorption.

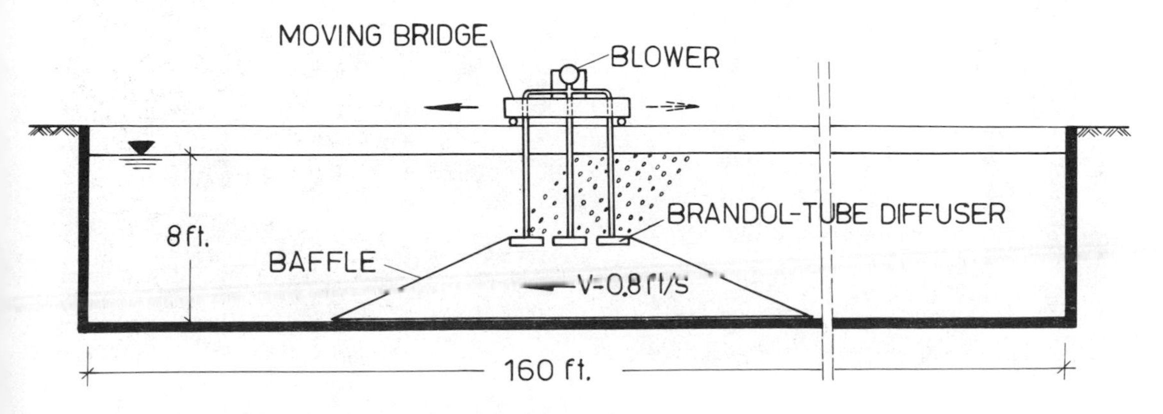

Figure 90. Diffused air system Danjes—cross section.

SIMPLEX-AERATOR (6 ft. CONE, 51 rev/min – v_p=16 ft/s, AER. EFF. ~3.1 lb/hp·h (FB.O))

FREEBOARD inch	OXYGEN CAPACITY $lb O_2/h$ ($kg O_2/h$)	PUMP. RATE Mio gal/d (m^3/h)	OXYG. CAPAC./ / PUMP. RATE ppm
0.0	50.0 (22.75)	13.9 (2200)	10.3
2.0	37.6 (17.10)	10.4 (1650)	10.3
4.0	30.8 (14.00)	7.3 (1160)	12.0
6.0	22.0 (10.00)	5.3 (840)	11.9

Figure 91. Simplex cone—oxygen capacity pumping rate.

Plate 1. Oxygenation by Simplex high-intensity cones.

relating the oxygenation capacity to the pumping rate, it can be shown that the water is almost saturated after one turnover. This is independent of the depth of immersion of the cone.

The same results were observed using a cone of 5 feet in diameter at 49 rpm or 13 ft/s at Emschergenossenschaft. From these data it follows that the quantity of water pumped is the limiting factor for high-intensity cones.

The oxygenation capacity of the 5-foot cone at 49 rpm and at 4 inches freeboard was a little bit higher ($\alpha = 1.15$), using tap water with detergents. For final effluent (content of detergents, 2–4 mg/l) OC was a little lower than tap water without detergents. By increasing the freeboard, better oxygenation capacities were obtained.

Simcar Cone

Simcar cones do not use a draft tube. The outer side of the cone has angle-formed steel plates effecting the oxygen input (Fig. 92). A Simcar cone of 7.5 feet in diameter had been tested in Hamburg in a tank 20 feet wide, 20 feet long, and 10 feet deep. The oxygenation capacity was determined for tap water and for final effluent.

For tap water, the peripheral speed was 16 ft/s, the freeboard was zero, and 70 lb O_2/h were transferred into the liquid. An increase in freeboard resulted in a linear decrease in the oxygen input (Fig. 93).

A peripheral speed of 16 ft/s led to splashing troubles in the small tanks, and the speed was reduced to 14 ft/s. It became evident that the oxygen input increased linearly, with water rising above the cone (negative freeboard). Final effluent transferred less oxygen ($\alpha = 0.9$).

With a decrease in oxygen supply, the energy input decreased linearly with an increase in freeboard. It is interesting to note that the operation of the cone required less energy for final effluent than for tap water (Fig. 94). When the ratio of oxygenation capacity over energy requirements was considered, aeration efficiency was more favorable at higher speeds.

At a peripheral speed of 14 ft/s, the oxygenation efficiency amounted to 3 lb O_2/HP-h; at 16 ft/s, 3.3 lb O_2/HP-h. The aeration was influenced by the rotational speed but remained constant at different immersion depths.

An increase in depth of the tank to 13 feet raised the oxygenation capacity of the cone with a peripheral speed of 14 ft/s by 20 percent. The oxygenation efficiency, however, remained unchanged. No deposits of sludge were encountered in these deep tanks with rounded cones.

Vortair Cones

Emschergenossenschaft tested a Vortair cone in a tank 20 feet in width, 20 feet in length, and 12 feet in depth. The volume was about 5,000 ft^3. A tank of 23,000 ft^3 was operated in parallel. When the rotational speed was kept constant, somewhat more oxygen was transferred into the larger tank (Fig. 95). Just the opposite happened to the oxygenation efficiency (Fig. 96). The optimum value for the small tank was less than 4 lb/HP-h, and less than 3 lb/HP-h for the large tanks at the optimal speed of 15 ft/s. This may easily be explained by the fact that when the whole water volume is circulated, the friction losses are smaller in the smaller tank. As to large basins, the opposite holds true, for the cone has to supply more energy, thus reducing the oxygenation efficiency. (The energy values had been transferred from a continuous gear, which was used during the investigation.) Figure 97 gives a velocity cross section for the large tank.

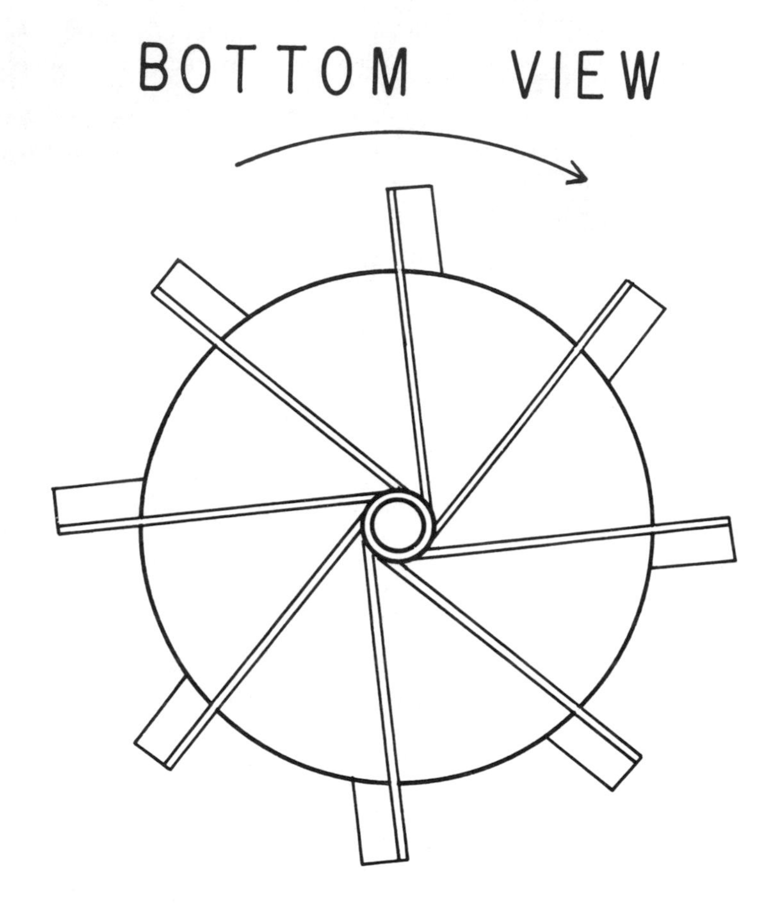

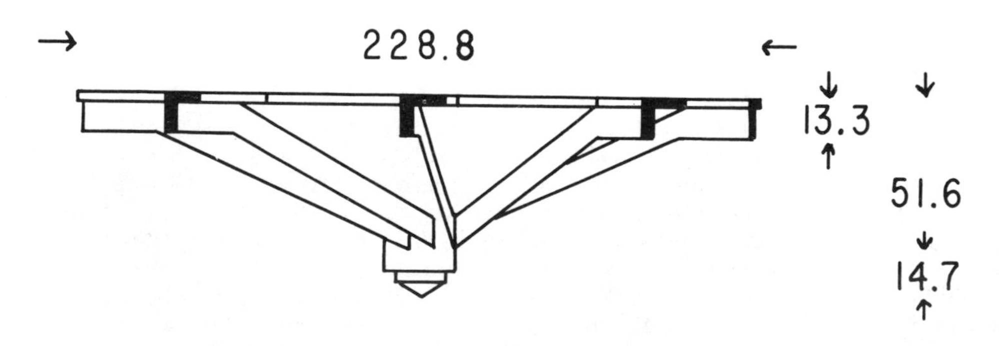

Figure 92. Simcar-Kreisel.

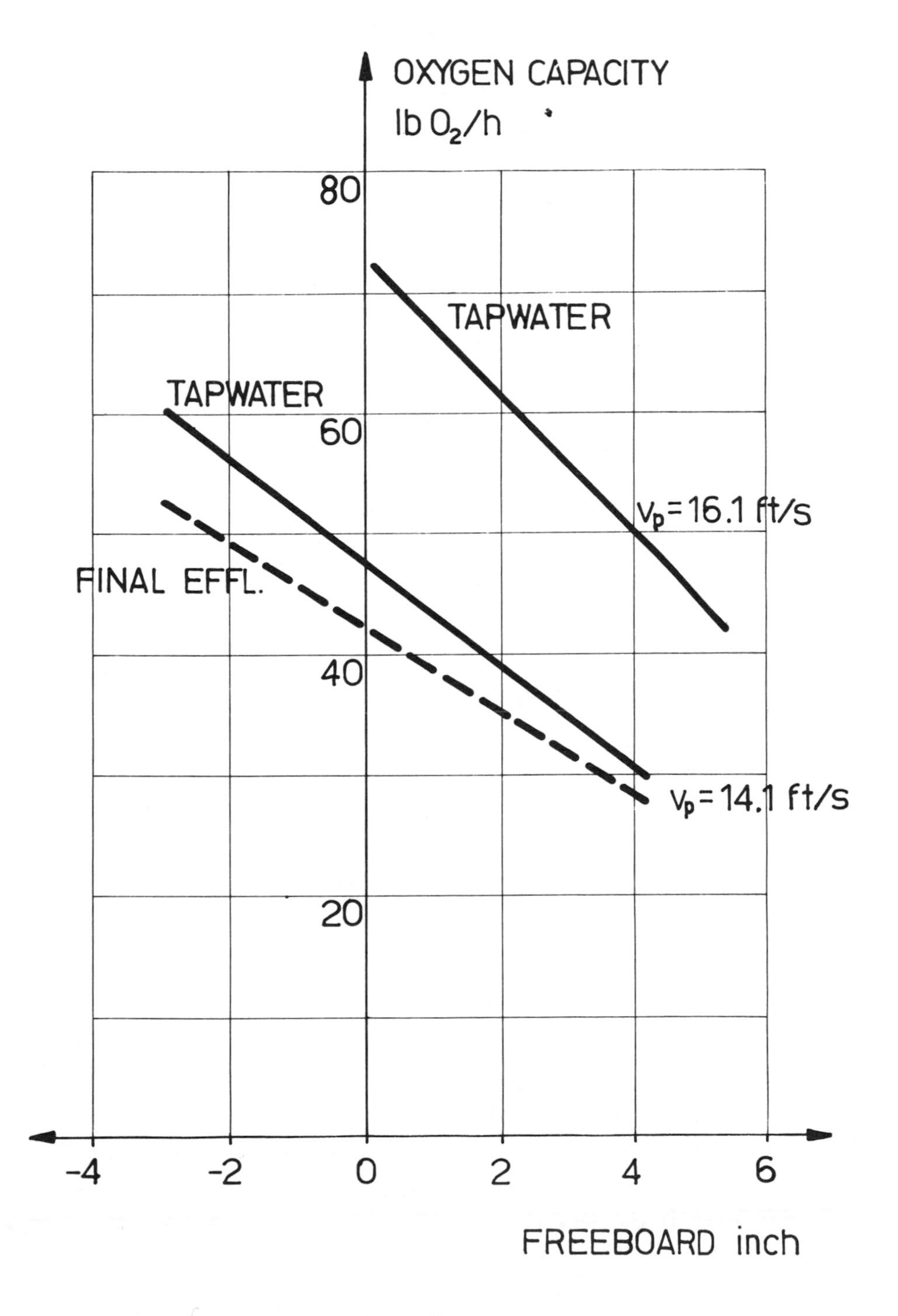

Figure 93. Simcar aerator—oxygen capacity.

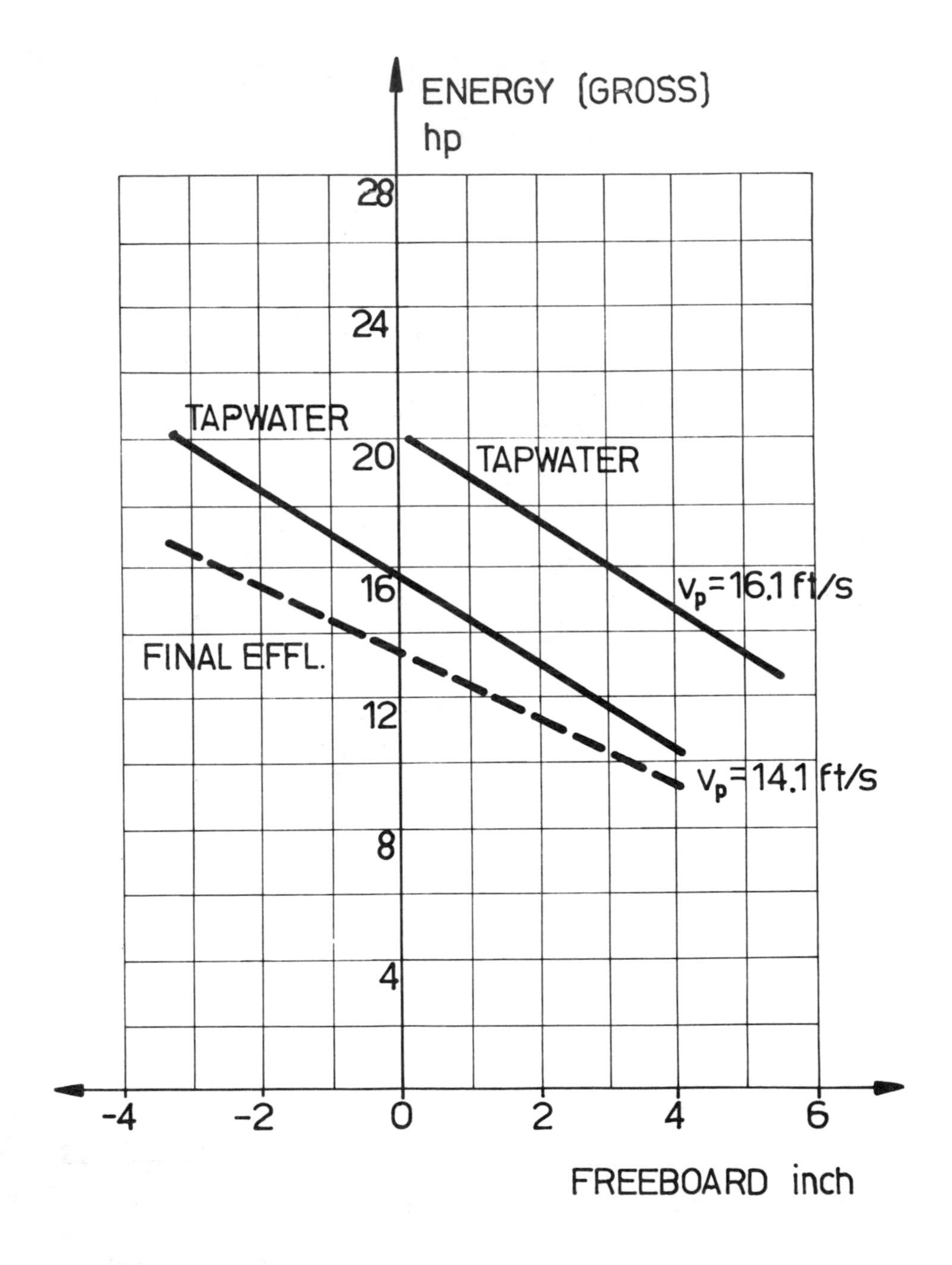

Figure 94. Simcar aerator—energy gross.

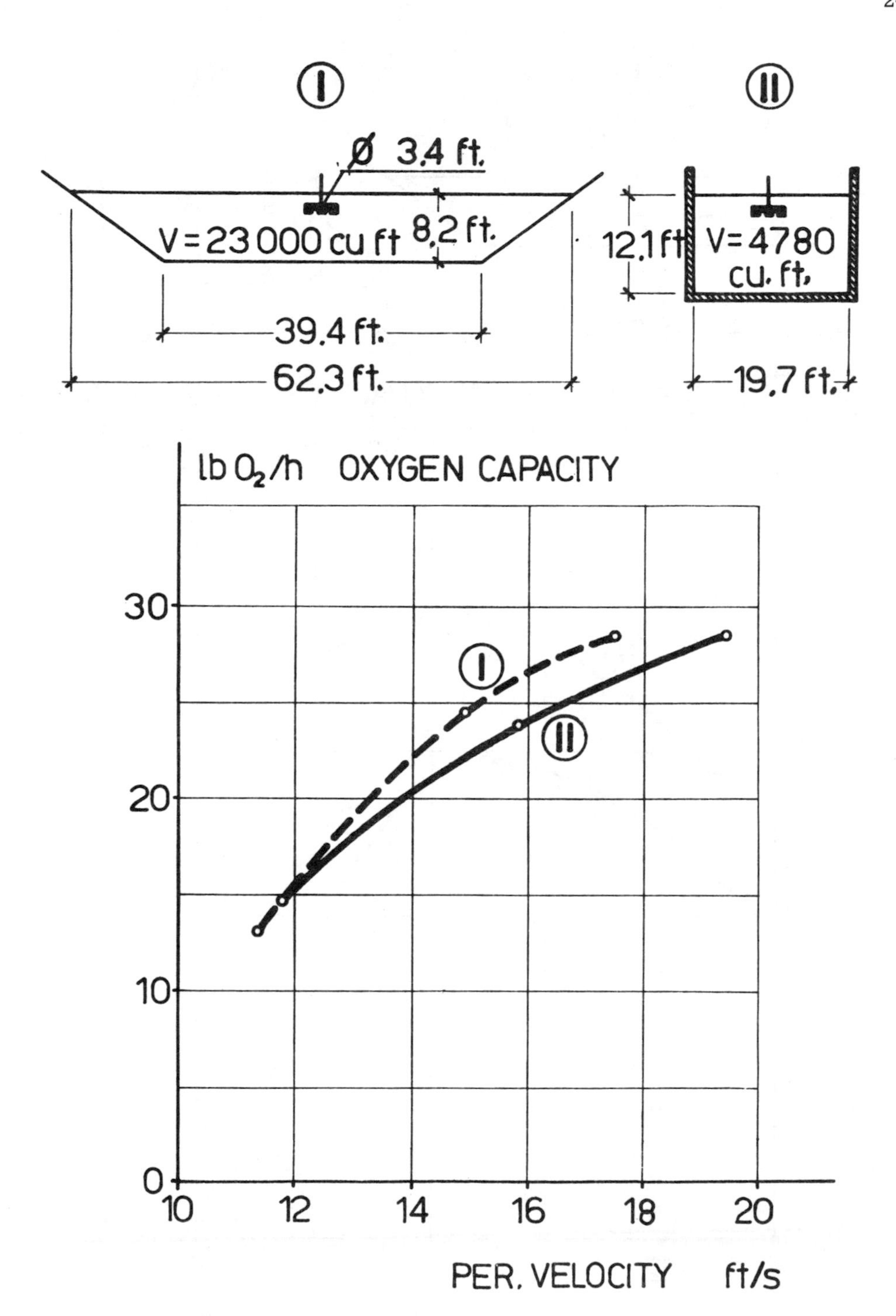

Figure 95. Vortair aerator—oxygen capacity.

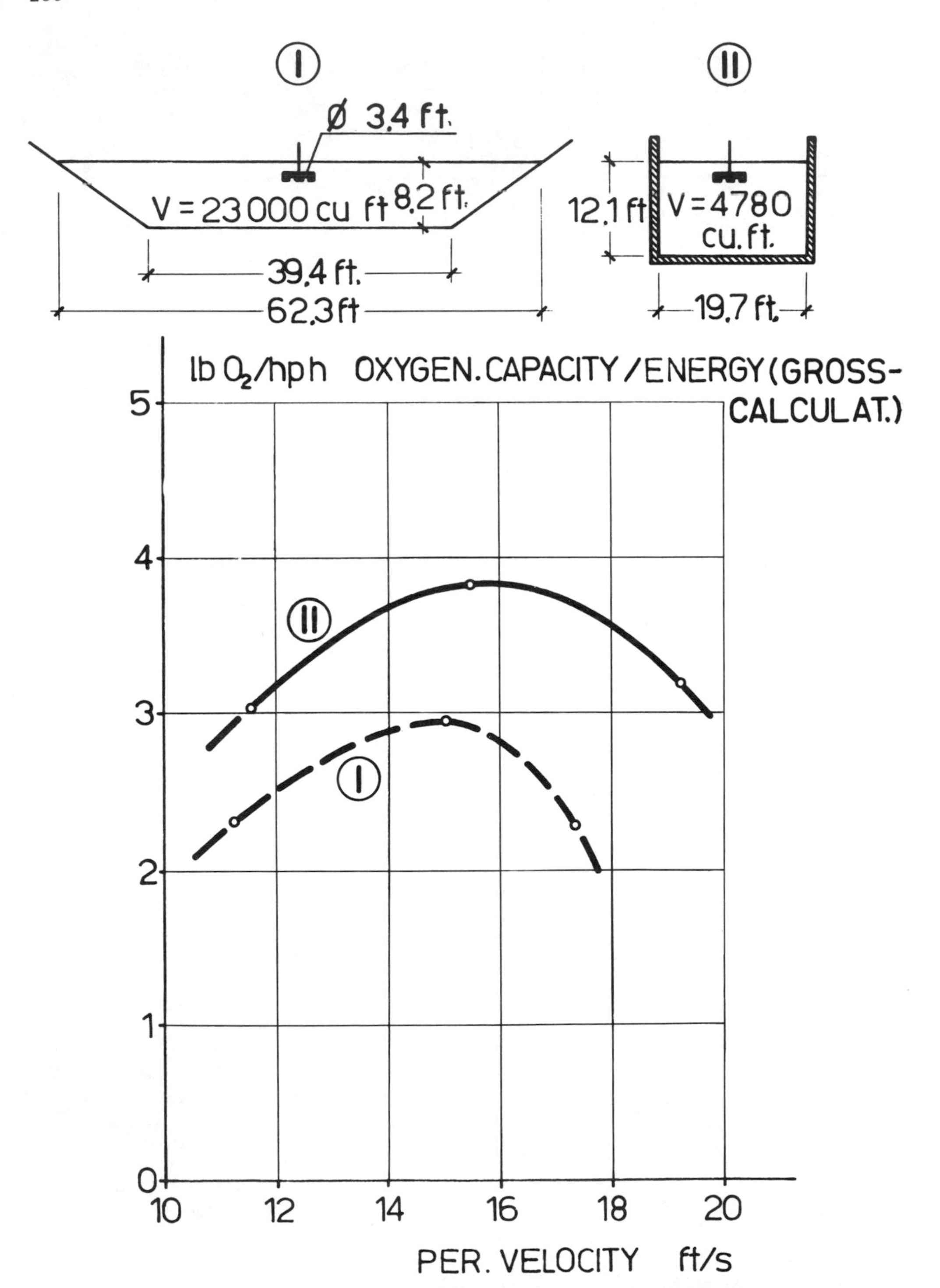

Figure 96. Vortair aerator—oxygen cap/en.

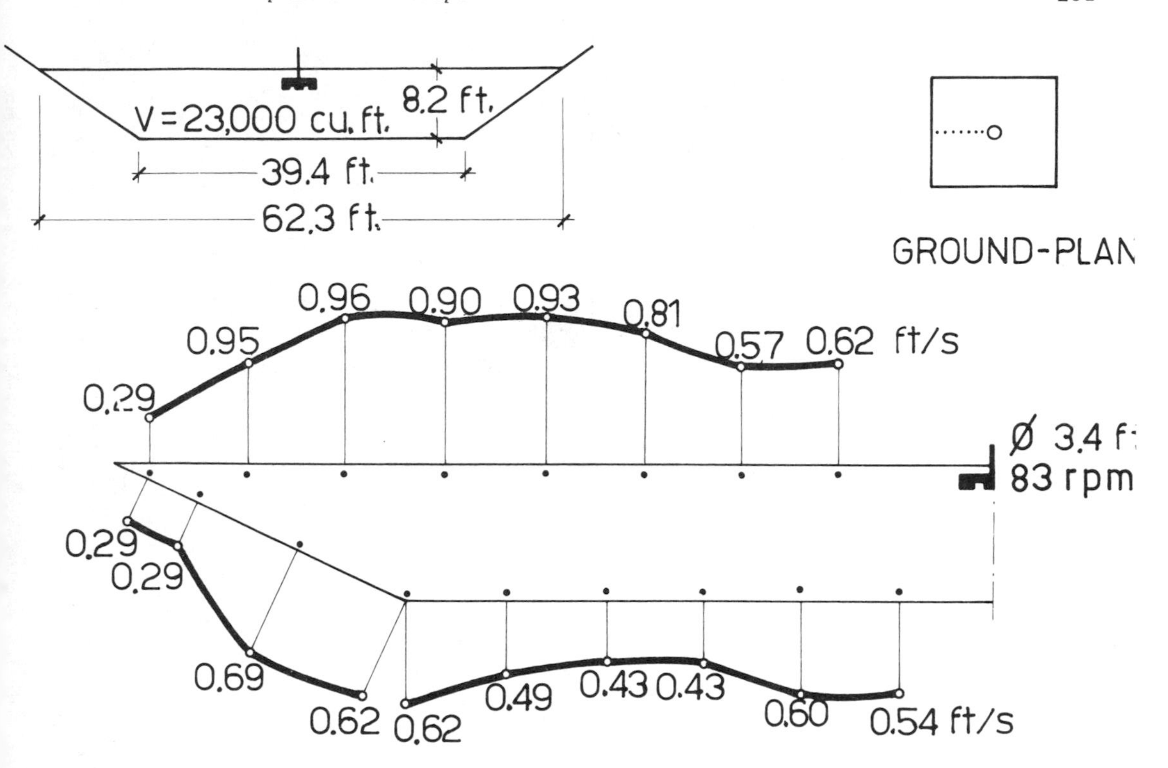

Figure 97. Vortair aerator—flow velocity.

BSK TURBINE

The BSK Turbine employs a turbine shaped to the flow of the water. The rotation sucks air, and air and water are mixed within the turbine and then discharged (Fig. 98).

The optimum values were attained at a peripheral speed of 15 ft/s using a 4-foot cone. Pilot investigations performed by the manufacturer showed an optimum oxygenation efficiency of 4.9 lb O_2/HP-h (Fig. 99). The depth of immersion has little influence upon the oxygenation efficiency. (The energy values had been transferred from a continuous gear similar to the Vortair cone used during the investigation.) Variation of the depth of immersion affected only a small increase in power requirements and in oxygenation capacity.

An increase of power requirements of 30 percent results for every 8 inches of additional depth of immersion. Turning back the direction of the rotation of the unit enlarges the range of control by 20 percent. Any operation should require two speeds.

ROTATING BRUSHES

The main sewage treatment plant at Hamburg provides larger aeration tanks to reduce the number of units. An improvement developed by Passavant employed the following:

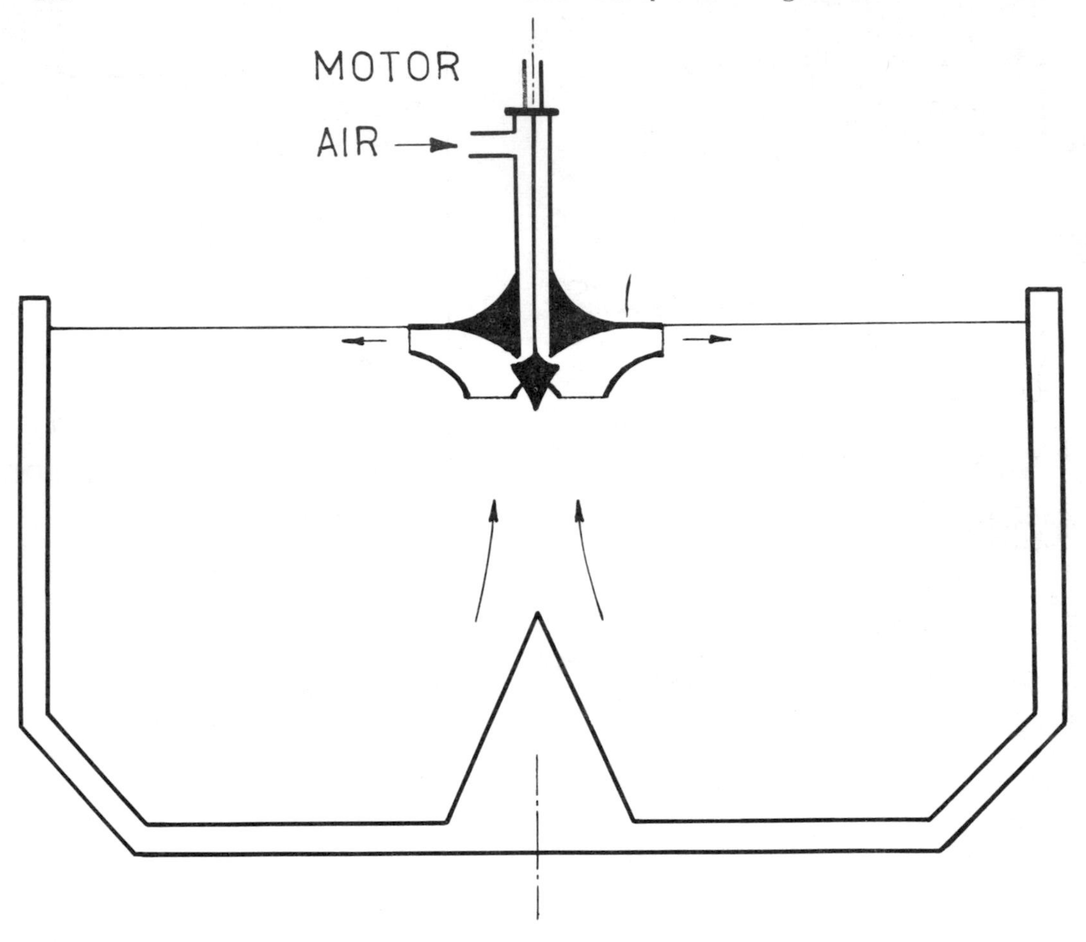

Figure 98. BSK Turbine—cross-section detail.

1. Increase the diameter of the aerators from 50 cm. to 100 cm. Double the depth of immersion of the rotors to effect a duplication of the oxygenation capacity per running meter of brush. As a consequence, the width of the tank may be enlarged from 3 to 6 meters, keeping the tank depth constant. Intermediate walls are no longer necessary.

2. The distance between the bearings is 3 m. at present and will be increased to 6 m. The larger diameter makes the completion of a stiffer axis possible, reducing the number of bearings.

3. The bearings are proposed to be fat-pressure bearings which will reduce maintenance.

These changes led to the development of the Mammut-Rotor.

Preliminary investigations indicated the need for baffles to guide the flow of water with detergents in small and large tanks. The deep zone did not show any flow. Sludge deposits are to be expected during normal operation.

Oxygenation investigations using tap water in a tank with two baffles showed little increase in the oxygenation capacity with an increase in the depth of immersion from 3 to 9 inches (Fig. 100).

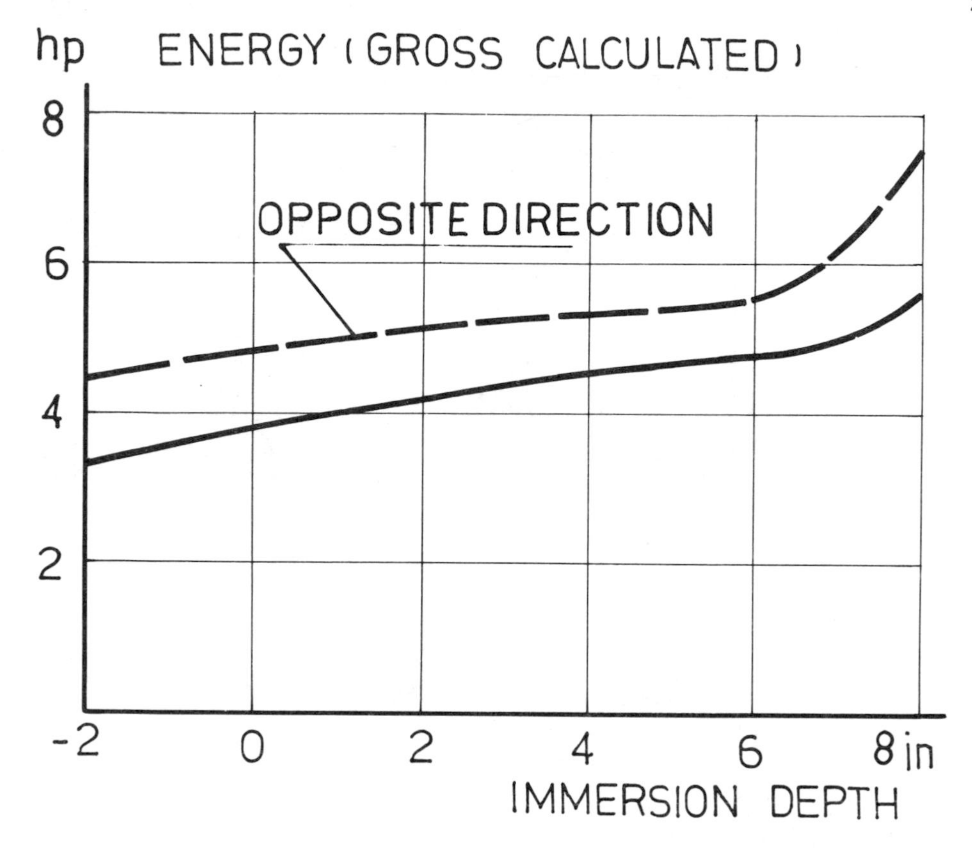

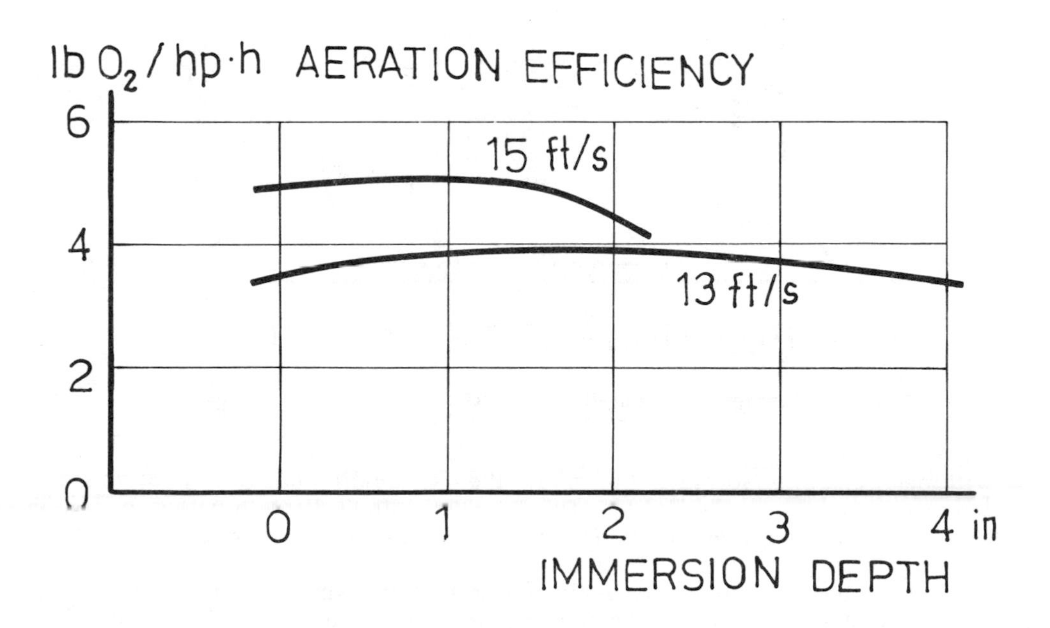

Figure 99. BSK Turbine—energy aeration efficiency.

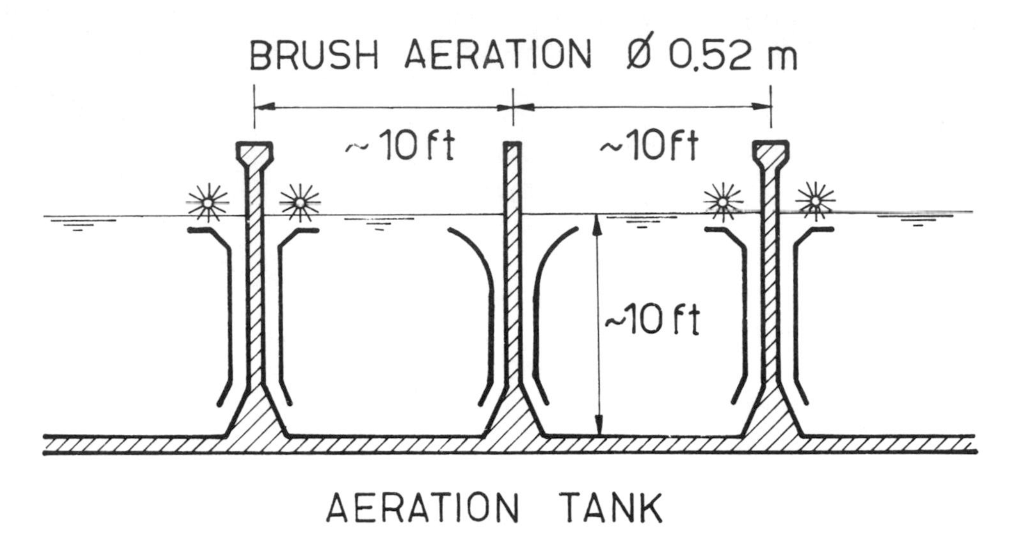

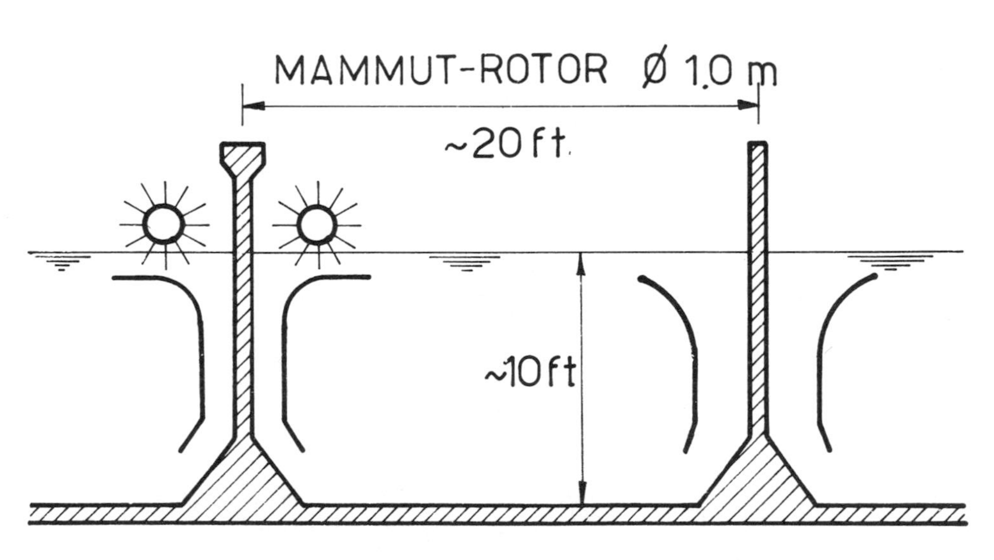

Figure 100. Development Mammut-Rotor—sections.

With detergents dissolved in tap water, the oxygenation capacity went up linearly with depth of immersion. The OC achieved was 60 lb O_2/h with 6 m. length of the rotor. These values are in the same range as those obtained with the Simcar cones.

To find out the quantity of water circulated by the Mammut-Rotor, a metering device was installed between the outer wall and the suction wall. The cross-sectional area and the metered liquid velocity were used to compute the quantity of water circulated (Fig. 101). This was considerably larger when using tap water with detergents or final effluent than plain tap water. The quantity of water with detergents circulated was proportional to the depth of immersion.

Higher liquid velocities were observed in the cones near the bottom when running the pilot plant with tap water. From this we draw the conclusion that some part of the water is circulating between the baffles instead of flowing linearally.

It was possible to compute the oxygen input per meter^3 of water moved (Fig. 102). Using this parameter, there is a startling difference between tap water

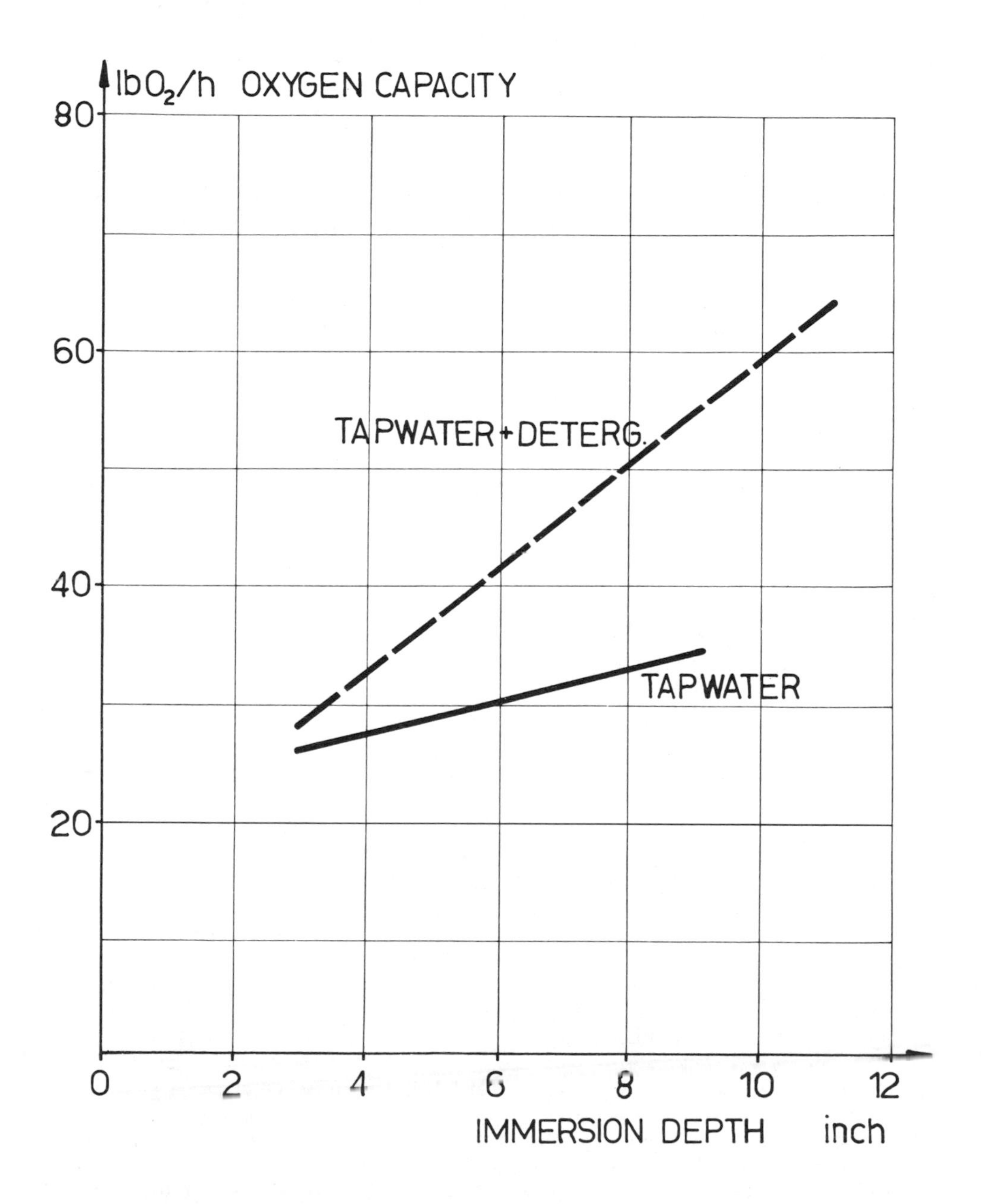

Figure 101. Mannut-Rotor—oxygen capacity.

without and with detergents and final effluent. As a mean value, 5 g O_2/m^3 of water was observed to circulate. Related to oxygen input of 1 kg O_2, the Mammut-Rotor circulated about twice the volume of water of the cones.

Immersion depths in the range of 25–30 cm. were investigated (Fig. 103). Final effluent showed a little higher value of oxygenation capacity than tap water. The measured maximum was 13.7 lb O_2 or 82 lb O_2 per 6 m. length. The content of detergents of the final effluent was 1.2–1.5 mg/l (as a consequence of the new biologically soft detergents used during the period of investigation, Spring 1965).

The tank which had a pressure baffle (without a suction baffle) using tap water showed better oxygenation efficiencies than the arrangement having a suction baffle, when final effluent was used. When the immersion depth was 1 ft., 88 lb O_2/h was transferred.

The opposite holds true for the energy input (Fig. 104). The largest value for final effluent using a pressure baffle was 27.5 kW with an immersion depth of 1 ft., compared with 25 kW for tap water. When suction baffles were applied, the required amount of energy was 22 kW for final effluent and 21 kW for tap water. In either case, energy requirements for final effluent were higher than for tap water.

This shows the importance of a suction baffle when aerating water containing detergents by means of the Mammut-Rotor. Aeration efficiency values are 2.70 lb O_2/HP-h for tanks with suction baffles, this being significantly above 2.0 lb O_2/HP-h for tanks with pressure baffles. Pressure baffles avoid deposits at the side of the tank opposite the brush.

Investigations on the Kessener brush 50 cm. in diameter in a cross section of 10 ft. by 10 ft. with two baffles increased the oxygenation capacity proportional to the peripheral speed of the brush to the power 2.6 for final effluent.

$$OC = 1.33 \times V_p^{\ 2.6} \times d_I \qquad (Kg\ O_2/m\ h)$$

V_p = peripheral speed (m/s)

d_I = immersion depth (m)

Flow conditions at higher speeds limit the tank circulation; and the oxygenation capacity decreases as compared to the formula shown above.

This equation shows good agreement compared to the investigations with the Mammut-Rotor. Previous tests showed a lower exponent on the peripheral speed for the increase of the energy requirements, showing as for cone aerators a more economic oxygen supply at higher rotational speeds. However, the shapes of the aeration tanks employed until now have acted as factors limiting circulation and mixing of the oxygen supplied by the brush.

A different situation prevails in continuous flow channels, as first proposed by Haworth. Edmondson increased the peripheral speed of the paddles by a factor of 2 up to 13 ft/s, achieving a higher oxygenation capacity twenty years ago in Sheffield. Here the exponent in the above equation was 2.5.

In accordance with Edmondson's recommendation, several Haworth-type plants had been rearranged, for example, the pilot plant in Manchester (Fig. 105). According to Jepson's report on operational results of various aeration devices in Manchester, a higher amount of energy was consumed by Haworth paddles than by Simplex cones and fine bubble aeration during the first fifteen years of operation—1935–1950. After the Haworth system was changed, energy requirements equaled those of Simplex cones. On the other hand, detergents present in the sewage increased energy requirements for fine bubble aeration.

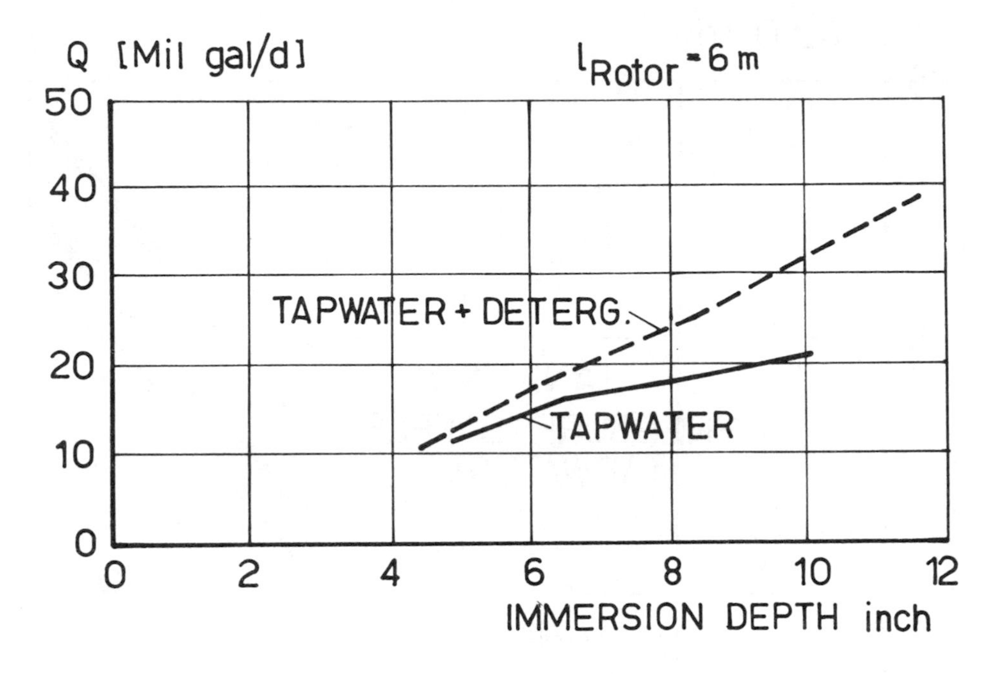

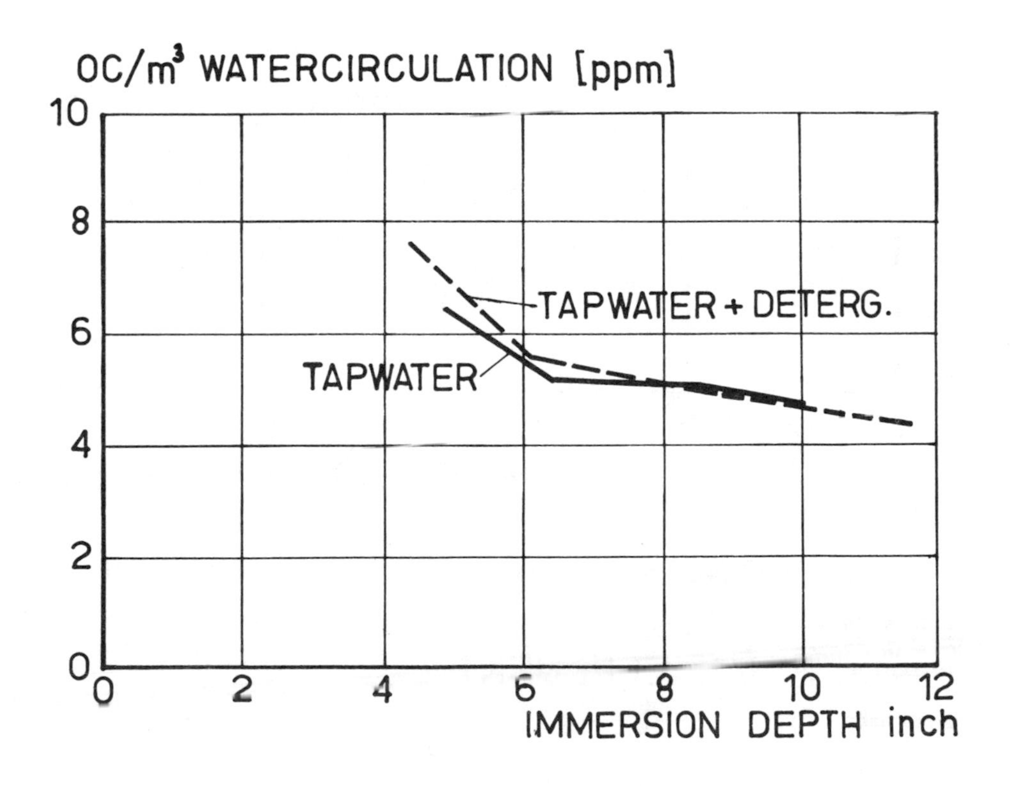

Figure 102. Mammut-Rotor—OC pump. rate.

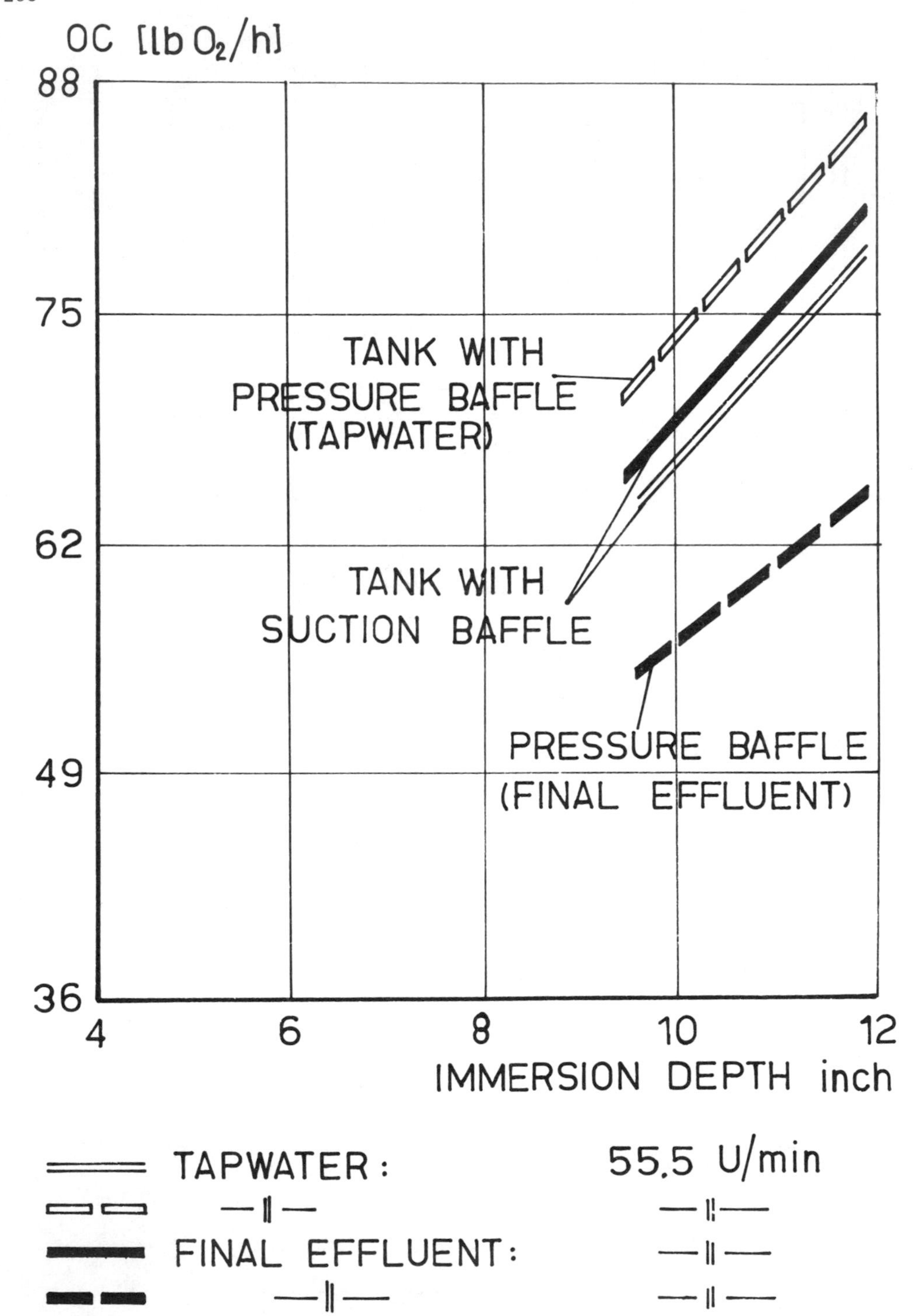

Figure 103. Mammut-Rotor—OC.

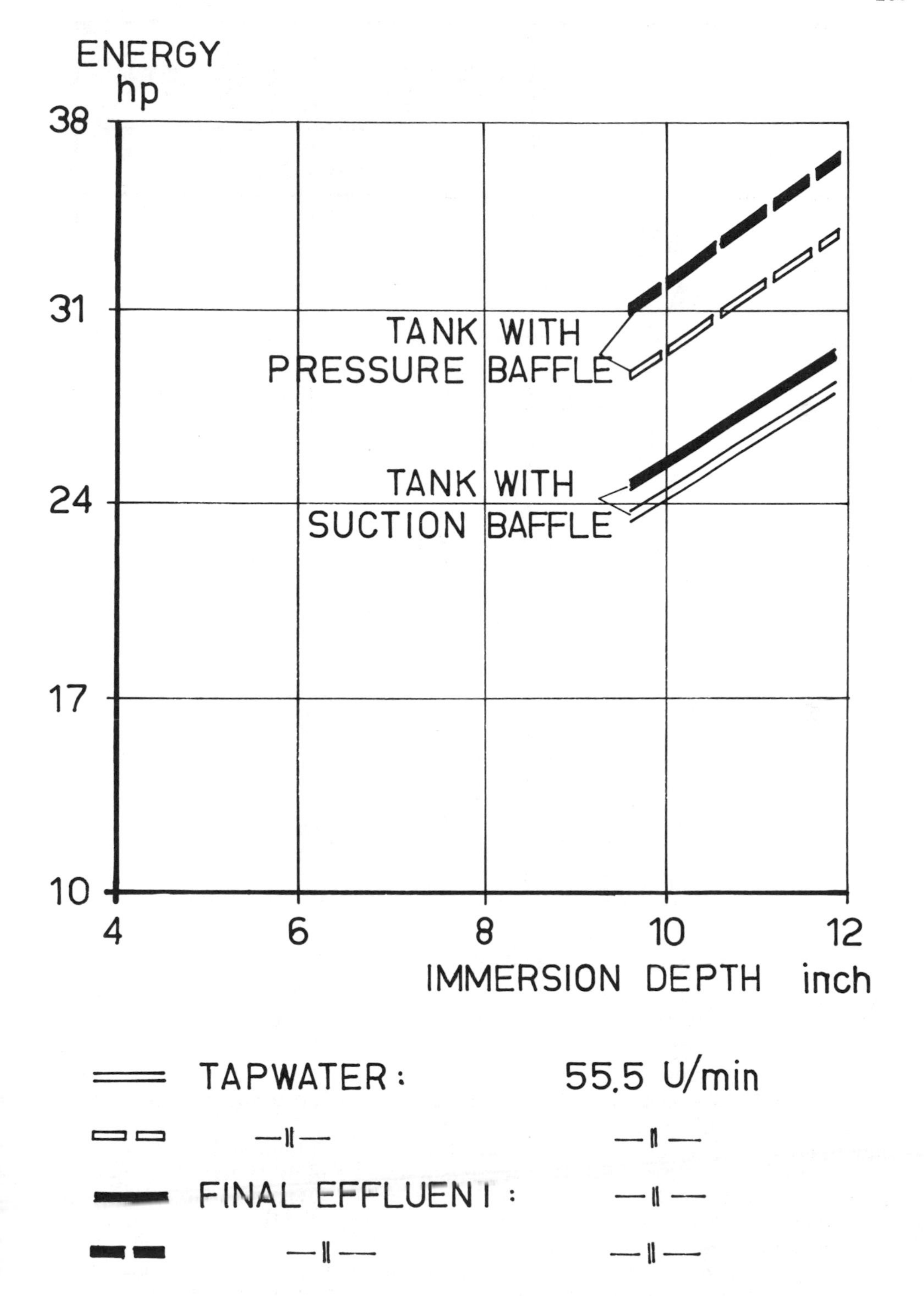

Figure 104. Mammut-Rotor—energy.

		1935-1950	1950-1953
		HP/Mio gal	
BIOAERATION PLANT		42.8	24.1
SIMPLEX PLANT		27.4	28.0
DIFFUSED AIR PLANT	UNIT 1	30.4	37.7
	UNIT 2	29.0	37.3
	UNIT 3	30.0	40.6

(JEPSON 1954)

Figure 105. Operation results—aeration energy.

Oxidation ditches operate with the same circulation principle as Haworth aeration (Fig. 106). Passavant has installed several oxidation ditches in Germany using the Mammut-Rotor for circulation tanks. A tank 50 ft. wide and 10 ft. deep has been employed. Several Mammut-Rotors (4 to 6) may be used in tanks of extended length. The distance between these devices has to take into consideration the requirements of mixing. The velocity will be high enough to avoid sludge deposits in long tanks.

A matching of oxygenation capacity to process needs is done by putting rotors in and out of service. Generally, repair is possible without putting a whole tank out of operation. This system may find application in the case of large, extended

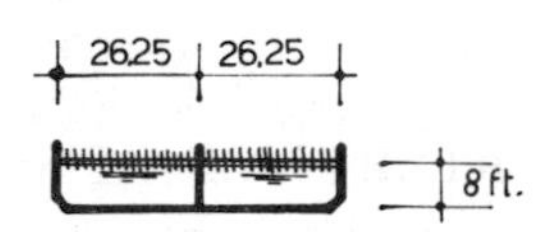

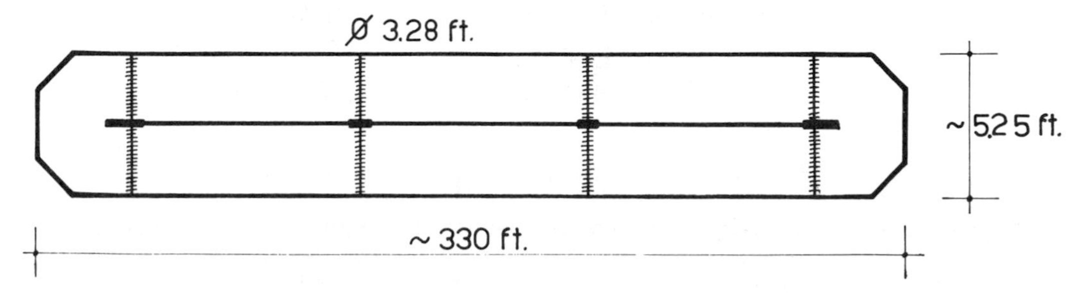

Figure 106. Mammut-Rotor—design Fa. Passavant.

aeration activated sludge plants. A simple dividing wall serves as a flow guide in the middle of the pond.

Haworth aeration and Kessener brush meet each other half way. The Mammut-Rotor may be considered as a row of Haworth aerators, having less diameter. Economics will dictate the type of aerator for any particular service.

MECHANISM OF INTERFERENCE OF SURFACE ACTIVE AGENTS WITH GAS TRANSFER IN AERATION SYSTEMS

K. H. Mancy
The University of Michigan, Ann Arbor, Michigan
W. E. Barlage, Jr.
Clemson University, Clemson, South Carolina

INTRODUCTION

In recent years considerable attention has been given to studying the effect of water soluble surface active agents (SAA) on aeration processes. Researchers in the fields of sanitary and chemical engineering reported conflicting results on the effect of SAA on gas transfer (1, 2). Studies on oxygen transfer using rising bubble contractors revealed that the presence of SAA increased the transfer rate (3, 4), decreased the transfer rate (5, 6), and last but not least had no effect on the oxygen transfer rate (7, 8). In certain surface aeration experiments it was quite puzzling to find that certain SAA, effective in the retardation of evaporation losses from reservoirs, had no effect on the aeration rate (9).

In spite of the above conflicting results, all point to a very important factor that needs to be considered. The presence of SAA in the aeration system may affect the hydrodynamic characteristics of air-water interface, the effect of which may significantly influence the rate of gas transfer. It is apparent that this has happened in the above instances, giving conflicting results. In fact Griffith (10) has shown that some SAA form caps of a nearly immobile surface on bubbles where the terminal velocity is related to the cap size and the amount of SAA present.

It was only recently that we were able to understand the reason behind the above conflicting results and to offer an explanation as to the effect of SAA on gas transfer in aeration systems. This was a result of extended investigations which lasted over five years and in which the physicochemical characteristics of the gas-water interface were investigated closely. The purpose of this paper is to present a comprehensive discussion of the problem as exemplified by studies on bubble aeration, surface aeration in stirred vessels, and liquid laminar jet systems.

Effect of SAA on Properties of Water Surface

In Figure 107 a schematic diagram of the structure of the water surface is shown. The water surface seems to be devoid of protons, since molecules at the phase boundary are oriented with their negative ends. Because of a lack of asymmetry in the intermolecular forces at the interface, the water surface exhibits an excess of free energy, approximately 72 ergs/cm^2, the mechanical equivalent of which is known as the surface tension. This high surface energy makes the water surface highly elastic with a tendency to contract spontaneously.

If SAA are added to the aqueous phase, they are driven to the water surface where they are adsorbed with their hydrophilic ends anchored in the water phase and the hydrophobic part facing the gaseous phase. In doing so they alter drastically the energy relationships of the interface. As a result the viscosity of water surface increases, it appears to lose its elasticity, and it exhibits plastic properties.

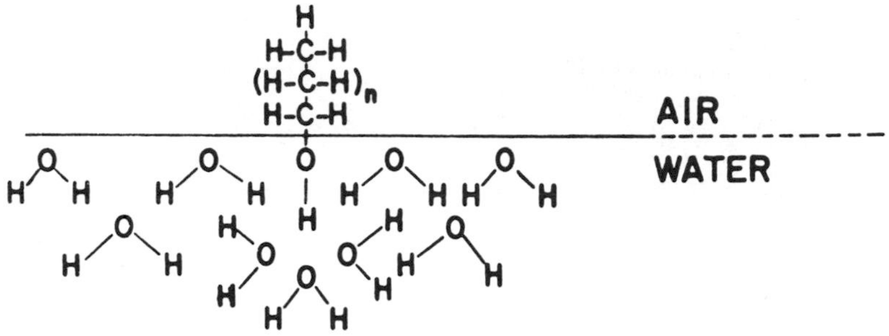

Figure 107. Orientation at air-water interface.

Based on the above discussion it is conceivable to differentiate between two effects of SAA, to be called "effects of the first kind" and "effects of the second kind." Effects of the first kind are related to the SAA adsorbed film itself, which may cover partially or totally the water surface and thus act like an insulating membrane separating the gas and the aqueous phase. This interfacial adsorbed film, F in Figure 108, not only will exert material resistance to gas transfer, but also will distort intermolecular forces between the water surface and the approaching gas molecules.

"Effects of the second kind" are related to the increase of the viscosity and the depression of the hydrodynamic activity of the water surface caused by the adsorption of SAA molecules. This effect can be understood by considering the structure of aqueous phase. Pure water contains temporary aggregates of water molecules arranged tetrahedrally, similar to the tetrahedral arrangement in ice (2). These icelike aggregates are in a rapid dynamic equilibrium with more disordered arrangements of water molecules. When SAA molecules are introduced in pure water, they tend to affect the equilibrium of the water structure, either by stabilizing the more ordered arrangements or by disrupting them. The hydrophilic parts of the SAA molecule will stabilize these water structures, while the hydrophobic parts will disrupt them. Accordingly, SAA molecules anchored to the water surface with their hydrophilic ends will act like magnet heads that immobilize several layers of crystalline water structures and attract a blanket of counter ions, as shown in Figure 108. This surface hydration layer is highly viscous (10^4 poises) and may extend several thousand angstroms in the aqueous phase (9). The increase of the viscosity of the water surface results in the elimination of all random surface motion, a phenomenon commonly called "surface stagnation" or "quiescence." The damping effect of SAA on surface motion is schematically illustrated in Figures 109 and 110. Liquid eddies driven by turbulence from the bulk may cause deformation of the water surface, as shown in Figure 109. In the presence of SAA adsorbed film this effect is opposed by a surface pressure, π, caused by a localized gradient in surface tension, which may be expressed as follows:

$$\pi = \text{grad } \sigma = \frac{\partial \sigma}{\partial \Gamma} \text{ grad } \Gamma \qquad (1)$$

where σ is the surface tension and Γ is the surface excess, which is approximately equal to the surface concentration of SAA. The positive sign on the right-hand side of Equation 1 indicates that the surface pressure, π, tends to move the surface from lower σ to higher σ. If the surface forces are larger than the bulk inertial forces, the net effect will be the immobilization and stagnation of the water surface.

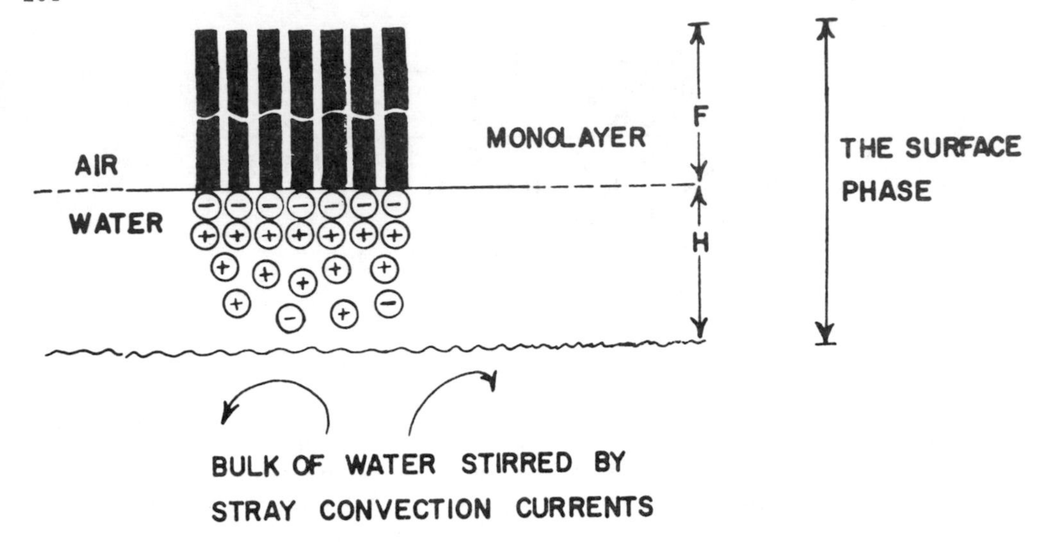

Figure 108. Structure of the surface phase.

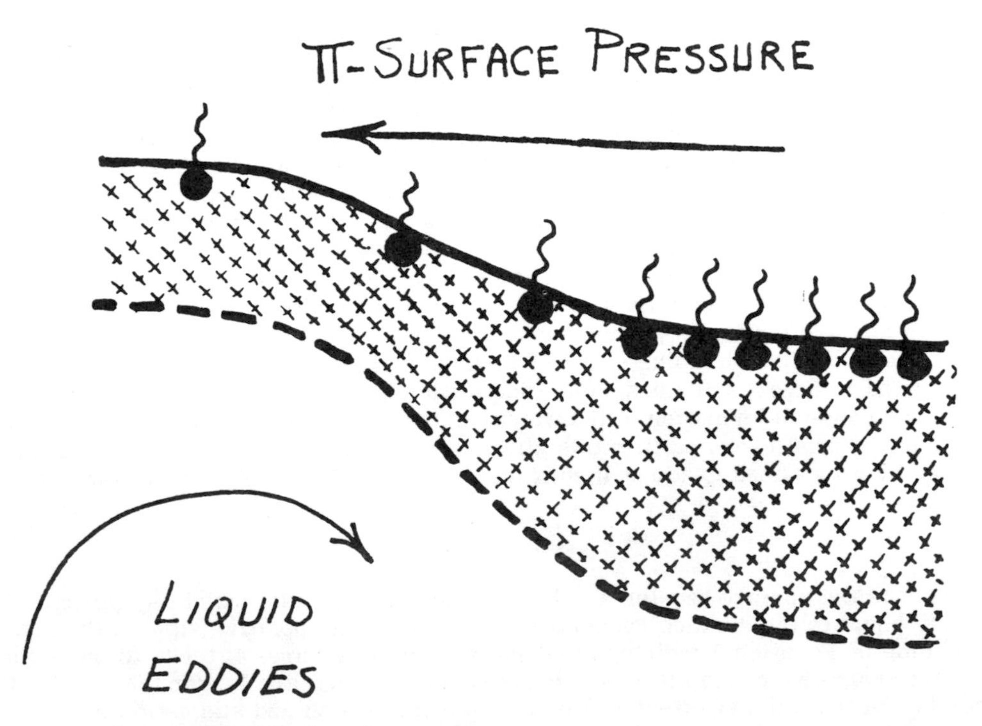

Figure 109. Retardation of surface motion.

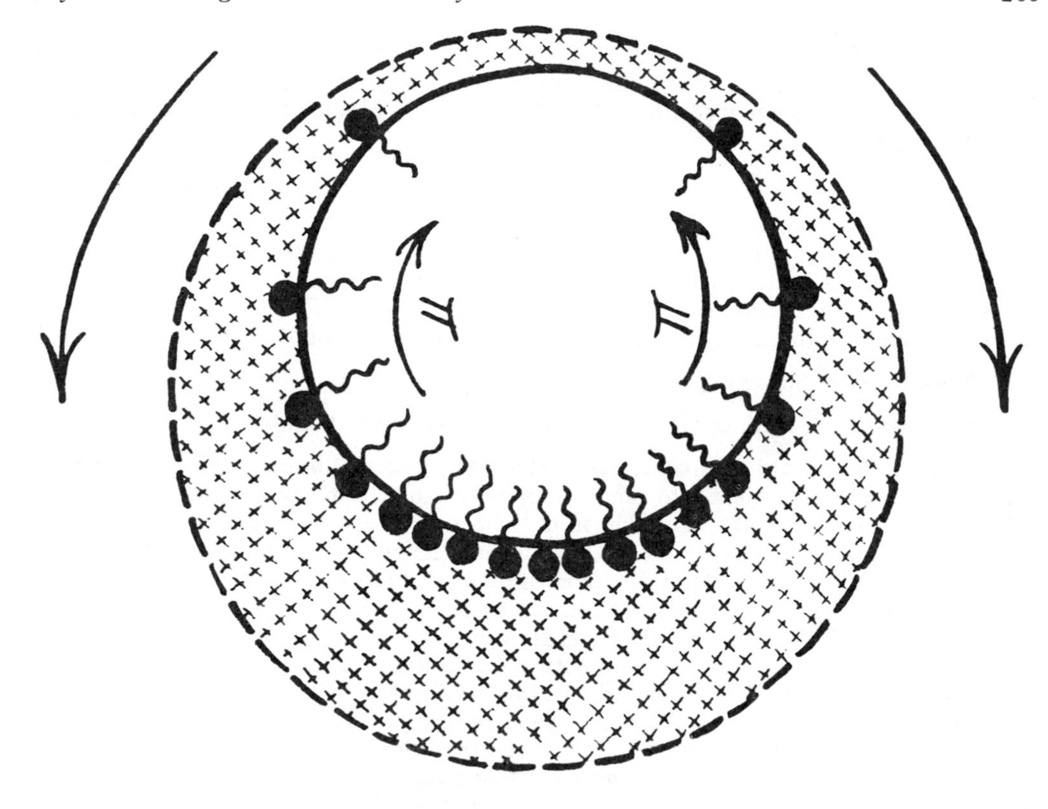

Figure 110. Retardation of bubble velocity.

SAA have also been noticed to influence bubble dynamics in diffused aeration systems (11-13). This effect can be in the form of a depression of circulation within the bubble wall immobilization of surface motion as discussed above, or the retardation of the velocity of bubble rise.

Bubble dynamics can be conveniently expressed by a Reynolds number, N_{Re}, as follows:

$$N_{Re} = \frac{Ur}{\nu} \tag{2}$$

where U is the bubble velocity, r is the bubble diameter, and ν is the kinematic viscosity. In presence of SAA it has been noticed that bubbles with $N_{Re} < 0.01$ travel as solid spheres and obey Stokes law (12). On the other hand bubbles in the range of $0.01 < N_{Re} < 50$ were observed to rise as solid spheres but do not obey Stokes law (12). This effect has been attributed to drag forces within the bubble wall caused by the presence of SAA. Figure 110 shows the structure of a bubble ascending in aqueous medium containing SAA. During the bubble rise the SAA film adsorbed on the bubble wall will be driven to the tail end of the bubble where it condenses, forming a solid cap. As a result a surface force will be set in the direction of the front end of the bubble, opposing the liquid drag forces which may cause a retardation in the velocity of bubble rise. For these surface forces to be of any significance they have to be comparatively greater than the viscosity resistance of the liquid. This is satisfied when

$$\frac{A_s}{4\pi r^2} => \frac{28\,v^2}{g r^3} \qquad (3)$$

where A_s is the area covered with SAA. The bubble velocity under these conditions (U_s) will be

$$U_s = -\left(\frac{4\pi}{3}\,\rho\, g\, r^3\right)^{0.5}\left(\frac{1}{k_f A_s}\right)^{0.5} \qquad (4)$$

where ρ is the liquid density and k_f is the liquid drag coefficient. Accordingly, the higher the SAA bulk concentration, the higher the A_s value and the slower the bubble velocity, as shown by Equation 4.

Larger bubbles in the order $N_{Re} > 800$ undergo fragmentation in presence of SAA. This occurs, however, when the hydrodynamic pressure, $\frac{\rho U^2}{2}$, exceeds the capillary pressure $\frac{\sigma}{r}$. Since the adsorption of SAA on the bubble wall will reduce the surface tension, which essentially is the force that holds the bubble together, large bubbles will fragment into smaller ones during their ascent.

The effect of SAA on the retardation of bubble velocity is clearly demonstrated from results reported by Levich (12), shown in Figure 111. These results indicate that the retardation did not occur with bubbles below 0.2 cm. in diameter. For bubbles with diameters larger than 0.2 cm., the presence of SAA resulted in a retardation of the bubble velocity, and this effect was higher the larger the bubble diameter. It is interesting to notice that bubble velocity in the presence of SAA was close to that of glass bubbles (adjusted for specific gravity). These results substantiate the findings of other investigators who observed that in the presence of SAA bubbles travel as if they are made of rigid spheres (13).

Based on the above discussion, we have two questions on hand. Do SAA influence the rate of gas transfer in aeration systems and if so, is this due to an effect of the first kind or an effect of the second kind?

EXPERIMENTAL PROCEDURES

Included in this section are brief discussions of three different experimental procedures used by the authors. References are made to the original work in order to avoid discussing in detail experimental setups and procedures. In addition, only those experimental techniques pertinent to the results presented in the next section of this paper are discussed.

Bubble Aeration System

The bubble aeration system employed by Mancy and Okun (13) is shown schematically in Figure 112. The system consisted essentially of a 1.5-liter glass cylinder through which the same water containing varying concentrations of sodium dioctyl sulfosuccinate, known as Aerosol O.T. (anionic SAA) in 0.001 M KCl solution was continuously recycled to the top of the cylinder and withdrawn from the bottom. A capillary was provided at the bottom of the column for oxygenation of the water along with a nitrogen diffuser for removing dissolved oxygen initially. Means were also provided to continuously bypass a small sample stream of the water for dissolved oxygen analysis in a polarographic cell. The development of a continuous recording system for determining dissolved oxygen in water containing surface active agents has been previously described by Mancy and Okun (14).

In addition to the above, means were also provided for quantitative photographic studies of the effects of varying concentrations of SAA and rates of oxygen flow on bubble formation, bubble volume, and bubble dynamics. These photographic studies provided a means for estimating the interfacial area to mass transfer in

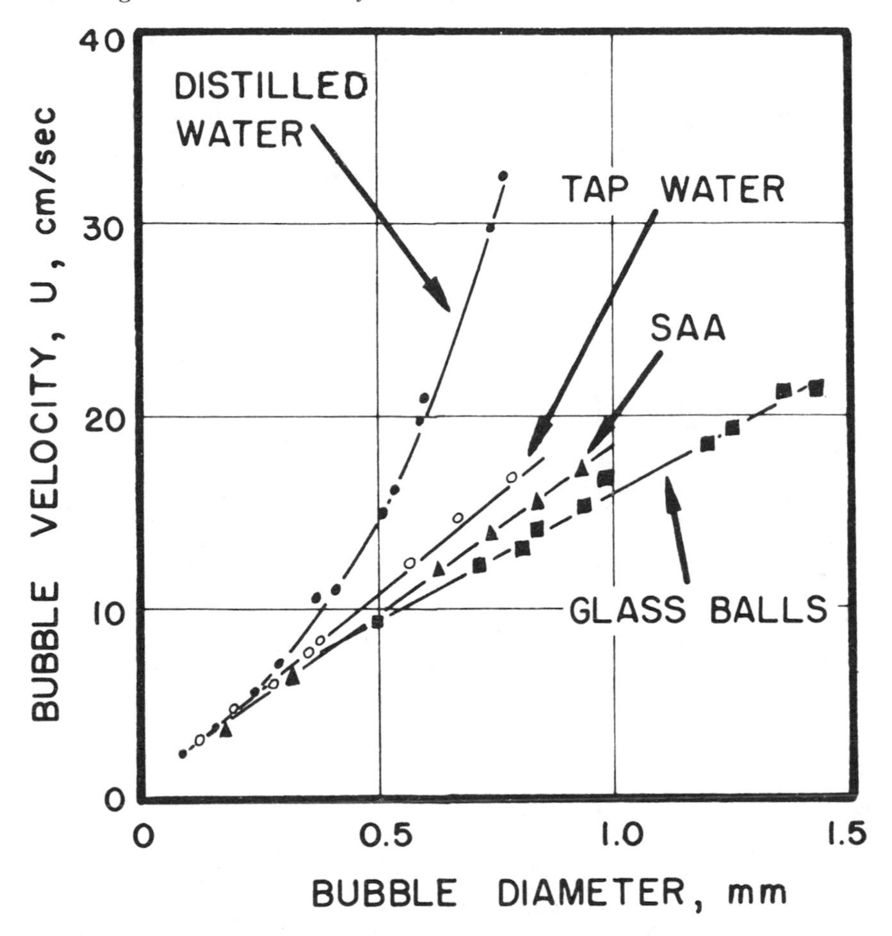

Figure 111. Effect of SAA on bubble velocity.

the aeration system. Such interfacial areas must be known, since in any fundamental mass transfer studies involving surface active agents and aeration rates, the effect of these materials on interfacial mass transfer areas and overall mass transfer coefficient must be separated, as well as their effect on any other hydrodynamic behavior of the system.

Stirred Vessel Aeration System

Although the bubble aeration system described above allowed the determination of an interfacial mass transfer area, this area was just an estimation, since spherical bubbles had to be assumed in the calculations. The photographic studies clearly indicated that the bubbles were not spherical in shape and that their geometry changed not only with varying concentrations of surface active agent, but also with position in the column. In addition, this aeration system did not allow for quantitative evaluation of other hydrodynamic behavior, such as internal bubble circulation, bubble oscillations, and behavior of the bulk of the liquid phase.

To overcome these difficulties, Mancy and Okun (15) employed a stirred cell aeration system to study the effect of varying concentrations of Aerosol O.T. on

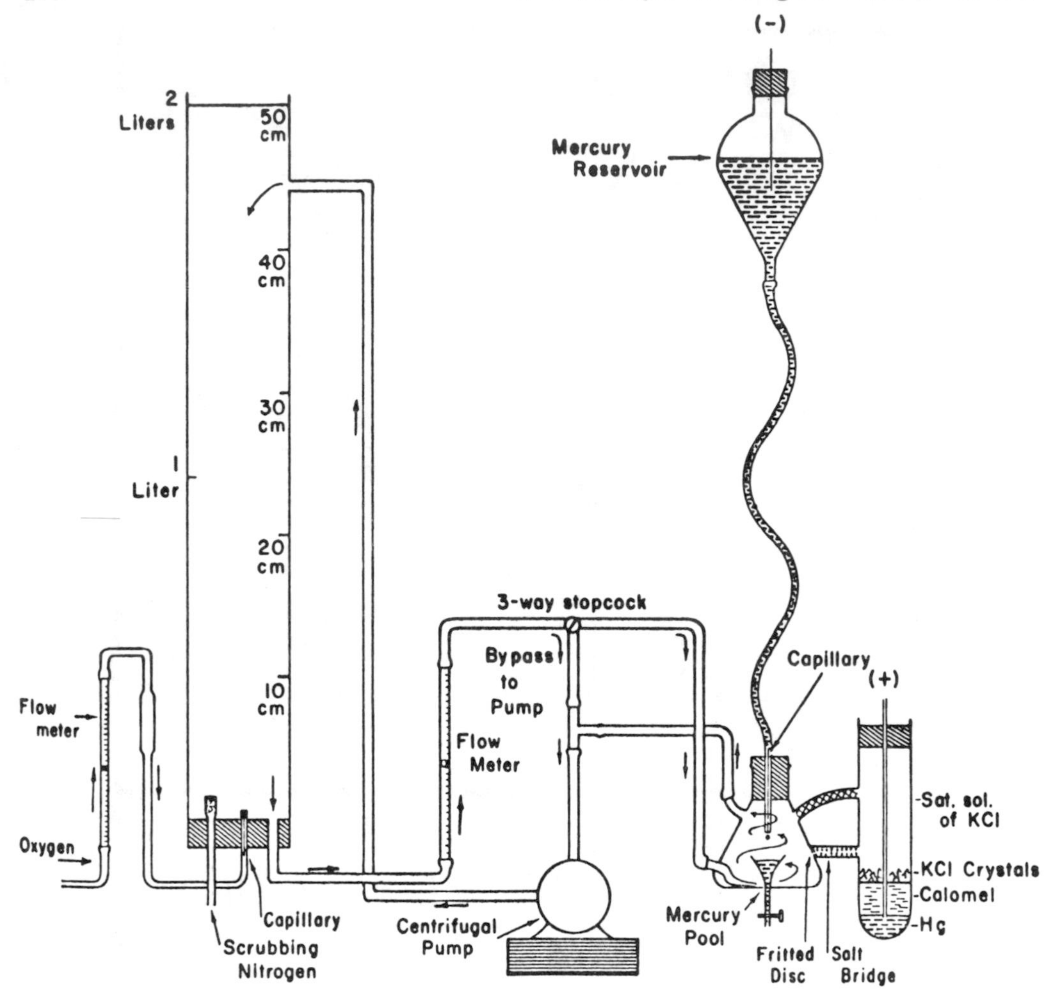

Figure 112. Bubble aeration system.

aeration rates. A schematic diagram of the system is shown in Figure 113. The system consisted essentially of an aeration vessel containing the test solution in a constant temperature bath. A magnetic stirring rod was located at the bottom of the vessel and was driven by a variable speed motor below the constant temperature bath. A Galvanic Cell Oxygen Analyzer (16) was immersed in the center of the aeration vessel at a fixed depth in the essentially oxygen-free water for continuously recording the rate of oxygen uptake in the system from the atmosphere. Various concentrations of Aerosol O.T. ranging from 0 to 50 milligrams per liter in 0.001 molar solutions of sodium chloride were employed. Initial and final dissolved oxygen determinations were made using the Winkler method. Mixing conditions within the vessel were varied by changing the geometry of the aeration system and the speed of the magnetic stirrer. As it was necessary that the air-water interface be as quiescent as possible in this aeration system, hydrodynamic conditions of the interface were determined by visual observations of the reflection of light transmitted from an incandescent lamp and by observing the movement of a film of sprinkled talcum powder spread on the water surface.

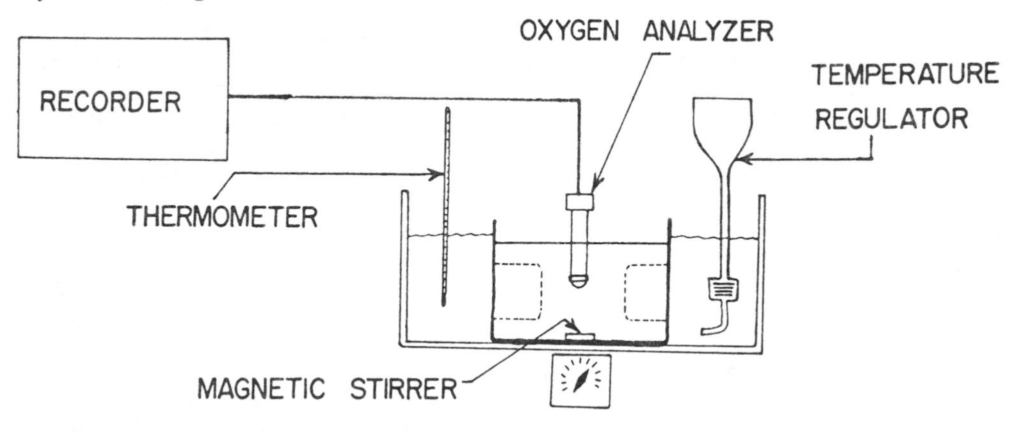

Figure 113. Stirred-vessel aeration system.

Surface rupture techniques (DuNouy Ring Method) were used to determine the surface tension for the various solutions. With the stirred vessel aeration system, the interfacial area to mass transfer and interfacial conditions could be accurately determined when the system was operated under quiescent conditions. This was a definite advantage of this system over the bubble aeration system. However, with the stirred vessel aeration system, hydrodynamic conditions within the bulk of the liquid phase could not be well defined and quantitatively calculated in an accurate manner.

Liquid Laminar Jet Mass Transfer System

The liquid laminar jet has all of the advantages of the aeration systems previously described, but without their inherent disadvantages. With the liquid laminar jet, interfacial mass transfer area between phases can easily and accurately be determined by use of a precision coordinate cathetometer to measure jet length and diameter. In addition, it is possible to control the "age" or exposure time of the mass transfer interface by simply controlling and measuring the jet length and/or velocity.

With the bubble aeration system "end effects," such as mass transfer during bubble formation and collapse, could not be experimentally determined. However, with the liquid laminar jet such end effects are minimized and can be evaluated by simply measuring gas absorption rates under operating conditions that are identical except for jet length. A quantitative measure of the end effects can then be determined by calculating the gas absorption rate at zero jet length.

Because the interfacial and bulk hydrodynamic conditions of the laminar jet are known, the diffusion equation may be solved for existing boundary conditions, and the experimental results compared with those calculated theoretically, assuming mass transfer by pure diffusion only. Thus it is possible to quantitatively determine interfacial resistances due to SAA for a given gas liquid absorption system.

The liquid laminar jet used by Caskey and Barlage (1) is shown schematically in Figure 114. The apparatus consisted essentially of an orifice, one or two millimeters in diameter, from which a gas-free laminar jet of water containing various concentrations of SAA was discharged into a contacting chamber maintained at a constant pressure of the absorbed gas. The apparatus was constructed to eliminate any gas loss except by absorption into the laminar jet. Thus by measuring the gas flow rate required to maintain a given pressure in the gas-liquid region, the rate of absorption could easily and accurately be determined. A soap-film flowmeter was used to measure the gas flow rate. To insure only single component mass transfer the gas was saturated with water initially.

Two types of jets were used in this study, a circular orifice, shown in Plate 2, and an elliptical orifice jet, shown in Plate 3. Carbon dioxide was chosen by Caskey and Barlage rather than air or oxygen, as it was desired to eliminate the possibility of an interfacial resistance resulting from a combination of the diffusing gas with the liquids. Some investigators (10, 7) have found an appreciable interfacial resistance using a "pure" system of oxygen and water. This has not been found with a "pure" system of carbon dioxide water.

Dodecyltrimethylammonium chloride and hexadecyltrimethylammonium chloride were chosen to study the effect of chain length on interfacial resistance to gas absorption. It has been found that these compounds do not change surface orientation with increasing surface concentration, do not form micelles below the critical micelle concentration, do not hydrolyze at the surface, and are consistent with the Gibb's isotherm. Sodium dodecyl sulphate and sodium hexadecyl were chosen to study the effect of chain orientation on interfacial resistance, since it has been demonstrated that the chain changes orientation with increasing surface concentration with these compounds. Bulk concentration of SAA to 800 mg/l were studied in 0.10 N NaCl solutions.

RESULTS

Bubble Aeration Systems

For single-component gaseous diffusion in a gas-liquid system the rate of mass transfer can be expressed in an equation of the form

$$\frac{dC_t}{dt} = K_L a \, (C_s - C_t) \tag{5}$$

where C_t is gas concentration in liquid at any time t, C_s is saturation or equilibrium concentration of gas in liquid, t is time, a is interfacial area to mass transfer per unit volume of liquid, K_L is overall liquid phase mass transfer coefficient, and $K_L a$ is overall liquid phase volumetric mass transfer coefficient.

If the product $K_L a$ can be assumed constant over the contacting time, Equation 5 may be integrated, and thus $K_L a$ will be

$$K_L a = - \frac{\ln \left[\frac{(C_s - C_{t2})}{(C_s - C_{t1})} \right]}{(t_2 - t_1)} \tag{6}$$

If the interfacial area to mass transfer and the volume of contacting liquid are known, the quantity, a, may be calculated from the relation

$$a = \frac{A}{V} \tag{7}$$

where A is interfacial area to mass transfer and V is volume of contacting liquid.

Mancy and Okun (13), using the bubble aeration system previously described, determined the effect of varying concentrations of Aerosol O.T. and oxygen flow rate on the volumetric mass transfer coefficient, $K_L a$, with both capillary tube and glass diffuser oxygen inlets. Results are shown in Figure 115. With the capillary oxygen inlet, it will be noticed that $K_L a$ initially decreases very rapidly with increasing Aerosol O.T. concentrations, reaching a minimum at a concentration of about 20 mg/l, but then gradually increases at the higher concentrations

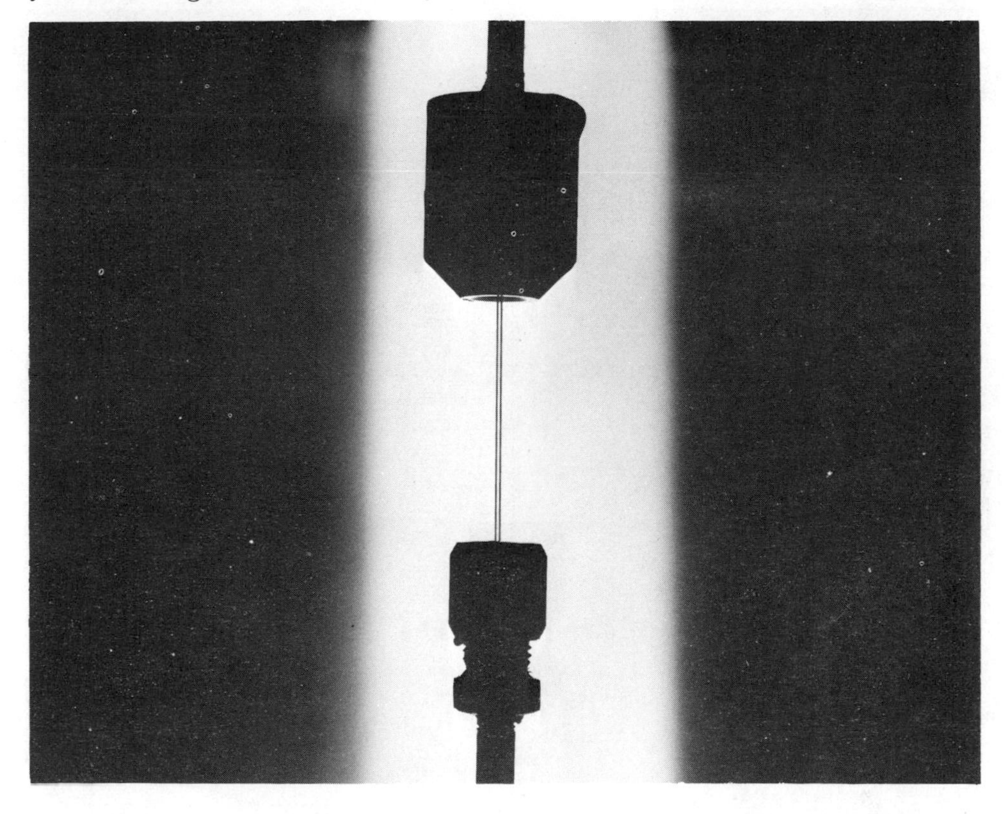

Plate 2. Liquid-laminar jet—circular orifice.

of SAA. This is not true, however, with the glass diffuser, where $K_L a$ shows a continuous increase with increasing Aerosol O.T. concentration.

From the photographic studies made with this bubble aeration system it was possible to estimate the interfacial mass transfer area, A. It was found that increasing concentrations of Aerosol O.T. increased the number of bubbles in the column at any instant, but decreased bubble volumes. This resulted in an increase in interfacial area, A, with increasing concentration of SAA, and thus it was possible to calculate the interfacial mass transfer area per unit volume of liquid, a, using Equation 7. Hence it was possible to determine the effect of varying Aerosol O.T. concentrations on K_L rather than $K_L a$.

Results are shown in Figure 116 for capillary tube oxygen inlet. It can be seen that K_L also shows a rapid initial decrease with increasing Aerosol O.T. concentration, reaching a minimum at a concentration of 20 to 40 mg/l. However, K_L does not increase again at the higher concentrations, as did the volumetric mass transfer coefficient, $K_L a$. This indicates that the recovery of the $K_L a$ at high SAA concentrations was primarily due to the increase of the interfacial area afforded by the formation of smaller bubbles for the same gas flow rate. However, Mancy and Okun (13) and others (17) have reported that under certain experimental conditions a slight recovery in the K_L value occurred at high SAA concentrations. It is believed, however, that this is primarily due to "end effects," such as mass transfer during bubble formation and collapse, a factor which cannot be easily determined experimentally.

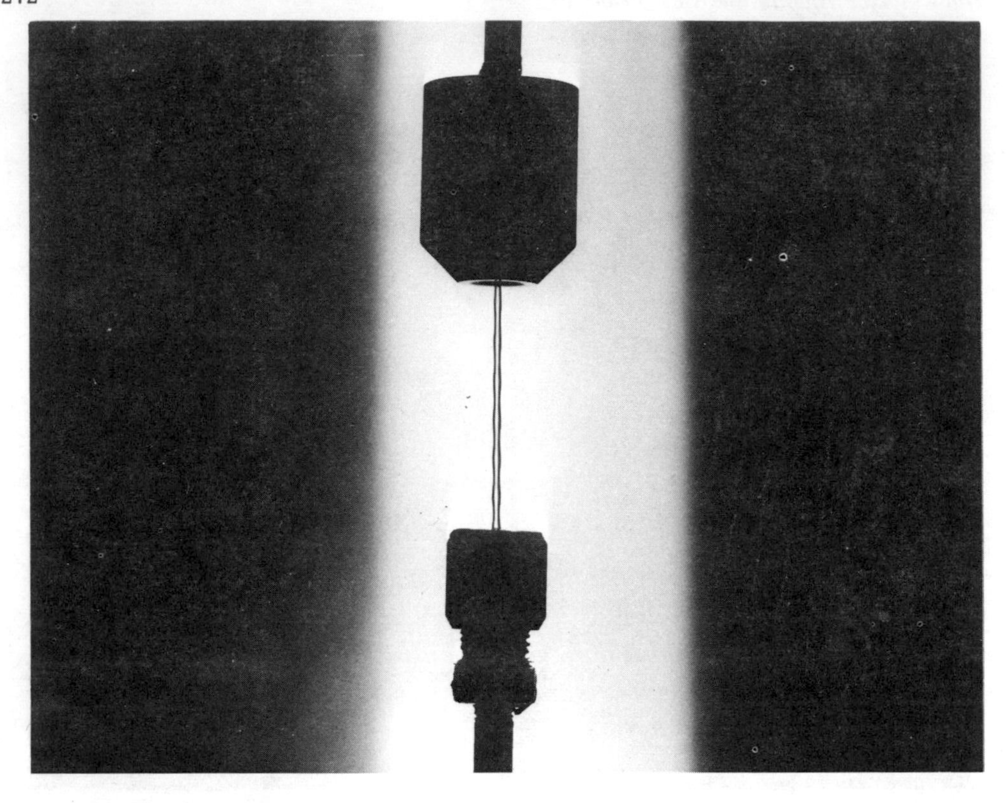

Plate 3. Liquid-laminar jet—elliptical orifice.

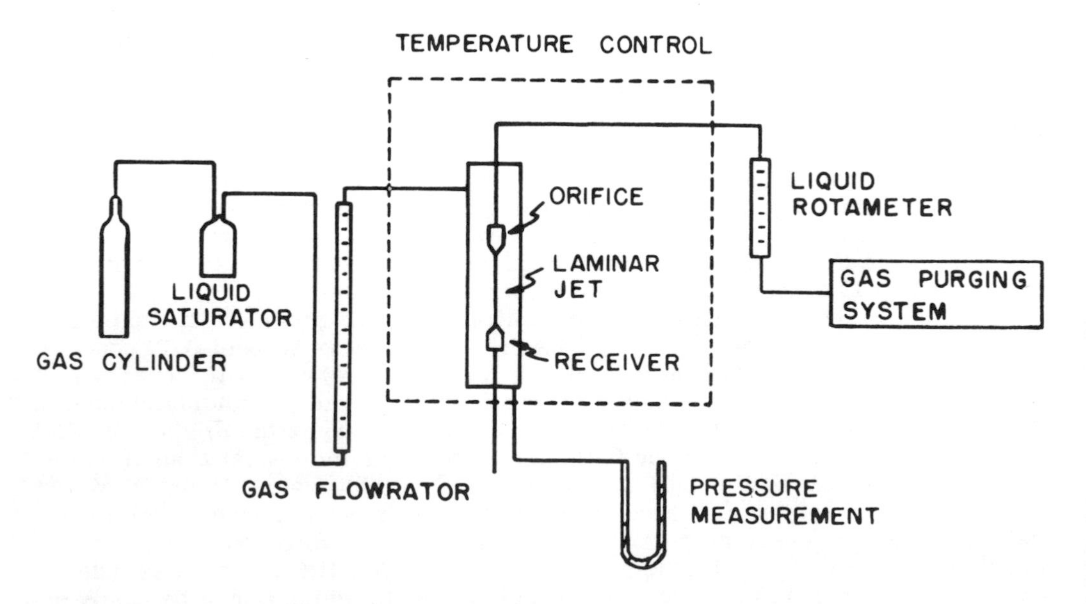

Figure 114. Liquid-laminar jet mass transfer system.

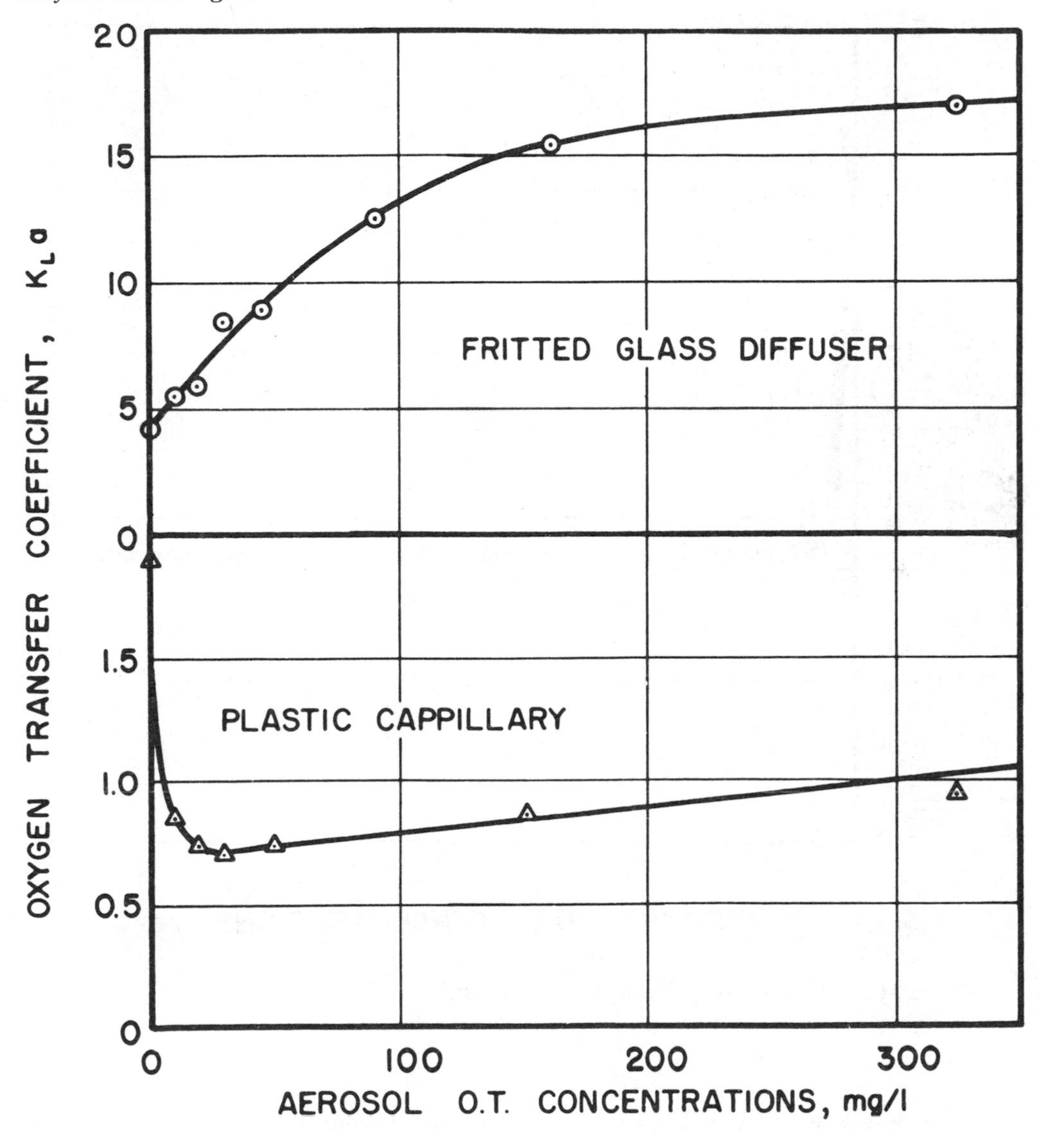

Figure 115. Oxygen transfer coefficient at varying SAA concentrations—diffused air system.

Stirred Vessel Aeration System

Rate processes may be described by the simple equation

$$\text{rate} = \frac{\text{driving force}}{\text{resistance}} \tag{8}$$

By comparing Equations 5 and 8, it can be seen that for single-component gaseous diffusion in gas-liquid systems, the resistance to mass transfer may be expressed as

$$R_T = \frac{1}{K_L} \tag{9}$$

where R_T is overall mass transfer resistance, min/cm.

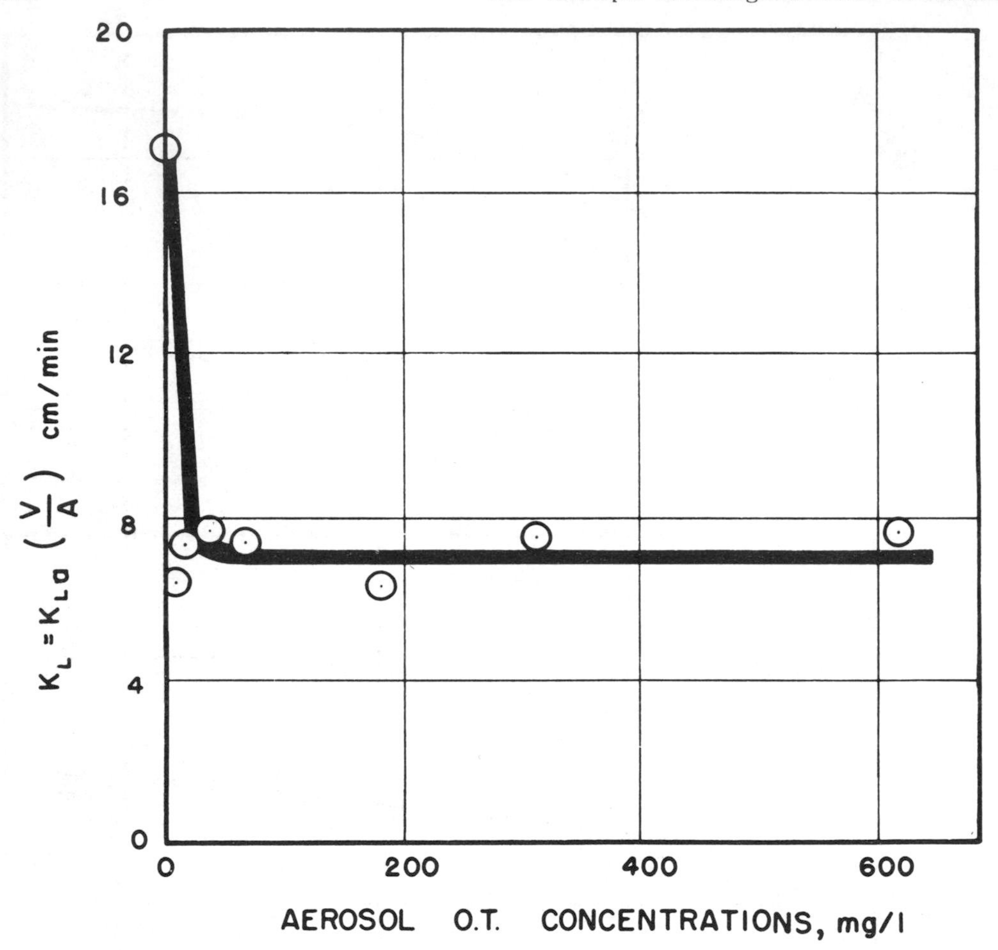

Figure 116. Absolute oxygen transfer coefficient.

Using the stirred vessel aeration system previously described, Mancy and Okun (15) determined the effect of varying concentrations of Aerosol O.T. and degrees of mixing on the overall mass transfer coefficient, K_L, and also on R_T. Oxygen uptake from the atmosphere was measured using three different aeration vessels, with typical results being shown in Figure 117.

To better describe the mixing conditions within the aeration vessel, the mixing Reynolds number, N_{Re}, was used to correlate R_T rather than stirrer speed. By definition,

$$N_{Re} = \frac{\text{inertial forces}}{\text{viscous forces}} \tag{10}$$

$$= \frac{d^2 Ne}{\mu} \tag{11}$$

where N_{Re} is mixing Reynolds number, d is tip-to-tip length of stirring rod, N is speed of stirring rod, ρ is liquid viscosity, and μ is fluid viscosity.

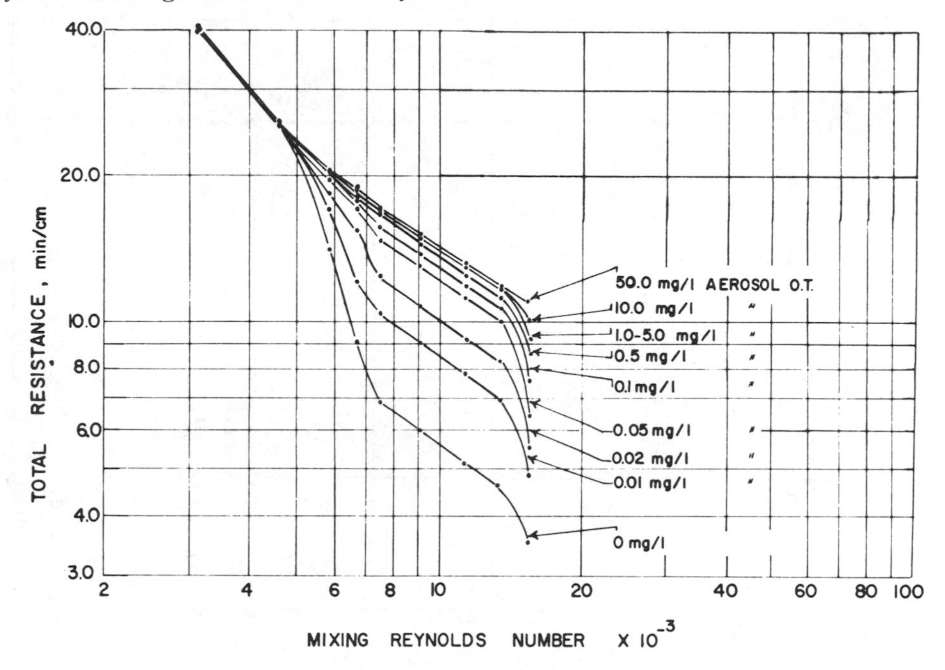

Figure 117. Total resistance at different mixing rates.

An examination of Figure 117 shows three distinct mixing regimes or regions. In Regime I, below N_{Re} of 5×10^3, there was no effect of increasing SAA concentrations on the total resistance to mass transfer, although R_T did decrease with increasing N_{Re}. In Regime II, above N_{Re} of 7×10^3, the effect of varying concentrations of SAA becomes measurable, with ln R_T decreasing with increasing ln N_{Re} for a given concentration of SAA. The slopes of the lines in this region were found to be the same for each concentration by means of regression analysis. Regime III exists for N_{Re} values greater than 1.5×10^4. This region is characterized by rapidly decreasing values of R_T for increased N_{Re}, with the effect of varying concentrations of SAA becoming less pronounced.

In Regions I and II visual observations of surface movement indicated the air-water interface in the mixing vessel to be quiescent. However, in Region III this interface was found to be in motion as a result of surface renewal from within the bulk of the water. From the magnitude of the mixing Reynolds number for each mixing region, Regions I, II, and III may be classified as laminar, transition, and turbulent regions, respectively. The effect of SAA concentration on R_T is more directly seen in Figure 118 where N_{Re} is the independent parameter rather than concentration.

For the stirred vessel aeration system used by Mancy and Okun, it could be assumed that most or all of the resistance to mass transfer existed in the liquid phase of the system. Thus R_T is due entirely to mass transfer resistances within the liquid or water phase of the aeration system. In addition, it was proposed that the total liquid phase resistance in the absence of SAA be further defined in terms of the following series resistances:

$$R_T = R_L + R_B \tag{12}$$

where R_L is mass transport resistance across the liquid surface, and R_B is mass transport resistance in bulk of liquid.

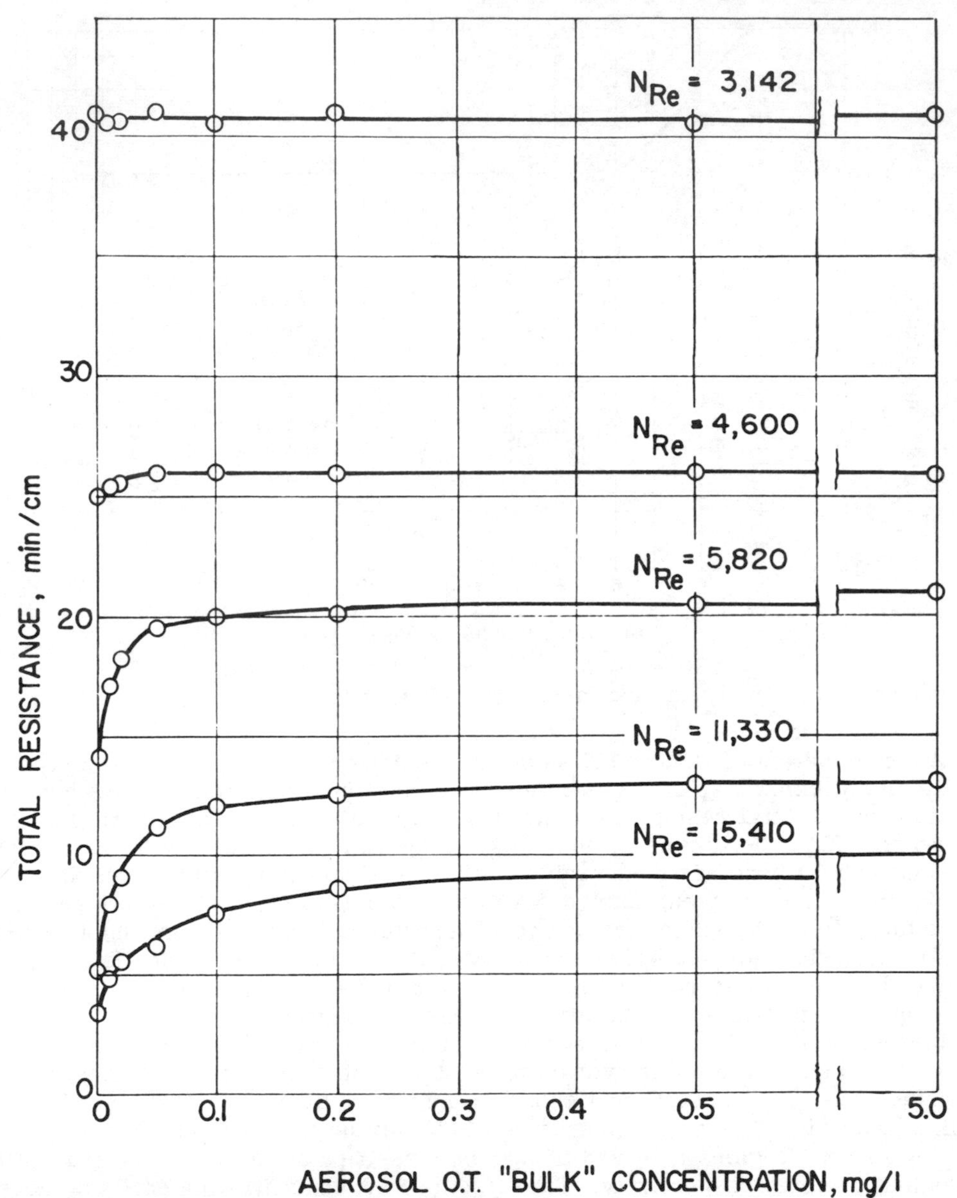

Figure 118. Effect of Aerosol O.T. concentration on the total resistance.

Based on the above discussion concerning the effect of SAA on the physico-chemical characteristics of the water surface, Mancy and Okun depicted that in the presence of SAA, the liquid surface resistance is composed of two resistances in series. The first of these resistances, R_F, is a results of "effects of the first kind." This is a type of mechanical resistance caused by the adsorbed SAA film at the gas-liquid interface. The second resistance, R_H, is mainly caused by "effects of the second kind," a result of the highly viscous hydration layer, which is associated with SAA film and which is effective in suppression of the hydrodynamic activity of the water surface. Thus, in presence of SAA, R_T can be expressed as follows:

$$R_T = R_F + R_H + R_B \tag{13}$$

and

$$R_H = R_L + R_{HL} \tag{14}$$

where R_L is the surface resistance in absence of SAA, and R_{HL} is the additional resistance to gas transfer caused by effects of the second kind. Thus

$$R_T = R_F + R_L + R_{HL} + R_B \tag{15}$$

From the definitions of R_F and R_{HL} it is obvious that R_F should be a function of SAA surface concentration only, and R_{HL} a function of degree of mixing as well as SAA concentration. This can be expressed as follows:

$$R_F = f(\Gamma)^n \tag{16}$$

and

$$R_{HL} = f(\Gamma, \frac{1}{N_{\mathrm{Re}}})^l \tag{17}$$

Since R_B is a function of degree of mixing only, then a low mixing Reynolds number in the aeration system, R_B, should be much greater than $(R_F + R_H)$, and the presence of increasing SAA concentrations in the aeration system will have no effect on R_T. An examination of Figures 117 and 118 shows this to be true in Mixing Region I. However, at higher degrees mixing, R_B should decrease and the effect of SAA on $(R_F + R_H)$, and thus R_T should be noticeable. This is seen to be true in Mixing Region II.

In an attempt to determine the order of magnitude of SAA effects of first kind and effects of second kind on gas transfer, Mancy and Okun calculated the differences in R_T values in the presence and absence of SAA (ΔR_T). At a given mixing condition (ΔR_T) was calculated from Equations 13, 14, and 15; thus

$$\Delta R_T = [R_L + R_B] - [R_F + R_L + R_{HL} + R_B] \tag{18}$$

$$= R_F + R_{HL}. \tag{19}$$

From Equations 16 and 17 and for a given bulk or surface SAA concentration, R_F should be constant and independent of degree of mixing in the aeration system and R_{HL} should vary inversely with the degree of mixing. Accordingly, at very high degrees of mixing, that is, high values of mixing Reynolds number, R_{HL} will become very small and eventually will approach zero; thus

$$\Delta R_T \cong R_F \tag{20}$$

realizing that differences in total resistances, ΔR_T, can only be measured experimentally in Mixing Regime II, as seen in Figure 117. However, since surface renewal occurred at mixing Reynolds number below which Equation 20 can be assumed valid, it was necessary to extrapolate data of ΔR_T vs. N_{Re} for a given SAA concentration to a value of N_{Re}, where it would be assumed that $R_{HL} \cong 0$. This value of N_{Re} was taken to be the common value of N_{Re}, at which the extrapolated data for three different aeration systems intersected. At this point Equation 20 is satisfied, since R_F and thus ΔR_T are constant and identical for all three mixing systems. From these extrapolations, it was possible to determine the effect of varying SAA concentrations on R_F and R_{HL}. This is shown in Figure 119, from which it is noted that R_F is a function of SAA concentration only, while R_{HL} is a function of both SAA concentration and degree of mixing within the system.

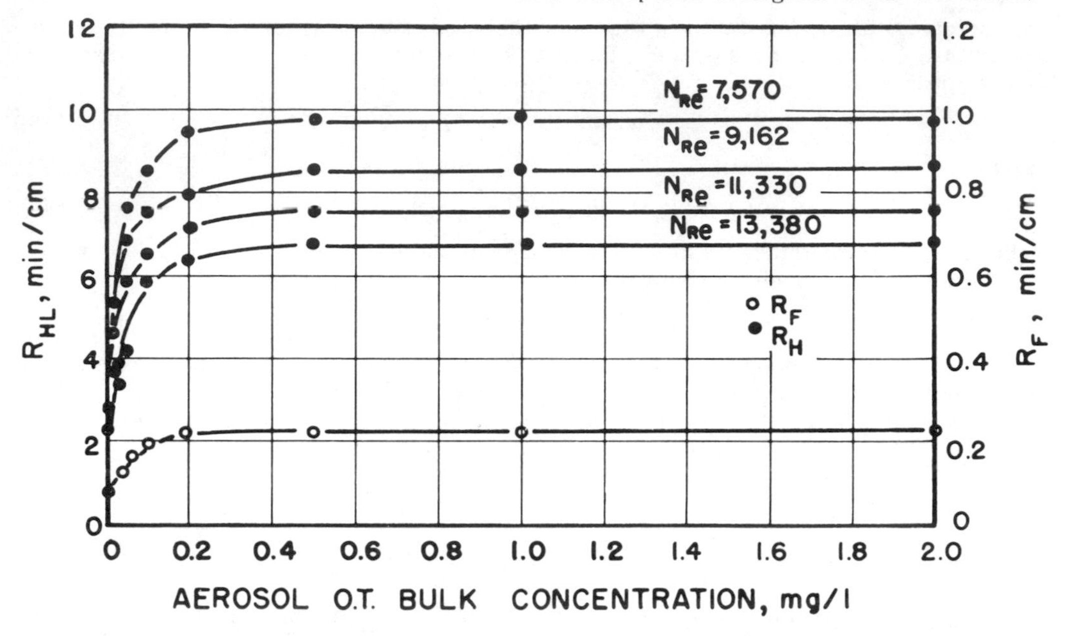

Figure 119. Effect of Aerosol O.T. concentration on R_F and R_{HL}.

From experimental data on the effect of bulk concentration of Aerosol O.T. on static or equilibrium surface tensions and the Gibb's adsorption isotherm, it was possible to calculate surface concentrations of Aerosol O.T. Using the data of Figure 119, it was thus possible to determine the effect of surface concentration on R_F and R_{HL}, as shown in Figure 120. In this figure the effect of surface concentration on R_{HL} is shown for a one-typical value of mixing Reynolds number, N_{Re} = 11,330.

Liquid Laminar Jet Mass Transfer System

As mentioned previously, since hydrodynamic conditions at the interface and within the bulk of the jet are known, the diffusion equation could be solved for existing boundary conditions, and the theoretical rates of absorption calculated for a "pure" system. Using the system "pure" carbon dioxide water, the investigators found that the measured total rate of gas absorption along the jet was within 1 percent of the calculated theoretical value, using literature values for the diffusion coefficient of CO_2 in water at the system temperature. Thus with this system it could be assumed that little or no interfacial resistance existed at the gas-liquid interface.

With the liquid laminar jet, diffusion to and orientation of molecules at the interface occurs the instant the liquid leaves the jet orifice. Thus for any quantitative determination of the effect of SAA on absorption rates, it was first necessary to determine the surface concentration of these materials as a function of jet length or exposure time. This was done by employing an elliptical jet orifice which produces an oscillating jet as shown in Figure 119. Using the equations of Bohr (18), and Defay and Hammelin (19), and measuring the changing distances between nodes of the oscillating jet due to changing surface tension, it was possible to calculate dynamic surface tension as a function of exposure time for a given SAA bulk concentration. A typical plot of dynamic surface tension vs. exposure time is shown in Figure 121 for 800 ppm of dodecyltrimethylammonium

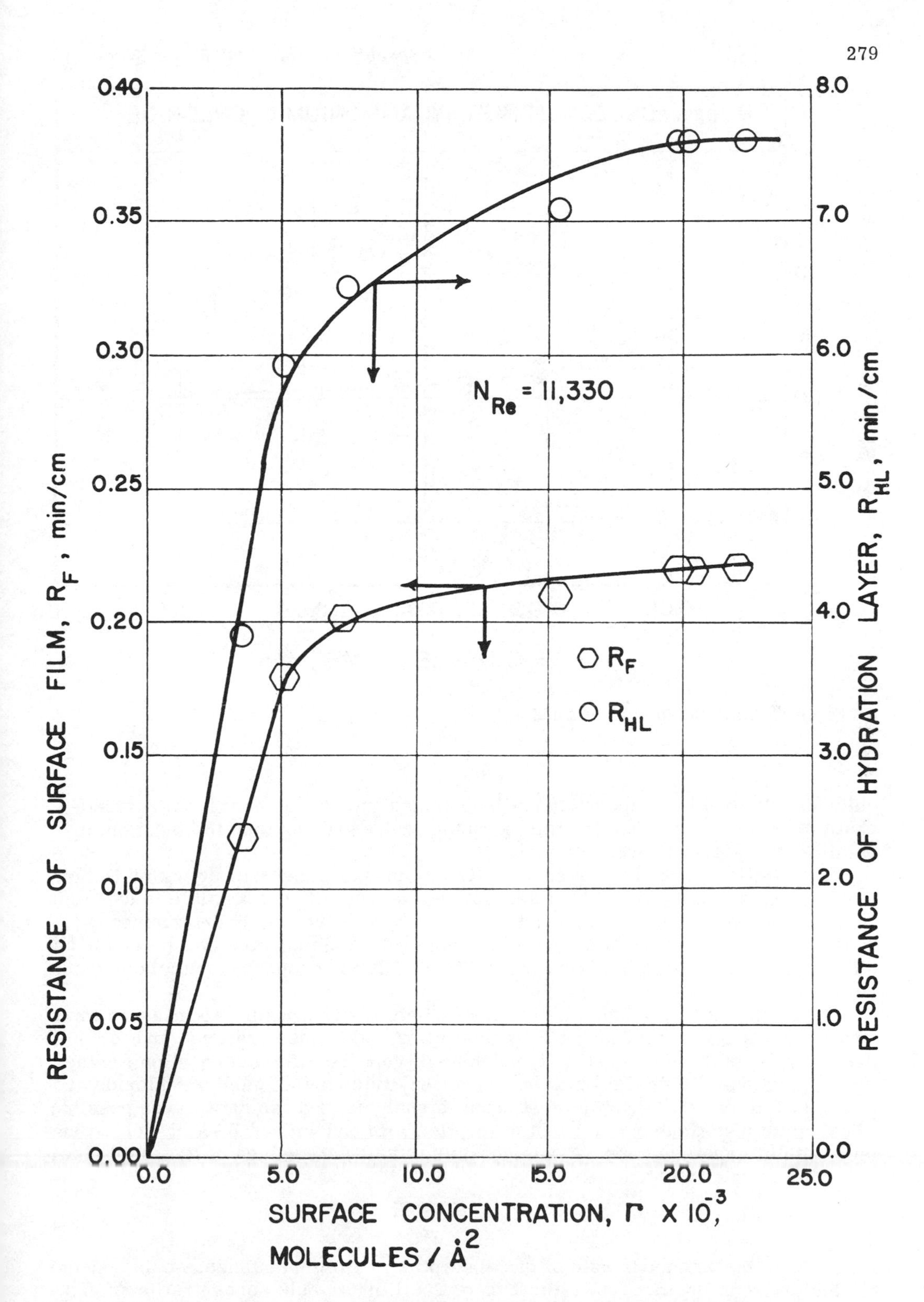

Figure 120. Values of R_F and R_{HL} at varying aerosol O.T. surface concentrations.

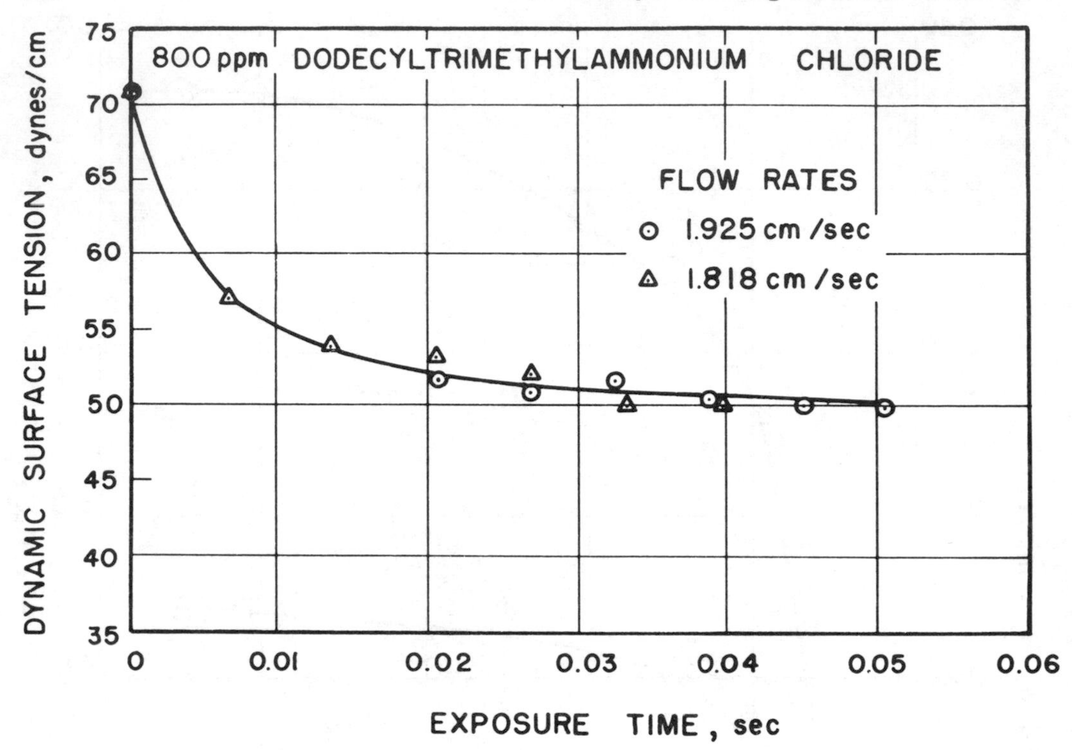

Figure 121. Dynamic surface tension.

chloride. Data of this type could not be obtained with the sodium hexadecyl sulphate, as orientation times for this substance were greater than the maximum obtainable exposure times of the jet.

From static or equilibrium surface tension measurements made with a DuNoüy tensiometer and using the Gibbs' adsorption isotherm, it was possible to calculate surface concentrations along the jet length, using the previously determined dynamic surface tension data. A typical plot of dynamic surface concentration as a function of exposure time is shown in Figure 122 for dodecyltrimethylammonium chloride.

By varying jet length using a circular orifice, it was possible to measure total absorption rates for varying jet lengths and SAA bulk concentrations, and to compare these with those theoretically calculated from the diffusion equation for the "pure" system. Typical results for the dodecyltrimethylammonium chloride are shown in Figure 123. From a least squares analysis of these data it was possible to calculate instantaneous rates of absorption with and without SAA present at any jet length or exposure time. It was possible to calculate values of R_{Ti}, using the following simple rate equation:

$$K_i = \frac{C_s - C_i}{R_{Ti}} \tag{21}$$

where K_i is instantaneous rate of gas absorption, C_i is instantaneous bulk concentration of gas in liquid, C_s is saturation or equilibrium bulk concentration of gas in liquid, and R_{Ti} is instantaneous overall mass transfer resistance.

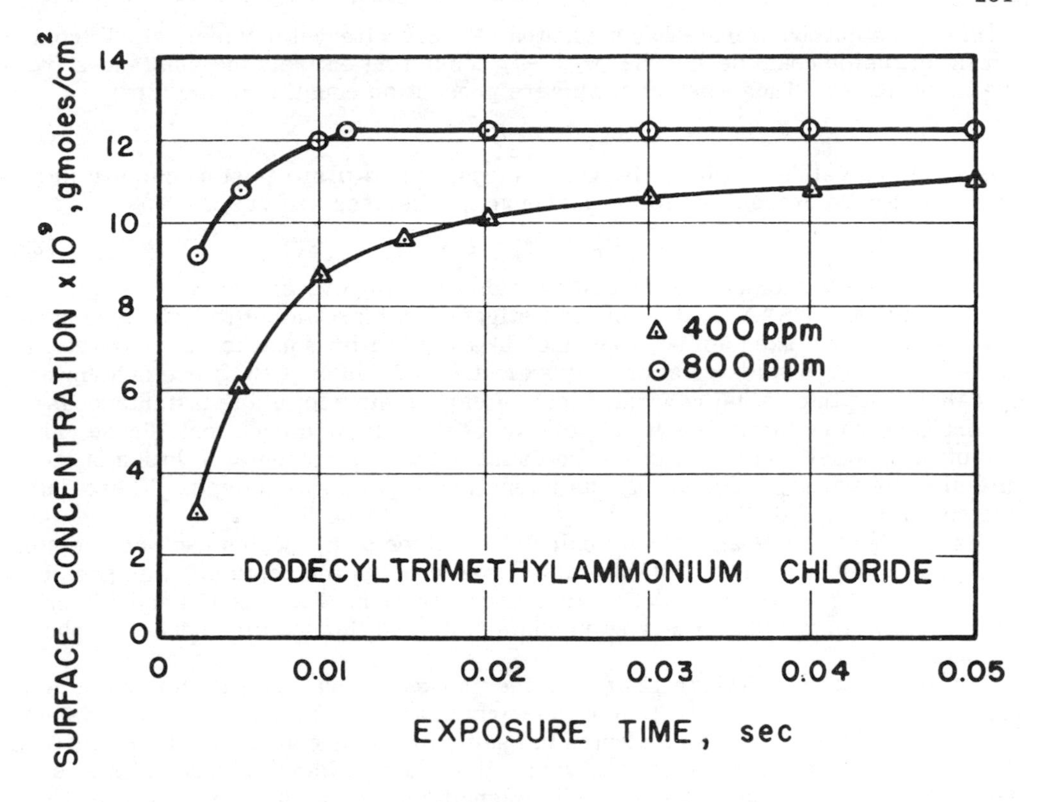

Figure 122. Dynamic surface concentration.

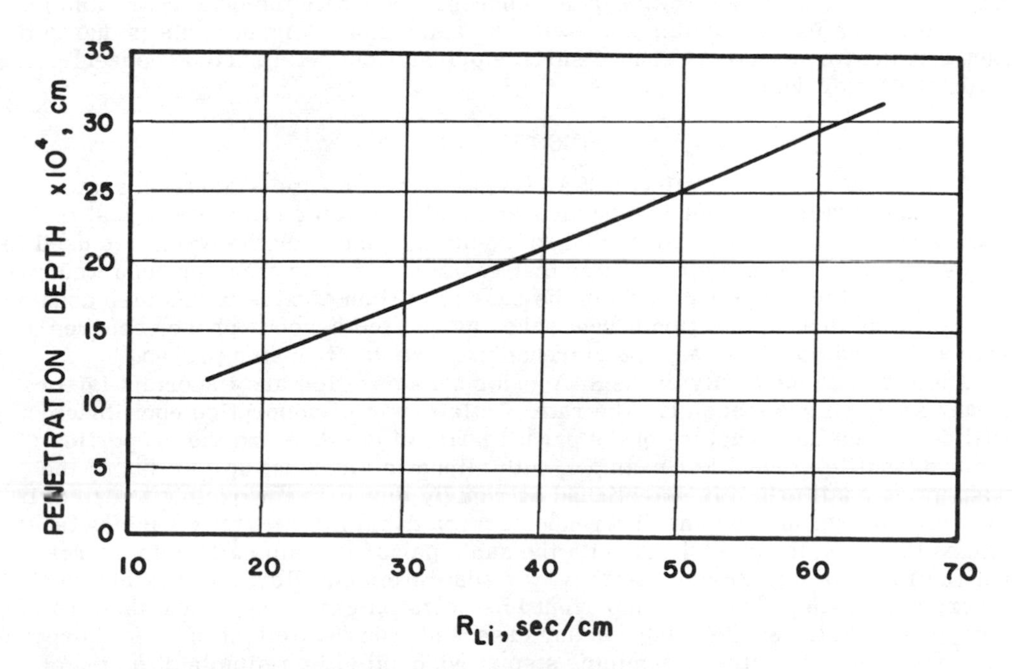

Figure 123. Penetration depth vs. film resistance.

Since the carbon dioxide was saturated initially with water vapor, single component diffusion could be assumed with R_{Ti} consisting entirely of resistances from the liquid phase. Thus when no SAA were present an equation of the form

$$R_{Ti} = R_{Li} \tag{22}$$

was assumed valid, where R_{Li} is instantaneous liquid film resistance below interface. With SAA present the following equation was assumed valid:

$$R_{Ti} = R_{Fi} + R_{Li} \tag{23}$$

where R_{Fi} is instantaneous resistance of adsorbed SAA layer.

Since all of the SAA used in this investigation are known not to hydrolyze at the surface, R_{Li} was taken as the resistance of a liquid film equal to the penetration depth of the carbon dioxide at any exposure time. Values of R_{Li} were determined by calculating interfacial concentrations of carbon dioxide, using instantaneous absorptions rates in the analytical solution of the diffusion equation. These values of interfacial concentrations were then used with a computer solution of the diffusion equation to calculate R_{Li} as a function of penetration depth. These data are shown in Figure 123.

Using Equations 21 and 23 with calculated values of R_{Li} which had been related to dynamic surface concentrations rather than penetration depths, it was possible to calculate R_{Fi} as a function of surface concentration. Figures 124 and 125 show such results for the quaternary ammonium salts and the sodium dodecyl sulphate, respectively.

An examination of Figure 124 shows the marked effect chain length has on R_{Fi} for a given surface concentration of the surface active material. A comparison of Figures 124 and 125 also indicates the same order of magnitude of R_{Fi} for both the dodecyltrimethylammonium chloride and sodium dodecyl sulphate. This is expected, since both have the same chain length and form no additional hydration layers within the liquid. However, an examination of these figures does indicate a greater increase in R_{Fi} with surface concentration with the quaternary ammonium salts than for the sodium salts with the same chain length. This is due to the fact that the former do not change surface orientations with surface concentration, while the latter do.

DISCUSSION

In a discussion on the effect of SAA on gas transfer rate in aeration systems, it is necessary to consider the physicochemical characteristics of the gas, the SAA, and the gas-liquid interface. From solubility data for the two gases used in this study it was possible to assume that resistance to gas transfer occurred entirely within the aqueous phase. In the case of carbon dioxide it was also assumed that any chemical interaction between the gas and the aqueous phase occurred at a rate which did not cause any interference with the gas transfer process.

The type and the purity of the SAA under consideration are important factors in any study on gas transfer. The rate of attainment of adsorption equilibrium will depend on the structure of the paraffin part of the SAA and the properties of the hydrophilic group. For example, with aliphatic alcohols, up to n-butyl, the adsorption equilibrium is established so rapidly that it is impossible to detect by the vibrating jet method any difference between dynamic and static surface tension values (20). On the other hand, with the same paraffin chain salts with hydrophilic groups of high surface activity, the adsorption equilibrium is established at a very slow rate. Thus it is important in studies on gas transfer and the SAA effect to control the surface age. In any case, the transient effect of SAA is dependent on whether the rate-determining step in adsorption is a simple diffusion of SAA molecules to the interface, or whether the velocity of attainment equilibrium

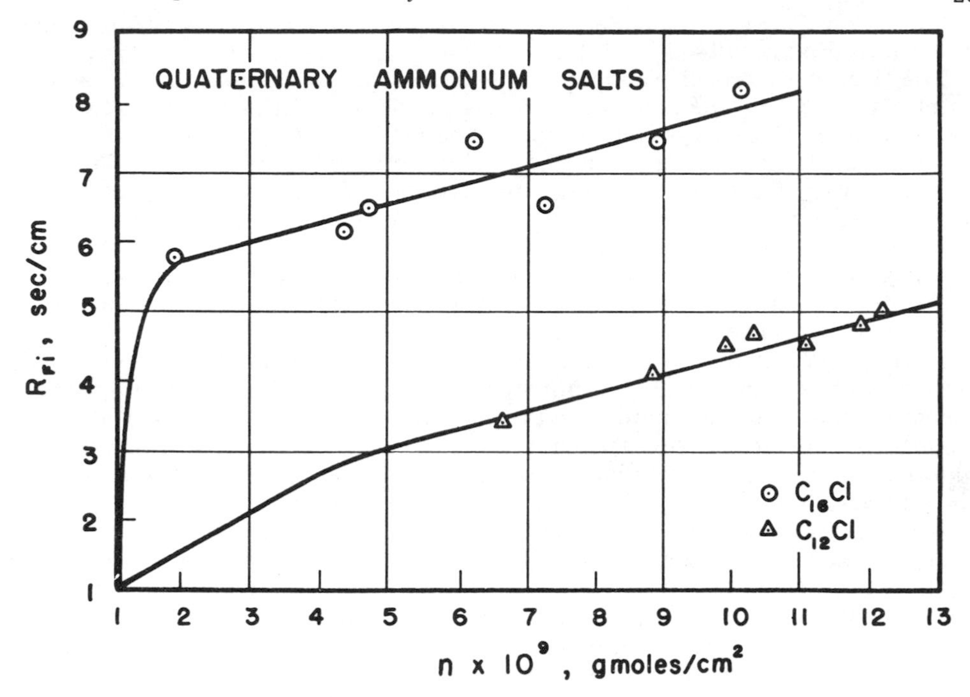

Figure 124. Interfacial resistance vs. surface concentration.

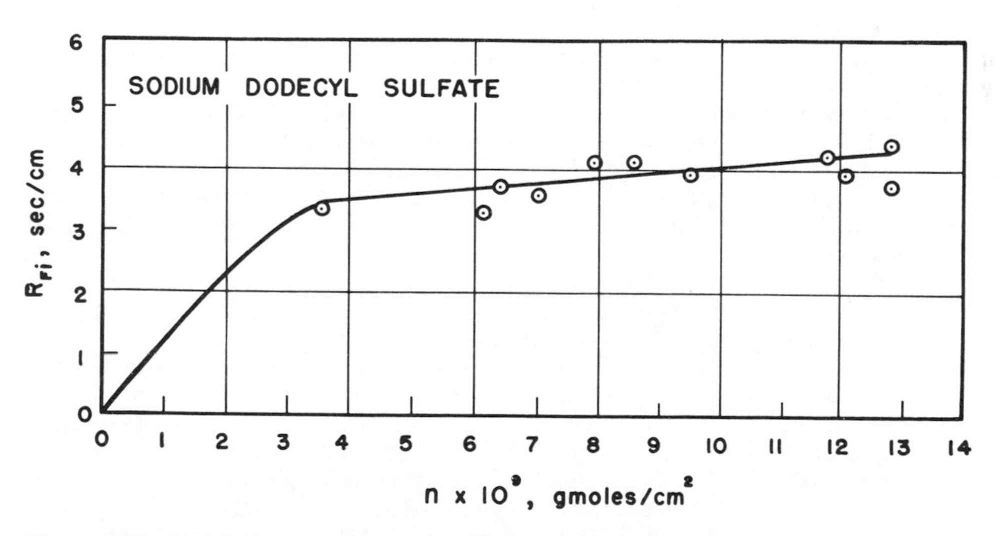

Figure 125. Interfacial resistance vs. surface concentration.

is determined by processes involving activation at an energy barrier at the interface, orientation in the surface layer, or other effects specific to the nature of the SAA molecule.

Concerning the purity of the SAA, it is important to point out that in any solution containing two or more SAA there will be a preferential adsorption at the interface, which is in general different from the concentration distribution in the bulk solution. Therefore, an SAA such as Teepol, a blend of alkyl sulfonates, may give misleading results.

The third and probably the most important factor in any fundamental study on the effect of SAA on gas transfer concerns the physicochemical characteristics of the interface. This has been discussed in detail in the Introduction and defined to be either as "effects of the first kind" or as "effects of the second kind."

Regardless of the mechanism of interference, our experimental results give all indications that SAA are effective in reducing the gas transfer rate and this effect is highly dependent on the aeration system. This dependency on the aeration system is believed to be a result of differences in the hydrodynamics of the contactor. Using this to advantage as a diagnostic criteria, it is possible to delineate the mechanism of SAA interference.

Photographic studies with bubble aeration system gave strong evidence of "effects of the second kind," manifested by changes in the process of bubble formation and bubble dynamics. In the presence of SAA it was observed that bubbles were detached from the capillary at a lower frequency and traveled like rigid spheroids at relatively lower velocity of ascent than in the absence of SAA. The photographic technique, however, is not adequate in defining the area of the gas-liquid interface and determining the hydrodynamics of the interface.

Stirred aeration systems provide the advantages of a defined interfacial area; besides it is possible to observe the hydrodynamic characteristics of the water surface under controlled bulk mixing conditions. Using this model, it was possible to ascertain the effect of mixing on gas transfer in presence and in absence of SAA. Hence, the SAA effect was detected only when the degree of mixing in the aqueous phase caused gas transport resistance in the bulk to be much smaller than that across the interface ($R_B \ll R_L$). Recent reported investigations on the effect of mixing on the aeration rate of certain industrial waste effluents (21) substantiated these findings.

Using stirred aeration systems it was also possible to analyze the effect of SAA on gas transfer rate into "effects of the first kind" (R_F) related to the transport resistance across the adsorbed SAA film itself and "effects of the second kind" (R_{HL}) related to the viscous hydration sublayer and surface stagnation. Our findings show that in presence of SAA the majority of resistance to oxygen transfer in stirred aeration systems is caused by "effects of the second kind." Other investigators (22) also used stirred vessels and found nearly identical gas transfer resistances with $C_8 - C_{16}$ alcohols. This was in accordance with our findings, that R_{HL} offered the majority of total interfacial resistance. Had the resistance of the adsorbed layer, R_F, been larger than R_{HL}, the gas transfer resistance would have been proportional to the alcohol chain length.

One of the main limitations of the stirred aeration model is that it does not lend itself to the study of transient gas transfer phenomena. In other words, such a system is inadequate for the study of SAA effect as a function of surface age. This is particularly important, especially in cases where adsorption of SAA at the interface proceeds slowly. In the liquid laminar jet model it is possible to control the surface age or exposure time quite accurately. Thus it was possible to study the effect of orientation of SAA molecules at the gas-liquid interface. Results shown in Figure 124 indicate that the slow attainment of a steady-state value of gas transfer resistance R_{Ti} in the case of sodium dodecyl sulphate is primarily due to surface orientation. This effect did not occur with dodecyltrimethylammonium chloride, which does not change surface orientation.

CONCLUSION

Upon comparing results from three different aeration systems, it was possible to develop a better understanding, on a fundamental level, of the mechanism of interference of SAA on gas transfer. The presence of SAA in the aeration system was found to cause a reduction in the rate of gas transfer, the extent of which depends on the hydrodynamics of the contactor and the chemical properties of the SAA used.

The interference of SAA with gas transfer can be either due to "effects of the first kind" or "effects of the second kind." The former are caused by SAA adsorbed film itself, which may cover partially or totally the water surface, block dissolution sites at the interface, or distort intermolecular forces between the gas molecule and the water surface necessary in the dissolution process. Effects of the second kind are related to the increase of the water surface viscosity, suppression of the hydrodynamic activity of the interface, and formation of viscous subsurface hydration layer.

Whether the resistance to gas transfer is that of the first or the second kind will depend on the structure and the physicochemical characteristics of the SAA molecule.

ACKNOWLEDGMENTS

The authors wish to extend grateful acknowlegments to Dr. D. A. Okun, chairman of the Department of Environmental Sciences and Engineering, University of North Carolina, who directed the studies on bubble and stirred aeration systems, and to Dr. J. A. Caskey, for his contribution to the studies on laminar fluid jets. The investigations reported herein were supported in part by the National Institutes of Health of the Public Health Service.

SYMBOLS USED

A = interfacial area, cm.^{2}
A_s = interfacial area covered with SAA, cm.^{2}
a = interfacial area per unit liquid volume, cm.$^{-1}$
C_i = instantaneous bulk concentration of dissolved gas, mg/l
C_t = bulk gas concentration at time t, mg/l
C_s = bulk gas concentration at equilibrium, mg/l
d = diameter of propeller, cm.
g = acceleration, cm^2/min
I = constant, dimensionless
$K_L a$ = overall or volumetric gas transfer coefficient, min.$^{-1}$
K_L = gas transfer coefficient, cm/min
K_i = instantaneous rate of gas absorption, mg/min/cm^2
N = number of revolutions, min.$^{-1}$
n = constant, dimensionless
N_{Re} = mixing Reynolds number, dimensionless
R_T = total gas transfer resistance in the liquid phase, min/cm
R_L = gas transfer resistance across liquid surface, min/cm
R_B = gas transfer resistance in the bulk of liquid phase, min/cm
R_F = gas transfer resistance due to SAA adsorbed film, min/cm
R_H = gas transfer resistance across liquid surface in presence of SAA, min/cm
R_{HL} = net resistance to gas transfer due to effects of the second kind and SAA hydration layer, min/cm
r = bubble diameter, cm.
t = time, min.
U = bubble velocity, cm/min
U_s = bubble velocity in presence of SAA, cm/min
V = volume of liquid phase, cm.^{3}
π = surface pressure, dyne/cm

σ = surface tension, dyne/cm
Γ = surface excess or surface concentration, moles/cm^2
ν = kinematic viscosity cm^2/min
μ = viscosity, cp

REFERENCES

(1) Caskey, J. A. "The Effect of Surfactant Chain Length and Surface Orientation on Gas Absorption Rates." Ph.D. Thesis, Clemson University (1965).
(2) Mancy, K. H. "Effects of a Surface Active Agent on Oxygen Transfer in Air-Water System." Ph.D. Thesis, The University of North Carolina (1962).
(3) Baars, J. K. "The Effect of Detergents on Aeration: A Photographic Approach to the Problem," *J. Inst. Sewage Purif.*, *4*, 358 (1955).
(4) Zieminski, S. A., C. C. Goodwin, and R. L. Hill. "The Effect of Some Organic Substances on Oxygen Absorption in Bubble Aeration," *Tech. Assoc. Pulp Paper Ind.*, *43*, 1029 (1960).
(5) Eckenfelder, W. W., and E. L. Barnhart. "The Effect of Organic Substances on the Transfer of Oxygen from Air Bubbles in Water," *Amer. Inst. Chem. Engr. J.*, *7*, 631 (1961).
(6) Hammerton, D., and F. H. Garner. "Gas Absorption from Single Bubbles," *Trans. Inst. Chem. Engr.* (Britain), *32*, 518 (1854).
(7) Raimondi, P., and H. L. Toor. "Interfacial Resistance in Gas Absorption," *Amer. Inst. Chem. Engr. J.*, *5*, 86 (1959).
(8) Timson, W. T., and C. G. Dunn. "Mechanism of Gas Absorption from Bubbles under Shear," *Ind. Engr. Chem.*, *52*, 799 (1960).
(9) Davies, J. T., and E. K. Rideal. *Interfacial Phenomena.* New York: Academic Press, Inc. (1961).
(10) Griffith, R. E. "The Absorption of Carbon Dioxide into Aqueous Monoethanolamine Solutions." Ph.D. Thesis, University of Tennessee (1957).
(11) Garner, F. H., and D. Hammerton. "Circulation inside Gas Bubbles," *Chem. Engr. Sci.*, *3*, 1 (1954).
(12) Levich, V. G. *Physiochemical Hydrodynamics.* Englewood Cliffs, New Jersey: Prentice Hall, Inc. (1962).
(13) Mancy, K. H., and D. A. Okun. "Effects of Surface Active Agents on Bubble Aeration," *J. Water Poll. Cont. Fed.*, *32*(4), 351 (1960).
(14) Mancy, K. H., and D. A. Okun. "Automatic Recording of Dissolved Oxygen in Aqueous Solutions Containing Surface Active Agents," *Analyt. Chem.*, *32*, 108 (1960).
(15) Mancy, K. H., and D. A. Okun. "The Effect of Surface Active Agents on Aeration," *J. Water Poll. Cont. Fed.*, *37*, 212 (1965).
(16) Mancy, K. H., D. A. Okun, and C. N. Reilley. "A Galvanic Cell Oxygen Analyzer," *J. Electroanalyt. Chem.*, *4*, 65 (1962).
(17) O'Connor, D. J. "Effects of Surfactants on Reaeration." Conference Biological Waste Treatment, Manhattan College, New York, New York (1960).
(18) Bohr, N. Philosophical Transactions, A209 (1909).
(19) Defay, R., and J. R. Hammerlin. "Measurements of Dynamic Surface Tensions of Aqueous Solution by the Oscillating Jet Method," *J. Coll. Sci.*, *13*, 553 (1958).
(20) Addison, C. C., and S. K. Hutchinson. "The Properties of Freshly Formed Surfaces, Part XI. Factors Influencing Surface Activity and Adsorption Rates in Aqueous Decyl Alcohol Solutions," *J. Chem. Soc.*, *4*, 3387 (1949).
(21) Ford, D. L., Civil Engineering Department, The University of Texas, Austin, Texas. Private Communications (1966).
(22) Goodridge, F., and D. J. Bricknell. "Interfacial Resistance in Carbon Dioxide-Water System," *Trans. Inst. Chem. Engr.*, *40*, 54 (1962).

FLOCCULATION PHENOMENA IN BIOLOGICAL SYSTEMS

W. C. Boyle, K. Crabtree, E. P. Iaccarino,
E. N. Lightfoot, and G. A. Rohlich
University of Wisconsin, Madison, Wisconsin

INTRODUCTION

For the past half century the activated sludge process has been extensively used and has found increasing application in the treatment of domestic and industrial wastes. In many respects practice has advanced more rapidly than has a basic understanding of the mechanism of the process.

Of primary importance in the process is the biological flocculation that takes place in the aeration tanks. Research efforts at the University of Wisconsin over the past five years have revealed considerable information on the qualitative aspects of flocculation. A qualitative description of the forces involved in floc formation is useful in determining conditions favoring flocculation, but will shed little light on flocculation rates, size distributions, or effects of aggregates.

It is, therefore, important to consider the quantitative aspects of flocculation—that is, the estimation of collision rates, the effectiveness of collisions, and the quantitative measure of adhesive and disruptive forces.

We have recently begun studying the quantitative aspects of flocculation of pure cultures of *Zoogloea ramigera.* It is clear as a result of our early observations that the available literature on colloid coagulation is of value and that much of it is applicable to bacterial flocs.

This paper will therefore:

1. Review the literature on colloid coagulation and indicate its usefulness and the gaps of knowledge which must be filled.
2. Review the qualitative theories proposed with respect to the cohesive forces.
3. Briefly discuss the qualitative theory of floc formation for *Zoogloea ramigera.*

QUANTITATIVE DESCRIPTION OF BACTERIAL FLOCCULATION

This section presents a review of current knowledge of the factors affecting the rate of aggregation of colloids and the size distribution of the resulting aggregates. The factors—Brownian motion, laminar shear, and turbulent transport—as they operate in colloidal suspensions, whether live or inanimate, are considered. In the analysis allowance is made for bacterial replication because its effects are not separable from the three factors.

The subject matter of this section is divided into three areas:

1. Population balances, which provide the formal basis for description.
2. The prediction of collision frequency, which depends primarily upon classical kinetic theory and hydrodynamics.
3. Characterization of disruptive forces, primarily hydrodynamic in the case of bacterial flocs, which tend to provide an upper limit for the size of primary aggregates.

Population Balances

Consider a well-mixed closed system containing a homogeneous pure culture of bacteria, and define n_x as the number concentration of aggregates containing a total of x bacteria each at any time t. The course of flocculation can then be formally described by a conservation, or "continuity," relation for each size of aggregate. For our purpose it will be convenient to write this relation in the form

$$\frac{dn_x}{dt} = C_x + D_x + R_x \tag{1}$$

Here dn_x/dt is the rate of increase of numbers of x-aggregates per unit volume and:

C_x = net rate of formation of x-aggregates resulting from *coalescence* of aggregates.

D_x = net rate of formation of x-aggregates resulting from *disruption* of preformed aggregates.

R_x = net rate of formation of x-aggregates resulting from bacterial *replication*.

Equation 1 is clearly nothing but a bookkeeping statement, and the choice of individual terms is to some extent arbitrary. More elaborate expressions have been developed for arbitrary countable entities (1) and for bacterial populations of nonuniform size and age (2).

The first term on the right side of Equation 1 has received the most attention to date and often dominates the other two. It will be convenient to rewrite it in terms of collision frequency and efficiency:

$$C_x = \frac{1}{2}\sum_{i=1}^{x-1} \beta_{i,\,x-i}\, A_{i,\,x-i}\, n_i n_{x-i} - n_x \sum_{i=1}^{\infty} \beta_{i,x} A_{i,x} n_i \tag{2}$$

where

$A_{jk}n_jn_k$, $(j \neq k)$ = rate of collisions per unit volume between pairs of aggregates containing j and k organisms, respectively,

$A_{jk}n_jn_k$, $(j=k)$ = twice the rate of collisions per unit volume between pairs of aggregates containing j organisms,

and

β_{jk} is the probability of a j-k collision being effective.

Effective collisions are defined as those resulting in formation of an aggregate containing $j + k$ organisms. The first term on the right side of this equation represents the formation of x-aggregates by coalescence of smaller flocs. The factor $\frac{1}{2}$ must be included, because in the summation each collision is counted twice. The second term represents the rate of coalescence of x-aggregates into larger flocs. Expressions for estimating the A_{jk} are presented in the next two sections.

The second term on the right side of Equation 1 is not always included in discussions of colloid or aerosol aggregation and may frequently be of little effect. It does, however, deserve mention, both because of its possible importance and because of some confusion concerning it in the published literature. It appears to have been used almost solely by Joly (3). These authors recommend for this term the expression

$$D_x = 2\left(\sum_{i=x+1}^{\infty} B_i n_i\right) - B_x\,(x-1)n_x \tag{3}$$

in which

B_in_i = rate of disruption of an i-aggregate into any two smaller aggregates, per unit volume and time.

However, unlike Equation 2, this expression is valid only for one kinetic model, that developed by Blatz and Tobolsky (4) for linear polymerization. In this model the particles forming any aggregate are arranged in a line, and the probability of breakage of each particle-to-particle link is the same. The first term of Equation 3 thus represents the splitting of higher polymers into two fragments, one containing x particles. The factor 2 is needed because there are two links in each larger polymer that can produce an x-aggregate (except when $i = 2x$, where two x-aggregates are formed by breakage of the central link). The second term represents the disruption of x-aggregates. The term $(x-1)$ is needed because there are $(x-1)$ links in the aggregate. It is extremely doubtful that Equation 3 is realistic for the types of aggregates encountered in biological flocculation—either bacterial or molecular. It appears likely, however, that the analysis of Joly and Barbu (5) is useful for describing the behavior of pairs of particles. In many practical operations the effect of disruptive forces will be minor and

$$D_x = 0 \qquad \text{(Adhesive forces dominant)} \tag{4}$$

Stability of flocs is discussed further in connection with analysis of disruptive forces.

The third term in Equation 1 is the only one peculiar to flocs of living bacteria. It may be expressed as

$$R_x = (k_G)_{x-1}\,(x-1)n_{x-1} - (k_G)_x\; x\, n_x \tag{5}$$

where

$$\approx -\frac{\partial}{\partial x}\left[(k_G)_x\; \phi_x\right] \tag{6}$$

$(k_G)_x$ = average growth constant (fractional rate of replication) for a floc of size x.

$\phi_x = \partial n/\partial x$ = frequency distribution of numbers of organisms relative to floc size, and n is the total number of organisms per unit volume.

Equation 6 will be suitable for all except the smallest flocs, and for these latter the growth constant will be essentially the same as for dispersed organisms. For larger flocs, k_G may, however, be considerably less because of diffusional limitations on substrate supply. It is assumed in Equations 5 and 6 that no organisms formed by replication leave the floc from which they formed.

Equations 1, 2, 4, and 6 provide a satisfactory formal basis for characterizing aggregation phenomena. It remains only to obtain explicit relations for the unknowns appearing in them to determine $\phi_x(x,t)$, the floc size distribution.

Estimation of Collision Frequency

In this section methods available for estimating the frequency of collisions between the particles of a colloidal suspension are discussed. The primary causative factors—Brownian motion, fluid shear, and turbulent transport—are introduced in turn, and their relative importance is discussed for conditions likely to be encountered in bacterial suspensions.

The factor of greatest importance is relative motion of adjacent particles necessary to bring them into contact. In quiescent suspensions or for very small particles, this relative motion is provided primarily by random thermal agitation of the molecules. Collision frequency under these conditions can be predicted from the classic analysis of Smoluchowski (6, 7). For agitated suspensions of particles above one micron in diameter, however, most of the relative motion is provided by convection of the fluid. In laminar flow, or where turbulent eddies are large compared to interparticle distances, this relative motion is provided primarily by the local shear rate. Here again a firm basis for predicting collision frequency has been provided by Smoluchowski (7). However, in turbulent systems eddy transport becomes an important source of relative motion if individual particles are large compared to the size of the smallest turbulent fluctuations. For this situation, very important in practice, recourse must be made to relatively unreliable semiempirical models of turbulent flow.

Also of great importance is estimation of the probability that a given collision will result in a permanent bond between the colliding particles. It is standard practice, especially in analysis of aerosol precipitation, to express this probability in terms of a collision efficiency. However, for bacterial aggregates it will be seen that this concept is not very useful and that no reliable means yet exists for estimating the probability of a collision being effective.

The Effects of Brownian, or Thermal, Motion

We consider here the effect of random thermal agitation on the relative motion of suspended particles. Discussion will be based almost entirely on the classic analysis of Smoluchowski (6, 7), which appears quite adequate for our purposes. Since this analysis is well known and adequately discussed in readily available texts (8), only a brief summary of Smoluchowski's methods and results will be given here. Throughout this and the succeeding sections all particles will be assumed to be spherical.

In this analysis attention is focused on any one particle, of radius R_i, chosen arbitrarily as the collector, and a collision is assumed to take place whenever the center of any second particle, of radius R_j, passes within a distance $(R_i + R_j)$ of the center of the collector. In order to estimate the frequency with which such collisions occur, the motion of the surrounding particles is assumed governed by Fick's second law of diffusion (8), with the effective diffusivity given by the Stokes-Einstein equation:

$$D_i = \kappa T / 6\pi\mu R_i \tag{7}$$

where D_i is the Brownian diffusivity of a particle of effective radius R_i through the fluid medium, κ is the Boltzmann constant, T the absolute temperature, and μ the viscosity of the suspending liquid. The Brownian diffusivity and other characteristic quantities of importance to this discussion are described in Table 45. For the origin of Equation 7, see Fuchs (8) or Einstein (9).

For the situation considered here, in which the collector is also diffusing, the effective diffusivity of the second particle to the collector is

$$D_{\text{eff}} = (D_i + D_j) \tag{8}$$

It may then readily be shown that the average number rate of condensation of particles of radius R_j on a collector of radius R_i is

$$N_{ij} = 8\pi\, n_j \frac{(R_i + R_j)}{2} (D_i + D_j) \left[1 + \frac{R_i + R_j}{\sqrt{\pi (D_i + D_j) t}} \right] \quad \text{where } (i \neq j) \tag{9}$$

where n_j is the number concentration of particles of radius R_j in the surrounding fluid. See for example Carslaw and Jaeger (10) for the heat-conduction analog.

It should be kept in mind that Equation 9, strictly speaking, is valid only at the very start of the flocculation process, and it may be noted that for this time the predicted flocculation rate is infinite. This is misleading, since in fact the rate of aggregation is discontinuous. It may be shown (8) that the average time elapsed up to the first collision.

$$t_1 = \frac{1}{8\pi n_j \left(\frac{R_i + R_j}{2} \right)} \left[1 + 15.3\,\phi_j \left(1 - \sqrt{\frac{2}{15.3\phi_j} + 1} \right) \right] \tag{10}$$

TABLE 45

CHARACTERISTIC QUANTITIES IN THE MECHANICS OF SPHERICAL HYDROSOLS

Brownian diffusivity $D = \kappa T / 6\pi\mu R_i$

Mean thermal velocity $\overline{U} = \sqrt{\dfrac{8\kappa T}{\pi m}} = \sqrt{\dfrac{6\kappa T}{\pi^2 \rho}}\ R^{-3/2}$

where m is particle mass and ρ particle density

Relaxation time $\tau = \dfrac{m}{6\pi\mu R} = \dfrac{mD_i}{\kappa T}$

"Effective mean free path" (stopping distance for initial velocity equal to the mean thermal velocity)

$$\ell = \overline{U}\tau = \frac{\overline{U} m D_i}{\kappa T} = \frac{\overline{U} m}{6\pi R\mu}$$

Typical numerical values at 303°K in water

$$\kappa T = 1.38 \times 10^{-16} \times 303 \text{ ergs} = 4.18 \times 10^{-14} \text{ ergs}$$

$$\mu = 0.8\text{cp} = 8 \times 10^{-3} \frac{\text{gm.}}{\text{sec. cm.}}$$

$$= 8 \times 10^{-3} \frac{\text{dyne sec.}}{\text{cm.}^2}$$

Diffusivity:

$$D_i = \frac{4.18 \times 10^{-14} \text{ dyne cm.}}{6\pi 8 \times 10^{-3} \text{ dyne}} \frac{\text{cm.}^2}{\text{sec.}} \frac{1}{R} = 277 \times 10^{-13} \frac{\text{cm.}^3}{\text{sec.}} \frac{1}{R}$$

Example: for $R = 1\mu = 10^{-4}$ cm.

$$D_i = \frac{2.77 \times 10^{-13}}{10^{-4}} = 277 \times 10^{-9} \frac{\text{cm.}^2}{\text{sec.}}$$

This is approximately correct for individual cells of *Zoogloea ramigera.*

Mean thermal velocity:

(for $\rho = 1$ gm/cm^3 = 1 dyne sec^2/cm^4)

$$\overline{U} = \sqrt{\frac{6}{\pi^2} 4.18 \times 10^{-14} \frac{\text{cm.}^5}{\text{sec.}^2}}\ R^{-3/2} = 1.592 \times 10^{-7} R^{-3/2} \frac{\text{cm.}^{5/2}}{\text{sec.}}$$

$$\overline{U}(R = 1\mu) = \frac{1.592 \times 10^{-7}}{(10^{-4})^{3/2}} = 0.1592 \text{ cm/sec}$$

Relaxation time:

(for $\rho = 1$ gm/cm^3)

$$\tau = \frac{4}{3}\pi R^3 \frac{\text{gm.}}{\text{cm.}^3} \cdot \frac{1 \text{ cm. sec.}}{6\pi R \times 8 \times 10^{-3} \text{ gm.}} = 27.8 R^2 \frac{\text{sec.}}{\text{cm.}^2}$$

$$\tau(R = 1\mu) = 278 \times 10^{-7} \text{ sec.}$$

Mean free path:

$$\ell = (1.592 \times 10^{-7})(27.8) R^{1/2} \text{ cm.}^{1/2} = 4.43 \times 10^{-6} R^{1/2} \text{ cm.}^{1/2}$$

$$\ell(R = 1\mu) = 4.43 \times 10^{-6} \times 10^{-2} \text{ cm.}^2 = 4.43 \times 10^{-8} \text{ cm.}$$

$$= 4.43 \times 10^{-4}\ \mu$$

$$\ell/R = 4.43 \times 10^{-4} << 1$$

Note: Since $\ell/R \propto R^{-1/2}$, this ratio will always be much less than unity for bacterial aggregates.

where ϕ_j is the volume fraction of particles of radius R_j in the fluid. For systems such as activated sludge the bracketed quantity of Equation 10 is unlikely to differ significantly from unity. It is therefore possible to ignore the transient term in Equation 9 and to assume pseudo steady-state conditions of flocculation at the rate

$$N_{ij} = 8\pi\left(\frac{R_i + R_j}{2}\right)(D_i + D_j)\, n_j \tag{11}$$

even at the start of flocculation. Since each of the i particles is equivalent to the others the rate of collision between particles of sizes i and j is

$$\Phi_{ij}\,\rho_{ij} = \Phi_{ij}\,\rho_{ji} = n_i n_j\; 8\pi\left(\frac{R_i + R_j}{2}\right)(D_i + D_j) \qquad (i \neq j) \tag{12}$$

For the special case of $i = j$, the corresponding result is

$$\Phi_{ii}\,\rho_{ii} = \frac{1}{2} n_i^{\,2}\; 8\pi R_i\,(2\,D_i) = n_i^{\,2}\; 8\pi R_i D_i \tag{13}$$

The factor 1/2 must be included to avoid counting each particle as both "collector" and "collected." If one now refers to Equation 2, it is clear that

$$A_{ij} = 8\pi\left(\frac{R_i + R_j}{2}\right)(D_i + D_j) \qquad \text{(for all } i, j) \tag{14}$$

$$A_{ii} = 2 \times 8\pi\, R_i D_i \tag{15}$$

where the A_{ij} are the bimolecular rate constants for collision. At the start of flocculation only single particles are present and $A_{ij} = A_{ii}$. The factor 2 is necessary in Equation 15, since particles of equal size are not counted twice in the first summation of Equation 2.

In principle Equations 14 and 15 must also be corrected both for discontinuities in surface concentration in the neighborhood of the collecting sphere and for the efficiency of collisions (which may be less than unity). To allow for these effects, we multiply the A_{ij} by efficiency β_{ij} (see Eq. 2).

Approximate expressions for the β_{ij} have been developed by Smoluchowski. These are discussed in such standard references as Fuchs (8). For uniform dispersions of hydrosols, or aqueous colloids, these expressions reduce to

$$\beta_{ii}^{\,0} \quad \frac{1}{\left(1 - 0.35\,\frac{\ell_i}{R_i} + 1.1\,\frac{\ell_i}{R_i\,\xi_i}\right)} \tag{16}$$

where

$$\ell_i = \overline{U}_i m_i D_i / RT \tag{17}$$

is the "effective mean free path" of the particles, $\overline{U}_i$ is the mean thermal velocity of the particle, m_i is its mass (See Table 45), and ξ_i is the efficiency of a single "collision." For colloids of unit specific gravity in water at 30°C.

$$\ell_i / R_i = 4.43 \times 10^{-6}\, R_i^{-1/2}\; cm^{1/2} \tag{18}$$

It follows then that for aggregates of bacteria of normal size ($R \sim 1$ micron)

$$\frac{\ell_i}{R_i} \leq 10^{-4} \tag{19}$$

and β_{ii} will be very nearly unity for all but very small ξ_i. The reason for this small sensitivity to collision efficiency is that the particles "collide" many times on each "close approach." Because the ℓ_i are so small, the β_{ij} for polydisperse systems may also be considered very nearly unity for finite collisions efficiencies.

It should, however, be kept in mind that Equation 14 was developed for inanimate particles. Motile bacteria may have much higher "effective diffusivities" than inanimate colloids of the same size and density—and thus may exhibit smaller efficiency factors. Indications of such behavior have been observed by the authors during phase-contrast examination of the early stages of flocculation of *Zoogloea ramigera*. In addition, the collision efficiency ξ_i may become extremely small in the presence of disruptive forces—always present in actual situations. It appears then that it may be preferable to write Equation 16 for colloids in the form

$$\beta_{ij} = 1; \quad \gamma_{ij} < 1 \tag{20a}$$

$$\beta_{ij} = 0; \quad \gamma_{ij} > 1 \tag{20b}$$

where γ_{ij} is the ratio of dispersive to adhesive forces. Unfortunately, it is very difficult at present to make a prior estimate of the γ_{ij}.

Returning now to Equation 14 and making use of the Stokes-Einstein equation, we see that

$$A_{ij} = \frac{2\kappa T}{3\mu}\left[(R_i + R_j)\left(\frac{1}{R_i} + \frac{1}{R_j}\right)\right] \tag{21}$$

The term in brackets may be written as

$$(R_i + R_j)\left(\frac{1}{R_i} + \frac{1}{R_j}\right) = 2 + \alpha + \frac{1}{\alpha} \tag{22}$$

where α is the ratio of particle radii. This quantity has a minimum value of 4 for $\alpha = 1$ but approaches α for large differences in size. Since the size of an aggregate formed by collision of a large and a small particle approximates the size of the larger, there is a strong tendency for the smaller particles to disappear from the suspension. The result is an asymmetric size distribution and some counteraction to polydispersity.

In the initial stages of flocculation, however, the size ratios are not large and the A_{ij} differ little from A_{ii}. Thus for coalescing emulsions it may be seen that the collision constant A_{ij} is never far different from A_{ii}. See Table 46.

If the rates of disruption and replication are negligible, Equation 14 may be combined with Equations 1 and 2 to give

$$\frac{dn_x}{dt} = 4\pi\left\{\frac{1}{2}\sum_{i=1}^{x-1} n_i\, n_{x-i}\,(D_i + D_{x-i})\,(R_i + R_{x-i})\,\beta_{i,x-i} - n_x \sum_{i=1}^{\infty} n_i\,(D_i + D_x)\,(R_i + R_x)\,\beta_{i,x}\right. \tag{23}$$

Smoluchowski (6, 7) obtained an approximate integration of the set of Equation 23 for an initially monodisperse system by assuming

$$\lambda = 2\pi(D_i + D_x)\,(R_i + R_x)\beta_{i,x}$$

to be a constant. The result of these integrations can be expressed as

$$n_x\,(t) = n_0\,\frac{(\lambda\, n_0\, t)^{x-1}}{(1 + \lambda\, n_0\, t)^{x+1}} \tag{24a}$$

$$n_{\text{tot}}(t) = \frac{n_0}{1 + \lambda n_0 t} \tag{24b}$$

where n_0 is the original number concentration of particles and n_{tot} the total number concentration at any time.

Equations 24 are most useful in the early stages of flocculation of very small

TABLE 46

SPECIFIC COLLISION CONSTANT

No. of Primary Drops, i	Radius	$(A_{i1})_s$	$(A_{i2})_s$	$(A_{i3})_s$	$(A_{i4})_s$	$(A_{i5})_s$
1	1	1				
2	$\sqrt[3]{2} = 1.26$	1.013	1			
3	$\sqrt[3]{3} = 1.44$	1.032	1.005	1		
4	$\sqrt[3]{4} = 1.59$	1.054	1.010	1.001	1	
5	$\sqrt[3]{5} = 1.71$	1.072	1.023	1.007	1.002	1

particles in a quiescent medium. Under these conditions the bacterial growth constant in Equations 5 and 6 may be considered constant at a value k_G.

In general, for the polydisperse system postulated, the total number concentration of particles can be calculated from an average collision constant $(A_{ij})_m$ by the equations

$$-\frac{dn_{\text{tot}}}{dt} = (A_{ij})_m \; n_{\text{tot}}^2 \tag{25a}$$

$$(A_{ij})_m = \int_0^\infty \int_0^\infty (A_{ij}\,\beta_{ij}) f(R_i,t) f(R_j,t) d\,R_i d\,R_j \tag{25b}$$

where $f(R_i, t)$ is the normalized radius frequency distribution. Equations 25 have been solved by Pshenai-Severin (11) for an experimental mass distribution. Total number concentration varied 12 percent from that calculated using A_{ii}. Also of interest is an earlier analysis of Todes (12).

Coagulation Resulting from Fluid Motion

It is again assumed here that particles collide and coagulate when their centers pass within a distance equal to the sums of their radii. In this simple theory no correction is made for hydrodynamic forces tending to prevent the particles from touching.

Again one particle is selected at random as the collecting particle.

1. *Laminar Streaming in a Constant Shear Field.* The relative velocity of any particle and the "collector" is clearly

$$U = \Gamma x = \Gamma r \sin \Theta \cos \phi \tag{26}$$

where r is the radial distance between particle centers (Fig. 126) and ϕ is measured from the positive x-axis in the plane $z = 0$. Looking at the system from below in the direction of the z-axis, we see that approaching particles are removed over a circular area of radius $(R_i + R_j)$.

The number rate of particle removal by any element of this target area A is

$$N_{ij} = n_i U dA = n_i \Gamma r\,(\cos \phi)\, dA \tag{27}$$

$$N_{ij} = 2 n_i \Gamma \int_0^{(R_i+R_j)} \int_{-\pi/2}^{\pi/2} r^2 dr \cos \phi \, d\phi \tag{28}$$

$$= 4/3\; n_i \Gamma\, (R_i + R_j)^3 \tag{29}$$

For a monodisperse sol

$$N_{ii} = \frac{32}{3}\, n_i\, \Gamma\, R_i^{\,3} \tag{30}$$

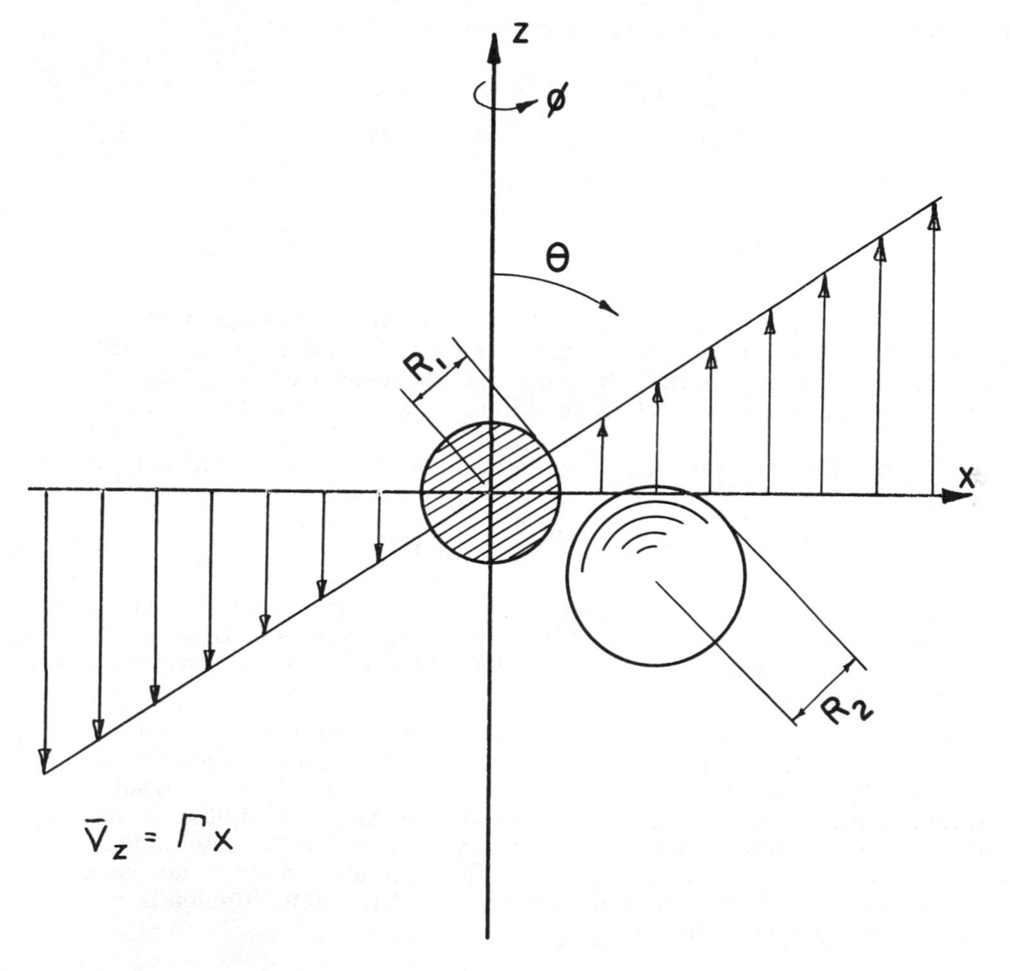

Figure 126. Laminar streaming in constant shear field.

Since each particle is equivalent and may be considered as a collector, we may write for a monodisperse sol at the start of coagulation

$$\left.\frac{-dn_i}{dt}\right|_{t=0} = n_i \left.N_{ii}\right|_{t=0} = \frac{32}{3} n_i^2 \Gamma R^3 \tag{31}$$

$$= \left(\frac{32}{3} \Gamma R^3\right) n_i^2 \tag{32}$$

Then the coagulation constant for shear-induced coagulation is

$$A_{ii}{}^S = \frac{32}{3} \Gamma R^3 \quad \text{(Shear-induced coagulation)} \tag{33}$$

This compares with that for Brownian coagulation of the last section:

$$A_{ii}{}^B = 16\pi R_i D_i \tag{34}$$

We then find the initial ratio of shear coagulation to Brownian

$$\frac{A_{ii}{}^{B}}{A_{ii}{}^{S}} = \frac{3}{2}\pi \frac{D_i}{\Gamma R_i{}^2} \tag{35a}$$

We may rewrite this expression with the aid of the Stokes-Einstein Equation

$$D_i = \frac{\kappa T}{6\pi\mu R_i} \quad \text{to obtain} \tag{35b}$$

$$\frac{A_{ii}{}^{B}}{A_{ii}{}^{S}} = \frac{1}{4}\ \frac{\kappa T}{\mu \Gamma R_i{}^3} \tag{36}$$

For bacteria with $R_{\text{eff}} = 1\mu$ in water at 30°C., the two mechanisms will be of equal effectiveness for shear rates of the order of 1 sec.$^{-1}$. Since this shear rate corresponds to only about 4×10^{-6} HP/1,000 gal, shear-induced coagulation can be expected to occur under almost all conditions of deliberate agitation. See Table 47.

For a polydisperse system we may define an unsymmetrical coagulation coefficient:

$$A_{ij} = \frac{4}{3}\Gamma(R_i + R_j)^3 \tag{37}$$

analogously to that for Brownian coagulation. It appears from Equations 32 and 37 that assumption of a size-independent coagulation constant will be quite unsuccessful for shear-induced flocculation. This situation does not, however, appear to have received much attention as yet.

2. *Coagulation in Turbulent Flow.* In the usual agitation of fluids on a large scale, flow tends to be turbulent, and efficiency of particle contacting is often higher than for either Brownian or laminar gradient coagulation. Turbulent coagulation is quite complex but semiempirical theories are available for this situation if (a) particles are of nearly the same density as the fluid so that they tend to follow the fluid motion closely, and (b) particles are large compared to the smallest scale of velocity fluctuations so that Brownian diffusion is negligible compared to turbulent diffusion.

TABLE 47

LOCAL AGITATION INTENSITY FOR WHICH FLUID SHEAR AND BROWNIAN MOTION GIVE EQUAL FLOCCULATION RATES FOR ONE-MICRON PARTICLES

$$\Gamma = \frac{4.18 \times 10^{-14}\ \text{dyne cm.}^3}{4 \times 8 \times 10^{-3}\ \text{dyne sec.}\ 10^{-12}\ \text{cm.}^3}$$

$$= \frac{4.18 \times 10^{-14}}{3.2 \times 10^{-14}} \approx 1\ \text{sec.}^{-1}$$

For the one-dimensional shear pictured, the local rate of dissipation of mechanical energy per unit volume is

$$E_v = \mu \Gamma^2$$

For H_2O at $\Gamma = 1/$ sec.

$$E_v = 8 \times 10^{-3}\ \frac{\text{dyne sec.}}{\text{cm.}^2} \cdot \frac{1}{\text{sec.}^2}$$

$$= 4.6 \times 10^{-6}\ \frac{\text{HP}}{1{,}000\ \text{gal.}}$$

The first of these requirements is met by almost all colloids, and bacterial flocs in particular. The second is believed to be met (13) when the collision radius

$$\frac{1}{2}(R_i + R_j) >> (D^2 \nu/\epsilon)^{1/4} \tag{38}$$

where D is the Brownian diffusivity and $\epsilon = \hat{E}_v/\rho$ the rate of viscous energy dissipation per unit mass of fluid (with the dimensions $1^2/t^3$). Under these conditions turbulent "diffusive" transport will predominate over Brownian to within the collision sphere. For aqueous suspension the inequality 38 will be met for $R_i > 1\mu$ at $\epsilon > 10^3$ cm.^{2}/sec.^{3}. Equation 38 will be reasonable under these conditions. Under the same agitation conditions the inequality will be reversed for $R_i < 0.1\,\mu$. Here Brownian diffusion will predominate in the neighborhood of the "collector" and turbulence will not affect coagulation.

Expressions for the effect of turbulence or coagulation rate have been offered by Levich (14). Levich considers the primary effect of turbulence to be an increase in the effective diffusivity of the particles, while Tunitskii (15) assumes an increase in gradient coagulation caused by velocity gradients at right angles to the line of particle centers. Both of these developments yield the expression

$$\frac{A\frac{T}{ii}}{A\frac{B}{ii}} = \frac{\alpha}{16\pi}\sqrt{\frac{\epsilon}{\nu}}\,\frac{R_i^{\;2}}{D_i} \tag{39}$$

for isodisperse suspensions. Here A_{ii}^T is the "turbulent" coagulation rate constant and is a model-dependent coefficient. The Levich development yields a value of 4, as obtained by Levich, and a value of 25, as by Obukhov and Yaglou (16). Equation 39 does not seem to have been checked experimentally. In view of this and the uncertainties in its development, it must be viewed with some reservations.

Disruptive Forces

The fundamental weakness in the above expressions for flocculation rate is the difficulty of estimating the probability β of a given collision, producing a stable aggregate of the colliding particles. If, as is often done, β is assumed constant, the above equations will predict a continuing flocculation—ultimately yielding a single aggregate containing all of the particles originally present. This is contrary to actual experience, for example, in the activated sludge process, where stable flocs of a rather wide size distribution are normally encountered. The basic reason for this discrepancy between prediction and observation is the failure of most predictive expressions to account adequately for dispersive forces.

Such forces arise from the same phenomena as those promoting flocculation: Brownian motion, fluid shear, and turbulent fluctuations. Each of these then plays a dual role, both providing the necessary relative motion required for particle-particle contacts and tending to prevent these contacts from being effective. Both adhesive and dispersive forces are also provided by the potential energy fields about the particles. The relative magnitudes of these aggregative and dispersive tendencies are discussed by Fuchs (8) and in considerably greater detail by Barbu and Joly (5). This latter analysis is of particular interest in that it considers simultaneously the effects of thermal motion, fluid shear, and the potential-energy fields of the particles. While not very realistic for the flat, globular, or starlike aggregates normally encountered in bacterial flocculation (for reasons discussed earlier) it may be useful for analyzing two-particle interactions. For this special case, the linear polymer model used by these authors appears valid.

There are also a number of more specialized analyses dealing only with disruptive forces. Among the earliest are those of Kuhn, concerning the effect of fluid shear (17). Like Barbu and Joly, Kuhn considered suspensions of linear aggregates of spherical particles, and developed expressions for their rate of rotation, and resultant tensile stresses, in a shear field. His results can be used to predict maximum aggregate size in a given flow field if the strengths of the interparticle bonds are known. The nature of these stresses can be simply visualized by considering the rotating dumbbell of Figure 127. The effect of fluid shear on aggregates of more probable shape is qualitatively similar. Unlike Joly and Barbu, Kuhn took into account the variation of shear-induced interparticle tensile stresses with position in the aggregate. He did not, however, consider hydrodynamic interaction between the particles constituting the aggregate. This has since been done by a number of authors for aggregates of various shapes, for example, ellipsoids of revolution and long cylinders. The older literature was reviewed and considerably extended by Burgers (18). Most of the analyses reported by Burgers are based on the Oseen point force approximation, for example, Happel and Brenner (19), and thus limited to long slender objects. However, Burgers also reviews the extensive exact analyses of D. B. Jeffery on ellipsoid motion in a shear field. It has since been shown by S. G. Mason (20) that the rotation of, and hence disruptive forces between, two attached spheres of equal diameter D in a shear field is closely approximated by that for an ellipsoid of revolution of length $2D$ and width D. Burgers' results for ellipsoids appear to be quite reasonable. However, those for cylinders are not, and the expressions of Broersma (21) are to be preferred. No analysis appears to have been made as yet for aggregates consisting of pairs of spheres of differing size. The groundwork for such an analysis, however, appears to have been laid by recent descriptions of two-particle interactions (19). The disruptive effects of turbulent fluctuations, although of considerable possible importance are as yet little understood.

Tensile Stresses in a Rotating Dumbbell

The disruptive effects of fluid shear are simply illustrated by considering the behavior of two spheres connected by a thin rigid shaft and rotating in a shear field. Such a system, first analyzed by Kuhn (17), is illustrated in the accompanying figure (Fig. 127).

For simplicity it will be assumed that:

1. The velocity gradient far from the spheres is constant, as shown in the figure, and the dumbbell is in the plane $Z = 0$.
2. The radii a of the spheres are much less than their distance of separation 2ℓ.
3. The Reynolds number $(a\Gamma\ell\rho_f/\mu_f)$, where ρ_f and μ_f are fluid density and viscosity respectively, is much less than unity.

Where assumptions (2) and (3) are valid the drag force F exerted on either sphere by the flowing fluid is given by the pseudosteady form of Stokes' law (8, 19):

$$F = 6\pi\,\mu\,a\,(\overline{V}_f - \overline{V}_s) \tag{40}$$

Where $\overline{V}_f$ is the velocity of the fluid, given by

$$\overline{V}_f = \Gamma\,\delta_x y \tag{41}$$

and $\overline{V}_s$ is the velocity of the sphere. Here Γ is the velocity gradient and δ_x a unit vector in the x-direction.

To determine the sphere velocity, and from it, the stress on the shaft, one may take advantage of the fact that the dumbbell can exert no torque on the fluid. (The angular momentum of the dumbbell is negligible at sufficiently low Reynolds number.) We may thus write that the torque

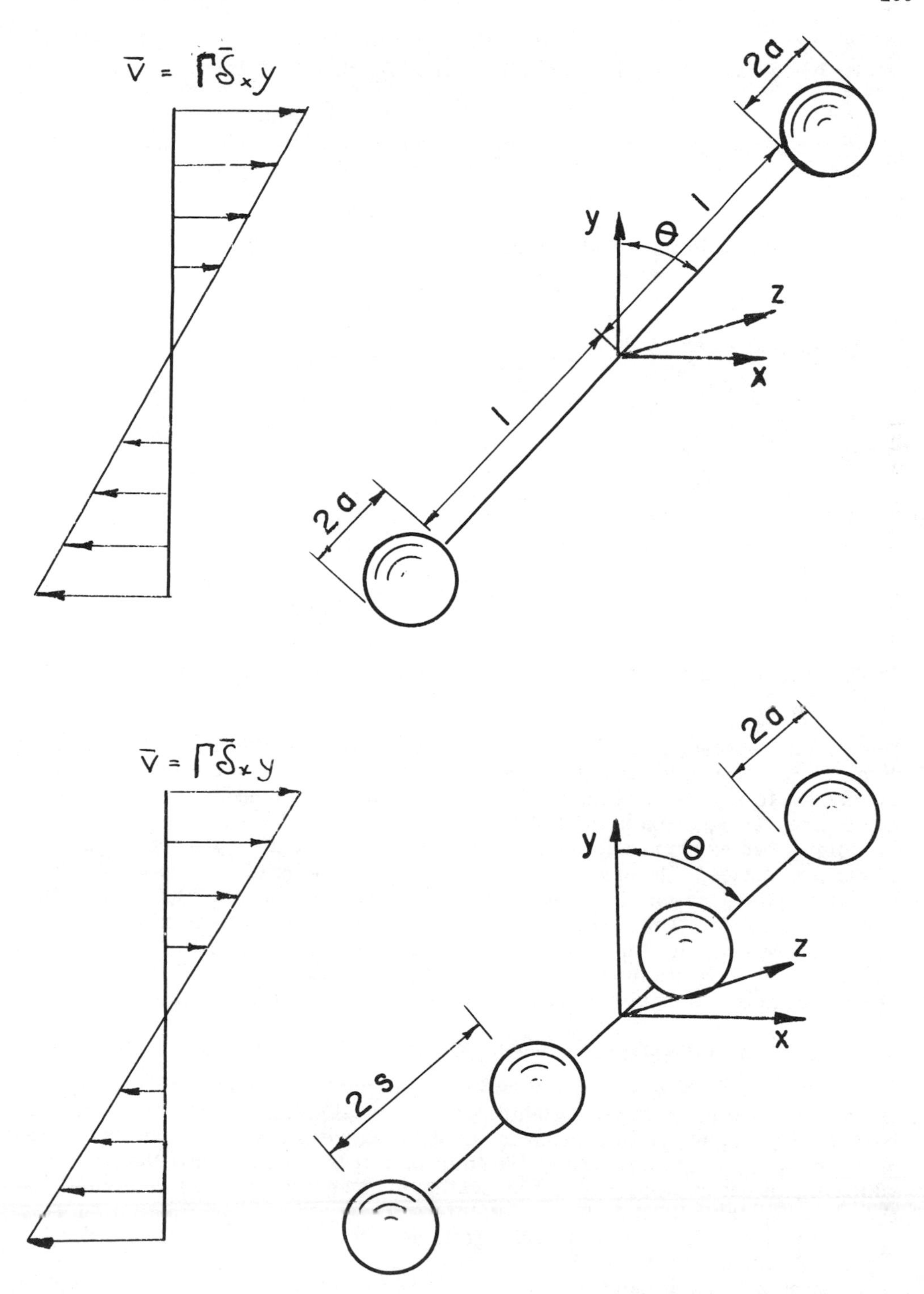

Figure 127. Kuhn's rotating dumbbell and rotating chain.

$$\overline{T} = \overline{r} \times \overline{F} = 0 \tag{42}$$

where $\overline{r}$ is a position vector from the origin. We thus find that

$$(V_{fy} - V_{sy})x - (V_{fx} - V_{sx})y = 0 \tag{43}$$

where the subscripts x and y refer to the x and y components of velocity. With the aid of Equation 41, we find

$$y\, V_{sx} = \Gamma y^2 + V_{sy}\, x \tag{44}$$

Since the dumbbells must follow a circular path, it follows that

$$-V_{sy}/V_{sx} = \tan\theta = \frac{x}{y} \tag{45}$$

and therefore that

$$V_{sx} = \Gamma y \Big/ \left(1 + \frac{x^2}{y^2}\right) = \frac{\Gamma y^3}{\ell^2} \tag{46}$$

$$V_{sy} = \frac{-\Gamma x y^2}{\ell^2} \tag{47}$$

It follows from Equation 42 that the drag force of the fluid must always be along the line of centers and of a magnitude:

$$F = 6\pi\mu a \sqrt{(V_f - V_s)^2} \tag{48}$$

$$= 6\pi\mu a \sqrt{\left(\Gamma y - \frac{\Gamma y^3}{\ell^2}\right)^2 + \left(\frac{\Gamma x y^2}{\ell^2}\right)^2} \tag{49}$$

The maximum tensile force will occur when $x = y$, $\theta = 45°$, and here

$$F_{\max} = 3\pi\mu a \Gamma \ell \qquad (\theta = 45°) \tag{50}$$

This, then, represents the maximum disruptive force of fluid shear on the aggregate. If $F_{\max}$ is greater than the strength of the bond between the two spheres, the bond will be broken as soon as this orientation is reached. The behavior of more probable aggregates is similar.

Corresponding expressions can be developed for chains of spheres, that is, linear aggregates. These will rotate about the mid-point of the chain, and the tensile stresses on the connecting links will increase toward a maximum at this center of rotation. The maximum, that is, central, tensile stress will increase with both the chain length and the velocity gradient in the fluid, and the chain will rupture if the strength of the central link is exceeded. As a result the maximum stable length of linear aggregates will decrease with increasing fluid shear rates.

QUALITATIVE DESCRIPTION OF BACTERIAL FLOCCULATION

The literature on waste treatment is replete with discussions of biological flocculation and its interrelationships with removal of organic matter. Also, the bacteriologist has been interested in bacterial aggregations with special emphasis on antibody agglutinations. From the literature it is indicated that the concepts on which explanations of microbial aggregation have been based may be divided into the following categories:

1. Capsular or gelatinous matrix agglomeration
2. Colloidal hypotheses
3. Protozoan agglomeration
4. Inert matrix and salt bridging hypotheses
5. Low energy concepts
6. Polymerization

Capsular or Gelatinous Matrix Agglomeration

Buswell and Long (22), in discussing the possible mechanism of bacterial flocculation in the activated sludge process, reported that the base of activated sludge flocs was composed of a bacterial slime layer to which other microorganisms adhered. This theory of slime attraction was subsequently accepted and discussed by several investigators: Cavel, (23), Theriault and McNamee (24), Heukelekian and Shulhoff (25), and White (26). Just as often, however, this theory was rejected by investigators, including Edwards (27), Dienert (28), McKinney (29), and McKinney and Weichlein (30), on the basis that many bacteria are wholly lacking in demonstrable slime or capsular material and yet readily form flocs resembling those formed in the activated sludge process. There appears to be serious question as to the importance of the gelatinous matrix as a cohesive force in flocculation.

Colloidal Hypotheses

It is tenable to assume that bacteria will act as colloids and therefore be influenced by the same factors which effect colloidal suspensions. This fact has led to a number of hypotheses regarding bacterial agglomeration. As early as 1897 Dunbar (31) proposed a theory for adsorption and absorption of colloidal and dissolved materials on floc in waste treatment processes. Biltz and Krohnke (32) stated, "Biological methods of sewage treatment are regarded as affording a means for the formation of absorption compounds between colloids of sewage and the slimy gelatinous coatings of filter materials." They considered that biological slimes are colloidal surfaces, and bacteria themselves, although associated with the slimes, were regarded as precipitants in reverse analogy to agglutination.

The agglomeration of bacterial cells by *p*H reduction (acid agglutination) has been reported by a number of bacteriologists: DeKruif (33), Eggerth and Bellows (34), Webster (35), and Lamanna and Mallette (36). The effect of reduction of *p*H on bacterial flocculation because of the reduction in cell surface charge to low value of potential (usually less than ± 15 millivolts), strongly supported the surface charge theory. Since cell surfaces are influenced by colloids in the medium (34, 36), flocculation *p*H values for a given organism will vary considerably. Baly (37) recognized that both the sewage colloids and the bacterial slime had negative charges, and suggested that it was the magnitude of the charge that was important; thus the more negatively charged bacterial floc adsorb the less negatively charged colloid. McKinney and Harwood (38) supported these concepts, stating that bacterial flocculation was probably brought about merely by reducing the surface charge on the cells below the "critical potential" and bringing them into contact through agitation.

Experiments performed by Joffe and Mudd (39) and later by McKinney (29) indicated, however, that it was possible to reduce the surface charges of bacteria below the "critical potential" without affecting flocculation. Tenny and Stumm (40) discussed bioflocculation in the light of colloidal theory. They also felt that the reduction in charge density, or decrease in electrostatic repulsion, was not a prerequisite for bioflocculation. It would seem, therefore, that reduction in surface charges is not the most significant factor in bacterial agglomeration.

Protozoan Theories

In 1943 Hardin (41) found that certain protozoa could cause the flocculation of some bacteria. This observation was supported and extended by Watson (42). He considered that the floc formation was caused by the adhesion of bacteria to the mucus surrounding the cilates. Similar observations were also reported by Pillai *et al.* in 1947 (43). However, in 1956 McKinney and Gram (44), in experiments designed to demonstrate competition prey-predator, and flocculation relationships in activated sludge, found that even in the presence of protozoa pure cultures of bacteria remained free and contributed to the BOD of the effluent. They concluded that protozoa played an important part in the clarification of sewage, but not in the process of flocculation. Curds (45) reported that India ink particles were flocculated by *Paramecium caudatum*; the particles were bound together by a "sticky" mucoprotein, which resulted in a change in surface charge and subsequent flocculation.

Inert Matrix and Salt Bridging Hypotheses

In 1935 Butterfield (46) stated that inert substances were needed to provide a framework for a stable floc. This view was supported by Whitehead and O'Shaughnesy (47). Hartmann (48) reported that it is common practice in Europe to start up activated sludge plants and maintain high solids concentrations by use of inorganic salts. These salts act as the base for cell aggregation. Without this inert matrix, bacteria will grow on the walls of the aeration tanks until a film develops, which, when sufficiently heavy, sloughs from the walls. Only then will flocs appear in the sewage.

In 1964 Gils (49) showed that *Alcaligenes faecalis* and *Vibrio percolans* required calcium and ferric ions for flocculation while *Zoogloea* strains formed flocs without these two ions. He believed that polyvalent ions may be required for the formation of bacterial flocs, but the bacteria must first have a layer of slime. In that same year, Mill (50), working with cultures of *Saccharomyces cervesia*, indicated that flocculation was dependent upon calcium ions, and no other metal ions could replace them. Sodium ions appeared to antagonize flocculation of the cells. Based on his experiments, Mill suggested that flocculation was caused by salt bridging between two carboxyl groups. This bond was further stabilized, he felt, by hydrogen bonding.

Low Energy Theory

The low energy theory developed by McKinney and others (29, 30) is composed of two principal ideas: "food to bacterial mass ratio, and energy level of the motile cells." McKinney noted that flocs of pure culture bacteria did not result until the bacteria were in an endogenous phase of metabolism. Observations during floc formation indicated that the bacteria became a part of the floc only when they lacked sufficient energy for motility to break away from the floc. "Thus the force of Brownian movement is sufficient to cause collision between individual cells. As two bacteria approach on a collision path the van der Waals force predominates, causing adhesion upon collision." McKinney reported that addition of fresh substrate to recently flocculated bacteria resulted in the dispersion of the cells as a result of additional energy. This theory receives considerable support from the fact that most activated sludge systems operate at low energy levels (that is, low substrate to bacterial mass ratios). Many systems which operate at higher food to microorganism ratios usually result in dispersed growth.

Polymerization

As early as 1953, there was evidence that bacteria could be flocculated by polymers of both natural and synthetic origin. Katchalsky (51) reported that *E. coli* and *S. aureus* were successfully flocculated with polylysene. Hodge and Metcalfe (52) flocculated bacteria with hydrophilic polymers of both ionic and nonionic structure. Tenny and Stumm (40) proposed that biological self flocculation results from the interaction of naturally produced polyelectrolytes which form bridges between individual microbial particles. They felt that it was plausible to interpret bioflocculation in terms of polyelectrolyte interaction. They state:

> Natural polymers, e.g., complex polysaccharides, poly amino acids, are excreted or exposed at surfaces predominantly during the declining growth in the endogenous respiration phases. It is possible that such polymeric substances are always, i.e., under all physiological conditions, excreted; but that under conditions of prolific growth, new surfaces are created faster than surfaces can be covered with such polymers. These polymeric molecules are of sufficient length to form bridges between microbial particles.

Crabtree *et al.* (53) had proposed a mechanism of floc formation based on the polymerization of the fatty acid β-hydroxybutyric acid. Evidence, which will be discussed in the subsequent sections, supports this theory for pure cultures of *Zoogloea* species. In that same year, Kuhn and Starr (54) discussed the clonal morphogenesis of *Lampropedia hyalina*. Their investigations show striking parallelisms with the Crabtree *et al.* (53) study with respect to agglomeration and accumulation of the polymer PHB.

STUDIES OF PURE CULTURES OF *ZOOGLOEA* SPECIES

For the past three years studies with pure cultures of floc forming microorganism *Zoogloea* species have been undertaken at the University of Wisconsin. Procedures as to the isolation, identification, growth, and metabolism of this microorganism appear elsewhere (53, 55).

Pure cultures of *Z. ramigera* I16-M (subsequently to be called *Zoogloea* species) will grow in the dispersed form in an arginine basal medium. The composition of this medium is shown in Table 48).

When glucose is added at the beginning of incubation, flocs are formed as growth proceeds. If glucose is added after the dispersed population has developed, the cells rapidly flocculate within half an hour, and clump completely in four to six hours. Microscopic examination of Sudan-black stained smears revealed that the cells in the flocs had accumulated large amounts of Sudanophilic granules; subsequently identified as poly-beta-hydroxybutyric acid (PHB). Since no capsule was demonstrable, it was assumed that the intracellular accumulation of the polymer was intimately associated with the flocculation of the organism.

Although these studies are wide in scope, one of the early objectives of the study was to investigate the mode of flocculation of this particular microorganism. As a starting point, several of the past speculations, hypotheses, and theories that had been formulated were evaluated, using pure cultures of *Zoogloea* species (53). These studies are briefly outlined below.

TABLE 48

ARGININE BASAL MEDIUM FOR GROWTH OF *ZOOGLOEA RAMIGERA*

Arginine H Cl	0.05%
$Mg\ SO_4 \cdot 7H_2O$	0.02%
K_2HPO_4	0.20%
KH_2PO_4	0.10%
B_{12}	2 mμg/ml
Biotin	2 mμg/ml

Protozoan Theory

The theory that the floc formation is due to the adhesion of bacteria to the mucus surrounding ciliated protozoa was discarded because the isolates were able to grow and flocculate readily in the absence of protozoa.

Inert Matrix Theory and Salt Bridge Theory

Cultures of *Zoogloea* species grown in the arginine basal medium without glucose continued to grow dispersed in the presence of magnesium pyrophosphate or magnesium orthophosphate. In fact, these two compounds were often formed in the basal medium whenever the culture raised the *p*H of the medium to 7.3 or higher. Neither calcium chloride ($CaCl_2 \cdot 2H_2O$, 10^{-2}M) nor ferric chloride ($FeCl_3 \cdot 6H_2O$, 10^{-3}M) had an appreciable effect on the rate of flocculation, the amount and shape of the flocs formed, or the settleability of the flocs. In addition, incorporation of chelating agents, such as EDTA or citric acid, to the washed polymer-containing cells in distilled water did not prevent the cells from flocculating. These experiments indicated that polyvalent metal bridging was not of significant importance in flocculation of *Zoogloea.*

Colloidal Theories

Dispersed cells of *Zoogloea* species grown in the arginine basal media (all ingredients being in true solution) flocculated immediately upon addition of glucose. Addition of colloidal suspensions of precipitated ferric oxide and/or heat-treated gelatin to dispersed cultures (without glucose) did not cause flocculation to occur. This experiment indicated that colloidal particles, either organic or inorganic or both, did not play an important role in agglomeration of *Zoogloea* species in the physiological ranges of *p*H.

Low-Energy Theory

Zoogloea species grown in an arginine basal medium did not flocculate, regardless of the phase of growth. Nonmotile cells (cells made flagella free) also did not flocculate in this medium. When the substrate to bacterial mass ratio was increased by adding glucose to the arginine basal media the cells flocculated rapidly. Hence the addition of an energy source such as glucose to the culture system caused exactly the opposite phenomenon one might expect from the low energy theory; the cells gained in potential energy by converting the glucose to the endogenous metabolite, PHB, and then they flocculated. It is conceivable that the ratio of nutrients to bacterial cells may be important, but the ratio must be qualified with respect to nutrient composition. The experiments with *Zoogloea* species indicate however, that motility is not a significant factor.

Gelatinous Matrix or Slime Theory

The organism *Zoogloea ramigera* has often been described as a floc-forming organism whose cells are imbedded in a "gelatinous matrix" or are encapsulated, but no investigators have as yet demonstrated the presence of capsules of a gelatinous matrix by either staining or chemical analyses. In the present investigations, trypticase soy broth enriched with glucose, fructose, or sucrose was used, because such media are believed to enhance the synthesis of capsules for many organisms. Smears prepared from cultures grown in these media were stained with three well-known capsular stains; also, wet mounts were made with litmus milk and India ink. All methods failed to demonstrate the presence of capsules or slime on the isolates. The question was raised whether *Zoogloea* organisms in the flocs may possess special types of capsules that are unstainable and not demonstrable with methods mentioned above. Thus attempts were made to harvest the capsule material, either by physical means or chemical extraction methods (56, 57). These methods did not demonstrate the presence of the hexosuronic acids which are commonly present in bacterial capsules. On the basis of these experiments it was concluded that capsules were not involved in flocculation of the *Zoogloea* species.

A MECHANISM OF FLOC FORMATION IN *ZOOGLOEA* SPECIES

Evidence supporting the PHB theory of flocculation for *Zoogloea* species is as follows (53):

1. Addition of glucose to carbon "starved" cells induced the synthesis of the polymer, PHB.
2. Accumulation of PHB preceded floc formation.
3. The initial effect of PHB storage was the disruption of the orderly process of cell division (that is, there was incomplete separation of the cell and uneven size of cells).
4. PHB-rich cells demonstrated adhesive properties, and the isolated native polymer, as well as the purified polymer, demonstrated similar properties.
5. Floc formation was prevented by metabolic blocking of PHB synthesis in *Zoogloea* species.
6. Endogenous dissimilation of PHB resulted in deflocculation of *Zoogloea* species. (PHB is a well-known endogenous metabolite.)

On the basis of these findings one may speculate further in proposing a mechanism of floc formation. *Zoogloea* species may flocculate by two general mechanisms:

1. The initiation of the rapid polymer synthesis, which disrupts the orderly biochemical process of cell division, causing cells to divide incompletely, leaving two cells attached.
2. Linkage of individual cells through ester bonds in the polyester-linked beta-hydroxybutyric acid.

In the growth of these microorganisms it was noted that rapid polymer synthesis caused the cells to divide incompletely; thus they remained attached in a regular pattern (Plate 4). These attached cells are capable immediately (or become so upon attaining maturity) of synthesizing the polymer; thus as they produce the polymer they in turn divide incompletely. Such cell divisions are seen to cause the cells in such a culture to occur in short chains, frequently in a regular lateral linkage. This incomplete cell division process is repeated continuously as long as a favorable growth condition is maintained. If such growth is permitted in standing tubes of broth, the cells form lacy tapelike flocs, as is shown in Plate 5.

It is conceivable that if such flocs are formed in a turbulent environment, such as in a mixed or aerated reactor, collisions of the polymer-rich incompletely divided cells and clumps are inevitable (Plates 6, 7). Adhesions of these small cell clumps may be at first aided by mechanical entanglement, but as the cells respire and accumulate more polymer, such cells and native polymer, released to the medium through lysis of the PHB-rich cells, may further enlarge and stabilize the clumps by linkage though ester bonds in the polyester-linked beta-hydroxybutyric acid. PHB initially is formed within the cells themselves, but as the PHB granules grow and fuse together, the cells become enlarged and appear pleomorphic. Under these conditions it is possible that the polymer would inflate the cells to a point where it lies in contact with the cell wall and may, in fact, stretch that wall so that only wall membrane separates the PHB from the outside liquid. The exact nature of this membrane is somewhat controversial,

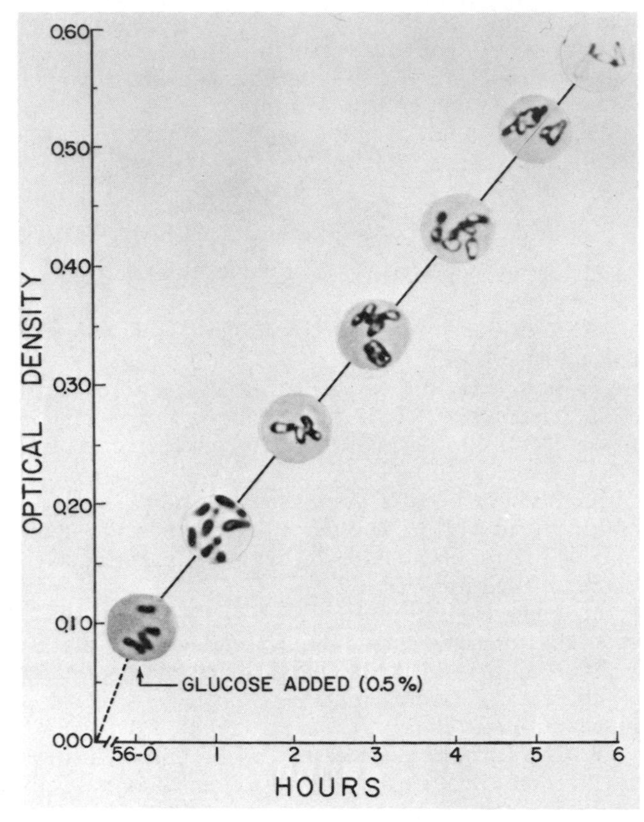

Plate 4. Morphological changes occurring during the synthesis of poly-β-hydroxybutyric acid. Glucose (0.5%) was added after fifty hours, and the incubation continued for six hours. Photomicrographs of cells, at different stages of polymer accumulation are superimposed on optical density curve.

and the exact phenomenon involved in the fusion or adhesion of two protruding membranes, with PHB backing each, is presently under investigation by examining thin sections of polymer-rich flocculating cells in electron-micrographs. That such membranes do exist is apparent but controversial from the present study of thin sections of *Bacillus cereus* (58), *B. megaterium* (59), and *Rhodospirilum rubrum* (60).

Thus the cells which initially aggregate in such ways become the eventual nucleus of larger flocs by linking more cells or cell clumps in the same physiological condition; increasing size will finally be limited by shearing forces of the turbulent fluid in the process. There is little doubt that many heterogeneous nonfloc-forming bacteria, yeast, fungi, and colloids will be entrapped or adsorbed during flocculation. In experiments with pure cultures of *Zoogloea* species, *Serratia marcesens*, and *S. faecalis* it was shown that nonfloc-forming organisms were entrapped by the flocs and that such heterogeneous flocs continue to grow synergistically.

Some of the factors affecting floc formation by the organism have been briefly investigated. The organism flocculated equally as well with arginine as a source of nitrogen as with a number of ammonium salts. However, it was observed that the concentration of nitrogen added was as significant as glucose in controlling the rapid accumulation of PHB as well as the flocculation. When the C/N ratio[1] exceeded 30:1 or was less than 10:1, it caused a deleterious effect on the settling

[1] C/N ratios were calculated based on the ratio of available carbon to available nitrogen for *Zoogloea*.

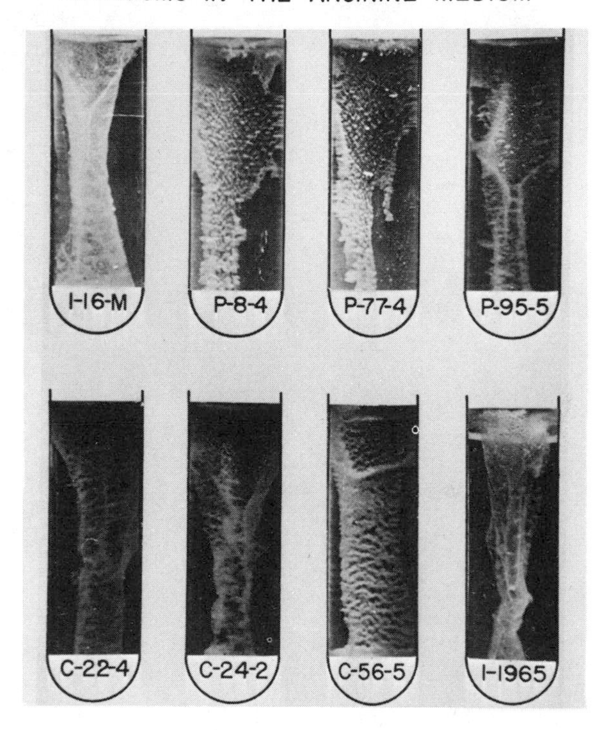

Plate 5. Photographs of the characteristic netted or lacy, tapelike growth by the isolates in standing broth medium. (The coded numbers represent particular isolates.)

characteristics of the flow; a ratio of 20:1 was the best of those tried. The effects of hydrogen ion concentration on flocculation indicated that a favorable range was between 6.0 and 8.5, with optimum near 7.0.

Rapid flocculation and production of "good" settleable flocs were produced most effectively in dilute medium (range of organics as found in sewage) so as to avoid excessive accumulation of PHB, which might cause the death of the cells. Again, although not conclusively proven, it appears as though cells of *Zoogloea* species continually accumulate the polymer, and apparently lack a feedback repressor for PHB synthesis. There was a striking reduction in the number of viable cells noted during the accumulation of polymer. For example, viable cell counts made immediately after the addition of glucose to dispersed cells were approximately 1.1×10^9 cells per milliliter, but the viable counts made at the end of the incubation (6 hours) were reduced to 7×10^7 cells per milliliter. Thus the massive accumulation of the polymer caused reduction in viable cells by more than 97 percent. It is speculated therefore that the cells in the internal portions of the flocs are inactive, whereas the cells near the periphery are highly active, utilizing substate and accumulating polymer.

One additional point of interest for this specific organism is in regard to its ability to survive in a heterogeneous culture, such as one would obtain in an activated sludge plant. Although typical municipal sewage contains well-balanced nutrients for growth of many heterogeneous microorganisms, the concentration is usually low. Thus a cell which can rapidly accumulate a carbon reserve would compete and survive to advantage. That the reserve should be insoluble in the cell (and thus nontoxic if in large quantities) is also an advantage. Under such an environment it is probable that some cells continue to compete for nutrient and

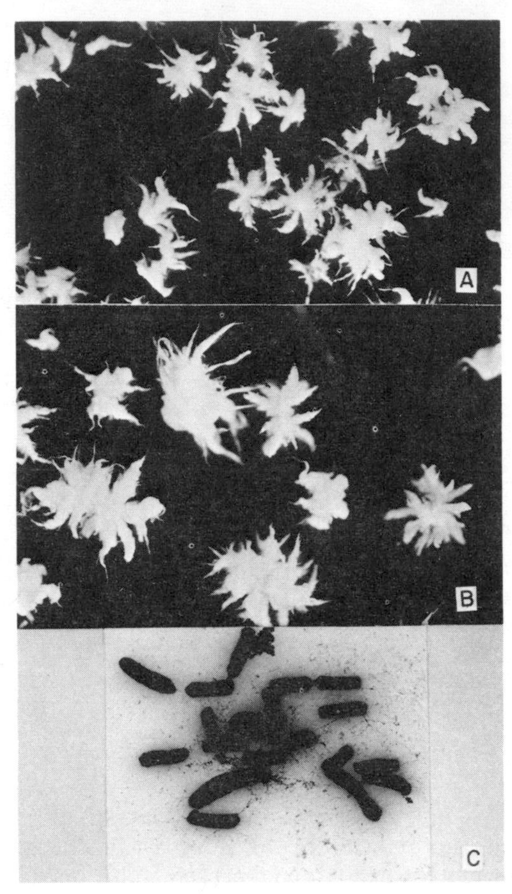

Plate 6. (A) Photographs of flocs of I-16M embedded in 0.2 percent agar. Magnification—×30. (B) Photographs of floc of P-95-5 embedded in 0.2 percent agar. Magnification—×30. (C) Electron micrograph of actively dividing cells of 1-16-M. Obtained from surface of standing broth cultures. Magnification—×7, 200×.

accumulate PHB; as well as serve as a nucleus of flocs. Such cells in the sludge held in the secondary settling tanks would have the chance to dissimilate the polymer to maintain their cellular integrity, while bacteria without such reserve may die off rapidly. The flocs settle out, coalesce, and are recycled again into the fresh nutrient environment of the incoming sewage; the process then repeats. Hence the organism with the ability to convert externally available nutrients or synthesis of PHB under the aerobic conditions and dissimilated under either aerobic or anerobic conditions has great advantage over other organisms which do not.

ACKNOWLEDGMENTS

A portion of the work reported in this paper was supported by the Division of Water Supply and Water Pollution Control through the Public Health Service Grant WP 00061.

SYMBOLS USED

a = sphere radius
A_{ik} = specific flocculation rate
$(A_{jk})_m$ = average collision constant
$(A_{jk})_s$ = specific collision constant
B_i = disruption constant

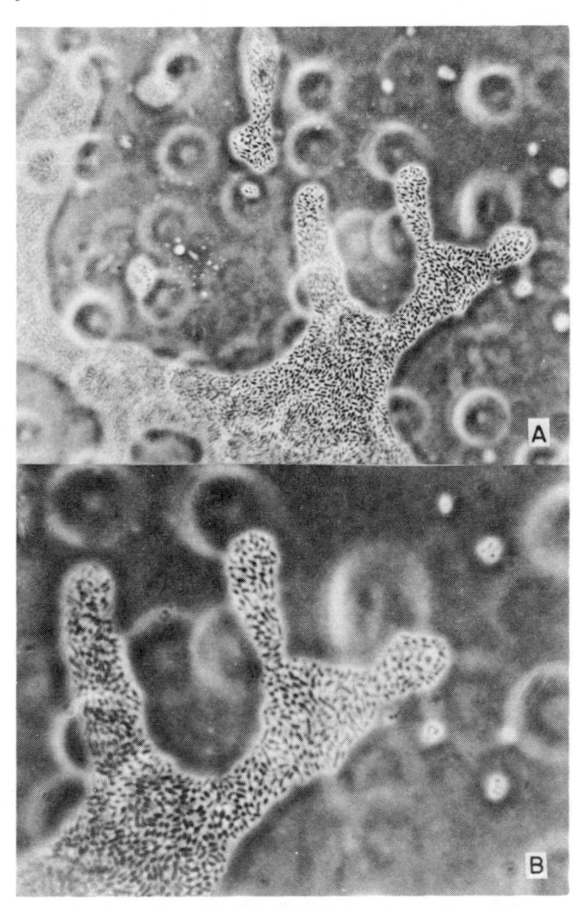

Plate 7. (A) Photograph of wet mount of I-16M showing typical "fingerlike" projections and several detached projections. Magnification—×980, Enlarged 1.5×. (B) Photograph of wet mount of I-16M showing "fingerlike" projections. Magnification—×980, Enlarged 3.0×.

C_x = rate of formation of x-aggregates by coalescence
D_i = effective Brownian diffusivity of i-aggregates
D_x = rate of formation of x-aggregates by disruption
E_v = rate of dissipation of mechanical energy per unit volume
$\bar{F}$ = force
k_G = fractional rate of bacterial replication
$(k_G)_x$ = average value of k_G in an x-aggregate
κ = Boltzmann constant
l_i = "mean free path" (stopping distance) of i-aggregates
m = particle mass
N_{ij} = rate of collisions between aggregates of j particles and a collector of i particles
n_x = number concentration of x-aggregates
r = position coordinate
$\bar{r}$ = position vector
R_i = radius of an aggregate containing i primary particles
R_x = rate of formation of x-aggregates by replication
t = time
T = absolute temperature
$\bar{T}$ = torque
U = relative velocity of particle and collector

$\bar{U}$ = mean thermal velocity
$\bar{V}_f$ = fluid velocity
$\bar{V}_s$ = sphere velocity
x = number of primary particles in an aggregate
α = ratio of particle radii
β_{jk} = probability of a j-k collision being effective
γ_{ij} = ratio of dispersive to adhesive forces
Γ = fluid shear rate
ϵ = rate of dissipation of mechanical energy per unit mass
μ = viscosity
ξ_i = single-collision efficiency of an i-aggregate
ρ = density
τ = relaxation time
ϕ = frequency distribution of numbers of organisms relative to aggregate size
Φ_{ij} = rate of collision between i and j particles
ν = kinematic viscosity
$\bar{\delta}_x$ = unit vector in x-direction

REFERENCES

(1) Randolph, A. D. "A Population Balance for Countable Entities," *Can. J. Chem. Engr.*, *42*, 280–281 (1964).
(2) Fredrickson, A. G., and H. M. Tsuchiya. "Continuous Propagation of Microorganisms," *Amer. Inst. Chem. Engr. J.*, *9*, 459 (1963).
(3) Joly, M. "Agrégation Provoquée par l'Écoulement dans les solutions de Macromolecules d'Origine Biologique," *Symposium on Bioheology*, edited by A. L. Copley. New York: John Inley and Sons (1965).
(4) Blatz, P. V., and A. V. Tobolsky. "Notes on the Kinetics of Systems Manifesting Simultaneous Polymerization-Depolymerization Phenomena," *J. Phys. Chem.*, *49*, 77 (1945).
(5) Joly, M., and Barbu. "The Globular-Fibrous Protein Transformation," *Disc. Far. Soc.*, *13*, 77 (1953).
(6) von Smoluchowski, M. "Drei Vortrage uber Diffusion, Brownsche Nikejykarbewegybg ybd Jiagykatuib vib Jikkiudteukegebn," *Z. Phys. Chem.*, *92*, 144 (1917).
(7) von Smoluchowski, M. "Versuch einer mathematischen Theorie der Koagulationskinetick kolloider Losungen," *Z. Phys. Chem.*, *92*, 129 (1917).
(8) Fuchs, N. A. *The Mechanics of Aerosols*. New York: MacMillan Publishing Company (1964).
(9) Einstein, A. *Investigations on the Theory of the Brownian Movement*. New York: Dover (1956).
(10) Carslaw, H. S., and J. C. Jaeger. *Conduction of Heat in Solids*. Second Ed. Oxford: Oxford University Press (1959).
(11) Pshenai, S.-Severin. "Raspredelenie Chastits Dispersnoi Po Raėmeram V Protsesse Koaguliatsii," *Dokl. Akad. Nank SSR*, *94*, 865 (1954).
(12) Todes, O. *Symposium on Problems of Kinetics and Catalysts*, ONTI, Moscow-Leningrad, 7, 137 (1949).
(13) Levich, V. G. *Physiochemical Hydrodynamics*. Englewood Cliffs, N.J.: Prentice-Hall, Inc. (1962).
(14) Levich, V. G. "Teoriia Koaguliatsii, Kolloidov V Turbulentom Potoke Zhidkosti," *Dokl. Akad. Nauk. SSSR*, *99*, 809 (1954).
(15) Tunitskii, N. *Zh. fiz, khim.*, *20*, 1136 (1946).
(16) Obukhov, A. M., and A. M. Yaglou. "Mikrostruktura Turbulentnogo Potoka," *Prikl. mat. melch.*, *15*, 1 (1951).
(17) Kuhn, W. "Uber Teilchenform und Teilchengrösse aus Viscosität und Stromungsdoppelbrechung" and "Dehnungsdoppelbrechung von Kolloiden in Lösung," *Z. Phys. Chemie A.*, *161*, 1, 427 (1932).

(18) Burgers, J. M. "Second Report on Viscosity and Plasticity," *Kon. Ned. Akad. Wet* (Eerste Sectie) *DL XVI.* Amsterdam: North Holland Pub. Co. (1938).
(19) Happel, J., and H. Brenner. *Low Reynolds Number Hydrodynamics.* New York: Prentice-Hall (1965).
(20) Mason, S. G., and W. Bartok. "The Behavior of Suspended Particles in Laminar Shear," *Rheology of Disperse Systems,* edited by C. C. Mill. London: Pergammon Press (1959).
(21) Broersma, S. "Viscous Force Constant for a Closed Cylinder," *J. Chem. Phys., 32,* 1632 (1960).
(22) Buswell, A. M., and H. L. Long. "Microbiology and Theory of Activated Sludge," *J. Amer. Water Works Assoc., 10,* 309 (1923).
(23) Cavel, L. "Sur l'adsorption des matières colloidales pour les 'boues actives'" *Ref. d' Hyg. et Med. Prev., 53,* 179 (1931).
(24) Theriault, E. J., and P. D. McNamee. "Adsorption by Activated Sludge," *Ind. Engr. Chem., 28,* 29 (1936).
(25) Heukelekian, H., and H. B. Schulhoff. "Studies on the Clarification Stage of Activated Sludge Process: IV. Preliminary Notes on the Clarifying Organisms in Activated Sludge," *Sewage Works J., 10,* 43 (1938).
(26) White, P. B. "On the Relation of the Alcohol Soluble Constituents of Bacteria to Their Spontaneous Agglutination," *J. Pathol, Bacteriol., 30,* 113 (1927).
(27) Edwards, G. P. "A Review of Activated Sludge Theory," *Sewage Works J., 7,* 17 (1935).
(28) Dienert, F. "Clarification of Sewage by Bacteria," *Comp. Pend. Acad. Sci., 200,* 1253 (1935).
(29) McKinney, R. E. "Biological Flocculation," *Biological Treatment of Sewage and Industrial Waste,* edited by Brother J. McCabe and W. W. Eckenfelder. New York: Reinhold (1956).
(30) McKinney, R. E., and R. G. Weichlein. "Isolation of Floc-Producing Bacteria from Activated Sludge," *Appl. Microbiol., 1,* 259 (1953).
(31) Dunbar, Dr. (translated by H. T. Calvert). *Principles of Sewage Treatment.* London: Charles Griffin and Co., Ltd. (1908).
(32) Biltz and Krohnke. "Veber organische colloide aus Stradtischen Abwasser und Deren Zustand saffinitat," *Ber., 37,* 1745 (1904).
(33) De Kruif, P. H. "Change of Acid Agglutination Optimum as Index of Bacterial Mutation," *J. Gen. Physiol., 4,* 347 (1922).
(34) Eggerth, A. H., and M. Bellows. "The Flocculation of Bacteria by Proteins," *J. Gen. Physiol., 4,* 669 (1922).
(35) Webster, L. T. "The Acid Agglutination of Mixtures of Oppositely Charged Bacterial Cells," *J. Gen. Physiol., 7,* 513 (1924).
(36) Lamanna, C., and M. F. Mallette. *Basic Bacteriology—Its Biological and Chemical Background.* 2nd ed. Baltimore: The Williams and Wilkens Co. (1959).
(37) Baly, E. C. C. "The Mechanism of the Activated Sludge Process of Sewage Disposal," *J. Soc. Chem. Ind., 50,* 22T (1931).
(38) McKinney, R. E., and M. P. Harwood. "Fundamental Approach to the Activated Sludge Process. I. Floc Producing Bacteria," *Sewage Ind. Waste, 24,* 117 (1952).
(39) Joffe, E. W., and S. Mudd. "A Paradoxical Relation between Zeta Potential and Suspension Stability in S and R Variants of Intestinal Bacteria," *J. Gen. Physiol., 18,* 599 (1934).
(40) Tenney, M. W., and W. Stumm. "Chemical Flocculation of Microorganisms in Biological Waste Treatment," 19th Purdue Ind. Waste Conf., 1963. *J. Water Poll. Cont. Fed., 37,* 1370 (1965).
(41) Hardin, G. "Flocculation of Bacteria by Protozoa," *Nature, 151,* 642 (1943).
(42) Watson, J. W. "Mechanism of Bacterial Flocculation Caused by Protozoa," *Nature, 155,* 271 (1945).
(43) Pillai, S. C., T. K. Wadhwani, M. I. Burbaxani, and P. V. R. Subrahamanyan. "Relative Efficiency of Bacteria and Protozoa in the Flocculation and Oxidation of Organic Matter Suspended in Water," *Cur. Sci., 16,* 340 (1947).

(44) McKinney, R. E., and A. Gram. "Protozoa and Activated Sludge," *Sewage Ind. Wastes, 28,* 1219 (1956).
(45) Curds, C. R. "The Flocculation of Suspended Matter by *Paramecium caudatum,*" *J. Gen. Microbiol., 33,* 357 (1963).
(46) Butterfield, C. T. "Studies of Sewage Purification: A Zoogloea-Forming Bacterium Isolated from Activated Sludge," *U. S. Public Health Report, 50,* 671 (1935).
(47) Whitehead, H. C., and F. R. O'Shaughnessy. "Improving the Efficiency of Activated Sludge," *Surveyor, 89,* 407 (1936).
(48) Hartmann, L. "Activated Sludge Floc Composition," *Water Sewage Works, 110,* 262 (1963).
(49) Gils, H. W. *Bacteriology of Activated Sludge.* Research Institute for Public Health Engineering, TNO, Holland, Report 32 (1964).
(50) Mill, P. J. "The Nature of the Interactions between Flocculant Cells in the Flocculation of *Saccharomyces cervisiae,*" *J. Gen. Microbiol., 35,* 61 (1964).
(51) Katchalsky, A. "Polyelectrolytes," *Endeavour, 12,* 90 (1953).
(52) Hodge, H. M., and S. N. Metcalfe, Jr. "Flocculation of Bacteria by Hydrophilic Colloids," *J. Bacteriol., 75,* 485 (1958).
(53) Crabtree, K., W. C. Boyle, E. McCoy, and G. A. Rohlich. "A Mechanism of Floc Formation by *Zoogloea ramigera,*" *J. Water Poll. Cont. Fed., 38,* 1968-1980 (1966).
(54) Kuhn, Daisy A., and M. P. Starr. "Clonal Morphogenesis of *Lampropedia hyalina,*" *Archiv. fur Microbiologie, 52,* 360 (1965).
(55) Crabtree, K. "Morphological and Biochemical Studies of *Zoogloea ramigera* Species in Pure Culture." Ph.D. Thesis, University of Wisconsin (1965).
(56) Guex-Holzer and J. Tomscik. "The Isolation and Chemical Nature of Capsular and Cell Wall Haptens in a *Bacillus* Species," *J. Gen. Microbiol., 14,* 14 (1956).
(57) Juni, E., and G. A. Heym. "Pathways for Biosynthesis of a Bacterial Capsular Polysaccharide. IV. Capsular Resynthesis by Decapsulated Resting-Cell Suspensions," *J. Bact., 87,* 461 (1964).
(58) Lundgren, D. G., R. M. Pfister, and J. M. Merrick. "Structure of Poly-Beta, Hydroxybutryric Acid (PHB) Granules," *J. Gen. Microbiol., 34,* 441 (1964).
(59) Pfister, R. M., and D. G. Lundgren. "Electron Microscopy of Poly Ribosome within *Bacillus cereus,*" *J. Bacteriol., 88,* 1119 (1964).
(60) Boatman, E. S. "Observations on the Fine Structure of Spheroplasts of *Rhodospirillum rubium, J. Cell Biol., 20,* 297 (1964).

INDUSTRIAL WASTE TREATMENT IN AERATED LAGOONS

John L. Mancini and Edwin L. Barnhart
Hydroscience, Inc., Leonia, New Jersey

INTRODUCTION

The design of biological treatment systems for individual wastes presents the engineer with the problem of selecting an economical and properly sized treatment system. Among the alternatives are activated sludge, conventional or high rate, extended aeration with associated aerobic digestion of sludge, aerated lagoons, and trickling filters. In many, if not most, instances it is desirable to conduct laboratory experiments and perhaps pilot scale studies to select the most effective and economical treatment system and to properly size the facilities.

Collection of data, regardless of scale, should be geared toward the establishment of a response system which will allow economic comparisons of alternative methods for obtaining the desired or required degree of treatment. If data collection is used exclusively as a tool for developing particular design criteria for a preselected system, it is often difficult or impossible to evaluate alternate treatment schemes. With the latter approach to data collection, the selected system generally can be designed to operate satisfactorily. The unanswerable question is the relative economics of the final system.

On the other hand, judgment must be employed to eliminate systems which are not applicable to the specific waste characteristics. Development of economical industrial waste designs requires a balance between experienced judgment, practical know-how, and experimental techniques which minimize the necessity for prejudging.

The purpose of this paper is to suggest a laboratory method which can be employed to evaluate, compare, and design activated sludge and aerated lagoon treatment systems from a single set of experimental data.

ATTRIBUTES OF AERATED LAGOONS

Biological waste treatment in the simplest form essentially consists of controlling environmental factors to enable a mixed culture of microorganisms to use the organic matter in the waste as a food source for synthesis and energy. In aerobic systems, such as activated sludge and aerated lagoons, organisms are suspended in a liquid medium with the waste to be treated. The culture is aerobic, requiring dissolved oxygen for respiration. Sufficient time is allowed for the organisms to utilize the organics as a food source. In activated sludge treatment, the mixture of treated wastewater and organisms is separated. The treated waste is discharged and the organisms are returned to the aeration tank for mixing with incoming waste. In aerated lagoons, organisms are wasted in the effluent at a rate proportional to the gross synthesis rate.

An essential difference between activated sludge and aerated lagoon systems is the degree of environmental control built into the system. Attempts are made in the activated sludge system to control the microorganism population by recycling of sludge. A major benefit obtained from sludge separation in the activated sludge or aerated lagoon system is the removal from the effluent of the oxygen demand associated with the settled sludge.

Aerated lagoon treatment systems can be designed to meet one of two basic objectives. In the first instance, they can be designed at high loading rates, providing an extremely economical means of converting soluble BOD to suspended BOD. Some stabilization of BOD is obtained from this system design even without sludge recirculation. In the second instance, aerated lagoons can be designed as low-rate systems to provide high overall BOD removals with a resultant reduction in solids.

High-rate aerobic lagoon systems provide a potentially economical solution when the effluent requirements are in the order of hundreds of parts per million, such as for pretreatment when discharging to a municipal treatment facility. Land requirements for this system are minimized, required operating time and skill are minimal, and the resulting effluent is generally treatable in a well-designed municipal plant. An additional advantage is associated with possible future conversion to activated sludge.

The basic advantages to aerated lagoon systems are:

1. Relatively low operating and capital costs
2. Low operating skill requirements
3. A high-quality effluent obtained with solids separation
4. At low loading rates, biological solids relatively stable
5. Resistance to upsets
6. Ability to treat high-strength wastes
7. Buffering capacity when *p*H is a problem
8. Relatively large heat transfer when high temperature wastes are to be treated

The basic disadvantages of aerated lagoons are:

1. Effluent quality without solids separation in the order of hundreds of mg/l
2. At high loadings solids separation possibly a significant problem
3. System temperature dependent with reductions in removals at low temperatures
4. Land area requirements normally greater than for activated sludge systems
5. Once upset by toxicity the lagoon possibly requires extended operating periods for complete recovery.

DATA COLLECTION

The basic objective of data collection should be to provide information from which a response function can be developed. The response function is then employed to evaluate multiple alternatives for their ability to answer specific long-term and short-term treatment needs and to provide information for the evaluation of treatment economics.

Laboratory evaluations should be the first step in a program of data collection. The degree of effort expended in the data collection program on laboratory and/or pilot plant work is contingent on the magnitude of the particular problem and the time available for solution.

Laboratory or pilot plant data can be evaluated to determine:

1. The response function for the waste under consideration
2. The ranges for the coefficients and system constants
3. Operating problems, such as: (a) toxicity effects, (b) sludge settling and separation problems, (c) unstable operating patterns when considering waste samples obtained at different times from the same waste discharge, (d) temperature effects, and (e) foaming problems.

System Response Function

The rates of BOD removal in activated sludge or aerated lagoon systems are related to the quantity of microorganisms available and the quantity of BOD present. Mathematically this is expressed as

$$\frac{ds}{dt} = K_2 X_a S \qquad (1)$$

where:

$\frac{ds}{dt}$ = rate of change of BOD with respect to time

S = BOD remaining
X_a = quantity of microorganisms present
K_2 = BOD removal rate (first-order kinetics)

Employing Equation 1 in a material balance around a completely mixed aerated lagoon or activated sludge system results in Equation 2:

$$\frac{S_a - S_e}{X_a t} = K_2 S \qquad (2)$$

S in Equations 1 and 2 is the BOD remaining. The BOD remaining in a completely mixed activated sludge or aerated lagoon system is equal to the effluent BOD concentration. Equation 2 becomes

$$\frac{S_a - S_e}{X_a t} = K_2 S_e \qquad (3)$$

The above development is based on the assumption of first-order kinetics. Several investigators have observed zero- and second-order removal rates for various substrates. Comparable mathematization can be developed for these reaction phenomena. This discussion will be limited to the assumption of first-order kinetics. The designer is primarily interested in obtaining a *reliable* response function for a system which will enable him to evaluate multiple alternatives. The reaction rate to be used in developing a response function can be governed by the collected data.

In Equation 3 the quantity S_e can be considered as the filtered BOD. If a particular waste has BOD associated with influent solids, then Equation 3 becomes

$$\frac{S_a - S_e}{X_a t} = \frac{\Delta \text{BOD}}{X_a t} = K_2 S_e + Z \qquad (4)$$

In this instance an apparent BOD removal occurs when the filtered influent BOD is zero. The BOD associated with the influent solids is not measured in the filtered effluent.

The change in solids can be obtained employing Equation 5.

$$\Delta SS = a \Delta \text{BOD} - Y X_a \qquad (5)$$

where:

ΔSS = change in solids
a = percent of removed BOD which is converted to solids
Y = percent of sludge under aeration which is oxidized
ΔBOD = removed BOD
X_a = solids under aeration

Similarly, the oxygen required for an aerated lagoon or activated sludge system is

$$\#O_2/\text{day} = Y'\Delta BOD + b'\, X_a \tag{6}$$

where:

$\#O_2$/day = total oxygen required
Y' = percentage of the removed BOD oxidized
$b'X_a$ = oxygen required to oxidize the sludge
ΔBOD = removed BOD

Data collection is aimed at evaluating the coefficients and the constants in Equations 4, 5, and 6. With this information, the designer can size activated sludge or aerated lagoon systems.

Specific Study Results and Numerical Example

The response equations resulting from the example laboratory study are:

BOD Removal:

$$\frac{S_a - S_e}{X_a\, t} = 0.034\, S_e + 0.10 \tag{7}$$

COD Removal:

$$\frac{S_a(\text{COD}) - S_e\,(\text{COD})}{X_a\, t} = 0.0276\, S_e\,(\text{COD}) + 1.1 \tag{8}$$

Solids Production:

Activated Sludge

$$\Delta SS\#/\text{day} = 1.05\#\ \text{BOD removed/day} - 0.25\# X_a \tag{9}$$

Aerated Lagoon

From a mass balance

$$X_a = \frac{Z + 1.05\, S_a - S_e}{(1 + 0.25t)} \tag{10}$$

Oxygen Requirements:

$$\#O_2/\text{day} = 0.662\#\ \text{BOD removed/day} + 0.355\#\ \text{Solids} \tag{11}$$

Calculations are presented in the Appendix to illustrate that the BOD and COD response functions provide comparable results when the measured BOD/COD relationship for influent and effluent are used. Figure 128 illustrates the two relationships obtained.

The substantial change in BOD/COD relationship before and after treatment tends to indicate a significant reduction in the rate of BOD exertion, which should be recognized in stream and estuary assimilation studies.

It should be noted that theoretically Equation 9 suggests that ΔSS can be made to equal zero. In practice, total oxidation of the organic solids formed cannot be obtained. Generally 10–25 percent of the removed BOD is retained as nonoxidizable organic solids. For the particular waste tested, there are indications that the nonoxidizable solids were as high as 30 percent of the BOD removed.

Correlations of the results of the laboratory study yielded a response function. These mathematical formulations were employed to size biological treatment facilities for the waste studied. Two examples are presented below for designing an aerated lagoon system and activated sludge treatment system.

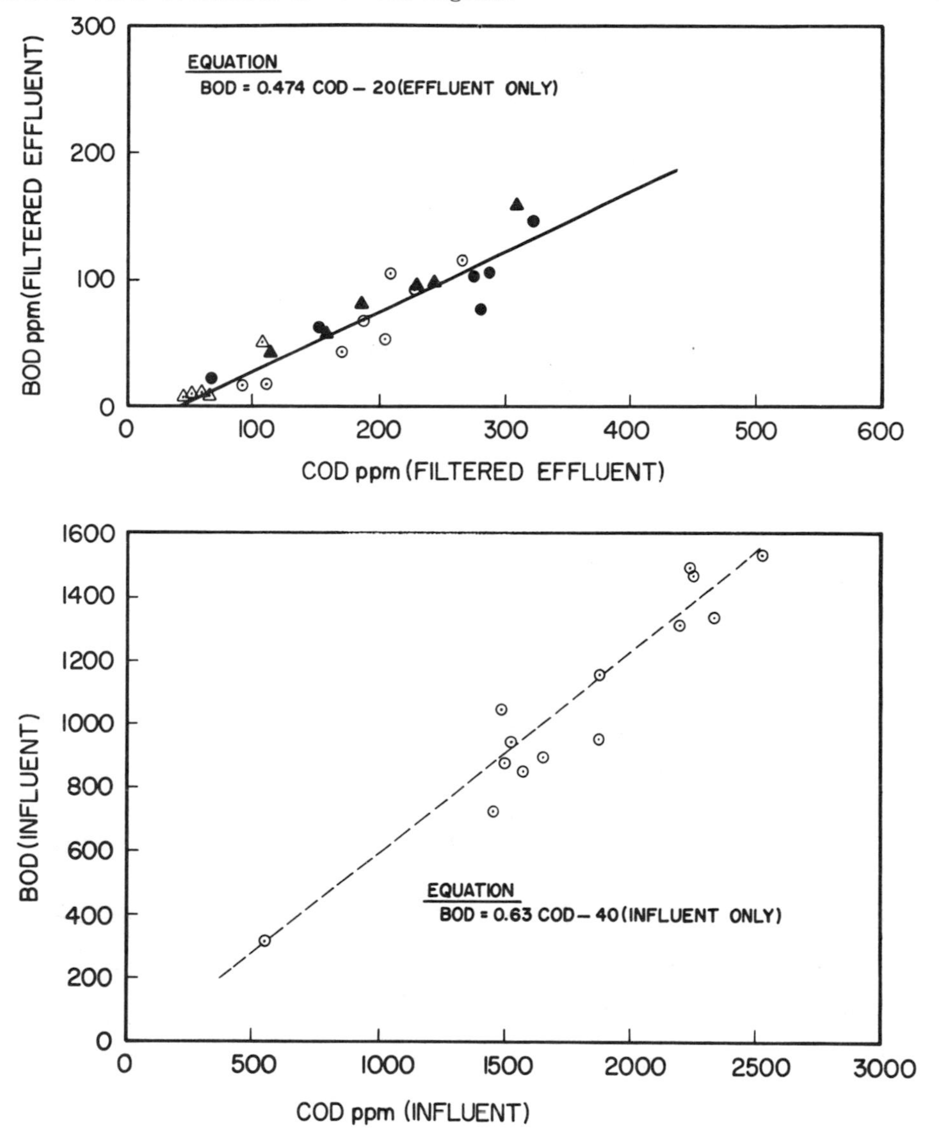

Figure 128. COD ppm (filtered effluent); COD ppm (influent).

1. *Design Example—Aerated Lagoon*

Assumptions: S_a = 750 mg/l (influent BOD)
Detention in aerated lagoon = 1 day
Flow = 0.5 MGD
No significant influent solids

Equilibrium Solids

$$X_a = \frac{Z + 1.05\,(S_a' - S_e)}{(1 + 0.25t)}$$

Assume:

Z = zero
S_e = 35 mg/l

$$X_a = \frac{1.05\,(750 - 35)}{(1 + 0.25 \times 1)} = \frac{1.05 \times 715}{1.25}$$

X_a = 600 mg/l

BOD (Filtered Effluent)

$$S_e = \frac{S_a - 0.10\,X_a \cdot t}{0.034\,X_a \cdot t + 1}$$

$$S_e = \frac{750 - 0.1 \times 600 \times 1}{0.034 \times 600 \times 1 + 1} = \frac{750 - 60}{1 + 20.4}$$

$$S_e = \frac{690}{21.4} = 32.2 \text{ mg/l}$$

Check assumption for S_e in solids concentration

32.2 = 35

Effluent BOD

BOD = Soluble + Suspended
BOD = 32.2 + 600 × 0.265 = 32.2 + 159 = 191 mg/l

Oxygen Requirements:

O_2/day = 0.62 (S_a - S_e) + 0.355# MLVSS
O_2/day = 0.62 (750 - 32) × 0.5 × 8.34 + 0.355 × 0.5 × 600 × 8.34
O_2/day = 1,860 + 836 = 2,696 # O_2/day
BOD removed = 559 × 0.5 × 8.34 = 2,330 # BOD_5/day

$$\frac{\#\text{ Oxygen}}{\#\text{ BOD}_5\text{(removed)}} = \frac{2,696}{2,330} = 1.15$$

2. *Design Example—Activated Sludge*

Assumptions: S_a = 750 mg/l (influent BOD)
Detention time = 12 hours
Flow = 0.5 MGD
X_a + 2,000 mg/l
Influent solids are insignificant
Effluent solids are 200 mg/l

Filtered Effluent BOD

$$S_e = \frac{S_a - 0.1\,X_a \cdot t}{0.034\,X_a \cdot t + 1}$$

$$S_e = \frac{750 - 0.1 \times 2,000 \times 0.5}{34 + 1} = \frac{750 - 100}{35}$$

$$S_e = \frac{650}{35} = 18.6 \text{ mg/l}$$

Effluent BOD

BOD = Soluble + Suspended
= 18.6 + 200 × 0.29 = 18.6 + 58 = 76.6 mg/l

Solids Requiring Disposal

#/day SS = 1.05 # BOD_5 removed/day - 0.25 # aeration solids
ΔSS = 1.05 × (750 - 18) × 8.34 × 0.5 - (0.25 × 8.34 × 0.5 × 0.5 × 2,000)
ΔSS = 2,160 #/day
Waste 200 mg/l in the effluent = 200 × 8.34 × 0.5 = 834 #/day
Solids requiring disposal = 2,160 - 834 = 1,326 #/day

Oxygen Requirements

O_2/day = 0.62 (S_a - S_e) 8.34 × 0.5 + 0.355 # MLVSS
= 0.62 (750 - 76.6) 8.34 × 0.5 + 0.355 × 8.34 × 2,000 × 0.5 × 0.5
= 1,740 + 1,480 = 3,220#/day
Lost in wasted solids = 1,326 × 0.29 = 384 # BOD
Not required because of solids wastening 384 × 0.62 = 238 # O_2
Total oxygen required = 3,220 - 238 = 2,982 #/day

$$\# O_2/\# BOD_{5\,(removed)} = \frac{2,982}{2,800} = 1.07$$

Figures 129–132 present the laboratory results, the prediction line, and the operating results from a prototype aerated lagoon system. There is reasonably

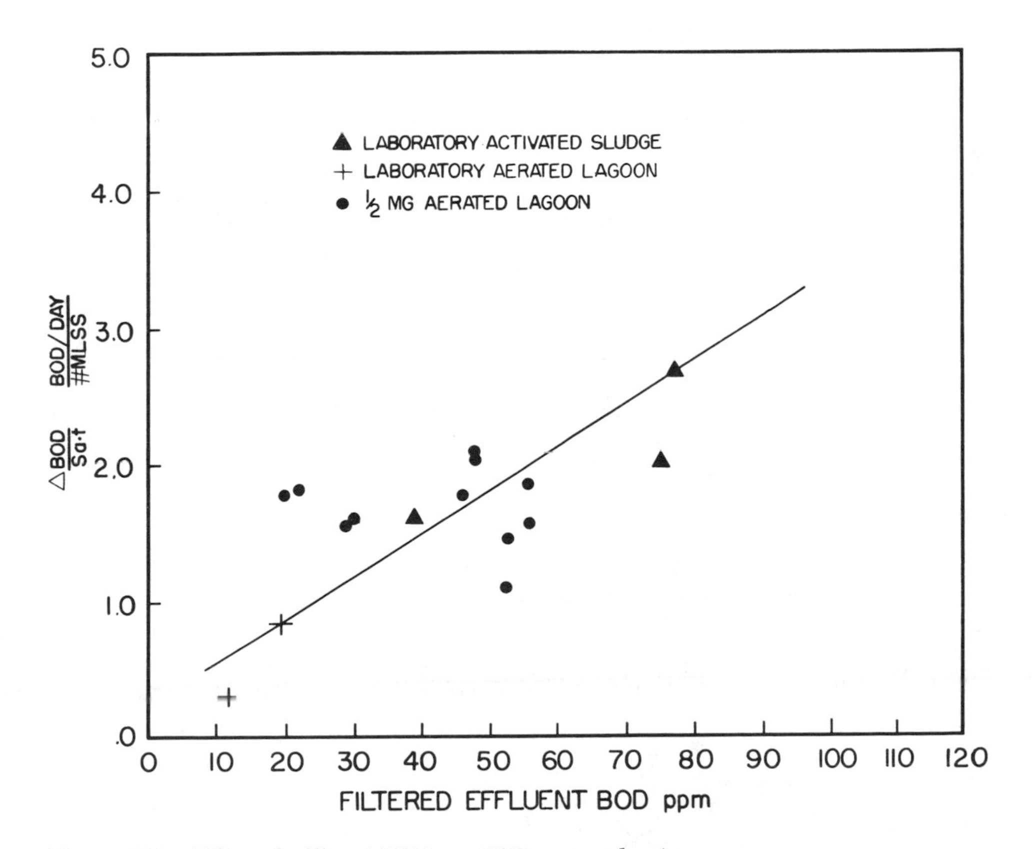

Figure 129. Filtered effluent BOD vs. BOD removal rate.

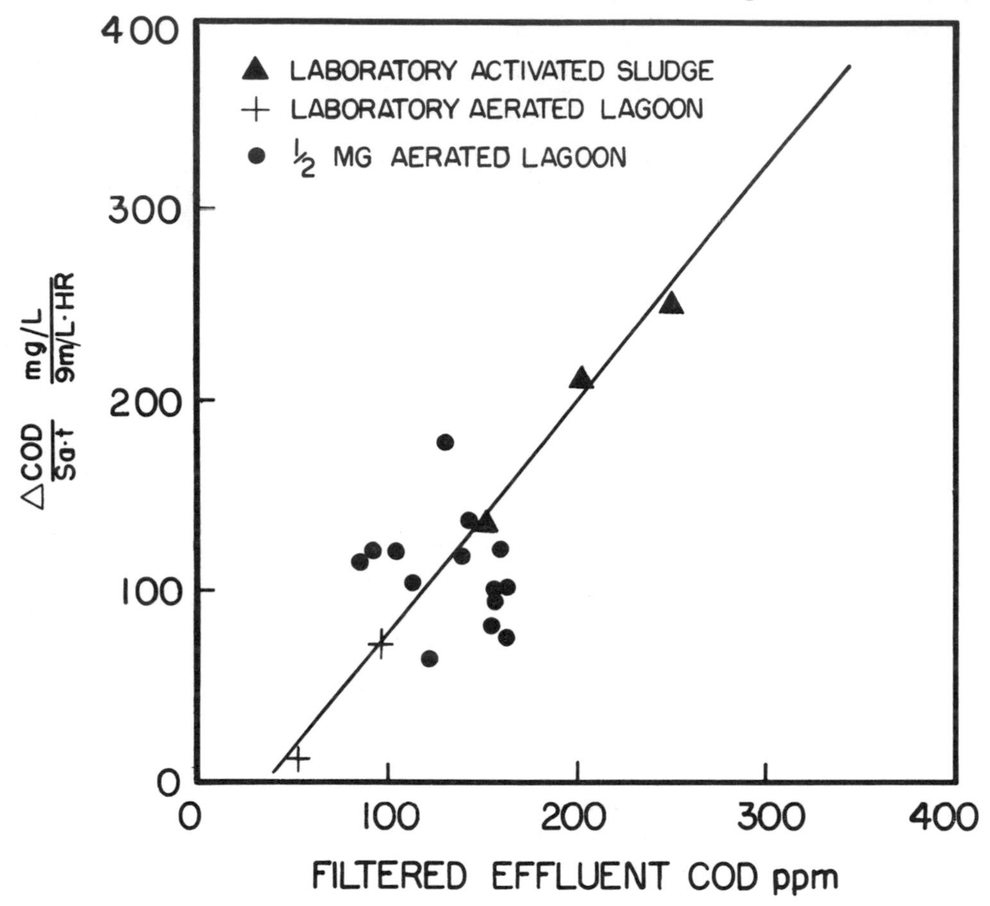

Figure 130. Filtered effluent COD vs. COD removal rate.

good agreement between the predicted and the observed operating results. The laboratory units were operated with an influent BOD of 1,200 mg/l. The retention periods in the aerated lagoon were two and five days, and in the activated sludge unit four, six, and nine hours. The observed data were obtained with an influent BOD averaging 2,000 mg/l from a one-day aerated lagoon system.

Temperature in Aerated Lagoons

The problem of aerated lagoon operation under extreme temperature conditions should be evaluated. The initial problem is to estimate the lagoon temperature. Equation 12 can be employed:

$$(T_i - T_w) = \frac{(T_w - T_a) f A}{Q} \tag{12}$$

where:

T_i = influent waste temperature
T_w = lagoon water temperature
T_a = air temperature
A = lagoon surface area (ft^2)

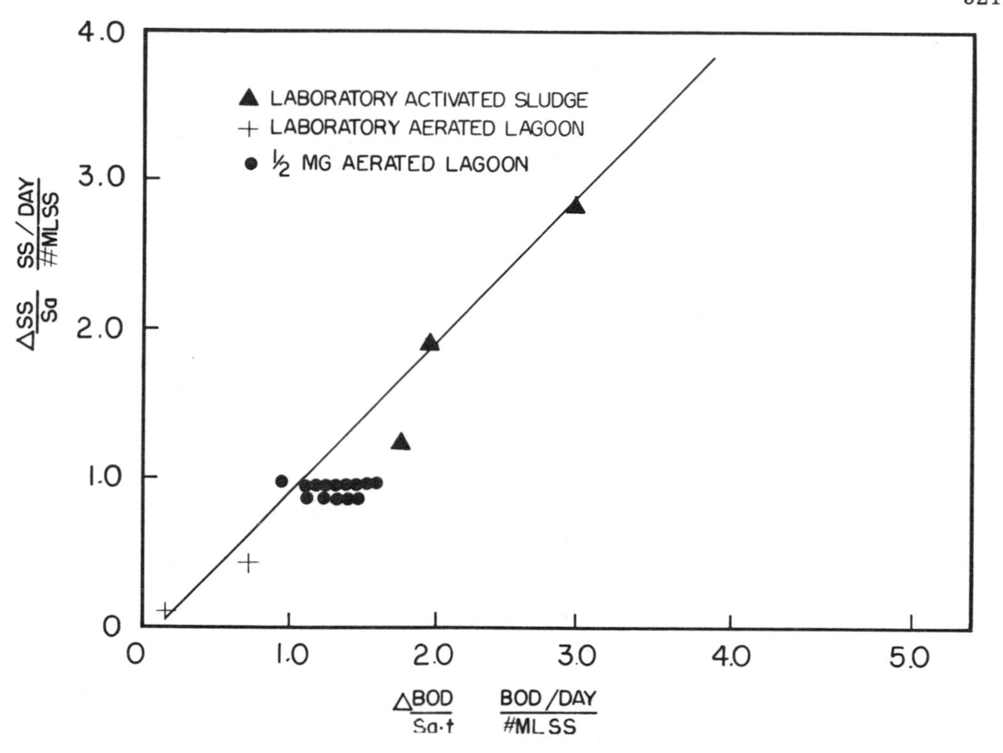

Figure 131. Suspended solids production as a function of BOD removal.

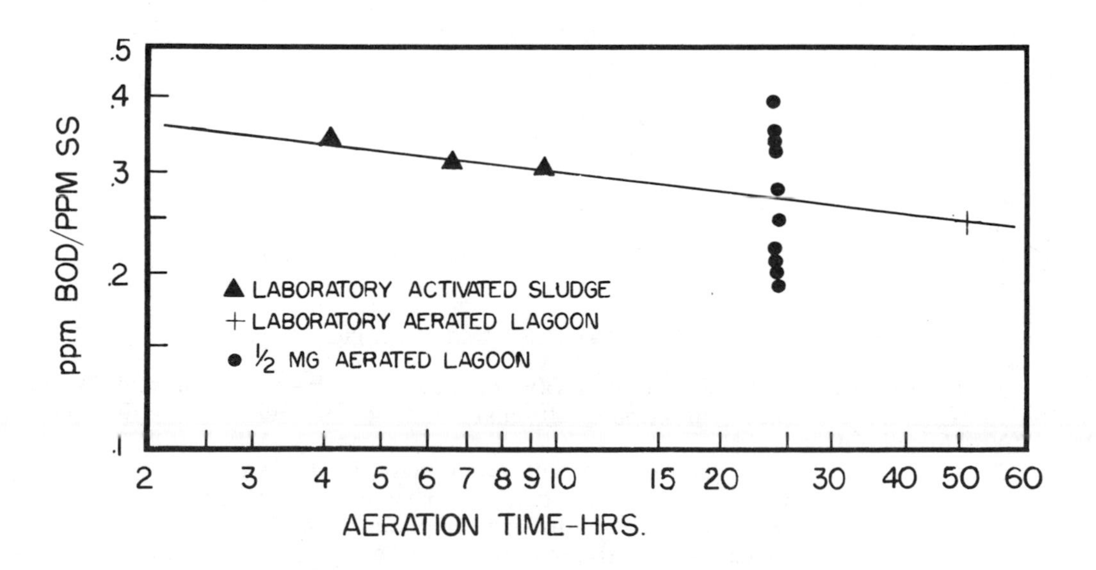

Figure 132. BOD of suspended solids as a function of aeration period.

Q = influent flow (MGD)
f = proportionality factor

In general, the value of f has been assigned at 12×10^{-6}; f is essentially a proportionality factor containing the heat transfer coefficients, the surface area increase (resulting from operation of the aeration equipment), wind, and humidity effects. Figures 133 and 134 present statistical plots of the calculated value of f for the Eastern United States and the Midwestern United States, respectively.

The value of f varies by orders of magnitude depending on wind, humidity, and other factors. It appears that a value of $f = 20 \times 10^{-6}$ is applicable for the Gulf Coast area of Texas. This value was developed based upon a limited amount of data and high-temperature summer information; that is, the waste was hot and tended to overheat during summer operation. A cooling tower was employed to control summer temperatures. This points out the potential problems associated with biological treatment of hot wastes in warm and mild climate areas. Excess temperatures can result in reduced biological treatment and should be considered in design of biological treatment facilities.

One the temperature of the lagoon has been predicted, for extreme temperature conditions, it is necessary to evaluate biological treatment efficiency at the predicted temperatures. Equation 13 has been used to predict performance.

$$K_t = K_{20^\circ C.}\ \theta^{(t-20)} \qquad (13)$$

where:

K_t = BOD removal coefficient at temperature (t)
K_{20} = BOD removal coefficient at temperature (20°C.)
t = temperature of the lagoon
θ = temperature coefficient
For aerated lagoons θ varies from 1.06 to 1.18.

A more direct solution is possible with the response function shown in this paper.

$$S_e\ (t) = S_e\ (20^\circ C.)^{\theta(t-20)} \qquad (14)$$

where:

$S_e\ (t)$ = effluent BOD at temperature (t)
$S_e(20^\circ)$ = effluent BOD at 20°C.
θs = coefficient
t = temperature of the lagoon

θ was found to be 1.065 for the waste used in the design example.

CONCLUSIONS AND RECOMMENDATIONS

1. Data collection can be geared toward establishing a response function which will permit an economic evaluation of alternate methods of obtaining the desired degree of treatment.
2. A laboratory technique for data collection has been presented which, if properly applied, can be employed to establish a response function for evaluating activated sludge, aerated lagoons, and low solids production systems.
3. The technique of handling activated sludge and aerated lagoon data in a continuous manner has provided an excellent tool for evaluating biological treatment systems. It is anticipated that the technique can be effectively applied over a wide

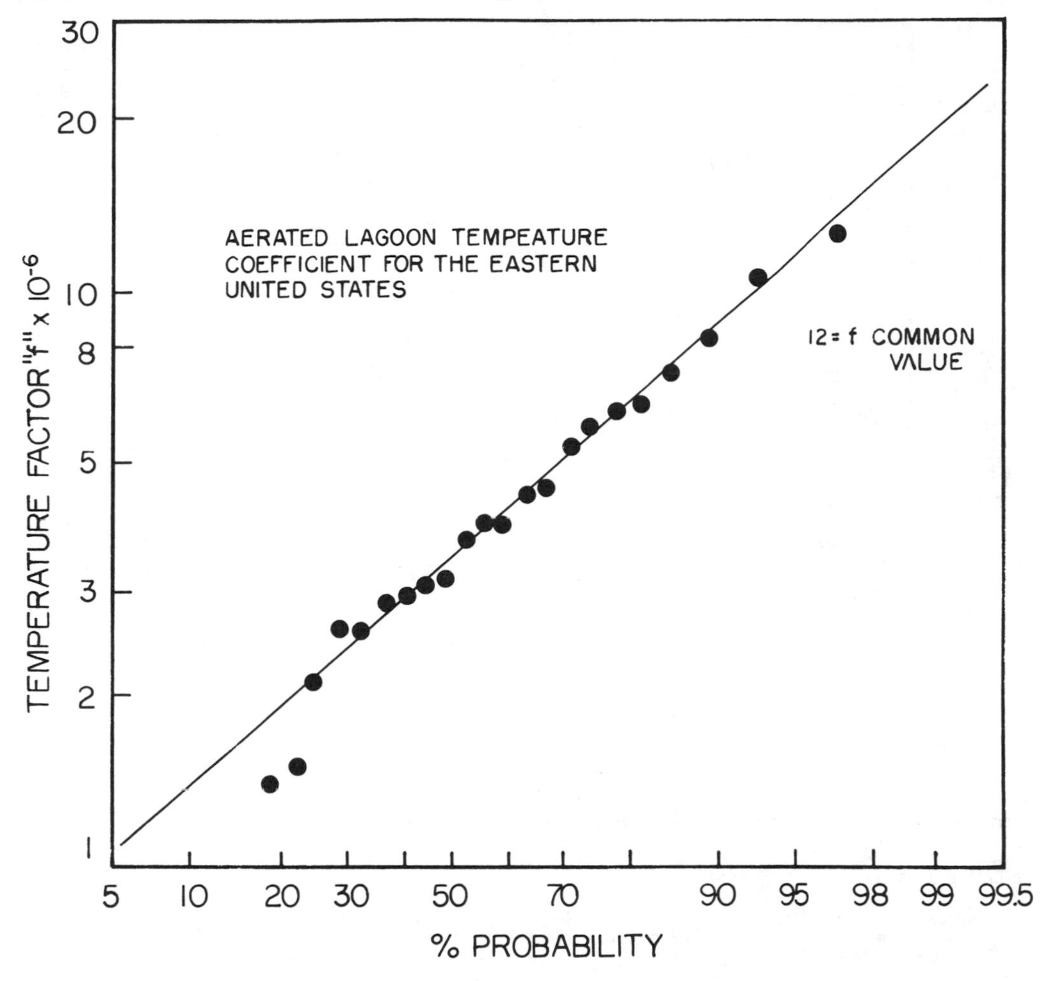

Figure 133. Aerated lagoon temperature coefficient for the Eastern United States.

range of waste types. It must be pointed out that additional experience in the use of this technique will provide a clearer insight into potential problems which might develop for this approach.

4. Performance predictions can be validly made for conditions of waste strength and aeration detention time other than those studied in the laboratory. The variations in waste strengths must be limited to substrate constituents having comparable removal characteristics.

5. It is possible, employing the techniques demonstrated, to determine the equilibrium solids in aerated lagoon systems and to determine the solids requiring handling and disposal in activated sludge systems.

6. A substantial change in the BOD/COD relationship was observed before and after treatment. This tends to indicate a significant reduction in the rate of BOD exertion which should be recognized in stream assimilation studies.

7. Methods of predicting aerated lagoon temperatures and performance have been illustrated.

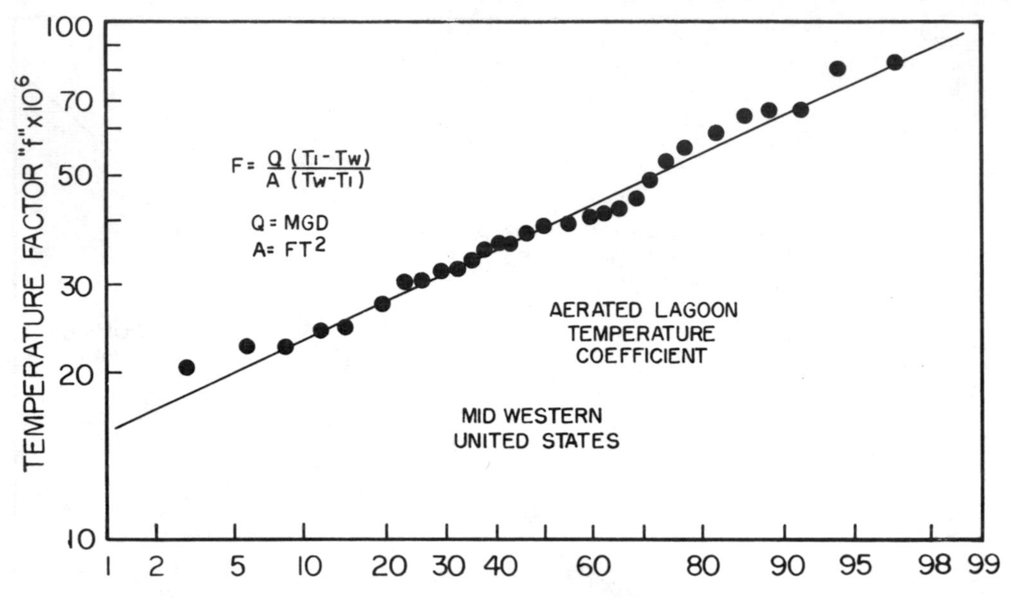

Figure 134. Aerated lagoon temperature coefficient for Midwestern United States.

APPENDIX

COMPARISON OF BOD AND COD RELATIONSHIPS

BOD Equation

$$\frac{S_a\,(\mathrm{BOD}) - S_e\,(\mathrm{BOD})}{S_a} = 0.034\, S_e\,(\mathrm{BOD}) + 0.10$$

COD Equation

$$\frac{S_a\,(\mathrm{COD}) - S_e\,(\mathrm{COD})}{\cdot\, X_a \cdot t} = 0.0276\, S_e\,(\mathrm{COD}) - 1.1$$

BOD/COD Relationship

S_a (BDO) = 0.63 S_a (COD) - 40 (Influent)
S_e (BOD) = 0.474 S_e (COD) - 20 (Effluent)

NEW CONCEPTS IN AERATED LAGOON DESIGN AND OPERATION

Clair N. Sawyer
Metcalf & Eddy, Engineers, Boston, Massachusetts

The aerated lagoon method of wastewater treatment satisfies a great need for economical high-degree treatment where adequate land areas are available for use. Land requirements are normally from 1 to 10 percent of those needed for oxidation or stabilization ponds and need not be much greater than is often required for high-rate trickling filters constructed with rock.

The capabilities of the aerated lagoon have been recognized only recently. Historically, aeration was first applied to simple lagoons which had failed to accomplish the desired degree of purification and, more often than not, had created serious odor problems (1,2). More recently, many oxidation ponds which have created odor problems due to overloading or other reasons have been converted to aerated lagoons, particularly where land for expansion was not available or additional development costs were excessive.

Necessity is often the mother of invention and aerated lagoons were certainly born of necessity. From small beginnings, in which science and engineering were relatively unimportant, the design and the application of aerated lagoons today has reached a high degree of development. Much of this can be credited to Professor Eckenfelder and his colleagues D. J. O'Connor, E. L. Barnhart, and J. L. Mancini (3-5).

The full potential of the activated sludge process was certainly not realized by its developers, Ardern and Lockett. New ways of harnessing activated sludge to accomplish desired objectives have been proposed during the first fifty years of its history and who would dare to say that no more will be developed. The aerated lagoon system of waste treatment is in its infancy and awaits full development. With our present knowledge of biological phenomena and the influence of environmental factors, a reasonable appreciation of the potential of aerated lagoons should come about rather rapidly. It is toward this end that these comments are directed.

SCOPE OF APPLICATION

Mixed Aerobic-Anaerobic Systems

Considering the origin of the aerated lagoon system, it is only natural that many of the early concepts of its application have had deep roots in lagoon behavior in which anaerobic processes play a significant role. On this basis, many aerated lagoons have been designed with facilities to distribute the waste uniformly throughout the basin and maintain aerobic conditions in surface layers of sufficient depth to intercept and prevent the release of obnoxious anaerobic decomposition products, such as hydrogen sulfide. In such a system, the heavier suspended solids, including biologically formed floc, are allowed to settle on the bottom of the lagoon where those matters subject to anaerobic decomposition are free to do so. The liquid and gaseous products of decomposition released at the sludge-water interface are carried by the circulating mixture into the aerobic zone above and utilized by the aerobic organisms, thus preventing the release of obnoxious gases to the atmosphere.

Aerobic Systems

In aerobic systems, mixing is adequate to prevent sedimentation of suspended solids except in very limited areas, and no dependence is placed upon anaerobic phenomena. In many ways, the aerobic lagoon systems can be considered an extension or new application of the modified activated sludge process in which time is substituted for sludge recirculation. The basic differences in lagoon behavior are shown in Figure 135.

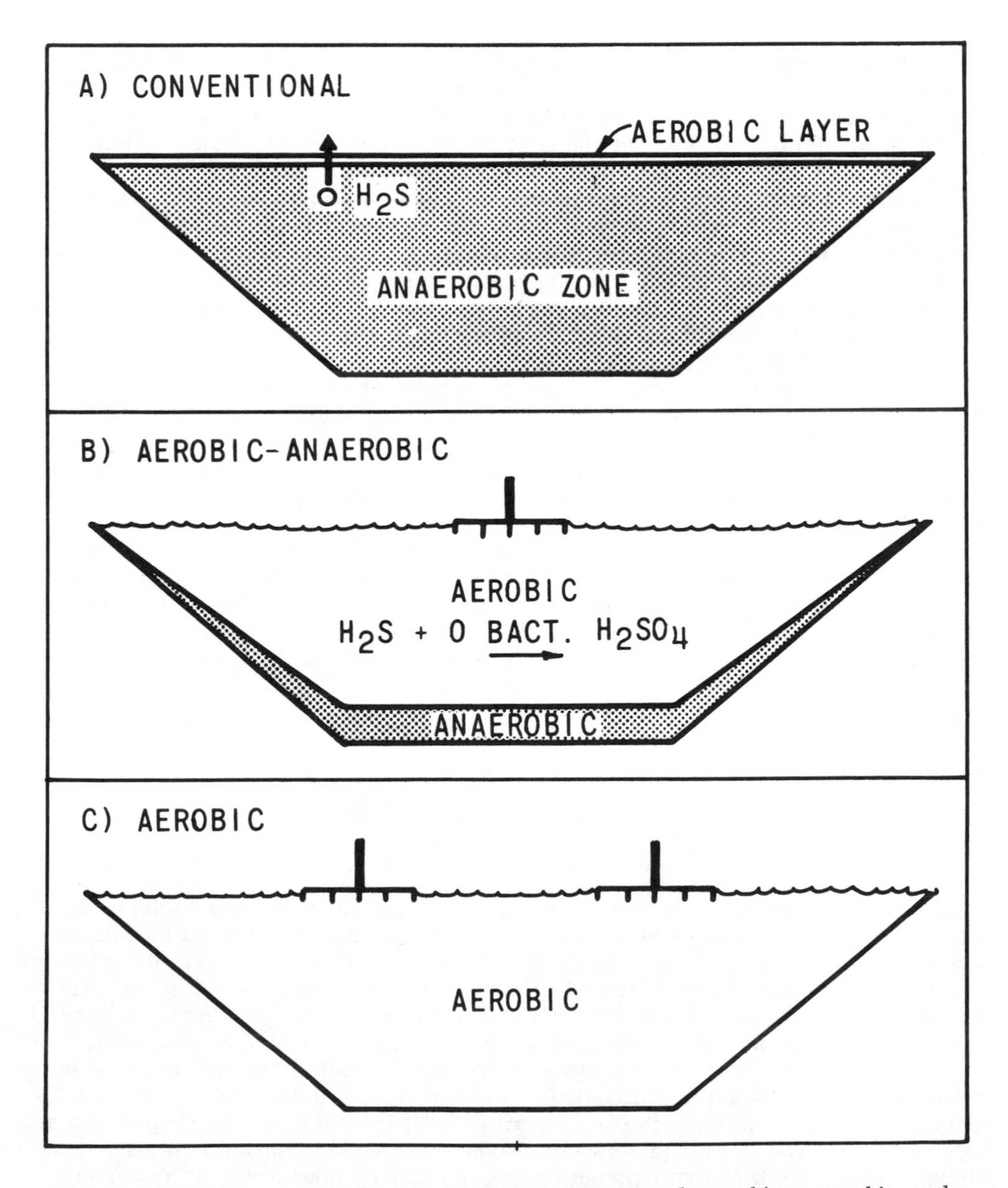

Figure 135. Fundamental differences between conventional, aerobic-anaerobic, and aerobic lagoons.

Aerobic Versus Aerobic-Anaerobic Lagoons

A major limitation of any of the aerobic methods of wastewater treatment which shorten the time over that required for anaerobic purification is the amount of putrescible sludge that accumulates and requires disposal. Conventional anaerobic lagoons are undoubtedly the least productive of sludges. The sludge problem is intensified the moment aerobic processes are substituted and increases in magnitude as rates of treatment are speeded.

Aerobic-anaerobic lagoons have a definite advantage in that they approach the total oxidation concept. Unfortunately, they cannot always be used, because of space limitations, wastewater characteristics, or other considerations. In general, they are applicable where BOD loadings do not exceed 5 lb/1,000 cu ft of lagoon capacity (80 grams per cubic meter), because at higher loadings such violent mixing is required to satisfy the oxygen requirements that sedimentation cannot occur within the lagoon. Aerobic-anaerobic systems have the definite advantage of minimizing the sludge disposal problem and the effluent is often suitable for direct discharge to the receiving water because of its low settleable solids content.

Aerobic lagoons have several advantages over most modifications of the activated sludge process but, of course, do have certain disadvantages, particularly heat losses in the colder climates. The choice between aerobic lagoons and activated sludge requires careful engineering evaluation in each instance. In general, aerobic lagoons produce sludge in amounts equal to the conventional activated sludge process. On wastes in which the majority of the BOD is in the soluble form, the effluent will carry suspended solids at about 50 percent of the influent BOD. The effluent, in most instances, must be settled to remove the settleable solids, and sludge disposal therefore is one of the attendant problems.

The aerobic lagoon has three definite advantages over the aerobic-anaerobic lagoon: (a) The oxygen requirement is considerably less per unit of BOD in the influent; (b) the lagoon does not store BOD at low temperatures and then release it as added load when temperatures increase; and (c) it is possible to overcome low-temperature effects by recycling sludge from the clarifier units as desired.

TEMPERATURE CONSIDERATIONS

Heat Losses

Lagoons are excellent heat-dissipating devices and this ability increases as the degree of agitation or turbulence increases. This particular ability makes aerated lagoon treatment especially attractive in the handling of high-temperature wastes, which often occur in the case of industrial wastes. By proper design, precooling facilities can usually be eliminated. On the other hand, heat losses can be a serious limitation in the application of aerated lagoons to treatment of low-temperature wastewaters, particularly in the colder climates during the winter months.

Ponds have long been used as cooling devices in place of cooling towers and a great deal is known about heat losses from them (6, 7). Conventional lagoons are ponds, and existing knowledge of heat losses from ponds is directly applicable to them. In general, heat loss is a function of losses due to evaporation, convection, and radiation, less any gain from solar heating. Losses due to evaporation and convection are both highly dependent upon wind conditions and, of course, increased by agitation of the water mass when artificial aeration is practiced. Barnhart and Eckenfelder (5) have given consideration to heat losses from aerated lagoons, and Mancini and Barnhart have discussed the matter further in this volume.

BOD Removal

Because aerated lagoons are dependent upon biological action in which mass inoculations with preformed organisms are not employed, as in the activated sludge process, it is only natural that they respond more radically to temperature and other environmental changes. With the growing interest in fairly uniform purification regardless of stream purification capacity, it becomes mandatory to design facilities which can maintain a reasonable degree of treatment at all times. As our knowledge of heat losses from aerated lagoons increases, it may become possible to obtain basic data for their design from carefully controlled laboratory studies, in some instances. However, in the absence of such refined information and for other reasons, particularly variable wastewater quality, operation of pilot plants under field conditions has been the favorite method of evaluation.

The information presented on Figure 136 shows data for 3.5-, 4.5-, and 5-day detention periods during an 18-month study of aerated lagoon treatment of cotton textile wastes. The temperature of the raw wastes varied from a high of 106°F. during July and August to a low of 73°F. in February. Each point on Figure 136 represents weekly average values in the aerated lagoon. Unfortunately, the 5-day

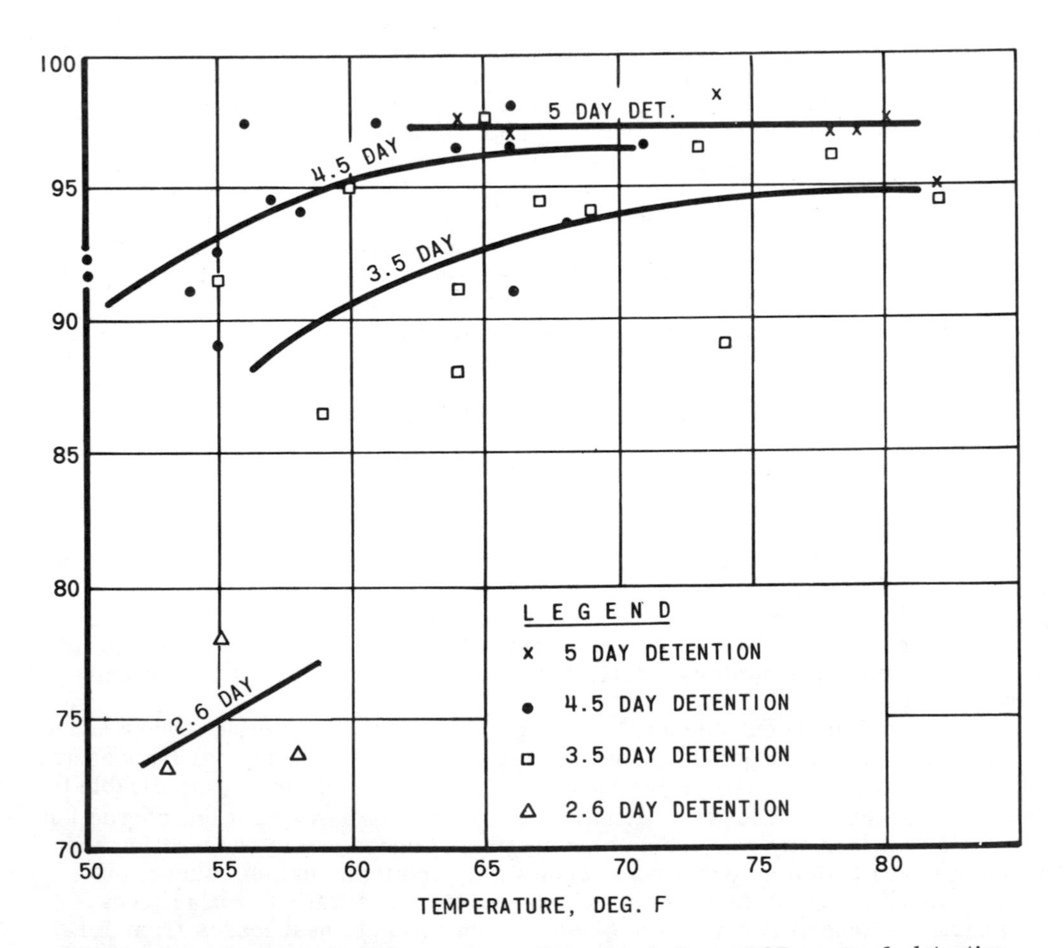

Figure 136. Pilot plant studies showing relationship between BOD removal, detention time, and temperature.

detention studies were terminated before the severest winter weather was experienced. The data show that a high degree of treatment, generally in excess of 90 percent BOD removal, was maintained at 4.5 days of detention at temperatures down to 50°F. Although lagoon temperatures were maintained at higher levels when the detention time was controlled at 3.5 days, the degree of purification was considerably inferior. Operation of the pilot plant at 2.6 days of detention with lagoon temperatures between 53° and 58°F. gave BOD removals in the range of 73–78 percent. This degree of purification was not acceptable and further studies were not conducted at this detention time.

The data presented on Figure 136 show that aerated lagoons with short detention times will be extremely sensitive to temperature changes in the range of 50°–70°F. and that reasonably stable operation in terms of purification can be expected with detention times of 4.5–5 days at all lagoon temperatures above 50°F. The study did not involve detention times greater than 5 days because of space limitations for the full-scale plant.

Temperature Compensation

Lowered temperatures can become a serious operating problem in two distinctly different situations. One deals with situations in which heat losses may be so great as to allow ice formation, and the other in which process failure may occur at temperatures considerably above the freezing point:

1. In situations in which conventional lagoons have been converted to aerated lagoons, usually of the anaerobic-aerobic type, the detention time is such that serious icing conditions may occur during the winter months. In one instance in which two lagoons were designed to operate in parallel, a satisfactory solution was found by operating the lagoons in series during the winter months. The method of operation for summer and winter is shown on Figure 137.

With the advent of colder weather, parallel operation is discontinued and all of the waste flow is diverted to one lagoon in order to conserve as much heat as possible. When this transfer is made, the lagoons are shifted from parallel to series operation, and both aeration devices are kept in service until ice formation forces the shutdown of the second aerator. It then operates as an anaerobic lagoon under ice cover. As the weather moderates in the spring, the ice near the aerator usually melts first. As soon as the mechanism is free of ice, the unit is started and continued in operation. In this manner of operation, odor problems have been overcome and a reasonable degree of purification, 60–75 percent, has been maintained through the coldest months of the year.

2. In instances in which aerated lagoons of the aerobic type must be constructed, it is reasonable to expect that the degree of treatment will suffer appreciably if lagoon temperatures drop below 50°F., or even at higher temperatures if detention periods of less than four days must be employed. In such cases, the lagoons should be made as deep as possible so as to minimize surface area and, therefore, heat losses. An illustration of application of this principle is at the Union Carbide plant at Institute, West Virginia. The aerated lagoons are 17 ft. deep. As a further means of maintaining purification capacity, provisions should be made to recycle sludge from the final clarifier (which is a normal component of aerobic lagoon systems) during the cold weather months. In other words, the aerated lagoon is operated quite like a modified activated sludge system, when desired. These elements of heat compensation are shown on Figure 138.

DESIGN TO MEET STREAM REQUIREMENTS

In many states of the Union, particularly in the Southeastern section of the country, where river flows are high during the winter months and ice cover is not

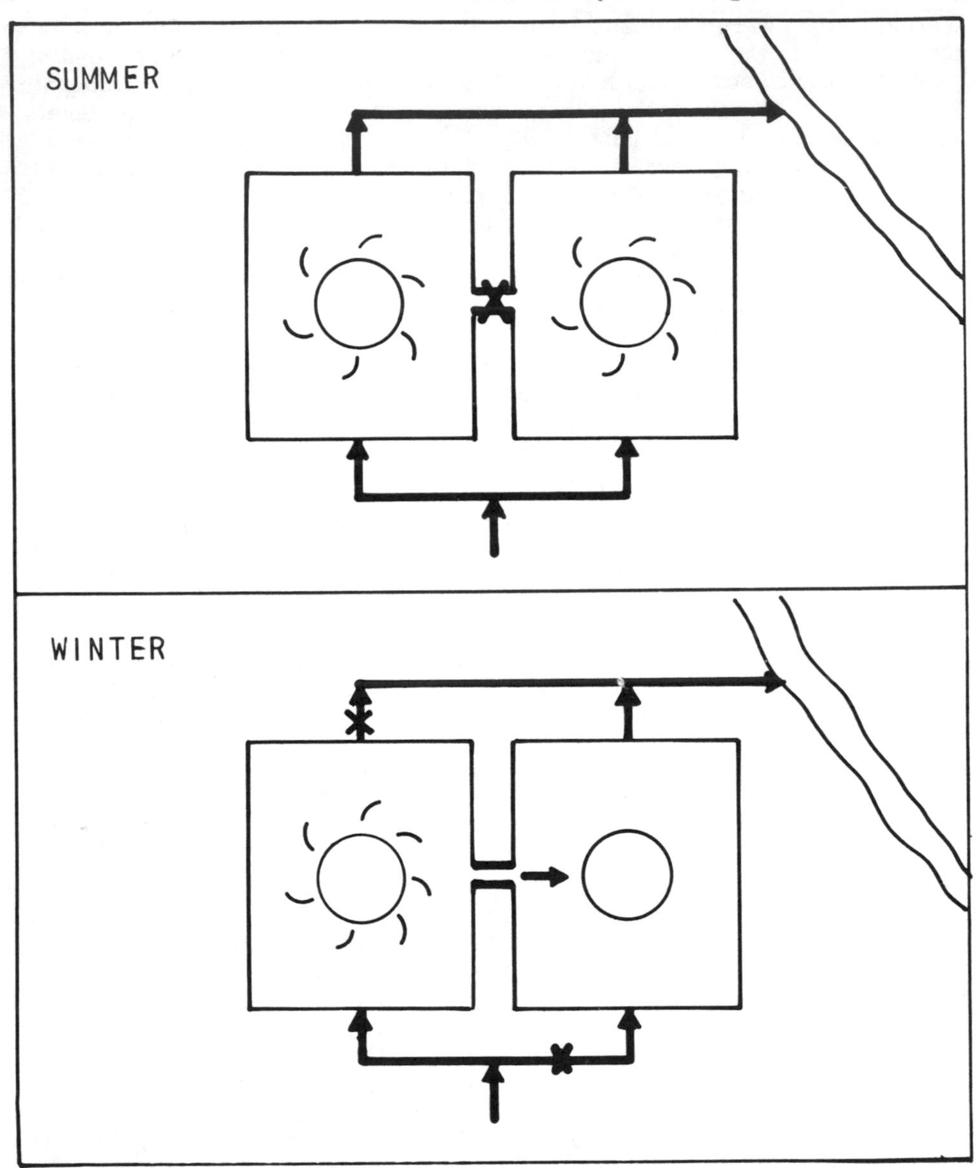

Figure 137. Temperature compensation—showing summer and winter operation of a two-lagoon anaerobic-aerobic system designed to minimize effect of icing problems.

a problem, the assimilative capacity of most rivers increases substantially during the winter months. In states in which stream standards have been established, the regulatory authorities often look favorably upon a degree of treatment dictated by stream conditions. In such instances, aerated lagoons are especially applicable because of the ease with which they can be moved into and out of operation, so that benefit can be taken of increased assimilative capacity of the river when it occurs.

In one industrial wastewater disposal problem in one of our Southern states,

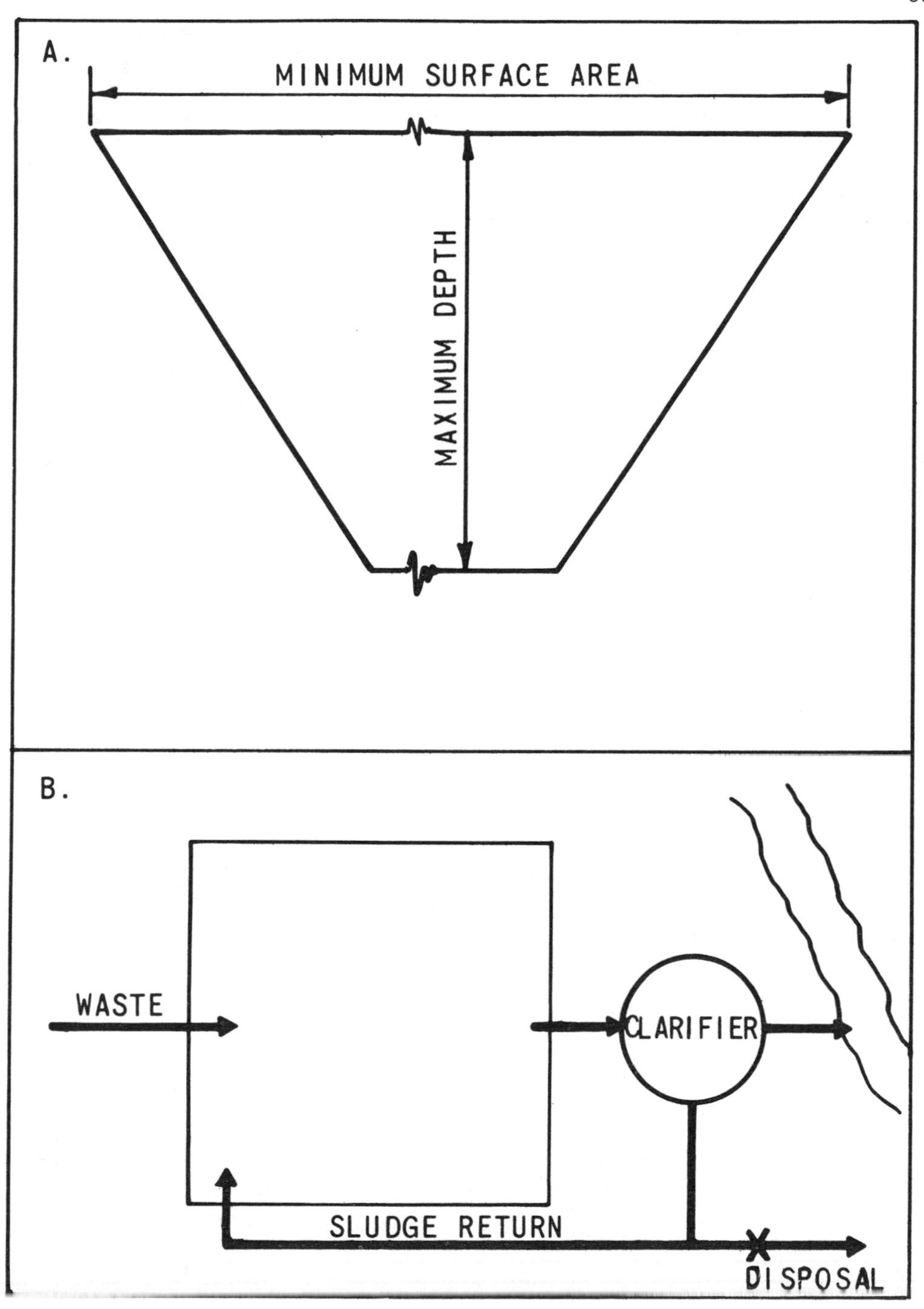

Figure 138. Temperature compensation (A) by maximum depth, (B) by recirculation of sludge.

the writer had an opportunity to recommend treatment facilities designed to utilize the purification capacity of a river to maximum degree. A study of stream flow records showed that minimum flows were about 50 cfs and that flows in excess of 190 cfs could be anticipated 50 percent of the time. Investigation showed that there was little possibility of industrial encroachment and little possibility of diversion or flow control upstream. On this basis, an extended study of the assimilative capacity of the river was conducted. This was relatively easy, as the untreated wastewaters were being discharged to the stream at regulated rates, seven days per week, during the period of survey.

With the assimilative capacity of the river established over a wide variety of flow and temperature conditions, a plan of waste treatment in four parallel aerated lagoons, as shown on Figure 139, was proposed. Each lagoon was to be operated separately as needed. The plan of operation was based upon the assimilative capacity of the river and is shown on Figure 140.

Studies of the wastewater from the industry showed that it contained about 15,000 lb. of BOD_5 per day during periods of maximum production. The river surveys established that the river had an assimilative capacity of about 60 lb. of BOD_5/day/cubic foot per second of flow under the prescribed river classification. From this information it was established that the river could handle all the wastewater flow without treatment at all river flows in excess of 250 cfs, or about 35 percent of the time. Calculations, based upon a 20-year probability curve for stream flow in the river, indicated that operation of one aerated lagoon would be required, on an average, about 65 percent of the time, a second lagoon about 53 percent of the time, a third lagoon about 32 percent of the time, and a fourth lagoon only 10 percent of the time.

The proposed plan of treatment was accepted by the state regulatory authority. The plant has been constructed and is now in successful operation.

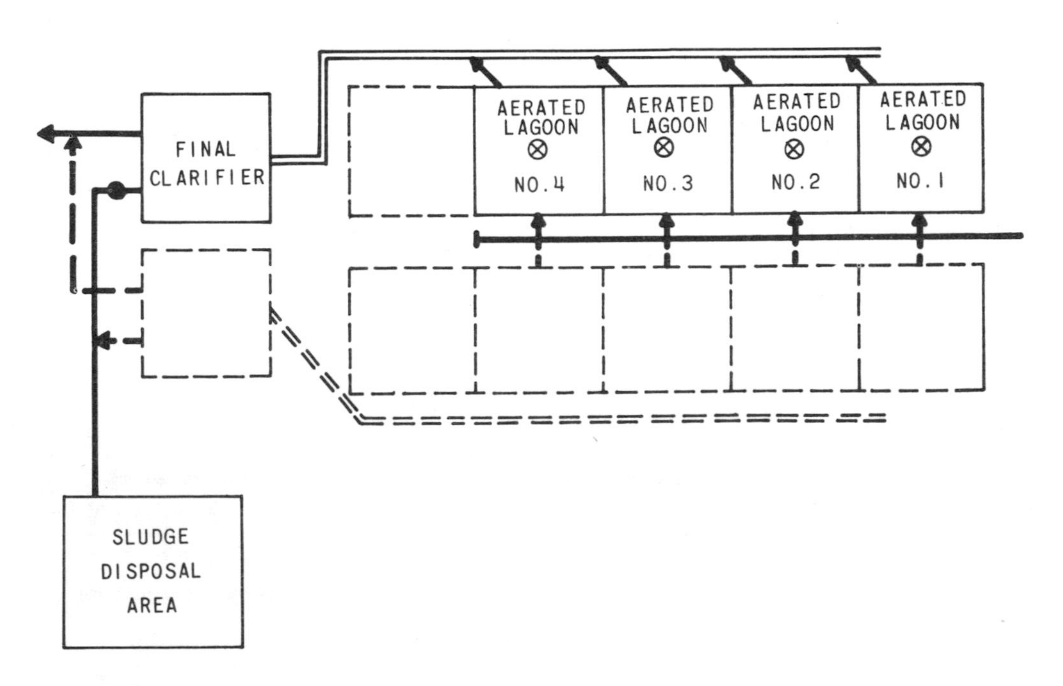

Figure 139. Proposed waste treatment system.

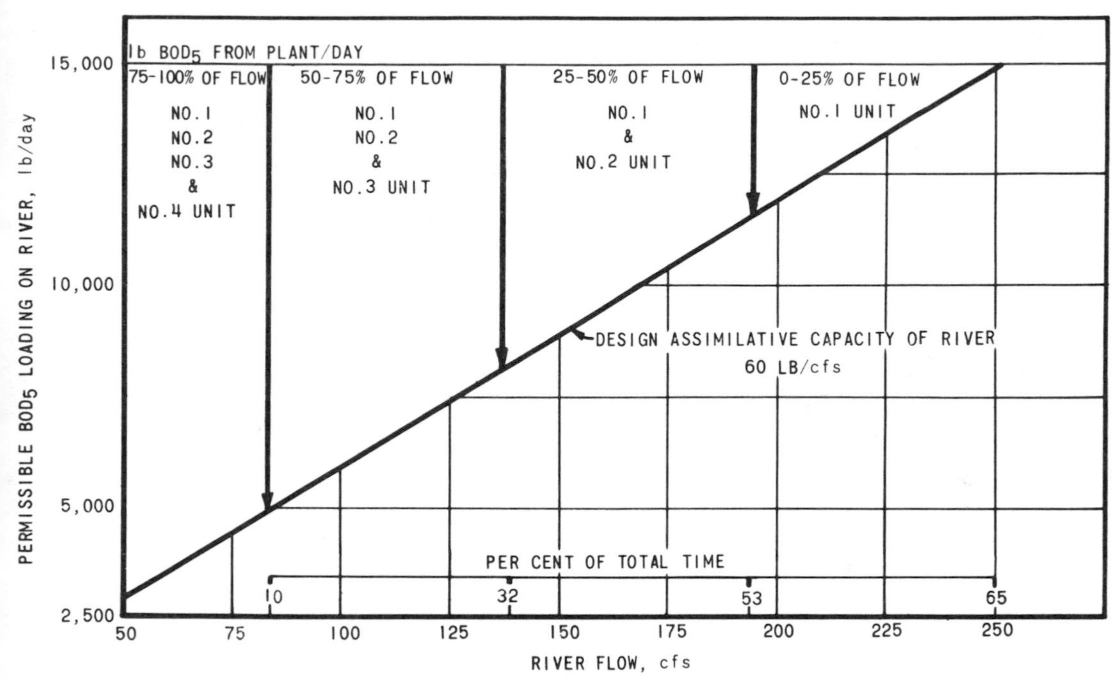

Figure 140. River assimilative capacity and aerated lagoon requirements.

DESIGN FOR WASTEWATER CHARACTERISTICS

A major advantage of the aerated lagoon over any other method of biological treatment is its ability to handle wastewaters of highly varying characteristics because of the great diluting capacity which it can provide. For this reason, pretreatment requirements are minimized and often unnecessary if proper consideration is given to design.

In order to take full advantage of aerated lagoons to overcome waste load variations, toxic properties, and high and low *p*H conditions, they must be operated as completely mixed systems. This poses no particular problem for systems that employ one aeration device, or even where two or three may be involved. It does, however, in large systems where many units may be installed in the same basin. In such systems, it becomes important to distribute the wastewaters properly and to remove the treated waste in such a fashion that each aeration device can operate at maximum efficiency. Let us assume that local conditions dictate use of one rectangular aeration basin with eight aeration devices, as shown on Figure 141. In such a system, wastewater should be distributed to all aeration units and the effluent should be withdrawn from at least two points. Ideally, the effluent should be withdrawn at two points on each side of the basin, but such additional facilities add to the cost and can seldom be justified.

SELECTION OF AERATION EQUIPMENT

Perhaps the greatest problem the designing engineer has, in relation to aerated lagoons, is the selection of aeration equipment. Solution of this problem is still clouded by the claims and counterclaims of equipment suppliers, for the

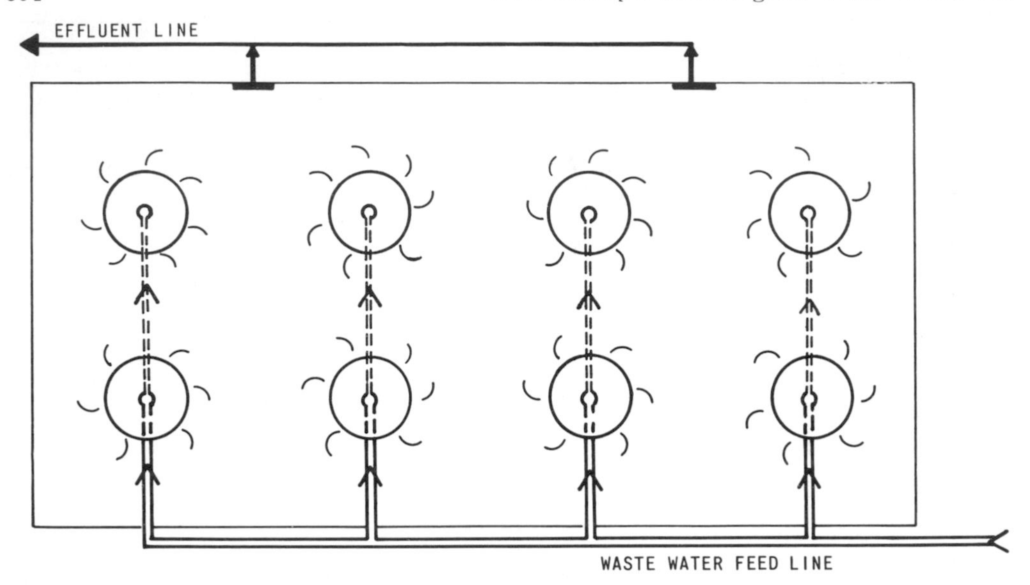

Figure 141. Proposed design for aerated lagoon with multiple aeration units for variable strength or toxic wastes.

market is highly competitive. In general, mechanical-type aerators of one type or another have been favored in all large installations over diffused air because of the greater mixing potential and economy of running electrical lines versus air lines over considerable distances. The selection of equipment depends to a major extent upon whether the lagoon is to be operated as an anaerobic-aerobic or as an aerobic system.

Anaerobic-Aerobic Systems

Successful operation of anaerobic-aerobic systems depends upon maintaining an aerobic layer of water of sufficient depth to prevent the release of obnoxious gases at the air-water interface. It does not depend upon mixing velocities sufficient to prevent solids deposition, but rather what might be termed "bathing velocities" sufficient to dissolve the products of anaerobic digestion at the sludge-water interface and carry them (e.g., CH_4, H_2S) into the aerobic zone for destruction by aerobic bacteria. An anaerobic-aerobic system which allows gas bubbles to form at the sludge-water interface will normally produce unsatisfactory results and may produce an aerial nuisance.

Surface aerators of practically any design are adequate for anaerobic-aerobic systems provided they have the capacity to supply oxygen sufficient to satisfy the total oxygen demand of the waste, which may range from 125 to 200 percent of the BOD_5 value, depending upon the BOD reaction rate constant.

Aerobic Systems

Successful operation of aerobic systems depends upon maintaining adequate mixing to keep essentially all biological growths in suspension at all times. This requires that flow velocities in the major portion of the bottom of the lagoon must be adequate to prevent deposition of solids or, if they are deposited, to ensure that they will be resuspended before anaerobic conditions develop. In general, mechanical aerators with draft tubes or deep secondary propellers are required to maintain adequate mixing velocities in lagoons with depths greater than 10 ft. Acceptance of other devices should be based open performance tests.

Aerobic lagoons accomplish purification by a combination of oxidation and synthesis in a manner comparable to activated sludge. In general, they produce about 0.5 lb. of suspended solids per pound of BOD_5, and the oxygen requirements are on the order of 0.8–1.2 lb. per pound of BOD_5 removed.

Choice of Equipment

The final choice of mechanical equipment for aeration purposes is not too difficult as long as the size of the units does not exceed 25 HP. For this size and smaller, practically all suppliers have, or have access to, test basins in which reasonable evaluations of oxygen transfer capacity and mixing ability can be made, or the purchaser can construct his own facility at reasonable cost. However, the testing of large-scale units, such as 50 and 75 HP or larger, under conditions comparable to service in aerated lagoons is impossible at the present time because no one has test facilities of adequate capacity.

It is claimed by several manufacturers that the larger size aerators are less efficient and that tests should be run with them regardless of the inadequacies of the small-scale test basins used. This forces the purchaser to make a choice based upon extrapolations involving geometry, time, and space. In instances when one or two units are being purchased, the purchaser should reserve the right to field test the equipment. This becomes impractical, however, in large basins where multiple units are to be installed.

In view of the potential market for mechanical aerators, there is a growing need for a testing station where mechanical aerators can be tested under prescribed conditions and certified as to their capabilities.

REFERENCES

(1) Ratliff, F. C. "The Use of a Circulating Lagoon in a Paper Mill Effluent Program," *Proceedings*. 12th Purdue Industrial Waste Conference, 502 (1957).

(2) Sawyer, C. N. "Practical Aspects of Aerated Lagoons." Symposium on Waste Water Treatment for Small Municipalities, Ecole Polytechnic, Montreal, Quebec (November 1965).

(3) O'Connor, D. J., and W. W. Eckenfelder, Jr. "Treatment of Organic Wastes in Aerated Lagoons," *J. Water Poll. Cont. Fed.*, *32*, 365 (1960).

(4) Mancini, J. L., and E. L. Barnhart. "Design Method for Aerated Lagoon and Activated Sludge Industrial Waste Treatment Systems." Paper presented at Water Pollution Control Federation Meeting, Atlantic City, New Jersey (October 14, 1965).

(5) Barnhart, E. L., and W. W. Eckenfelder, Jr. "Theoretical Aspects of Aerated Lagoon Design." Symposium on Waste Water Treatment for Small Municipalities, Ecole Polytechnic, Montreal, Quebec (November 1965).

(6) Thomas, B. L. "How to Calculate Heat Losses from Ponds," *Chem. Engr.*, *67*, 129 (1960).

(7) Velz, C. J., and J. J. Gannon. "Forecasting Heat Loss in Ponds and Streams," *J. Water Poll. Cont. Fed.*, *32*, 392 (1960).

ANAEROBIC TREATMENT OF SOLUBLE WASTES

Perry L. McCarty
Stanford University, Stanford, California

INTRODUCTION

In the anaerobic waste treatment process, microorganisms are used under anaerobic conditions to stabilize organic wastes by conversion to methane and carbon dioxide. The most significant advantage of anaerobic treatment over aerobic treatment is that the growth of excess microorganisms is minimized, thus decreasing the requirements for biological sludge disposal facilities and for the biological nutrients, nitrogen and phosphorus. In addition, the methane gas produced can serve as a source of fuel. This process has been used in the past mainly for the stabilization of concentrated municipal and industrial sludges. Anaerobic treatment, however, is equally adaptable to treatment of both dilute and concentrated soluble organic wastes.

The anaerobic treatment of relatively dilute soluble wastes has been made feasible through the development of various "anaerobic contact processes," which take advantage of the more rapid and efficient treatment obtained by maintenance of high concentrations of microorganisms in the reactor. Preliminary results from a particularly promising contact process for soluble wastes, termed the "anaerobic filter," are given in the following along with a summary of results from various other anaerobic processes.

MICROBIOLOGY AND BIOCHEMISTRY

It is desirable to have an understanding of the microbiology and biochemistry of anaerobic treatment in order to better appreciate the significant design parameters as well as the limitations of the process. An understanding of anaerobic treatment is simplified by considering that complex organic materials are converted to methane and carbon dioxide in two stages, as indicated in Figure 142. In the first stage, a heterogeneous group of facultative and anaerobic bacteria, commonly termed the "acid-formers," convert proteins, carbohydrates, and fats primarily into fatty acids by hydrolysis and fermentation. The methane-producing bacteria then utilize the organic acids in the second stage, converting them

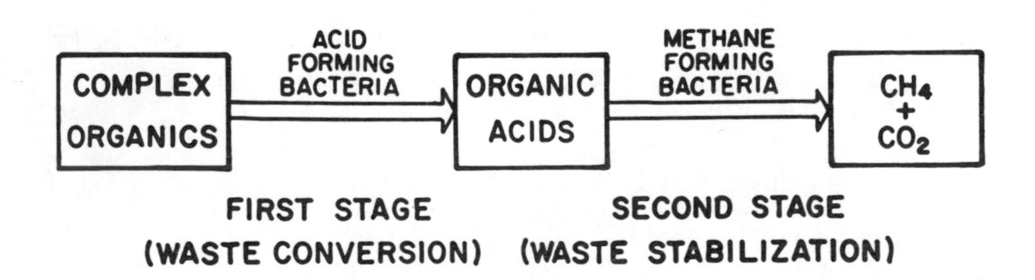

Figure 142. Two stages of anaerobic waste treatment.

into carbon dioxide and methane. Alcohols may be fermented also by methane-producing bacteria (this could be significant with certain types of waste). Although it appears possible that methane bacteria alone could carry on both stages of the fermentation, evidence is lacking to indicate that this actually occurs.

The first-stage conversion by acid-forming bacteria is brought about with little "stabilization" of BOD (biochemical oxygen demand) or COD (chemical oxygen demand) of the organic matter in suspension or in solution. Here, simply, a change in form takes place, a portion being converted to end products, such as organic acids, and the other portion being converted to new bacterial cells. It is in the second stage of methane formation that true "stabilization" of oxidizable organics takes place, and this is directly proportional to the quantity of methane produced. Exceptions to this, under anaerobic conditions, are removals resulting from the occasional formation of hydrogen or reduction of inorganic electron acceptors, such as sulfates, nitrates, and nitrites.

The quantity of methane evolved from the stabilization of a given waste can be estimated quite closely from the oxygen equivalent of methane gas:

$$CH_4 + 2O_2 \rightarrow CO_2 + 2H_2O \quad (1)$$

Mol. Wt.: 16 64

Thus, each 16 grams of methane produced and lost to the atmosphere corresponds to the removal of 64 grams of oxygen equivalent from the waste stream. Converting to gas volume, 5.62 cubic feet of methane produced (STP) corresponds to the stabilization of one pound of ultimate BOD (BOD_L) or COD.

The methane-producing bacteria comprise several different species of strictly anaerobic organisms (1). The major similar characteristic of these organisms is that they all produce methane from fermentation of simple organics under anaerobic conditions. However, each species has been found to have specific requirements and can ferment only a relatively restricted group of simple organic compounds. For this reason, several species of methane organisms may be required for the complete methane fermentation of even simple substrates.

Since anaerobic waste stabilization is proportional to methane fermentation, it is desirable to know the sources of methane. The major portion of methane formed in the treatment of most wastes results from fermentation of acetic and propionic acids. These volatile fatty acids are formed as intermediates in the anaerobic degradation of most complex wastes, and are fermented as follows:

Acetic Acid:

$$CH_3COOH \rightarrow CH_4 + CO_2 \quad (2)$$

Propionic Acid:

1st step $CH_3CH_2COOH + 1/2H_2O \rightarrow CH_3COOH + 1/4CO_2 + 3/4CH_4$

2nd step $CH_3COOH \rightarrow CH_4 + CO_2$

Overall: $CH_3CH_2COOH + 1/2H_2O \rightarrow 5/4CO_2 + 7/4CH_4$ (3)

The complete methane fermentation of acetic acid requires only one group of methane bacteria. Propionic acid, however, is fermented through acetic acid and its complete fermentation requires two steps, each of which is carried out by a separate group of methane bacteria.

The significance of acetic and propionic acids as precursors of methane is indicated in Figure 143, which shows the pathways by which mixed complex organic materials are converted to methane gas. The percentages shown are based on COD conversion and are for methane fermentation of complex materials with composition similar to municipal waste sludge. The percentages would be different for other wastes. It has been shown from tracer studies that about 70 percent

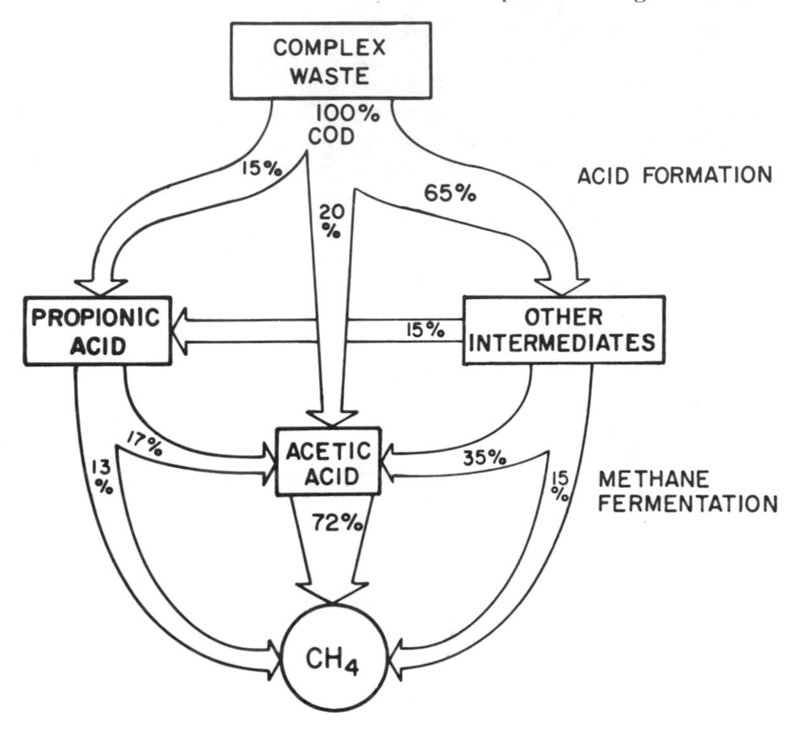

Figure 143. Pathways in methane fermentation of complex wastes such as municipal waste sludges. Percentages represent conversion of waste COD by various routes (16).

of the methane from carbohydrate, protein, or fatty acid fermentation comes from acetic acid (2). From anaerobic Warburg respirometer studies, it has been estimated that about 58 percent of the COD of hexose carbohydrates and about 28 percent of the COD of proteins passes through propionic acid during complete methane fermentation (3). No propionic acid is formed during methane fermentation of even-carbon fatty acids, while one mole of propionic acid is formed per mole of long chain odd-carbon fatty acid fermented. These figures indicate that approximately 85 percent of the total methane formed from the complete treatment of a complex waste results from methane fermentation of propionic and acetic acids. This shows the significance of the methane bacteria which ferment these two acids to the overall process. The remainder of the methane appears to result from various sources such as hydrogen and formic acid fermentation and from the methane fermentation associated with beta-oxidation of longer chained fatty acids.

ANAEROBIC TREATMENT PROCESSES

Several anaerobic treatment processes have been described in the literature and a summary of the nomenclature used appears justified. Schematic diagrams of three processes are given in Figure 144. Most of the early anaerobic systems were of the flow-through type with no special attempt made to keep a high mass of microorganisms in the system. The term "conventional" to describe such a system appears justified.

During the 1950's, several systems were described which attempted to mix

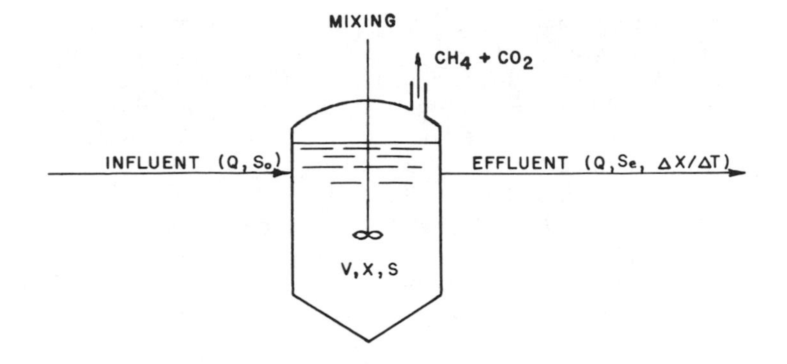

CONVENTIONAL PROCESS

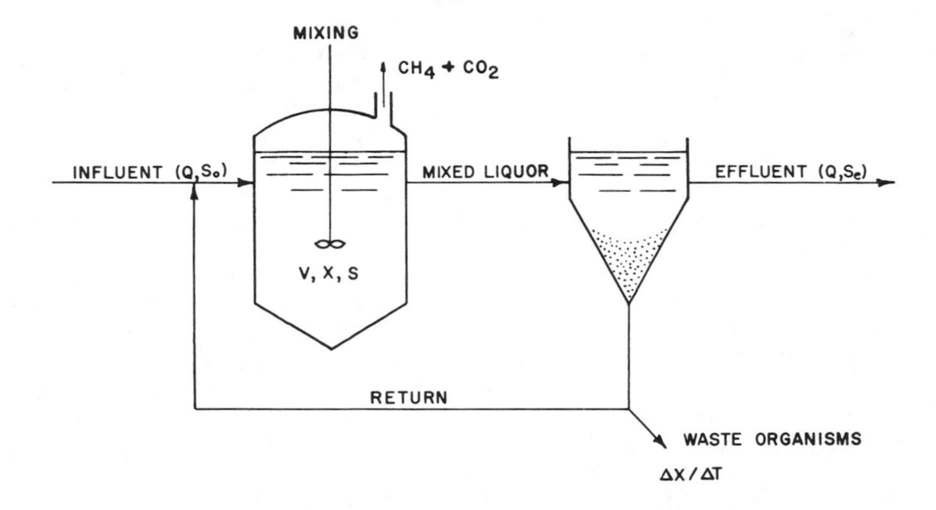

ANAEROBIC ACTIVATED SLUDGE PROCESS

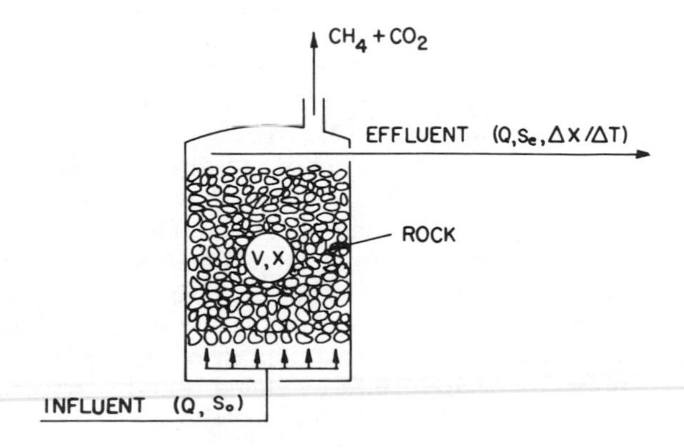

ANAEROBIC FILTER PROCESS

Figure 144. Basic anaerobic process designs.

raw waste with a large anaerobic biological mass maintained in the digester for more efficient and rapid treatment. Schroepfer, Fuller, Johnson, Ziemke, and Anderson (4), as well as Coulter, Soneda, and Ettinger (5), referred to such systems as "anaerobic contact processes." Schroepfer *et al.* (4) also stated in reference to their particular method that "the 'anaerobic activated sludge process' appears to be descriptive of the action involved." Their contact process labeled with this name is shown in Figure 144. The similarity of this process to its aerobic counterpart makes this nomenclature appear appropriate.

Stander and his co-workers (6) described a contact process in which the waste passed up through a sludge blanket maintained in the digester. This is somewhat similar to the first stage of the process described initially by Coulter et al. (5) for treatment of raw domestic sewage. The effluent from this stage was then passed upward through a rock-filled column for removal of suspended solids which may be carried in the first-stage effluent.

A newer anaerobic contact process which has been evaluated in the author's laboratory for soluble waste treatment is also pictured in Figure 144, and is termed the "anaerobic filter process" because of its similarity to an aerobic trickling filter. However, the anaerobic filter has a bottom feed so that the filter is completely submerged in the waste. In effect this filter is similar to the rock-filled column used by Coulter *et al.* (5). A similar device was used by Winneberger, Saad, and McGauhey (7) for raw sewage treatment.

The anaerobic filter offers perhaps more promise for treatment of dilute soluble wastes than any other anaerobic treatment scheme. The anaerobic microorganisms cling quite readily, although loosely, to surfaces. For this reason they remain on the rock in the filter in large masses, allowing efficient waste treatment even at moderate temperatures. In addition, much flocculant biological mass grows free of the rocks and becomes suspended in the pools between them. By using an upflow pattern, these free organisms tend to remain in the filter, increasing both the biological mass as well as the contact of the waste with the organisms. Preliminary results with the anaerobic filter have been most promising and will be given in a later section.

KINETICS OF WASTE TREATMENT

Reports on the kinetics of bacterial growth have been frequent during the past several years: Monod (8), Novick and Szilard (9), Herbert, Elsworth, and Telling (10), Novick (11), and James (12). Use of continuous culture growth kinetics similar to that developed in the above references or with slight modifications have been frequently used in recent years to describe biological waste treatment systems. Andrews, Cole, and Pearson (13), Agardy, Cole, and Pearson (14), Stewart (15), and McCarty (16) have used this model to describe anaerobic waste treatment kinetics. Although various other models have been used by others, this particular model was chosen, as it has some theoretical basis and yields a continuous function which describes both substrate-limited and substrate-unlimited growth. Here, only a summary of what appears to be the most important considerations for waste treatment design and operation will be given.

The growth of microorganisms as a function of time after they are mixed with organic wastes has been approximated by Heukelekian, Orford, and Manganelli (17), Eckenfelder and Weston (18), and Marr, Nilson, and Clark (19) by equations similar to the following:

$$dX/dt = y(dS/dt) - bX \qquad (4)$$

where:

dX/dt = growth of microorganisms in mass per unit time

dS/dt = rate of waste utilization in mass per unit time
X = mass of microorganisms present
y = growth yield constant
b = microorganism decay rate in units/time

Equation 4 states that the rate of growth of microorganisms is proportional to the rate of waste utilization (dS/dt) minus the rate of microorganism decay (bX). The rate of waste utilization can be approximated by an expression similar to that used by Monod (8) to describe the relationship between concentration of a limiting nutrient and growth rate of microorganisms:

$$\frac{dS}{dt} = \frac{kXs}{K_s + s} \tag{5}$$

where:

k = maximum rate of waste utilization at high waste concentration
K_s = waste concentration at which dS/dt is 1/2 the maximum rate
s = concentration of waste surrounding the microorganisms

If Equations 4 and 5 are combined, the rate of growth of microorganisms as a function of waste concentration can be obtained:

$$\frac{dX/dt}{X} = \frac{yks}{K_s + s} - b \tag{6}$$

where:

$\frac{dX/dt}{X}$ = specific growth rate = fractional growth per unit time

In a continuously fed completely mixed waste treatment system simulated by the conventional process or anaerobic activated sludge process, a steady state will be reached when the average quantity of microorganisms produced each day just equals the average quantity of microorganisms wasted from the total treatment system per day ($\Delta X/\Delta t$) from Fig. 144). At this point, the specific growth rate will equal the ratio of microorganisms wasted to microorganisms in the system, $(\Delta X/\Delta t)/X$, and the effluent waste concentration will equal s given by Equation 6. The kinetics are more complicated for the anaerobic filter.

The reciprocal of specific growth rate is more convenient for use and gives the biological solids retention time (SRT), which is the average retention time of microorganisms in the system and can be defined as follows:

$$\text{SRT} = \frac{X}{\Delta X/\Delta t} = \frac{\text{suspended solids in system}}{\text{suspended solids removed per day}} \tag{8}$$

Use of suspended solids as an indication of microorganism mass is adequate in the above formulation, since the average retention time of the microorganisms will approximately equal the average retention time of the mixed suspended solids in the digester.

The rate of waste treatment, $\Delta S/\Delta t$, from Figure 144 is $(S_0 - S_e)Q$, and the percent efficiency of waste treatment is $(S_0 - S_e)\ 100/S$. For high efficiencies of treatment, the concentration of waste in the effluent, S_e, must be small. Figure 145 indicates the relationship between effluent concentration, treatment efficiency, and SRT, based on Equations 6 and 7. As SRT decreases, the concentrations of waste in the effluent increases and efficiency decreases. There is a minimum SRT below which the treatment process fails. This point is reached when the microorganisms are removed from the system faster than they can reproduce themselves and "washout" or loss of microorganisms responsible for treatment results. This minimum SRT is reached when $S_e = S_0$, and can be approximated from the following by considering b to be negligible:

$$\mathrm{SRT}_{\mathrm{min.}} = \frac{1}{yk}\left(\frac{K_s + S_0}{S_0}\right) \tag{9}$$

The minimum SRT is a function of the fraction of organic waste converted to biological cells, y, the maximum rate of waste utilization, k, and the raw waste concentration, S_0. The value of y is much lower in anaerobic treatment than in aerobic treatment. It is for this reason, other factors being equal, that $\mathrm{SRT}_{\mathrm{min.}}$ for anaerobic treatment is much longer than for aerobic treatment.

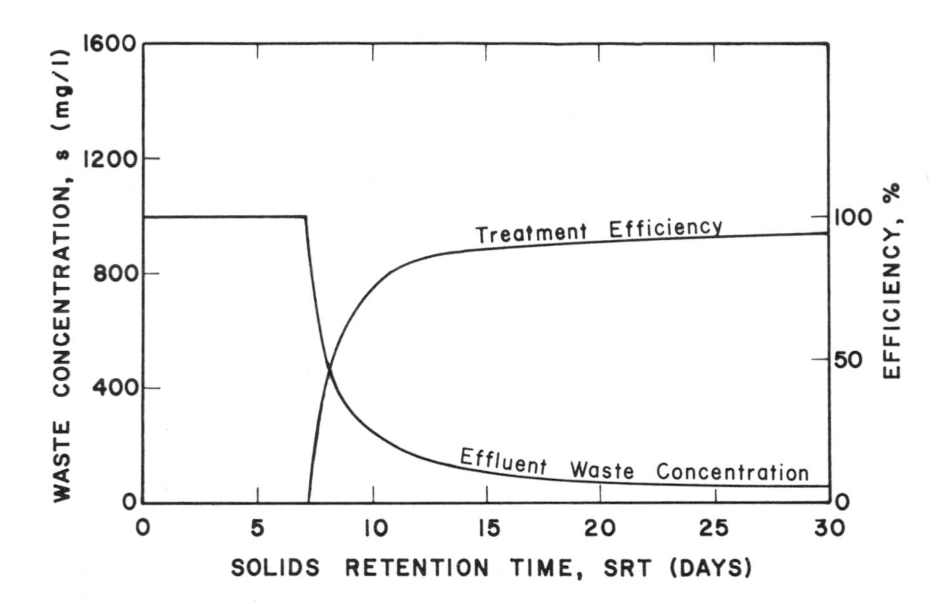

Figure 145. Relationship between solids retention time, effluent waste concentration, and treatment efficiency, based on assumed values of 1,000 mg/liter for S, 100 mg/liter for K_s, 0.05 for a, 0.04/day for b, and 4 gm/gm-day for k.

With the conventional process indicated in Figure 142, the SRT is equal to the hydraulic detention time (V/Q). With the anaerobic activated sludge and the anaerobic filter process, however, the removal of excess microorganisms and the removal of effluent from the system can be carried out independently of each other so that a long SRT required for efficient treatment can be maintained while operating at a relatively short hydraulic detention time.

APPLICATION OF KINETICS TO ANAEROBIC TREATMENT

Continuous culture kinetics have been used primarily to describe the growth of a single species of microorganisms in a dilute solution of a pure organic substrate. However, the anaerobic waste treatment process is much more complex, as indicated previously, and requires many different species of microorganisms to efficiently treat complex wastes containing a variety of organic materials. The kinetics of pure culture growth can be used to describe the kinetics of a complex process such as this when one step in the process is sufficiently slow to govern the rate of the overall process. It has been found that the rate-limiting step in the anaerobic treatment of municipal sludge is the methane fermentation of the important intermediates, acetic and propionic acid. A much longer SRT is required for successful fermentation of these acids than is required for protein or carbohydrate fermentation (16). Of the degradable materials studied, only the long chain fatty acids have a comparable SRT requirement. It can thus be expected that with most soluble organic wastes, acetic and propionic acid fermentation will also represent the limiting step, although there may be exceptions to this.

The kinetics of methane fermentation of acetic and propionic acids have been evaluated (20) at temperatures of 25°, 30°, and 35°C.; $SRT_{min.}$ at these temperatures for these acids lies between 3 and 5 days. At lower temperatures, $SRT_{min.}$ increases significantly so that anaerobic treatment below 20°C. becomes difficult. A knowledge of $SRT_{min.}$ is of interest to indicate the limiting design below which process failure will result. In practice, a safety factor must be used so that such failure will not occur. Thus, actual SRT values ranging from 2 to 10 times greater than $SRT_{min.}$ are commonly used. In general, the longer the SRT value used, the more reliable and efficient will be the operation, but the higher will be the cost. The best SRT to use is decided by the required degree of treatment and good engineering judgment. The critical SRT is the same for the conventional and for anaerobic contact processes. The conventional process is used for concentrated wastes where economical treatment can be obtained with hydraulic detention times equal to the desired SRT. The economical treatment of dilute wastes, however, requires hydraulic detention times much below the desired SRT, so here the anaerobic contact processes are more applicable.

ANAEROBIC BIOLOGICAL GROWTH

The most important advantages of the anaerobic waste treatment process are the high percentage of the waste which is stabilized by conversion to methane gas and the low percentage conversion of organic matter to biological cells. The small quantities of sludge growth minimizes the problems of biological sludge disposal, as well as the requirements for the inorganic nutrients, nitrogen and phosphorus.

The biological growth resulting from anaerobic treatment of different types of wastes varies considerably, as shown in Figure 146 (21). Thus, the growth cannot be predicted from a knowledge of the waste strength alone. The two extremes in growth are represented by fatty acid wastes, which produce the lowest growth, to carbohydrates, which produce the highest. Other types of waste can be expected to vary between these two extremes. Corresponding growth under aerobic conditions may be as high as 0.4 pound/pound BOD_L.

The quantity of waste converted to biological suspended solids decreases with increase in SRT. When cells are maintained for long periods of time, they decay, as indicated by Equation 4, with the result that the net growths are less. Thus, greater waste stabilization and lower biological cell production are obtained at long SRT values.

The biological requirements for inorganic nitrogen and phosphorus may be determined from the cell growth indicated in Figure 146 and the fraction of nitrogen and phosphorus in the cells. From these considerations, the nitrogen requirement is about 11 percent and the phosphorus requirement is about 2 percent of the cell volatile solids weight. Thus, if the solids production were 0.1 pound/pound BOD_L, the nitrogen and phosphorus requirements would be 0.011 pounds and 0.002 pounds/pound of BOD_L, respectively.

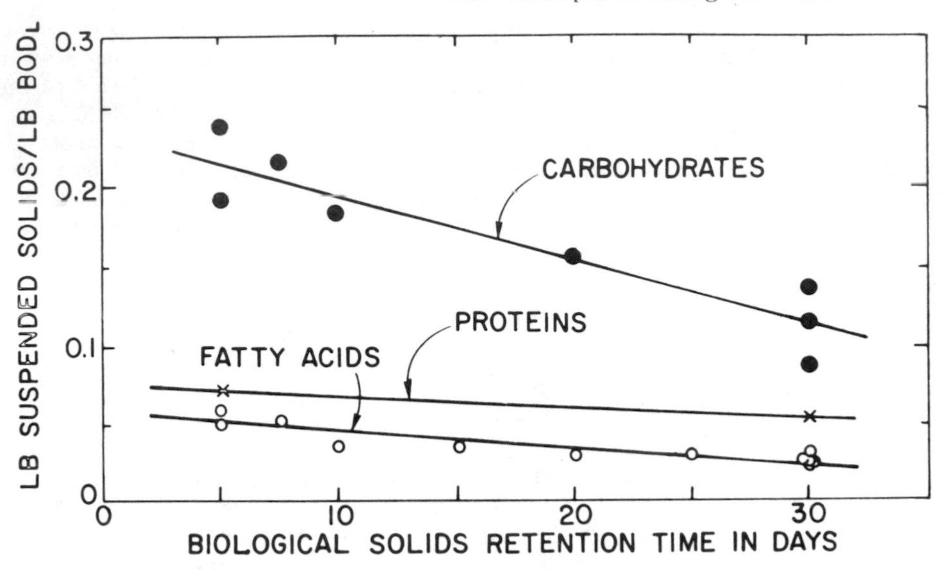

Figure 146. Biological solids production resulting from methane fermentation.

ANAEROBIC FILTER OPERATION

Insufficient methane for waste heating is produced from anaerobic treatment of dilute soluble wastes so that treatment at ambient waste temperature is a practical necessity. However, efficient waste treatment at temperatures of 20° to 25°C. requires a long SRT. This is not economically feasible with the conventional process, and therefore either the anaerobic activated sludge or the anaerobic filter process is more appropriate. The anaerobic activated sludge process operates quite well with meat packing and other wastes containing a significant suspended solids concentration. The microflora become attached to the solids and are readily removed in the final settling tank for recycle back to the digester. However, with soluble wastes, many of the bacteria remain dispersed and a significant number may be lost in the effluent, making a long SRT difficult to maintain. The anaerobic filter appeared to be a process which might overcome this problem and was explored in the author's laboratory during the past year.

In the anaerobic filter the bacteria grow attached to the filter stone and remain in the filter, making a long SRT possible. The laboratory filter used in this study was simple in construction and was designed for a feasibility evaluation of the process, rather than to determine the most efficient design parameters for operation. A schematic diagram of the filter is shown in Figure 147. A 3-liter bottle was filled to the 2.5-liter mark with 1–2-inch quartzite stone. Feed was introduced at the bottom of the bottle through a simple tube and was withdrawn at the top so that the filter remained completely submerged. The stone volume was approximately 1.5 liters, while the liquid volume was about 1.0 liters. Gas was collected and metered. Feeding was continuous during the week, but the rate was reduced over each weekend.

The feed composition and the rate of feed were varied over the 10-month period of operation, as indicated in Tables 49 and 50. The organic materials listed in Table 49 were mixed with settled sewage and sufficient sodium bicarbonate to give an alkalinity of 2,500 mg/l. The sewage carriage water served as a source

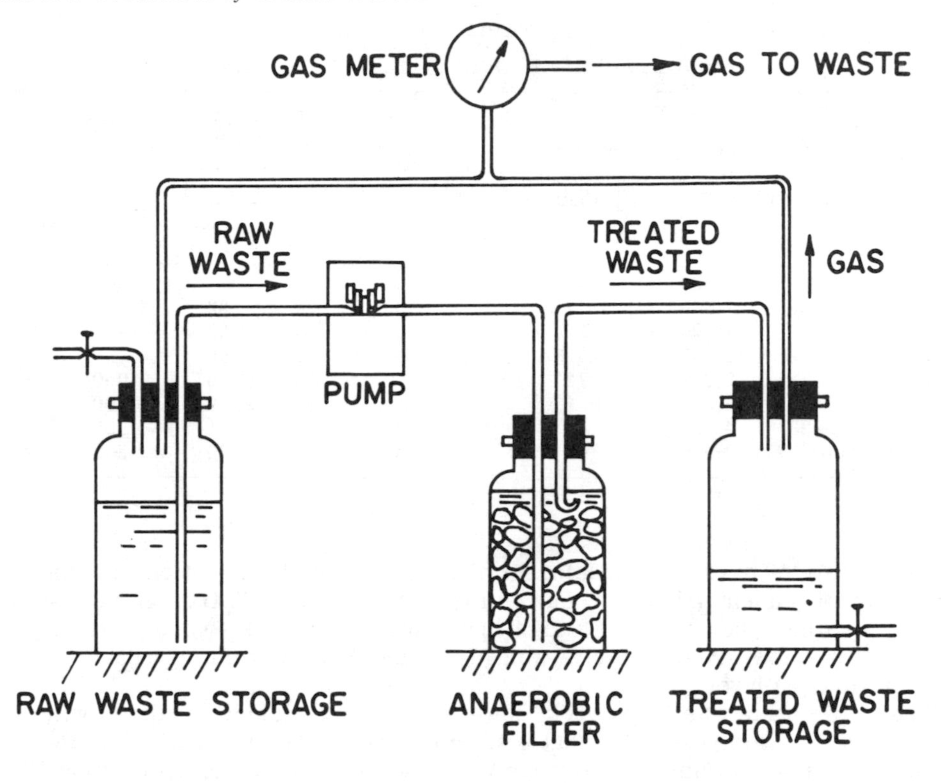

Figure 147. Schematic diagram of laboratory anaerobic filter.

of seed organisms and of nutrients for biological growth. During the first period, 1,500 mg/l of methanol, which is readily used by one group of methane bacteria (16), was used as the feed. Within 10 days, active methane fermentation had begun. On Day 32 acetate was added to the feed, and on Day 124 propionate was added. These acids were chosen because their fermentation represents the limiting step in anaerobic treatment and their efficient utilization would be required for the process to be feasible. From Day 124 the two acid salts were added in equal equivalent amounts, giving the total volatile acid concentrations listed in Table 49.

Results of operation are listed in Table 50. Approximately 30 days were required after introduction of acetate before it was used at a significant rate and

TABLE 49

ANAEROBIC FILTER FEED COMPOSITION

Feed Period	Days of Operation	Total Days	Feed Composition	COD mg/l	Volatile Acids* mg/l
1	1–31	31	Methanol	2,140	0
2	32–123	92	Methanol + Acetate	2,360	275
3	124–269	146	Methanol + Acetate + Propionate	2,650	500
4	270–285	16	Acetate + Propionate	–	650
5	286–307	22	Acetate + Propionate	2,240	1,550

*As equivalent acetic acid.

TABLE 50

RESULTS OF ANAEROBIC FILTER OPERATION

Feed Period	Days of Operation	Feed Volume ml/Day	Theoretical Detention-Time Hours	Loading lb COD per 1,000 cu. ft. per Day	Removal Eff. Percent		Gas Production	
					COD	Volatile Acids	ml/Day	Percent Methane
1	11–31	2,000	12	107	88	–	1,540	89
2	32–68	2,000	12	123	74	22	1,440	90
2	69–91	2,000	12	123	78	60	–	–
2	92–123	2,000	12	123	82	80	–	–
3	124–226	2,000	12	131	86	85	1,950	85
3	227–269	4,000	6	266	80	80	3,380	85
4	270–285	4,000	6	–	–	81	950	91
5	285–307	4,000	6	224	82	76	2,300	91

approximately 60 days passed before a high efficiency of utilization was obtained. This is about the normal time required to start an anaerobic treatment system beginning without the benefit of a significant anaerobic sludge seed; it is required to permit the slow-growing acetic-acid-using methane bacteria to reach a significant population level.

When propionate was introduced, however, it was efficiently utilized within only one week. It is postulated that a sufficient concentration of this acid was present in the settled sewage carriage water so that during the preceeding 123 days of operation a somewhat active propionic-acid-using methane bacterial population became established in the filter.

On Day 270 the methanol was eliminated from the feed, and on Day 286 the concentrations of propionate and acetate were increased. The anaerobic filter immediately responded to these changes. Operation proved to be very stable and not harmed by decreased feed rate over the weekend or by daily temperature changes of a few degrees centigrade.

The loadings indicated in Table 50 are exceptionally high when compared with normal aerobic treatment and yet the production of excess biological solids was almost negligible. In the latter two months of operation, the suspended solids in the effluent had reached a level of only 20–40 mg/l, and this settled readily. Also, no suspended solids had to be removed from the filter during the entire period of operation. The methane production indicated at least 70–80 percent of the waste was stabilized by conversion to methane gas. Thus, a nearly ideal treatment process is indicated with high loading rates, negligible biological solids for disposal, treatment of relatively dilute wastes at ambient temperatures (25°C.), and little or no power requirements. Since the anaerobic filter is submerged, the head loss would be small even compared to that with an aerobic trickling filter. The only significant adverse factors were the long time required before instigation of volatile acids fermentation and the presence of a sulfide odor in the effluent due to reduction of sulfates contained in the carriage water.

On the last day of operation the filter was opened and examined for quantity and nature of biological growth. The accumulated growth, which was readily washed from the stones, had a total weight of 11.6 grams and a volatile content of 68 percent. This is a significant growth, and based on an average suspended solids concentration of 20 mg/l in the filter effluent, would indicate an SRT in the filter of over 100 days.

Several anaerobic free-swimming protozoa were present throughout the filter. Bacteria, however, predominated and those of the most prevalent group were connected in long entwined chains characteristic of *Methanobacterium sohngenii*, an acetate utilizer (22). When growths were carefully lifted from the stones and examined, as many as 50 to 100 of these chains were observed bundled together in a spiral fashion, like a many-stranded cable. Of much lesser abundance were packets of large sarcina characteristic of *Methanosarcina*.

Because of the promise of the anaerobic filter process, studies are currently underway to determine the significant factors for filter design. Several six-foot-tall units are presently being operated with sample ports at different levels. Complex soluble wastes are being used and the first-stage conversion to fatty acids, as well as the second-stage fermentation to methane and carbon dioxide, is being evaluated. It is also planned to look into the possibility of recycle to determine if any significant advantage can be obtained. The use of an aerobic treatment unit to reduce the anaerobic conditions of the filter effluent, as well as to produce a higher degree of treatment efficiency, is also under study.

OTHER APPLICATIONS

Operational data for the anaerobic treatment of strictly soluble wastes are fairly limited. This is due partly to a fairly prevalent belief that anaerobic treatment is an inefficient process and also that it is for solids destruction only, rather than for general waste treatment. This, however, is not the case, as indicated by the results of treatment of various wastes listed in Table 51.

These data are results from both laboratory and pilot plant studies of the conventional and the anaerobic contact process. Five-day BOD loadings of over 100 lb/1,000 cu ft/day are indicated in most cases, along with BOD removal efficiencies generally over 90 percent. Values for BOD stabilized were computed from reported values of methane production, using 5.62 cu. ft. of methane produced to correspond to the stabilization of 1 pound of BOD_L, and assuming this is equivalent to 0.65 pounds of BOD_5. The values are shown for comparative purposes and indicate that in most cases a high proportion of the BOD which is removed is actually converted to methane gas.

It would be desirable to know the SRT which was associated with the operational results listed in Table 51 so that the significance of this parameter could be evaluated better. In the case of the conventional process, the SRT is equal to the hydraulic detention time. In the contact processes, however, these two parameters are relatively independent of each other. Insufficient information was usually given here to allow a proper evaluation of SRT. In any event, the data available do indicate the potential of anaerobic treatment for the stabilization of relatively soluble industrial wastes.

PROCESS LIMITATIONS

Concentrated soluble industrial wastes frequently contain toxic or inhibitory concentrations of both inorganic and organic materials. Several instances of anaerobic treatment failures listed in the literature can be traced to this cause. Thus, it is desirable to understand the influence of toxic materials so that such problems can be anticipated when investigating the application of the anaerobic process to waste treatment. The concentrations of alkali and alkaline earth-metal salts, such as those of sodium, potassium, calcium, or magnesium, may be quite high in industrial wastes, and are frequently the cause of inefficiency in, or failure of, anaerobic treatment (31, 32). This "salt" toxicity is associated primarily with the cation, rather than the anion portion of the salt. The nature of the inhibitory effect of these salts is quite complex, but general guidelines can

TABLE 51

ANAEROBIC TREATMENT PERFORMANCE FOR THE CONVENTIONAL AND CONTACT PROCESSES

Waste	Hydraulic Detention Time Days	Digestion Temperature °C.	BOD_5					Reference
			Raw Waste mg/l	lb/1,000 cu ft/Day			Percent Removed	
				Added	Removed	Stabilized		
Conventional Process:								
Butanol	10.0	–	17,000	114	80	75	70	Buswell (23)
Acetic acid	30.0	35	620,000	975	965	876	99	McCarty *et al.* (24)
Butyric acid	30.0	35	400,000	1,000	980	910	98	McCarty *et al.* (24)
Contact Processes:								
Maize starch	3.3	23	6,280	110	97	85	88	Hemans *et al.* (25)
Whiskey distillery	6.2	33	25,000	250	237	164	95	Painter *et al.* (26)
Cotton kiering	1.3	30	1,600	74	50	42	67	Pettet *et al.* (27)
Citrus	1.3	33	4,600	214	186	141	87	McNary *et al.* (28)
Brewery	2.3	–	3,900	127	122	–	96	Newton *et al.* (29)
Meat packing	1.3	33	2,000	110	104	77	95	Pettet *et al.* (27)
Meat packing	0.5	33	1,380	156	142	66	91	Steffen *et al.* (30)
Meat packing	0.5	35	1,430	164	156	–	95	Schroepfer *et al.* (4)
Meat packing	0.5	29	1,310	152	143	–	94	Schroepfer *et al.* (4)
Meat packing	0.5	24	1,110	131	119	–	91	Schroepfer *et al.* (4)

be given to indicate when inhibition may be suspected, and how it may be controlled. In general, cation concentrations up to 100–400 mg/l may be stimulatory, rather than inhibitory to the process. Concentrations ranging from 1,000 to 5,000 mg/l usually have an adverse effect on the process, and the higher concentrations may so strongly retard the methane bacteria that anaerobic treatment may not be practical. Combinations of cations act in a different manner than single ions. The divalent cations are less toxic if a stimulatory concentration of a monovalent cation such as sodium or potassium is present. If high concentrations of these salts cannot be eliminated from the waste, then waste dilution may be indicated.

Ammonia is usually formed from anaerobic degradation of wastes containing proteins or urea. Ammonia may be present during treatment, either in the form of the ammonium ion (NH_4^+) or as dissolved ammonia gas (NH_3). These two forms are in equilibrium with each other, the relative concentration of each depending upon the *p*H of the solution. At *p*H values near 7.0, concentrations of ammonia nitrogen up to 1,000 mg/l will have no adverse effect (33). Higher concentrations, however, can be detrimental, especially at higher *p*H values which cause a shift toward the more toxic NH_3 form. Ammonia nitrogen concentrations above 3,000 mg/l, at any *p*H, are quite detrimental.

Sulfides in anaerobic treatment can result from introduction of sulfides with the raw waste, or from biological production in the digester by reduction of sulfates and other sulfur-containing inorganic compounds, as well as from anaerobic protein degradation. Sulfate salts usually represent the major precursors of sulfides in industrial wastes. Sulfides, when formed, may be precipitated by heavy metals, may remain as soluble sulfides in the digester, or may escape from solution as a gas (20). A sufficiently high concentration of sulfides in solution can be quite toxic to the methane-producing bacteria. In general, concentrations of soluble sulfides from 50 to 100 mg/l can be tolerated with little adverse effect. Concentrations up to 200 mg/l may require acclimation by the methane bacteria, and higher concentrations than this generally are quite toxic.

Low concentrations of heavy metal salts such as of copper, zinc, and nickel can be quite toxic to anaerobic treatment. However, these metals combine with sulfides to form extremely insoluble and biologically inert precipitates (34, 35). As long as an excess of sulfides is available, either from sulfate reduction or from some other source, these heavy metals can be tolerated. The author is aware of at least two cases where the addition of sodium sulfide to munifipal digesters cured serious heavy metal problems. Hexavalent chromium can also be toxic to anaerobic treatment. However, this metal ion, if introduced slowly, may be reduced to the trivalent form which is relatively insoluble at normal digester *p*H levels, and consequently is not very toxic.

In general, elimination of potentially toxic materials from the waste is the most advisable solution. If this is not feasible, then dilution of the waste below the "toxic threshold" may be indicated. If too much dilution is required, however, the waste may reach the point where a high efficiency of treatment becomes difficult.

SUMMARY

The anaerobic treatment of soluble wastes has some significant advantages over aerobic treatment: high loading rates are possible with little production of biological solids for disposal, power requirements are lower, and the methane produced by anaerobic treatment is a useful end product. The development of various "anaerobic contact processes," which produce more rapid and efficient treatment, has made possible the economical treatment of relatively dilute wastes at ambient temperatures. It is felt that efficient anaerobic treatment of soluble wastes with BOD concentration as low as 500 mg/l is now feasible. Wastes with lower BOD can also be treated anaerobically, although the waste treatment efficiency will not be of the same magnitude expected for aerobic treatment. This is because the "driving force" required for rapid anaerobic treatment is higher so that treated effluents with less than 50 mg/l BOD are difficult to produce. Nevertheless, the advantages of anaerobic treatment may dictate in the future that the best process for dilute wastes will be operated in two stages, with anaerobic treatment being used for maximum waste stabilization, followed by an aerobic process for polishing of the effluent.

The best parameter for controlling the operation of anaerobic treatment is the biological solids retention time (SRT). A minimum SRT exists, below which the critical methane-producing bacteria are removed from the system faster than they can reproduce themselves. This $SRT_{min.}$ represents the "breaking point" of the system, and, as in all engineering design, a safety factor must be applied to prevent the system failure which occurs at this point. For this reason, SRT values of two to ten times $SRT_{min.}$ should be used. The higher the safety factor, the more stable and efficient the operation.

When very high SRT values are maintained, highly efficient treatment can be obtained and at lower temperatures. Also, the system is more stable and readily responds to changes in organic or hydraulic loading, as well as to changes in temperature. The "anaerobic filter" is one of the most promising of the contact processes for soluble waste treatment, as it permits the maintenance of exceptionally high SRT values of up to 100 days. With this process it appears that most of the advantages of anaerobic waste treatment can be realized.

ACKNOWLEDGMENT

This report was supported in part by Research Grant WP-584 from the Federal Water Pollution Control Administration.

REFERENCES

(1) Barker, H. A. *Bacterial Fermentations*. New York: John Wiley and Sons (1956).

(2) Jeris, J. S., and P. L. McCarty. "The Biochemistry of Methane Fermentation Using C^{14} Tracers," *J. Water Poll. Cont. Fed., 37,* 178–192 (1965).

(3) McCarty, P. L., J. S. Jeris, and W. Murdoch. "Individual Volatile Acids in Anaerobic Treatment," *J. Water Poll. Cont. Fed., 35,* 1501–1516 (1963).

(4) Schroepfer, G. J., W. J. Fullen, A. S. Johnson, N. R. Ziemke, and J. J. Anderson. "The Anaerobic Contact Process as Applied to Packinghouse Wastes," *Sewage Ind. Wastes, 27,* 460–486 (1955).

(5) Coulter, J. B., S. Soneda, and M. B. Ettinger. "Preliminary Studies on Complete Anaerobic Treatment," *Proc. ASCI,* 82(SA5), 1089-1–1087-9 (1956).

(6) Stander, G. J. *Full-Scale Anaerobic Digestion of Effluents from the Production of Maize Starch.* Council for Scientific and Industrial Research Special Report No. W20, Pretoria, South Africa, 36–39 (1963).

(7) Winneberger, J. H., W. I. Saad, and P. H. McGauhey. *A Study of Methods of Preventing Failure of Septic-Tank Percolation Fields.* University of California Sanitary Engineering Research Laboratory Report (1961).

(8) Monod, J. "La Technique de Culture Continue; Théorie et Applications," *Ann. Inst. Pasteur, 79,* 390 (1950).

(9) Novick, A., and L. Szilard. "Experiments with the Chemostat on Spontaneous Mutations of Bacteria," *Genetics, 36,* 708–719 (1950).

(10) Herbert, D., R. Elsworth, and R. C. Telling. "The Continuous Culture of Bacteria: A Theoretical and Experimental Study," *J. Gen. Microbiol., 14,* 601–622 (1956).

(11) Novick, A. "Growth of Bacteria," *Ann. Rev. Microbiol., 9,* 97–110 (1955).

(12) James, T. W. "Continuous Culture of Microorganisms," *Ann. Rev. Microbiol., 15,* 27–46 (1961).

(13) Andrews, J. F., R. D. Cole, and E. A. Pearson. *Kinetics and Characteristics of Multi-Stage Methane Fermentation.* Sanitary Engineering Research Laboratory Report No. 64-11, University of California, Berkeley, California (1964).

(14) Agardy, F. J., R. D. Cole, and E. A. Pearson. *Kinetic and Activity Parameters of Anaerobic Fermentation Systems.* Sanitary Engineering Research Laboratory Report 63-2, University of California, Berkeley, California (1963).

(15) Stewart, M. J. *Reaction Kinetics and Operational Parameters of Continuous Flow Anaerobic Fermentation Processes.* Sanitary Engineering Research Laboratory Report No. 2, University of California, Berkeley, California (1958).

(16) McCarty, P. L. "Kinetics of Waste Assimilation in Anaerobic Treatment," *Developments in Industrial Microbiology.* Washington, D.C.: American Institute of Biological Sciences (1966).

(17) Heukelekian, H., H. E. Orford, and R. Manganelli. "Factors Affecting the Quantity of Sludge Production in the Activated Sludge Process," *Sewage Ind. Wastes, 23,* 945–958 (1951).

(18) Eckenfelder, W. W., and R. F. Weston. "Kinetics of Biological Oxidation," *Biological Treatment of Sewage and Industrial Wastes,* edited by J. McCabe and W. W. Eckenfelder. Vol. 1. New York: Reinhold (1956).

(19) Marr, A. G., E. H. Nilson, and D. J. Clark. "The Maintenance Requirement of *Escherichia coli.,*" *Ann. New York Acad. Sci., 102,* 536–548 (1963).

(20) Lawrence, A. W. "Kinetics of Methane Fermentation in Anaerobic Waste Treatment." Ph.D. Thesis, Stanford University (1967).

(21) Speece, R. E., and P. L. McCarty. "Nutrients Requirements and Biological Solids Accumulation in Anaerobic Digestion," *International Conference on Water Pollution Research, 1962.* New York: Pergamon Press (1964).

(22) Breed, R. S., E. G. D. Murray, and N. R. Smith. *Bergey's Manual of Determinative Bacteriology.* 7th Ed. Baltimore: The Williams and Williams Company (1957).

(23) Buswell, A. M. "Fermentations in Waste Treatment," *Industrial Fermentation,* edited by L. A. Underkofter, and R. J. Hickey. New York: Chemical Publishing Company (1954).

(24) McCarty, P. L., and C. A. Vath. "Volatile Acid Digestion at High Loading Rates," *Inter. J. Air Water Poll., 6,* 65–73 (1962).

(25) Hemens, J., P. G. J. Meiring, and G. J. Stander. "Full-Scale Anaerobic Digestion of Effluents from the Production of Maize-Starch," *Water Waste Treat.,* (May–June 1962).

(26) Painter, H. A., J. Hemens, and D. G. Shurben. "Treatment of Malt Whiskey Distillery Wastes by Anaerobic Digestion," *Brewer's Guard.* (1960).

(27) Pettet, A. E. J., T. G. Tomlinson, and J. Hemens. "The Treatment of Strong Organic Wastes by Anaerobic Digestion," *J. Inst. Public Health Engr.,* 170–191 (July 1959).

(28) McNary, R. R., R. W. Wolford, and M. H. Dougherty. "Experimental Treatment of Citrus Waste Water," *Proceedings,* 8th Industrial Waste Conference, 1953, Purdue Engineering Extension Series 83, 256–274 (1954).

(29) Newton, D., H. L. Keinath, and L. S. Hillis. "Pilot Plant Studies for the Evaluation of Methods of Treating Brewery Wastes," *Proceedings,* 16th Industrial Waste Conference, 1961, Purdue Engineering Extension Series 109, 332–350 (1962).

(30) Steffen, A. J., and M. Bedker. "Operation of Full-Scale Anaerobic Contact Treatment Plant for Mean Packing Wastes," *Proceedings,* 16th Industrial Waste Conference, 1961, Purdue Engineering Extension Series 109, 423–437 (1962).

(31) Kugelman, I. J., and P. L. McCarty. "Cation Toxicity and Stimulation in Anaerobic Waste Treatment. II. Daily Feed Studies," *Proceedings,* Nineteenth Industrial Waste Conference, 1964, Purdue Engineering Extension Series No. 117, 667–686 (1965).

(32) Kugelman, I. J., and P. L. McCarty. "Cation Toxicity and Stimulation in Anaerobic Waste Treatment," *J. Water Poll. Cont. Fed., 37,* 97–116 (1965).

(33) McCarty, P. L. "Anaerobic Waste Treatment Fundamentals," *Public Works* (September–December 1964).

(34) Lawrence, A. W., and P. L. McCarty. "The Role of Sulfide in Preventing Heavy Metal Toxicity in Anaerobic Treatment," *J. Water Poll. Cont. Fed.*, *37*, 392–406 (1965).

(35) Masselli, J. W., N. W. Masselli, and M. G. Burford. *The Occurrence of Cooper in Water, Sewage and Sludge and Its Effects on Sludge Digestion.* New England Interstate Water Pollution Control Commission Report (June 1961).

A DISCUSSION OF "ANAEROBIC TREATMENT OF SOLUBLE WASTES"

John F. Andrews
Clemson University, Clemson, South Carolina

Dr. McCarty has proposed the use of an "anaerobic trickling filter" with hydraulic upflow for the treatment of soluble wastes. This is certainly a step in the right direction, since the use of such a process results in the retention of microorganisms in the reactor and allows operation at low hydraulic residence times. In effect, the process carries out biological oxidation and solids-liquid separation in the same unit instead of requiring separate units for the biological oxidation and solids-liquid separation.

Dr. McCarty has stated that his proposed process is limited to soluble wastes and has performed his experiments using the soluble substrates methanol, formic acid, acetic acid, and propionic acid. He has shown in these experiments that the process gives a high percentage of COD removal with a low solids concentration in the effluent. However, by using soluble substrates which are directly metabolized by the methane bacteria he has neglected solids ("acid forming bacteria") produced in the conversion of such soluble wastes as sugars to volatile acids. Speece and McCarty (1) have shown that this can be significant in that as much as 0.46 grams of solids can be produced per gram of glucose COD utilized. They also indicate that the major portion (0.406 gm.) of these solids are produced in the conversion of glucose to volatile acids. Only 0.054 grams of solids are produced in the subsequent conversion of these volatile acids to methane and carbon dioxide. The solids produced are destroyed at a relatively low rate and may result in clogging of the filter media and/or pass over in the effluent from the reactor.

The filter media used by Dr. McCarty may be unnecessary. A vertical multistage reactor, such as that proposed by Gates *et al.* (2), would make more efficient use of the reactor volume, reduce the danger of clogging, and permit the digestion of both soluble and insoluble wastes. This upflow reactor consists of a mixed lower chamber in which anaerobic decomposition occurs, a solids separator just above the lower chamber which returns solids to the lower chamber, intermediate baffles to prevent oxygen from the aerobic compartment from reaching the anaerobic chamber and separator, and an upper aerobic chamber for odor control.

It is encouraging to see research aimed toward increasing microorganism residence times with decreased hydraulic residence times, since this results in increased substrate removal rates per unit volume of reactor and therefore permits the use of smaller reactors. However, the value of solids retention and/or solids separation with recycle to the reactor has been amply demonstrated by theory (3), in the laboratory (4), and in the treatment of certain industrial wastes (5).

Research emphasis should now be placed on field studies using the "real" substrates (sewage sludge, etc.) and solids retention and/or solids separation apparatus of a size that will permit field evaluation and scale-up.

REFERENCES

(1) Speece, R. E., and P. L. McCarty. "Nutrient Requirements and Biological Solids Accumulation in Anaerobic Digestion," *Advances in Water Pollution Research,* edited by W. W. Ekenfelder. Vol. 2. New York: The Macmillan Co. (1964).

(2) Gates, W. E., J. H. Smith, S. Lin, and C. H. Ris. "An Anaerobicaerobic Process for Industrial Wastewater Treatment. I. The anaerobic process." Presented at the National Meeting of the Water Pollution Control Federation, Atlantic City, New Jersey (1965).

(3) Andrews, J. F., R. D. Cole, and E. A. Pearson. *Kinetics and Characteristics of Multistage Methane Fermentations.* Berkeley: Sanit. Eng. Research Lab., University of California (1964).

(4) Schroepfer, G. J., and N. R. Ziemke. "Development of the Anaerobic Contact Process. I. Pilot-plant Investigations and Economics," *Sewage Ind. Wastes, 31,* 164, 1959.

(5) Steffen, A. J. "Treatment of Packing House Wastes by Anaerobic Digestion," *Biological Treatment of Sewage and Industrial Wastes,* edited by J. McCabe and W. W. Eckenfelder. Vol. II. New York: Reinhold Publ. Co. (1958).

NEW DEVELOPMENTS IN THE ANAEROBIC DIGESTION OF SLUDGES

Joseph F. Malina, Jr., and Ernest M. Miholits
The University of Texas, Austin, Texas

INTRODUCTION

The treatment and the disposal of the primary and biological sludges produced during the treatment of wastewaters frequently pose more serious problems than the treatment of the liquid wastes alone. The anaerobic digestion of these sludges is employed at many wastewater treatment installations to stabilize a portion of the organic matter and thereby reduce the volume of sludge that must be disposed of. The destruction of pathogenic organisms and the production of usable products, such as a combustible gas and a stable, innoccuous sludge which can be used as a soil conditioner or fertilizer, are ancillary benefits derived from anaerobic digestion.

The final sludge disposal scheme to be used determines the degree to which anaerobic digestion of the sludge must be carried out. The digested sludge is air-dried on sand beds in many plants. In this case a high degree of solids destruction is desired. Burning of the sludge is also practiced; at other installations the stabilized sludge is pumped or barged for dilution in the ocean. A wet combustion system which is operated at a relatively low temperature and pressure has been developed and shows promise of application to sludge disposal. Incineration of sludge is employed at many plants; however, the moisture content of the sludge must be reduced and the solids concentrated prior to incineration. The dewatering of the sludge may be accomplished by centrifugation, gravity thickening, or elutriation and vacuum filtration.

MECHANISM OF ANAEROBIC DIGESTION

In the anaerobic digestion of wastewater sludges, an orderly and controlled dissimilation of the substrate occurs, without molecular oxygen acting as the hydrogen acceptor, in such a manner that energy and building material are made available to the cell and a portion of the organic material is converted to methane and carbon dioxide. The microbial population is composed of facultative and anaerobic bacteria which utilize chemically bound oxygen in the form of carbon dioxide, nitrates, sulfates, or organic compounds as the final hydrogen acceptor. The facultative organisms can also use molecular oxygen during metabolism; therefore, these microbes protect the strict anaerobic bacteria from any small amounts of free dissolved oxygen which may be introduced into the digestion system with the feed sludge.

Particulate material cannot pass through the bacterial cell wall and membrane; therefore, these substances cannot be directly utilized by bacteria. Most microorganisms require dissolved substances from which energy, as well as organic and inorganic nutrients necessary for growth and metabolism, may be derived. Therefore, the microbial stabilization of wastewater sludges is in essence a sequential process. The particulate organic components of the sludge are first converted to simpler dissolved compounds, primarily organic acids which are subsequently utilized by the bacteria resulting in the release of methane and carbon dioxide gas. This liquefaction and hydrolysis is accomplished by a group of saprophytic bacteria which secrete extracellular enzymes. These bacteria attach themselves to the sludge solids. The bacterial enzymes do not diffuse into the medium but remain at the bacterial site; thus this close association between the sludge solids, bacteria, and enzymes allows for a more rapid breakdown of the organic material in the digester. During this acid production phase there is almost no change in the amount of organic material in the system. The environment may be characterized by a decrease of the *p*H and an increase in the concentration of organic acids. If the *p*H decreases below 6.0, the organic acids will continue to accumulate and gasification will not take place. Some alkaline products result during the degradation of particulate material and tend to provide the buffering capacity for the system.

The conversion of the dissolved organic acids to gaseous end products is carried out by strict anaerobic bacteria which are generally classified as methane bacteria, which are sensitive to changes in temperature, *p*H, and concentrations of fatty acids and other organic and inorganic compounds. The stabilization of the wastewater sludge is actually accomplished during gasification and the organic content of the system decreases markedly during the production of methane and carbon dioxide gas. This sequential mechanism is illustrated in Figure 148, which represents a summary plot of data observed during batch digestion studies (1). Although the mechanism of anaerobic digestion of sludge is sequential in nature, liquefaction and gasification take place simultaneously and synchronously in a well-buffered actively digesting system.

The composition of the feed sludge controls to some extent the final products of digestion. The average chemical constituents of sludges are presented in Table 52 (2). The composition of most municipal wastewater sludges may be generally categorized as carbohydrates, proteins, and lipids. The anaerobic degradation of these sludge constituents is presented in a generalized fashion in Figure 149. Many of the carbohydrates exist as large polysaccharides such as cellulose and starch (3, 4), which are hydrolyzed by extracellular enzymes to monosaccharides, primarily glucose with some fructose and mannose (5). These monosaccharides are used as a source of microbial energy resulting in end products which include methane, carbon dioxide, organic acids, and alcohols. Lipids are hydrolyzed to glycerol and fatty acids. The glycerol is anaerobically degraded in a manner similar to carbohydrates (6). Long chain fatty acids are broken down to shorter chain fatty acids by the sequential elimination of two carbon fragments ($-CH_2CH_2-$) which probably involves the Knoop's beta-oxidation scheme. The resultant end products are primarily acetate and propionate, which are subsequently converted to methane and carbon dioxide.

The nitrogenous constituents of the sludge include proteins, products of protein degradation, and urea and other nitrogen-containing compounds. Urea is hydrolyzed microbially to carbon dioxide and ammonia. Proteins are extracellularly hydrolyzed to peptides and amino acids which can then enter the bacterial cell for further degradation or utilization.

Carbohydrates and lipids are utilized much more quickly and completely than proteins during anaerobic digestion (7). The interrelationship and interactions of these three major groups of compounds are numerous and a detailed discussion is beyond the scope of this paper; however, two examples may be pertinent to this presentation. Many bacteria cannot form extracellular enzymes required to hydrolyze proteins unless an energy supply such as glucose is available (8); however, the glucose is released during degradation of carbohydrates, and other microorganisms require a small initial supply of ammonia nitrogen or amino acids to initiate the synthesis of extracellular enzymes (9).

The primary precursors to the production of methane during digestion are the organic fatty acids, mainly acetic, butyric, and propionic acids. Approximately

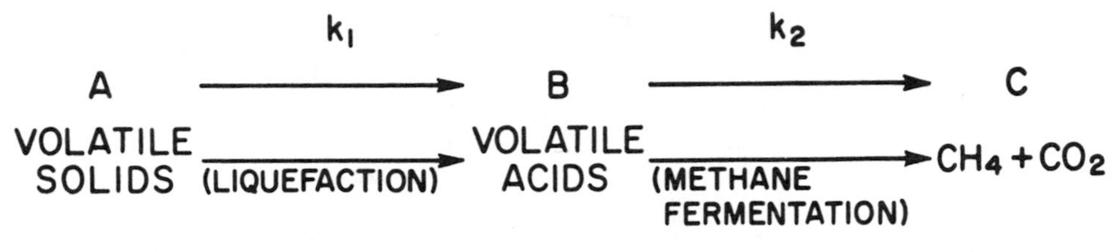

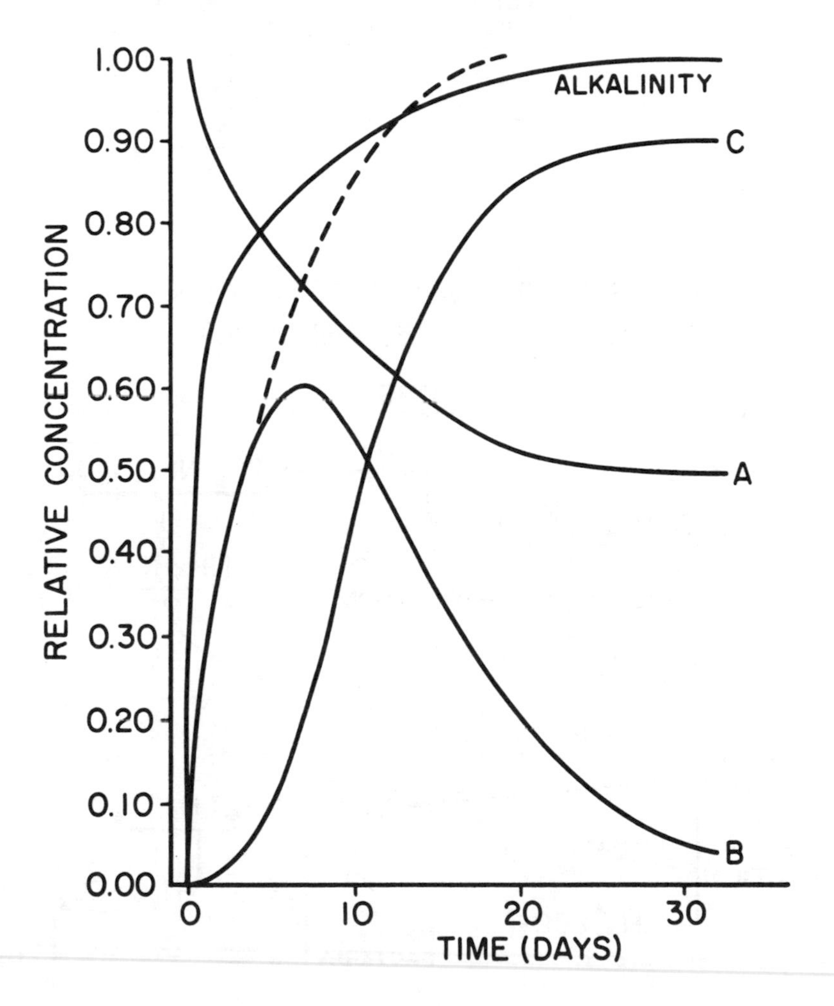

Figure 148. Sequential mechanism of anaerobic sludge disgestion.

TABLE 52

AVERAGE CHEMICAL CONSTITUENTS OF SEWAGE SOLIDS AND SLUDGES, PERCENT ON DRY WEIGHT BASIS

	Fresh	Activated	Digested
Organic matter	60–80	65–75	45–60
Total ash	20–40	25–38	40–55
Insoluble ash	17–35	22–30	35–50
Pentosans	1.00	2.10	1.50
Grease and fat (Ether)	7–35	5–12	3.5–17
Hemicelluloses	3.20	–	1.60
Cellulose	3.80	7.0 (Incl. lignin)	0.60
Lignin	5.80	–	8.40
Protein	22–28	37.50	16–21
Nitrogen (N)	4.50	6.20	2.25
Phosphoric (P_2O_5)	2.25	2.50	1.50
Iron (Fe_2O_3)	3.20	7.20	6.00
Chlorides (Cl)	0.50	0.50	0.50

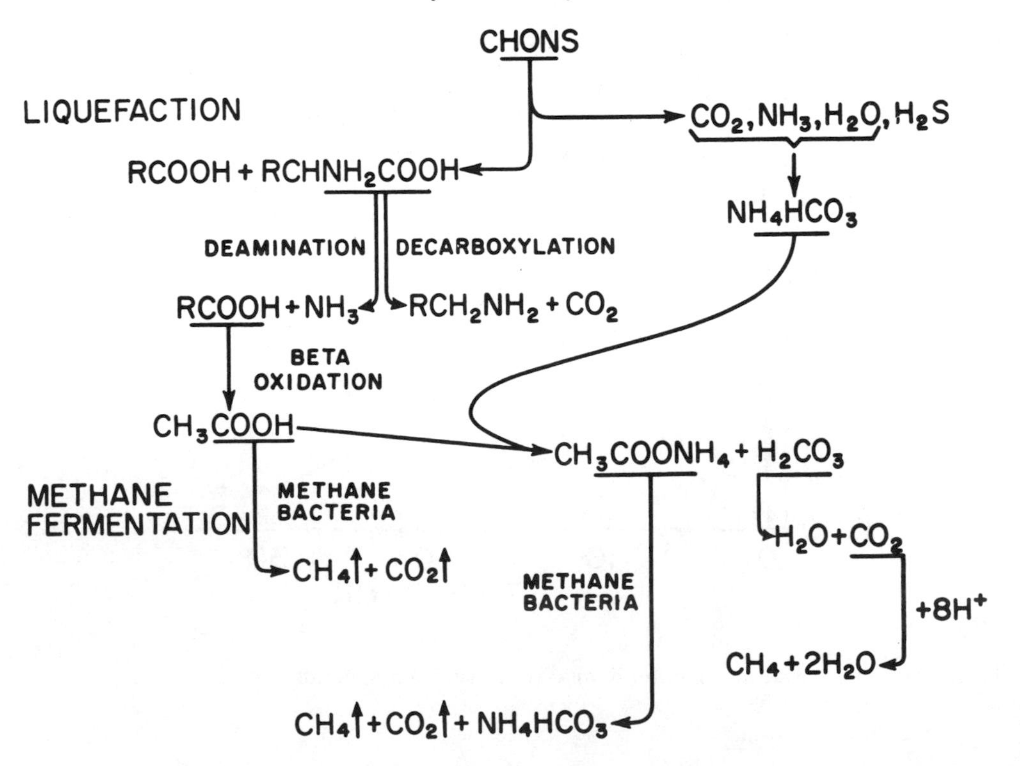

Figure 149. Anaerobic degradation of complex organic substances.

70 percent of the methane produced during anaerobic digestion is formed from acetic acid, and approximately 15 percent of methane results directly from the degradation of propionic acid. The reduction of carbon dioxide to methane and the decomposition of other intermediate compounds account for the remainder of the methane produced (10).

The energy resulting from anaerobic digestion of organic solids is relatively low compared to energy resulting from complete aerobic oxidation to carbon dioxide and water. The low energy yield of anaerobic metabolism may be attributed to the energy contained in the methane gas, which is not available to the microorganisms. Because of this low energy yield, the biological growth during anaerobic digestion is relatively small. Less than 10 percent of the proteins and fatty acids are synthesized into cells under anaerobic conditions. The energy from the anaerobic conversion of carbohydrates to organic acids results in greater cell synthesis than that reported during the anaerobic utilization of proteins and fatty acids.

Two physiologically different groups of bacteria are responsible for the anaerobic stabilization of wastewater sludge, namely, the acid-producing organisms and the methane bacteria. Since in most cases the rate-limiting reaction in anaerobic digestion is the production of methane and carbon dioxide from the dissolved intermediate compounds, the environment should be optimum for the methane-forming bacteria. The methane bacteria are particularly sensitive to temperature and *p*H. These bacteria are active in two temperature zones, namely, in the mesophilic range between 86° and 95°F. (30°-35°C.) and in the thermophilic range between 122° and 140°F. (50°-60°C.).

The curves presented in Figure 150 illustrate the temperature effects on digestion. Gas production is much higher at temperatures about 95°F. (35°C.) and 131°F. (55°C.). However, at temperatures near 113°F. (45°C.) the gas production is lower. The results of lab scale digestion studies (12) indicate that at 109.5°F. (42.5°C.) liquefaction progressed at a rate similar to that observed at 90.5°F. (32.5°C.) and 126.5°F. (52.5°C.). These data seem to indicate that the bacteria responsible for the conversion of organic acids to methane are insufficiently active at this intermediate temperature range. The results of laboratory and field evaluations of thermophilic digestion are not in complete agreement regarding the benefits accrued from operating digestion units in the range of 122°–131°F. (50–55°C.). The increased cost of providing the additional heat required to maintain the thermophilic condition is not offset by increased gas production or more complete digestion. Therefore, the optimum temperature recommended for efficient anaerobic digestion is between 85° and 95°F. (30° and 35°C.). The optimum *p*H for efficient methane production ranges between 6.2 and 7.8 (14); however, a more practical limit is 6.8 and 7.4 (15).

HIGH-RATE DIGESTION

The rate of anaerobic sludge stabilization has been accelerated by maintaining a relatively constant temperature throughout the digestion tank and by mixing the digesting sludge. This "high-rate" digestion process is capable of treating sludge in a relatively short detention time of between 10 and 15 days compared to the 30 or more days required for digestion tanks in which stratification took place and scum problems were prevalent.

A high rate of volatile solids destruction was maintained by intimately mixing raw and digested sludge prior to addition to the digestion tank (16). A ratio of 1:1 of raw to digested sludge on a weight of volatile solids basis was successfully digested in about 10 days without any artificial mixing of the sludge in the digestion tank. The reported advantage of this system is that the mixture of raw

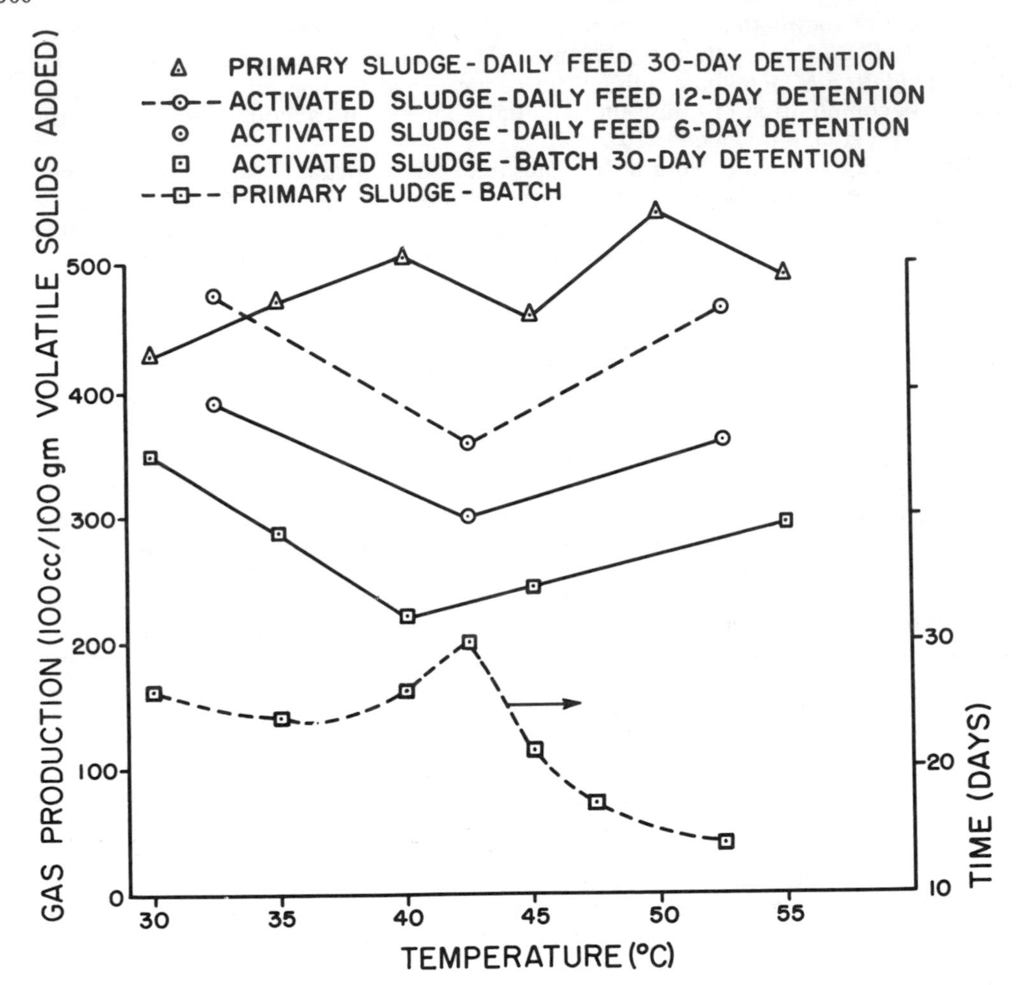

Figure 150. Effects of temperature on gas production during anaerobic digestion.

and digested sludge is added at the top of the digester and moves downward as digested sludge is withdrawn from the cone at the bottom of the digester. The sludge that is withdrawn for disposal, therefore, contains no raw sludge.

Temperature Control

The importance of temperature on the anaerobic digestion process was discussed previously in this paper. It should be pointed out, however, that not only must the temperature be maintained relatively constant within the recommended temperature range of 85°–95°F. (30°–35°C.), but the temperature of the entire mass of digesting sludge must be uniform to avoid thermal stratification or pockets or cold sludge. External heat-exchange units have solved many of the problems of sludge heating which were encountered when sludge digestion units were heated by passing hot water through coils which were located within the tank and which invariably would become coated with baked sludge, thereby reducing the transfer of heat to the digesting sludge. Pumping the digesting sludge from the tank through the external heat-exchange unit permits the seeding of raw sludge with digesting sludge; however, this external mixing does not markedly affect the circulation pattern in the tank.

Mixing

The initial attempts at providing some degree of mixing or agitation of the digesting sludge were primarily directed at breaking the scum or maintaining the scum moist so that the evolving gas could escape.

Advantages of mixing the digestion tanks other than eliminating the scum include (a) eliminating thermal stratification and maintaining a uniform temperature throughout the tank; (b) providing intimate contact between the raw feed sludge and the digesting sludge, thus eliminating isolated pockets of raw sludge; (c) maintaining close contact between the microbial population and the food supply; (d) rapidly removing metabolic waste material which may cause a local environment that is inhibitory to bacterial activity; and (e) presenting a "mixed liquor" condition in all parts of the digestion tank, so that the addition of new material to the tank results in the displacement of "mixed liquor" rather than supernatant liquor or sludge. The major disadvantage of completely mixing a digestion tank is the need for a facility which will enhance the separation of the digested solids from the aqueous phase of the "mixed liquor."

Various mixing systems have been marketed by different manufacturing companies. These systems provide adequate mixing by recirculating digestion gas or by mechanical agitation or circulation. Four systems employ gas recirculation for mixing. The first application of gas recirculation was originally employed to break the scum layer. This system is called the Pearth process and is marketed by the Pacific Flush Tank Company and the Ralph B. Carter Company. Some of the essential elements of this system are shown in Figure 151. A compressor which is mounted on the cover of the digestion tank transfers digestion gas from the gas dome sequentially through a series of pipes which are located at a distance of about one half the tank radius. The gas is released at a point about 10 to 12 feet below the liquid surface. The Pearth system may be modified to approach complete mixing by extending the recirculating pipes to a greater depth and by increasing the rate of gas recirculation. The location of the gas recirculation pipes away from the center of the tank prevents disturbance within the cone of the tank and permits the classification of the bottom materials, thereby minimizing the amount of raw sludge which is withdrawn and resulting in a more concentrated sludge for transfer to a secondary digester or sludge dewatering or disposal scheme.

The quantity of recirculated gas required to mix a digestion tank varies with the volume of sludge undergoing digestion. In the Pearth process the gas must be distributed through a series of pipes, and the number of discharge points varies with the tank diameter. Some of the operating data collected by the Pacific Flush Tank Company (17) are tabulated in Table 53, while similar data reported by the Ralph B. Carter Company are presented in Table 54. These data are presented to illustrate the variation in the rate of gas recirculation, the horsepower, and the number of discharge points required for mixing different sizes of digestion units.

The release of compressed gas at the bottom of the cone in the digestion tank is the basis for the Catalytic Reduction Process (CRP) marketed by the Chicago Pump Division of the Food Machinery and Chemical Corporation. The compressor is located adjacent to the digestion tank, and the recirculated gas is released through "Shearfusers" which are shown in Plate 8. The dispersed gas sets up circulation of the sludge as the recirculated gas rises in the center of the tank. The circulation pattern is illustrated in Plate 9. The entire volume of the tank is utilized for digestion and no solids separation or concentration takes place.

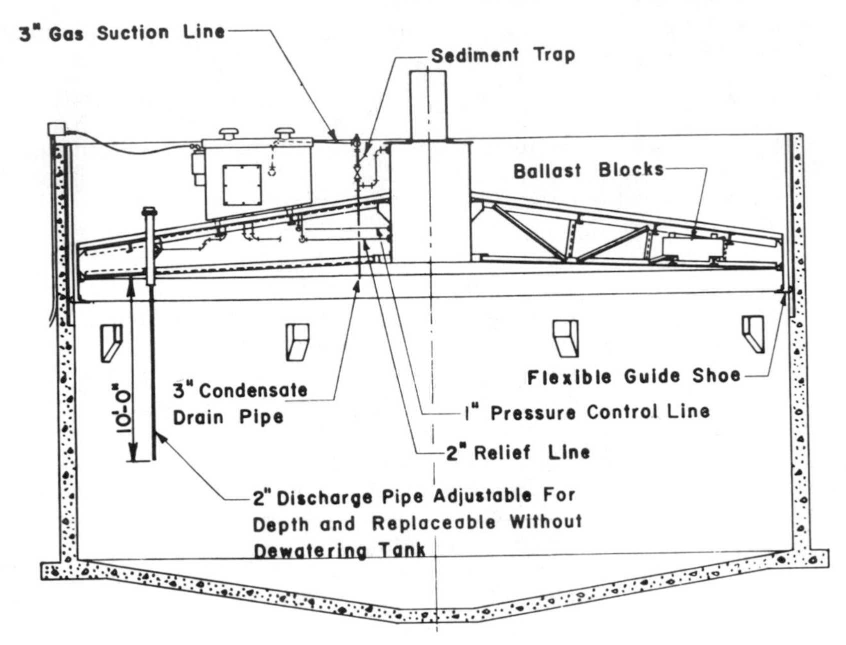

PFT - Pearth System

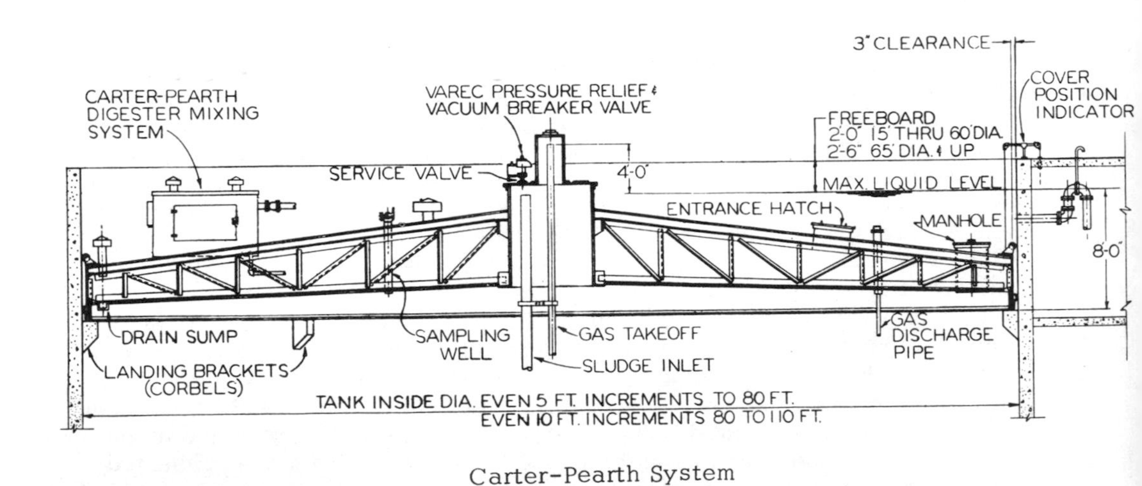

Carter-Pearth System

Figure 151. Pearth gas recirculation systems.

The rate of gas recirculation required for mixing the digester varies with the size of the tank. Some operating data collected for various installations of the Catalytic Reduction Process are presented in Table 55 (18).

Recirculated gas is employed to provide mixing by an action similar to that of a gas lift pump in the "Gas lifter" process marketed by Walker Process Equipment, Incorporated (19). This system is illustrated in Figure 152. The recircu-

TABLE 53

P.F.T.—PEARTH "MULTI-POINT" GAS RECIRCULATION DATA

Diameter of Digester Range in Feet	No. of Units in Analysis	No. of Gas Discharge Points per Unit	Diameter of Circle of Influence at Discharge Point (ft.)	Rate at Area of Influence cfm/1,000 cu. ft. of Digester Capacity	Gas Discharge Rate: C.F.M. per Foot of Diam.		Gas Discharge Rate: C.F.M. per 1,000 cu. ft. of Digester Capacity		Actual HP Used per 1,000 cu. ft. of Digester Capacity	
					Range of Units	Avg.	Range	Avg.	Range	Avg.
25–30	2	Single	—	—	—	5.30	10.60–10.80	10.70	0.370–0.380	0.375
	4	4	15	28.5	2.50–3.70	2.90	3.70–6.30	5.08	0.167–0.321	0.252
31–40	9	5	20	22.6	1.90–3.10	2.70	2.80–4.00	3.43	0.142–0.330	0.210
41–50	9	6	20	22.6	2.20–3.20	2.60	2.20–3.50	2.53	0.112–0.227	0.149
51–60	8	7	25	20.5	2.50–2.70	2.53	1.62–3.00	2.20	0.082–0.150	0.115
61–70	13	8	25	20.5	2.14–3.08	2.44	1.30–2.28	1.91	0.077–0.170	0.120
71–80	11	8	25	20.5	2.00–2.67	2.19	1.14–1.55	1.31	0.057–0.136	0.074
81–90	6	8	30	19.0	1.67–2.35	1.80	0.70–1.27	0.84	0.035–0.095	0.051
91–100	10	8	30	19.0	1.50–2.10	1.87	0.60–0.98	0.71	0.033–0.054	0.042
101–110	8	8	30	19.0	1.80–2.38	1.95	0.50–0.94	0.66	0.038–0.070	0.049

TABLE 54

GAS RECIRCULATION DATA – CARTER-PEARTH METHOD OF DIGESTER MIXING

Digester Diameter (ft.)	Number of Gas Discharge Points per Tank	Gas Discharge Rate		Nameplate Horsepower
		$\left(\frac{\text{cfm}}{\text{ft. (Diam.)}}\right)$	$\left(\frac{\text{cfm}}{\text{1,000 cu. ft.}}\right)^*$	$\left(\frac{\text{hp}}{\text{1,000 cu. ft}}\right)^*$
20	3	3.0	8.8	0.73
30	3	2.0	3.9	0.32
40	5	2.4	2.7	0.27
50	5	2.2	2.5	0.17
60	5	2.5	2.4	0.16
70	5	2.1	1.8	0.12
80	5	1.9	1.4	0.09
90	6	2.3	1.5	0.11
100	6	2.1	1.2	0.09
110	6	1.9	1.0	0.07

*At 22 ft. SWD—Compute other depths proportionately.

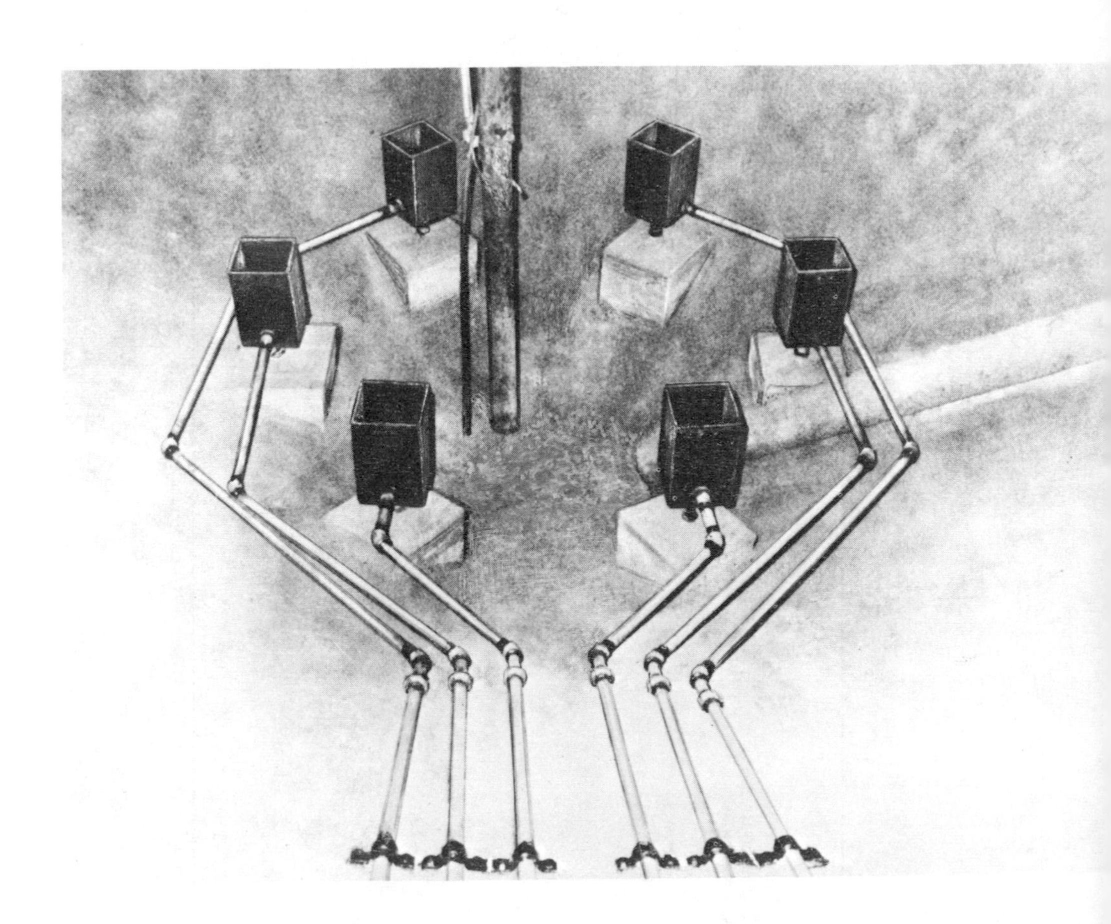

Plate 8. CRP shearfusers.

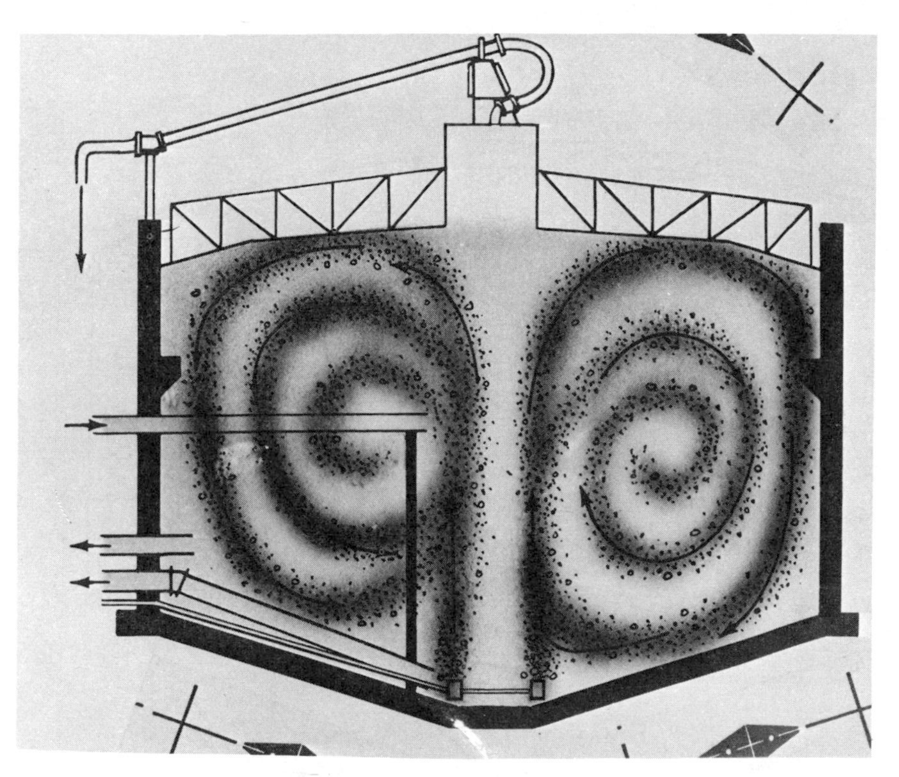

Plate 9. CRP digestion system.

TABLE 55

CATACYTIC REDUCTION PROCESS
REQUIRED RATE OF GAS RECIRCULATION
AND HORSEPOWER FOR SPECIFIC SIZE TANKS

Digester Size	Vol. Cu. Ft.	Required CFM	Required HP
20' dia. × 19' SWD	6,000	20 at 9 psi	1 1/2 HP
25' dia. × 20' SWD	10,000	25 at 9 psi	2 HP
30' dia. × 21' SWD	15,000	30 at 10 psi	3 HP
35' dia. × 21' SWD	20,000	35 at 10 psi	3 HP
40' dia. × 20' SWD	25,000	40 at 9 psi	3 HP
45' dia. × 22' SWD	35,000	45 at 10 psi	3 HP
50' dia. × 23' SWD	45,000	50 at 11 psi	5 HP
55' dia. × 23' SWD	55,000	55 at 11 psi	5 HP
60' dia. × 23' SWD	65,000	60 at 11 psi	5 HP
65' dia. × 24' SWD	80,000	65 at 11 psi	5 HP
70' dia. × 26' SWD	100,000	70 at 12 psi	5 HP
75' dia. × 26' SWD	115,000	75 at 12 psi	5 HP
80' dia. × 26' SWD	130,000	80 at 12 psi	7 1/2 HP
85' dia. × 26' SWD	150,000	85 at 12 psi	7 1/2 HP
90' dia. × 27' SWD	175,000	90 at 12 psi	7 1/2 HP
100' dia. × 30' SWD	235,000	100 at 14 psi	10 HP
110' dia. × 30' SWD	285,000	110 at 14 psi	10 HP
125' dia. × 30' SWD	375,000	125 at 14 psi	15 HP

Note: Standard design conditions of 1 cfm per foot of tank diameter and a diffusion area equal to 1/10 of the tank diameter applies when the tank radius to depth ratio does not exceed 2:1. For ratios greater than 2:1, an increase in cfm and diffusion area is required.

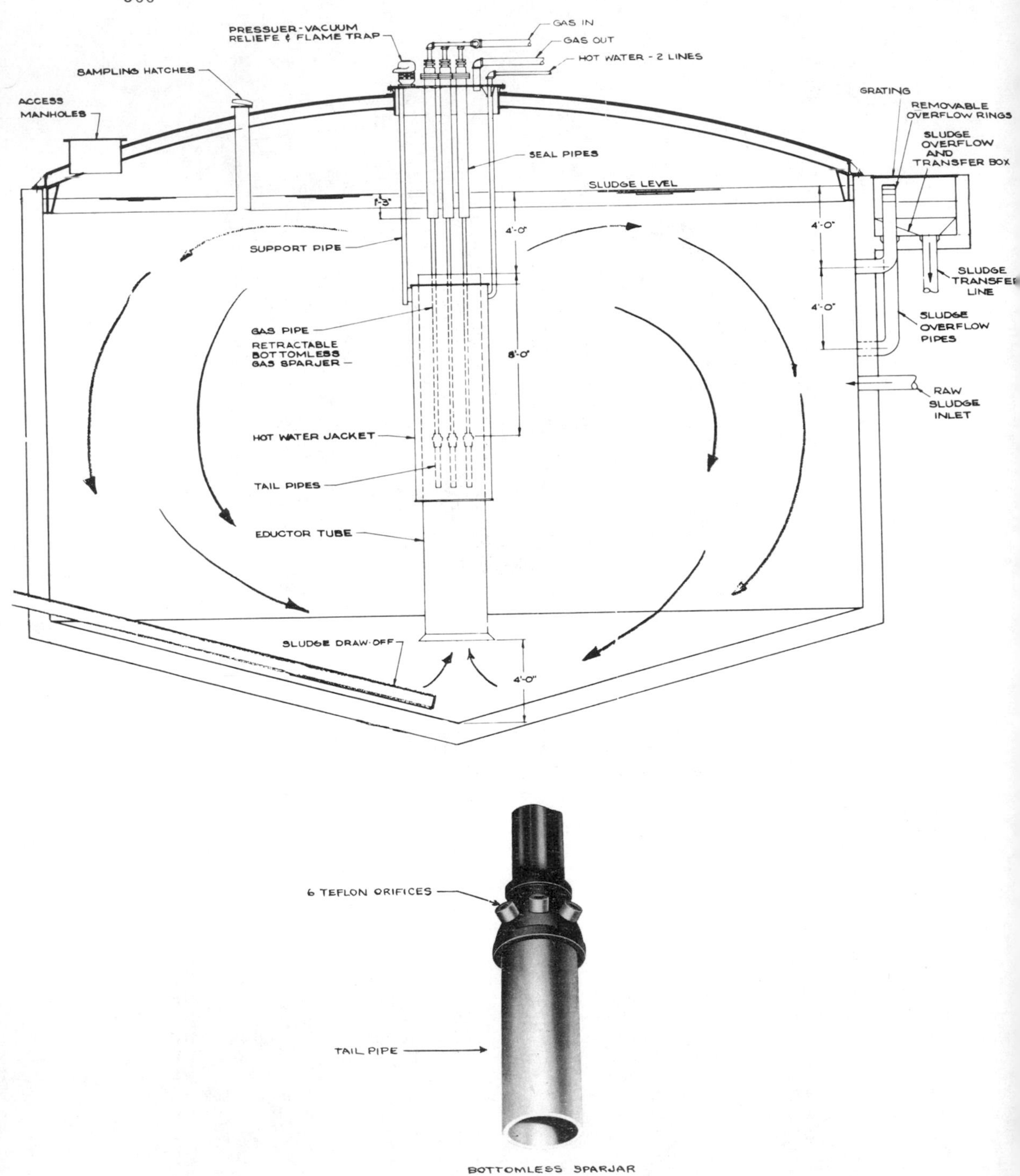

Figure 152. Gaslifter digestion system.

lated gas is transferred from the gas dome by a roof-mounted compressor through a number of pipes positioned at about mid-depth in a vertical draft tube located in the center of the tank. The number of sparjers used depends on the size of the tank. As the gas is released, sludge is carried upward through the draft tube to the surface, where the sludge is directed radially toward the tank periphery. This circulation pattern provides complete mixing of the entire tank volume. Published operating data indicate that the power required by the "Gas Lifter" system of mixing a digestion tank is between 0.1 and 0.12 horsepower per 1,000 cubic feet of digester capacity, and results in gas recirculation rates of 4.9–6.0 cubic feet per minute of gas per cubic foot of tank capacity (20). The draft tube may be converted to a heat exchanger by placing a hot water jacket around the periphery of the tube.

The "Aero-Hydraulic" system for mixing digestion tanks, which is marketed by the Ralph B. Carter Company, also employs compressed recirculated gas (21). The compressed gas accumulates in a "piston bubble" generator (Fig. 153) at the base of a vertical barrel and is released as a single large bubble which acts as an expandable piston as the gas rises through the barrel. The gas bubble forces the sludge upward through the barrel out the top, while at the same time sludge is drawn into the barrel behind the bubble. Upon leaving the barrel the bubble explodes and the gas continues to travel freely to the surface. The release of a bubble from the generator at the same time the previous bubble leaves the barrel provides continuous flow of sludge and establishes a circulation pattern. These "Bubble Guns" are usually located at a distance of one half the radius of the tank, and the number used depends on the size of the tank. Gas is distributed sequentially through one or two of these barrels, depending on the size of the digester. Plate 10 shows the barrel prior to installation. Data relating the rate of gas recirculation, number of discharge points, and horsepower to digestion tank size are presented in Table 56.

The claimed advantage of using a number of "Bubble Guns" is that the multiple point application of unidirection energy maximizes mixing by establishing interfering currents (22). The barrel may serve as a heat exchanger by adapting this unit with a double wall and recirculating hot water through the annular space. The inner wall of the barrel is the heat-exchange surface and the velocity of the rising sludge helps to prevent caking of the sludge.

Various mechanical methods of mixing the digesting sludge have been employed. The "Densludge" system, developed by Dorr-Oliver, Incorporated, includes a thickening tank to remove as much water as possible from the sludge prior to adding the sludge to the digestion tank; the mixing is maintained by a number of mechanical draft tube mixers located to provide maximum mixing. Thickening the sludge prior to digestion eliminates the need for a secondary digester.

A method of recirculating sludge externally has also been developed by Dorr-Oliver, Incorporated. The "Dynomix" system involves drawing sludge from the central portion of the digester by means of a pump and discharging the sludge tangentially through nozzles near the surface to break the scum, and near the bottom of the tank.

The Process Equipment Division of Eimco Corporation has developed and marketed a draft tube mixing device for application in anaerobic digestion systems. The sludge is circulated from the top of the digestion tank by means of a propeller pump and discharged at the bottom of the tank. These draft tube mixers may be placed within the tanks or mounted externally around the periphery of the digester.

The use of a turbine mixing device consisting of vertical plates mounted at the periphery of a circular horizontal plate attached to a vertical shaft has been

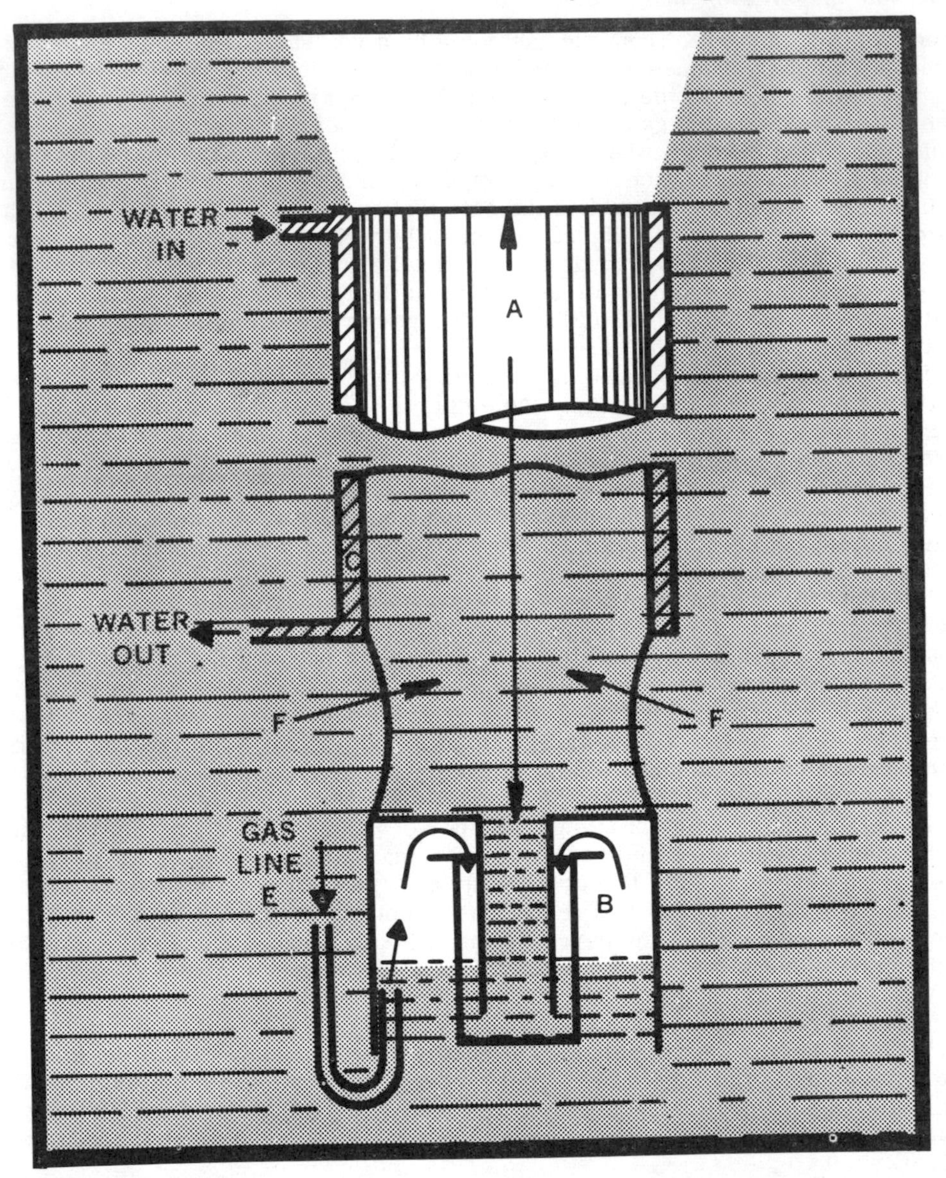

Figure 153. Carter Aero-Hydraulic "piston bubble" generator and heating gun.

developed by Infilco, Incorporated, to completely mix the sludge in anaerobic digestion tanks (23). The circulation pattern is from the bottom of the central portion of the tank and radially along the surface to the periphery. This system is illustrated in Figure 154.

Loading and Detention Time

The operation of "high-rate" or accelerated digestion systems requires a solids loading as nearly as continuous as possible, uniform temperature, and uniform distribution of raw and digesting sludge within the biological unit.

Plate 10. Installation of an Aero-Hydraulics heating and mixing unit.

TABLE 56

GAS RECIRCULATION DATA
CARTER AERO-HYDRAULIC METHOD OF DIGESTER MIXING

Digester Diameter (ft.)	Number of Gas Discharge Points per Tank	Gas Recirculation Rate		Nameplate Horsepower
		(cfm / ft. (diam.))	(cfm / 1,000 cu. ft.)*	(hp / 1,000 cu. ft.)*
20	1	0.33	0.97	0.2200
30	3	0.44	0.85	0.1900
40	3	0.33	0.48	0.1100
50	3	0.26	0.30	0.0670
60	4	0.22	0.21	0.0490
70	4	0.19	0.16	0.0350
80	5	0.17	0.12	0.0270
90	5	0.15	0.10	0.0220
100	6	0.13	0.08	0.0170
110	6	0.12	0.06	0.0144

*At 22 ft SWD—Compute other depths proportionately.

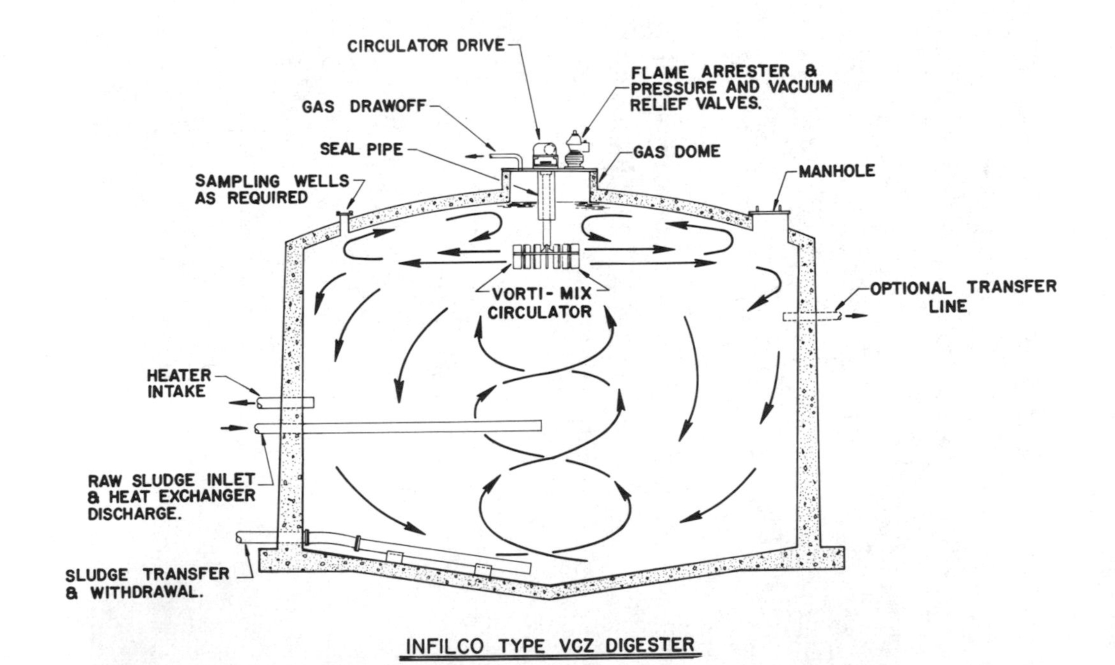

Figure 154. Infilco mechanically mixed digestion system.

Accelerated digestion results in a reduction of detention time, an increase in gas production, and greater destruction of volatile material. The loading to digestion systems should be expressed in terms of weight of volatile solids per volume of digestion capacity per day (lb VS/1,000 cu ft/day or kg VS/m^3/day) instead of on a volume per capita basis.

The literature is replete with data which indicate effective "high-rate" digestion at volatile solids loadings between 100 and 300 lb/1,000 cu ft/day (1.6–4.8 kg/m^3/day) and at detention times of 8 to 25 days. Much of these data have been compiled by Estrada (24).

The variation in the volatile solids loadings and detention time is controlled in most plants by the efficiency of the sedimentation basins which in effect determine the concentration of sludge that is pumped to the digester. Most equipment manufacturers generally recommend volatile solids loadings of 200 lb/1,000 cu ft/day (3.2 kg/m^3/day), if the volatile solids concentration is about 70 percent. As the concentration of volatile solids drops below about 70 percent, a total solids loading of about 300 lb/1,000 cu ft/day (4.8 kg/m^3/day) is recommended as the maximum.

The detention time recommended for effective high-rate digestion is about 15 days, although some of the pilot plant and field data indicate that an 8–10-day detention time would be sufficient for adequate digestion. The loading and detention time affect the efficiency of the digestion, which is generally measured in terms of volatile solids destruction and gas production. A reduction of volatile solids in excess of 50 percent is usually considered satisfactory; however, the ultimate disposal of the digested sludge determines the degree of digestion required.

The total volume of gas produced increases as the loading increases and longer detention times result in more complete gasification. However, it must be determined whether the increased yield of gas will offset the cost of additional digester volume required to provide a longer holding time. The quality and the composition of the gas produced in the digestion process are not significantly changed by increasing the loading and/or the detention time.

A series of curves which show the relationship among solids loading, detention time, and sludge concentration were developed (25). These curves are presented in Figure 155. According to Figure 155, in order to operate a digestion system at the recommended volatile solids loading of 200 lb/100 cu ft/day at a detention time of 10 days, the volatile solids concentration in the feed sludge would have to be about 3.2 percent and about 4.6 percent for a 15-day detention time. Most primary sludge contains about 60–80 percent volatile matter; therefore, the required total solids concentration in the feed sludge would have to be between 4.0 and 5.3 percent for the 10-day detention and between 5.7 and 7.6 percent for the 15-day detention. Separate continuously operated thickening tanks would be required at most treatment plants to insure continuous volatile solids loadings of 200 lb VS/1,000 cu ft/day, because of difficulties encountered in estimating the sludge concentration.

The ability of the mixing devices to completely circulate the contents of a digestion system is not without limits. The relative content of fixed and volatile solids in the sludge appears to affect mixing. Mixing by gas recirculation in laboratory units may be hindered as the total solids content of the digesting sludge exceeds 5 percent (25). Although the solids content in the digester is less than that in the raw sludge, Sawyer (25) suggested that feed sludges should not be concentrated to more than 8 percent total solids if the volatile solids content is less than 70 percent, that is, the fixed solids exceed 30 percent. The effects of total solids concentration and volatile solids content on the viscosity of digesting sludge were reported (27), and these data indicated that this property of sludge may be responsible for localized zones in which the effects of mixing are not fully realized because of the inadequate sheer force.

The effects of solids concentration on the biochemical reactions by which anaerobic digestion proceeds should be mentioned at this time. At high solids concentration the amount of water available to carry away and dilute the end prod-

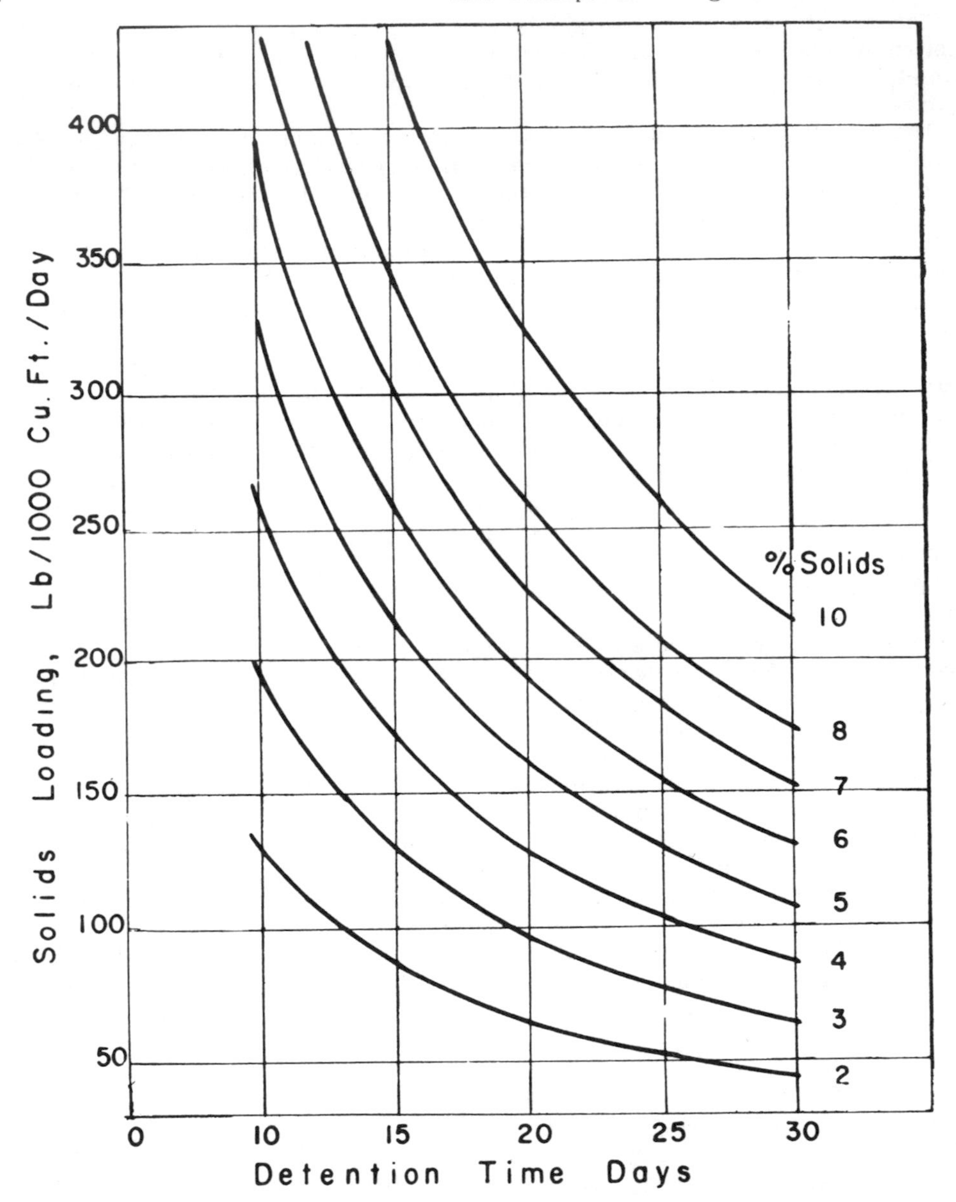

Figure 155. Relationships between sludge solids, digester loadings, and detention time.

ucts of microbial metabolism is reduced and may lead to a localized environment which is inhibitory to the methane-forming bacteria.

Although the results of laboratory studies indicate a maximum recommended solids content of 8 percent in order to insure adequate mixing, it should be pointed out that the degree of mixing or agitation in the laboratory does not exactly simulate field conditions. At the present time digester loadings are controlled to a great extent by the sedimentation process and not mixing. The effective use of a sludge density meter which estimates the solids concentration in the sludge by radiation techniques control sludge pumping has been demonstrated (28). At this plant volatile solids loadings of 280 lb/1,000 cu ft/day (4.48 $kg/m^3/day$) were maintained and effective digestion was possible in about 8 days without any artificial mixing. The natural mixing caused by the rising gas produced at this loading was sufficient, although digesting sludge was recirculated to seed the incoming sludge. The rate of sludge recirculation was such that the entire tank volume was displaced once in a 24-hour period. However, this plant has recently installed artificial gas recirculation systems, and effective treatment at volatile solids loadings of 430 lb/1,000 cu ft/day (6.88 $kg/m^3/day$) is anticipated.

It seems that the available equipment or modifications of this equipment is capable of mixing large volumes of concentrated sludges and that methods of concentrating solids and of maintaining a relatively uniform volatile solids loading to the anaerobic digestion units constitute the major limitation to digester loadings.

Solids Separation after Digestion

The contents of a high-rate digestion system are a type of "mixed liquor." Although some solids concentration inadvertantly takes place in the central cone of mixed digestion tanks, the effluent must undergo some type of solids separation prior to disposal of the sludge. Two-stage digestion has been employed to permit the separation of the solids from the liquid carrier. The second stage is usually unheated, and very little improvement in solids destruction or gas production takes place. Woods (7) evaluated a two-stage digestion at the Village Creek Treatment Plant in Fort Worth, Texas. This system was lightly loaded at 43 lb VS/1,000 cu ft/day (0.68 $kg/m^3/day$) and had a detention time in the heated primary digester of 39 days. The second stage was not heated. The results of this study are graphically summarized in Figure 156. These data indicate that most of the stabilization takes place in the first stage, and that negligible gas production and waste stabilization occur in the second stage. It should be pointed out that the supernatant resulting from solids separation contains a considerable amount of volatile solids and organic constituents and cannot be disregarded in evaluating digester performance or estimating the load on the treatment plant. The results of carbon and nitrogen balances (7) also indicate that carbon is removed from the sludge primarily in the form of gas during the first stage, and that most of the nitrogen entering the plant remains in the supernatant leaving the second stage. These data are presented graphically in Figure 157.

Difficulties have been encountered in concentrating the sludge from high-rate digestion systems in secondary units. Sawyer (25) pointed out that some of these difficulties may be caused by inadequate capacity in the secondary digesters, which are usually of the same size as the primary digesters. He suggested that the secondary digesters be designed with two to four times the capacity of the primary digesters to improve the separation of the sludge and supernatant. Elutriation of the sludge between the two stages of digestion seemed to have solved this problem at the Owl's Head Plant in New York City, where solids contents of 17 percent were obtained.

INTERNAL CONTROL OF DIGESTERS

Careful external control of the operating temperature of, degree of mixing in, volatile solids loading to, and hydraulic detention time of an anaerobic digestion system will usually result in maintaining a relatively constant environment. However, careful external control will not necessarily provide an environment in

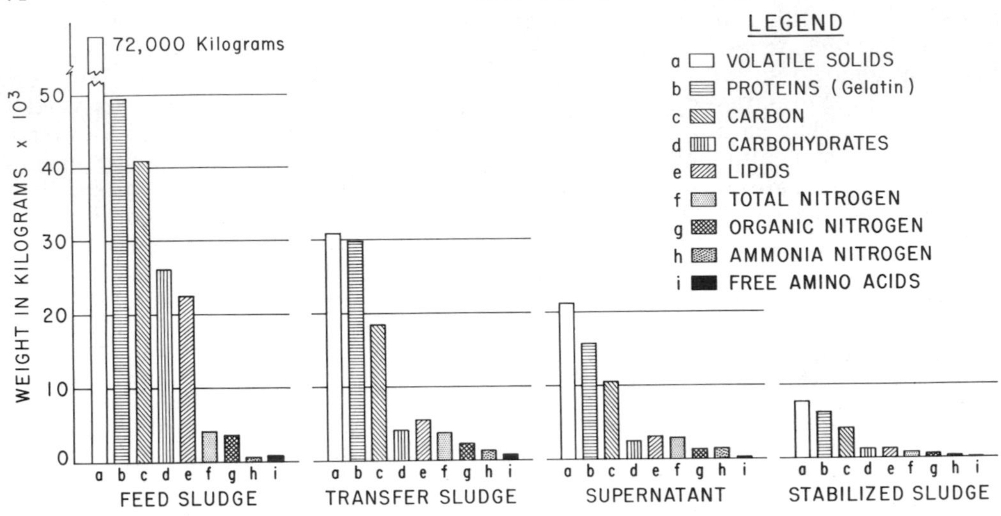

Figure 156. Weights of organic constituents in various sludges from July 15, 1963, to August 15, 1963.

which the activity of the microbial population responsible for the decomposition and the stabilization of the sludge is optimum.

Digestion systems may fail because of a sudden increase in the concentration of the feed sludge. The heterogeneity of sludge and the daily variation in the concentration and the composition of the sludge at most treatment plants may easily cause digestion difficulties. The continuous addition of sludge of a high solids content may result in insufficient mixing in a portion of a high-rate digestion tank, and the accumulation of intermediate products may cause methane production to cease in these localized areas of stagnation. Eventually the environment within the tank is changed sufficiently to cause digester failure. Buzzell (27) presented data which substantiated the effects of solids concentration on digester performance.

The introduction into digestion systems of materials which are toxic to methane bacteria will cause a breakdown in the gasification phase and cause digester failure. Most digestion failures are typified by the inability of the methane bacteria to utilize the volatile acids which are produced at a rate that would maintain an environment suitable for methane bacteria; therefore, the volatile acids accumulated in the system. Thus, many reports indicate that high concentrations of volatile acids will cause digester failure. A more accurate appraisal is that a sudden increase in the concentration of volatile acids is the result of a stuck digester and not directly the cause of digester failure. The upper limit of volatile solids concentration before digester failure, as suggested by many investigators, is between 2,000 and 3,000 mg/L. However, McCarty (29) showed that the "toxicity" associated with the volatile acids in fact was attributable to the type and the concentration of cations associated with the alkaline substances which provide the buffering capacity for the system. The neutralization of concentrations of volatile acids up to 10,000 mg/L as acetic acid was possible with calcium or magnesium hydroxide without any inhibitory effects on the digestion process; however, the same results were not observed when the hydroxides of sodium, potassium or ammonia were used (28) (29). The buffering capacity of an actively digesting system was reported by Schulze (29) (30), who observed that a sudden increase in the volatile acid concentration from 1,208 to 47,100 mg/L resulted

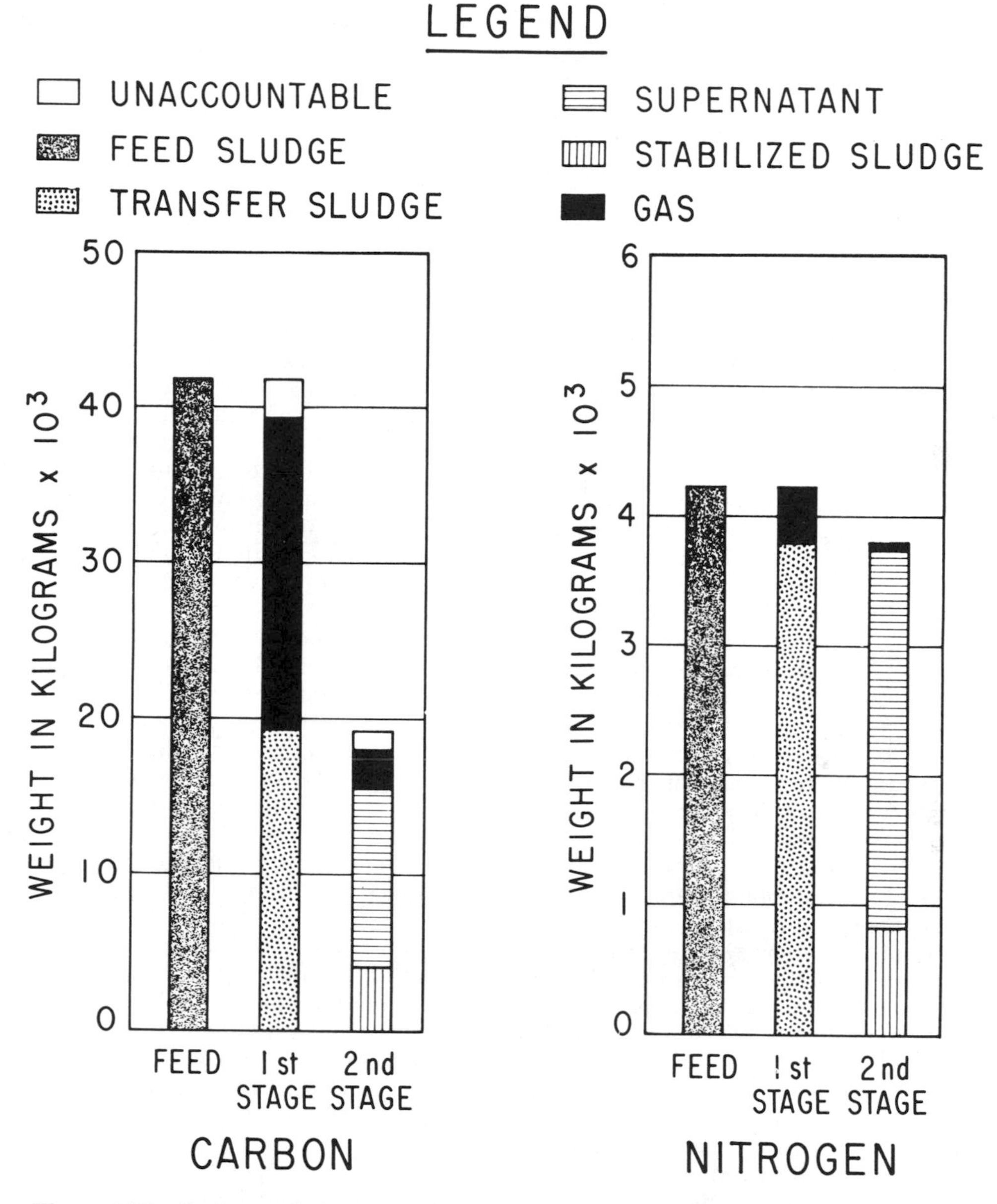

Figure 157. Carbon and nitrogen balances from July 15, 1963, to August 15, 1963.

in a drop in *p*H from 7.3 to 6.9. Schulze (31) also pointed out that the cations present in the system influenced the effect of volatile acids on digestion. The results of these studies also indicated that at a raw sludge concentration of 10 percent the excessive accumulation of volatile acids was more inhibitory than the concentration of ions.

Pohland (32) also indicated that the concentration of volatile acids cannot be considered as an isolated factor in digester failure. The concept of "volatile acid salts" alkalinity, which results from the neutralization of volatile acids by reaction with the alkalinity yielding carbon dioxide was presented. Based on the ability of alkaline materials to neutralize acids, Pohland (32) proposed that about 83.3 percent of the volatile acids concentration contributes to the alkalinity as "volatile acid salts." Since alkalinity is expressed as $CaCO_3$ and volatiles acids as acetic acid, the reaction of the two will result in a volatile acid salt.

$$CaCO_3 + 2CH_3COOH \rightarrow (CH_3COO)_2\,Ca + H_2CO_3$$

The "volatile acid salt" may then react to neutralize the acids:

$$(CH_3COO)_2\,Ca + H_2SO_4 \rightarrow CaSO_4 + 2CH_3COOH$$

Therefore, when the "volatile acid salts" alkalinity exceeds the total alkalinity, free volatile acids are present and will cause a decrease in *p*H, and inhibition of the process is impending.

The inhibitory effects of nitrogenous compounds on anaerobic digestion have also been reported. High concentrations of amino acids can cause inhibitory conditions to develop in an anaerobic system. The addition of a concentration of 5 mM/L of amino acids into laboratory scale digesters decreased the rate of gas production by 20–80 percent of that of the control, depending on the amino acid added. At this concentration of amino acid the *p*H was unchanged but the volatile acid concentration and alkalinity increased slightly. However, the addition of less than 100 μM/1 of amino acid resulted in an increase in the rate of gas production from the sludge mass; the degree of increase varied for the five amino acids studied by a factor of 2 to 25 times (33). Ammonia which results from the breakdown of amino acids has been reported to effect anaerobic digestion. Failure of the digestion process when the ammonia concentration exceeded 1,250 mg/L was reported at high solids loadings, but at low loadings 5,000 mg/L of ammonia was tolerated. Digester failure was induced by adding high concentrations of solids or NH_4HCO_3 which resulted in the development of high volatile acids concentrations. The *p*H, carbon dioxide content, volatile acids, and ammonia are interrelated in the anaerobic system. The optimum *p*H was reported to be 7.1 (34). The *p*H of the environment influences the effects of ammonia, since the equilibrium between ammonia and ammonium ion is *p*H sensitive. Free ammonia, which is toxic, is favored at high *p*H values.

The above discussion indicates that there is no single parameter which can be isolated as the best indicator of the environment within the digester. In the recent past, the rate of gas production was considered the best indication of digester performance; however, this parameter does not describe the environment within the digester and usually when gas production drops off, the environment is upset and remedial measures are drastic. The above discussion showed that the anaerobic environment is well buffered; therefore, *p*H cannot by itself be used as an indicator of a suitable environment.

The parameters which would provide an insight into the condition of the environment early enough to avert digester failure are the volatile acids concentration, alkalinity, and the carbon dioxide content of the gas along with *p*H. Sudden large changes in these parameters will signal impending digester failure much sooner than a drop in the rate of gas production. The onset of digester failure is signaled by a sharp increase in the free volatile acid concentration and the carbon dioxide content of the gas and a decrease in the *p*H and possibly the alkalinity. The daily gas production may also drop slightly. Digester upset may usually be controlled by maintaining the *p*H near neutral by the addition of lime and/or by reducing the loading on the digester.

Daily evaluation of the *p*H, volatile acid concentration, alkalinity of the sludge, and carbon dioxide content of the gas is imperative to good digestion, and relatively simple and inexpensive analytical techniques are available. Electronic *p*H meters are available and relatively simple to use. A direct titration method of evaluating the volatile acid concentration has been developed (35). This method consistently yielded results which were higher than those obtained by the distillation method (27). However, since relative values are important in digester control this shortcoming of the direct titration method is not significant. Alkalinity may easily be estimated by titrating the sample with a standard sulfuric acid solution to an end point of *p*H 4.5 (36). The color of the supernatant frequently precludes the use of any indicator solutions in this analysis.

The carbon dioxide content of the gas may be evaluated by using gas chromatographic techniques; relatively simple and inexpensive gas partitioners are available. Another simple technique for estimating the carbon dioxide content of a digester gas is to pass a known volume of gas through a carbonate free-sodium hydroxide solution to absorb the CO_2 as Na_2CO_3. Barium chloride solution is thus added to precipitate the Na_2CO_3 as $BaCO_3$, and the excess NaOH is titrated with 1 normal hydrochloric acid solution (35).

The internal digester controls discussed above are generally applicable to remedy impending or temporary digester upset. However, the presence of toxic materials in the sludge may result in more permanent digester upsets. The results of recent research activities have been directed to the toxic effects of cations and anions on anaerobic treatment (36) (37). A controlled medium was used in these studies and the results cannot be directly applied to the heterogeneous multicomponent environment in an actual anaerobic digestion. These data, however, may be helpful in attempting to determine the cause of digester failure if other methods do not provide a remedy. The ability of sulfides to react with heavy metals in a digester to form insoluble precipitates, thus eliminating the toxic effects of copper, zinc, and nickel, has been demonstrated (38). Sodium sulfide may be used to remove the heavy metals up to a concentration of 10 percent on a dried volatile solids basis without inhibitory effect if sufficient sulfides are not present in the anaerobic environment.

SUMMARY

The complexity of the biochemical reactions by which wastewater solids undergo liquefaction and gasification indicates that careful external and internal control of the variables is necessary. Optimum digestion conditions include mixing the contents of a digestion tank either mechanically or by means of recirculated gas and maintaining the temperature within the tank ebtween 86° and 95°F. (30°–35°C.). Under these conditions the recommended volatile solids loading is 200 lb/1,000 cu ft/day (3.2 kg/m^3/day); a detention time of 10 days should be sufficient although 15 days may be preferable. Maintaining the solids loading and the hydraulic displacement as uniform as possible will improve digester performance.

The different chemical parameters which characterize the environment within the digester are all interrelated, and one variable may directly or indirectly affect the others. Therefore, daily laboratory analysis of the volatile acids, the alkalinity, and the digesting sludge of the gas, *p*H, and carbon dioxide are essential for efficient digestion with a minimum number of problems.

REFERENCES

(1) Malina, J. F., Jr. "Thermal Effects on Completely Mixed Anaerobic Digestion," *Water Sewage Works, 95,* 52 (1964).
(2) Rudolfs, W. "Fertilizer and Fertility," *Water Works Sewage, 90,* 261 (1963).
(3) Balmat, J. L. "Chemical Composition and Biological Oxidation of Particulate Fractions in Domestic Sewage." Ph.D. Dissertation, Rutgers University (1955).

(4) Heukelekian, H., and B. Heinemann. "Studies on the Methane Producing Bacteria," *Sewage Ind. Wastes J., 11,* 436 (1939).

(5) Oginsky, E. L., and W. W. Umbreit. *An Introduction to Bacterial Physiology.* San Francisco: W. H. Freeman and Co. (1959).

(6) White, A., P. Handler, and D. Stetten. *Principles of Biochemistry.* New York: McGraw-Hill Book Co., Inc. (1959).

(7) Woods, C. E., and J. F. Malina, Jr. "Stage Digestion of Wastewater Sludge," *J. Water Poll. Cont. Fed., 37,* 1495 (1965).

(8) Clifton, C. E. *Introduction to Bacterial Physiology.* New York: McGraw-Hill Book Co., Inc. (1957).

(9) Roberts, R. B., D. B. Cowie, P. H. Abelson, E. T. Bolton, and R. J. Britten. *Studies of Biosynthesis in* Escherichia coli. Washington, D.C.: Carnegie Institute of Washington Publication 607 (1957).

(10) Jeris, J. S., and P. L. McCarty. "The Biochemistry of Methane Fermentation Using C^{14} Tracers," *J. Water Poll. Cont. Fed., 37,* 178 (1965).

(11) Golueke, C. G. "Temperature Effects on Anaerobic Digestion of Raw Sewage Sludge," *Sewage Ind. Wastes J., 30,* 1225 (1958).

(12) Malina, J. F., Jr. "The Effect of Temperature on High-Rate Digestion of Activated Sludge," *Proceedings,* 16th Purdue Industrial Waste Conference, Purdue University, Lafayette, Indiana, Engineering Bulletin, 46, 2, 232 (1962).

(13) Fair, G. M., and E. W. Moore. "Time and Rate of Sludge Digestion and Their Variation with Temperature," *Sewage Works J., 6,* 3 (1934).

(14) Rudolfs, W. *Principles of Sewage Treatment.* Washington, D.C.: National Lime Association, Bulletin 112 (1955).

(15) McCarty, P. L. "The Methane Fermentation." Presented at the Rudolfs Research Conference, Rutgers University, New Brunswick, New Jersey (1963).

(16) Keefer, C. E. "Effects of Premixing Raw and Digested Sludge on High-Rate Digestion," *Sewage Ind. Wastes J., 31,* 388 (1959).

(17) Schlenz, H., Pacific Flush Tank Inc., Chicago, Illinois. Private Correspondence (April 1966).

(18) Fields, S. E., Chicago Pump, FMC Corporation, Chicago, Illinois. Private Correspondence (April 1966).

(19) Dreier, D. E., Walker Process Equipment Incorporated, Aurora, Illinois. Private Correspondence (January 1966).

(20) Dreier, D. E. "Boosting Digester Performance through Effective Mixing." Paper presented at Michigan Sewage and Industrial Wastes Association Annual Meeting (1961).

(21) Steffen, A. J., Ralph B. Carter Company, Hackensack, New Jersey. Private Correspondence (April 1966).

(22) Boschen, W. O., Ralph B. Carter Company, Hackensack, New Jersey. Personal Communication (April 1966).

(23) Garland, C. F., Infilco, Tuscon, Arizona. Private Correspondence (April 1966).

(24) Estrada, A. A. "Design and Cost Considerations in High Rate Digestion," *Proc. Sanit. Engr. Div. ASCE, 86* (SA3), 111 (1960).

(25) Sawyer, C. N. "Anaerobic Units," *Proceedings,* Symposium on Advances in Sewage Treatment Design, Sanitary Engineering Division, Metropolitan Section, American Society of Civil Engineers, New York (1961).

(26) Sawyer, C. N., and J. S. Grumbling. "Fundamental Considerations in High-Rate Digestion," *Proc. ASCE, 86*(SA2), 49 (1960).

(27) Buzzell, J. C., Jr., and C. N. Sawyer, "Biochemical vs. Physical Factors in Digester Failure," *J. Water Poll. Cont. Fed., 35,* 205 (1963).

(28) Garrison, W. E., J. D. Parkhurst, and C. A. Nagel. "Gas Recirculation—Natural, Artificial," *Water Works Wastes Engr., 1,* 58 (1964).

(29) McCarty, P. L., and R. E. McKinney. "Volatile Acid Toxicity in Anaerobic Digestion," *J. Water Poll. Cont. Fed., 33,* 223 (1961).

(30) Schulze, K. L. "Studies on Sludge Digestion and Methane Fermentation, I. Sludge Digestion at Increased Solids Concentrations," *Sewage Ind. Wastes, 30,* 28 (1958).

(31) Schulze, K. L., and B. N. Raju. "Studies on Sludge Digestion and Methane Fermentation, II. Methane Fermentation of Organic Acids," *Sewage Ind. Wastes, 30,* 164 (1958).

(32) Pohland, F. G., and D. E. Bloodgood. "Laboratory Studies on Mesophilic and Thermophilic Anaerobic Sludge Digestion," *J. Water Poll. Cont. Fed., 35* (1963).

(33) Miholits, E. M., and J. F. Malina, Jr. *Uptake and Utilization of Amino Acids during Anaerobic Digestion.* Technical Report EHE 11-6505, CRWR 11. Austin: The University of Texas (1965).

(34) Albertson, O. E. "Ammonia Nitrogen and the Anaerobic Environment," *J. Water Poll. Cont. Fed., 33,* 978 (1961).

(35) DiLallo, R., and O. E. Albertson. "Volatile Acids by Direct Titration," *J. Water Poll. Cont. Fed., 33*(4), 256 (1961).

(36) Woods, C. E., and J. F. Malina, Jr. *Anaerobic Stabilization of Waste Water Sludge and Glycine Uptake.* Technical Report, Austin: The University of Texas (1963).

(37) Kugelman, I. J., and P. L. McCarty. "Cation Toxicity and Stimulation in Anaerobic Waste Treatment," *J. Water Poll. Cont. Fed., 37,* 97 (1965).

(38) Lawrence, A. W., and P. L. McCarty. "The Role of Sulfide in Preventing Heavy Metal Toxicity in Anaerobic Treatment," *J. Water Poll. Cont. Fed., 37,* 392 (1965).

A DISCUSSION OF "NEW DEVELOPMENTS IN THE ANAEROBIC DIGESTION OF SLUDGES

John F. Andrews
Clemson University, Clemson, South Carolina

Dr. Malina has described several new developments which should be of interest to engineers involved in the design of anaerobic digesters. Two of the topics which he has covered—mixing, and the need for continuous feeding—are of sufficient importance to warrant additional emphasis.

Dr. Malina has listed the various functions served by mixing in anaerobic digestion. However, more emphasis should be placed on the importance of mixing in increasing reaction rates. Most of the mixing procedures in use today have been designed on an empirical basis and have not employed the theory and techniques reviewed by Parker (1). There is little doubt that reaction rates in anaerobic digesters can be increased by increasing mixing, thus resulting in smaller reactors. However, little data are available on increased reaction rates versus cost of mixing, especially for biological reactions occuring in now-Newtonian fluids. Pilot plant studies using modern techniques (strain gage dynamometers, gas chromatographs) are desperately needed in this area and should result in significant advances in the anaerobic digestion of wastes. Pilot plants for this purpose are being designed at Clemson University. The criticism may be raised that increased mixing will result in increased foaming; however, foam control methods used in the fermentation industry should be applicable to anaerobic sludge digestion.

Another important factor in the biological degradation of any inhibitory or toxic material in a continuous mixing process is the need for continuous feeding or an approximation as close to this as is possible. The microorganisms involved respond to the instantaneous concentration of feed, not the concentration averaged over the period of a day. For example, the "instantaneous" increase in concentration will be four times as high if a digester is fed a given quantity of sludge once per day instead of one fourth this quantity four times per day. For a more detailed mathematical description of continuous feed versus intermittent feed in biological systems, the reader should consult Málek (2). It is easy to see the significance of this when such substances as phenols (inhibitory or toxic in relatively low concentrations) are being metabolized in a complete mixing activated sludge process. The same principle should hold when a substrate (such as sewage sludge) is converted at a high rate to inhibitory substances (volatile acids) which are more slowly metabolized.

REFERENCES

(1) Parker, N. H. "Modern Theory and Practice on the Universal Operation: Mixing," *Chem. Engr.*, 166–220 (June 8, 1964).

(2) Málek, I. "Development and Further Perspectives of the Continuous-Flow Method of Cultivation of Microorganisms," *S.C.I. Monograph No. 12. The Continuous Culture of Micro-organisms*. New York: The Macmillan Co. (1961).

KINETICS OF BIOLOGICAL TREATMENT

Erman A. Pearson
University of California, Berkeley, California

INTRODUCTION

Sanitary engineers were among the first in the biological sciences to work with large-scale chemostats—more commonly known today as the continuous-flow cultivation of microorganisms. This was the result of applying biological systems to the treatment of the nonuniform but continuous flow of wastes from urban areas.

Significant progress has been made in the practical application of biological systems to municipal and industrial waste treatment. However, most of the progress in waste treatment technology has been the result of field experimentation, largely on a trial and error basis. Much of the research in waste treatment has been devoted to the development of rational or semirational explanations of the phenomena observed in practice.

Very substantial amounts of money and investigative effort have been devoted to biological waste treatment research. Maximum benefit has not accrued from much of the research effort because of the lack of an adequate theoretical basis upon which to design meaningful experiments and to obtain interpretable data. Of necessity, much of the waste treatment research has been undertaken within an empirical framework of analysis directed to specific system characteristics of interest or to practical problems to be resolved. It appears that limitations in either interest or funds have retarded the development of quantitative kinetic descriptions of biological processes. Moreover, the lack of specific and accurate analytical methods for characterization of the active biological population of processes has not accelerated the analytical modeling of waste treatment processes.

The principal objectives of this paper are as follows:

1. To present a consistent and rational basis for a kinetic description of biological processes.

2. To indicate the value of kinetic descriptions in process evaluation and in the analytical comparison of different biological process (viz., aerobic and anaerobic).

3. To encourage the development of sufficient data in field evaluations and laboratory researches to permit kinetic descriptions of the biological processes. This point needs emphasis, since many investigators indicate little concern for kinetic data.

An urgent plea is made to all investigators in the biological process field to collect and publish sufficient data on process characteristics so that those interested in kinetic analyses of processes can benefit from the large volume of data being developed. Unfortunately, most of the process data existing in the literature to data are sufficiently incomplete so that the data cannot be analyzed or compared on a rational and analytical basis. Essentially all research on biological processes should include kinetic descriptions of the process. Without such descriptions one cannot evaluate accurately or scientifically the effect of a particular variable or environmental factor. It is only by means of kinetic descriptions of processes that waste treatment technology can be taken out of the "black box" and "witchcraft" association and put on a sound technological basis.

SUBSTRATE REMOVAL

The traditional objective of biological waste treatment, namely the removal of soluble organic substrate from the feed stream, usually expressed in terms of biochemical oxygen demand, BOD_5, or chemical oxygen demand, COD, is the major consideration of this kinetic analysis. However, an example is included showing the analysis and the operation of a biological process as a cell-producing system which could be used to remove from the feed stream any constituent incorporated in cell tissue. Obvious possibilities include process design to maximize cell production and removal, thereby maximizing the removal of essential nutrients such as nitrogen and phosphorus along with the cell tissue.

The proper kinetic description for the removal of organic substrate has been the subject of much discussion to date and will receive increased attention in the future. It is not the purpose of this paper to evaluate the many kinetic models that have been proposed by various investigators for waste treatment systems. Nor will a review be made of the kinetic theories put forward by the rapidly increasing number of microbiologists working with the continuous cultivation of microorganisms. This latter group has been concerned largely with pure culture, noncell recycle systems. Instead, attention will be directed to the basis for and development of kinetic equations which can be utilized in the analysis and the design of waste treatment systems.

After a thorough appraisal of kinetic descriptions of biological systems available in 1956, Stewart (1) selected the Michaelis-Menten kinetic model to represent substrate removal kinetics for his work on methane fermentation kinetics. This model, developed from an analysis of reaction rates in an enzyme catalyzed reaction, results in a kinetic expression equivalent to that proposed by Monod (2) based upon empirical analysis of bacterial growth as well as that of surface controlled reactions such as Langmuirs adsorption isotherm.

Michaelis-Menten Enyzme Substrate Removal Kinetics

The general equation for enzyme substrate reactions as applied to waste treatment systems was reported first by Stewart (1) and later by Agardy (3). It is reviewed briefly here for completeness of the kinetic presentation.

$$\mathrm{Enz} + S \underset{k_2}{\overset{k_1}{\rightleftharpoons}} \mathrm{Enz}S \underset{k_4}{\overset{k_3}{\rightleftharpoons}} \mathrm{Enz} + P$$

Enzyme, Substrate, Enzyme Substrate Complex, Enzyme, Product Nonreactive

At steady state

$$k_1 (\mathrm{Enz})(S) - k_2 (\mathrm{Enz}S) = k_3 (\mathrm{Enz}S) - k_4 (\mathrm{Enz})(P)$$

$$\frac{(\mathrm{Enz})}{(\mathrm{Enz}S)} = \frac{k_2 + k_3}{k_1 (S) + k_4 (P)} = \frac{k_2 + k_3}{k_1 (S)} \quad \text{if} \quad k_4 (P) \cong 0$$

If we assume the enzyme plus enzyme-substrate complex is proportional to the total "active solids" concentration, we obtain

$$(\mathrm{Enz}_t) = (\mathrm{Enz}) + (\mathrm{Enz}S)$$

$$(\mathrm{Enz}) = (\mathrm{Enz}_t) - (\mathrm{Enz}S)$$

Substituting:

$$\frac{(\mathrm{Enz}_t) - (\mathrm{Enz}S)}{(\mathrm{Enz}S)} = \frac{k_2 + k_3}{k_1 (S)} \text{ or } \frac{(\mathrm{Enz}_t)}{(\mathrm{Enz}S)} = \frac{k_2 + k_3 + k_1 (S)}{k_1 (S)}$$

Let

$$K = \frac{k_2 + k_3}{k_1}$$

Then

$$\frac{(\mathrm{Enz}S)}{(\mathrm{Enz}_t)} = \frac{(S)}{K + (S)} \text{ or } (\mathrm{Enz}S) = \frac{(\mathrm{Enz}_t)(S)}{K + (S)}$$

If one assumes that the growth rate μ is proportional to the enzyme substrate complex concentration,

i.e., $\mu \propto (\mathrm{Enz}S)$ when $(S) \rightarrow \infty$, $\mu \rightarrow (\mathrm{Enz}_t) \cong \hat{\mu}$ where $\hat{\mu}$ is the maximum growth rate at infinite substrate concentration.

Therefore

$$\mu = \frac{\hat{\mu}\,(S)}{K_s + (S)} \tag{1}$$

where K_s is the substrate concentration at one half maximum growth rate (i.e., $\hat{\mu} = \frac{\hat{\mu}}{2}$) . Figure 158 shows a plot of μ versus S as well as a reciprocal plot of the M-M growth equation showing a graphical method of obtaining the rate constants $\hat{\mu}$ and K_s.

One of the powerful advantages of the M-M growth model is that it is a continuous function which is first order at low concentrations of substrate (such as in standard rate activated sludge systems) and approaches zero order at high substrate concentrations. In addition, it appears that the M-M kinetic expression is being used with increasing frequency in fundamental studies on the continuous cultivation of microorganisms. Experience in the laboratory during the past eight years dealing with growth kinetics of anaerobic organisms (mixed cultures) over an extremely wide range of growth rates indicates that the M-M model fits the experimental data as well or better than any other expression.

Process Materials Balance

Substrate

Along with the kinetic description of microbial growth one must consider the constraints imposed by the physical system in which the growth reaction is carried out. Figure 159 shows a definition sketch for the reaction system and a process materials balance for substrate made around the system, which includes a reactor and cell separator with cell recycle. For purposes of simplicity in kinetic analysis (arithmetic) two simplifying assumptions are made as follows:

1. The reactor volume, V, includes the volume of the cell separator, and the cell concentration, X_a, is the mean cell concentration in the reactor. In laboratory studies, both the separator volume and the cell mass in the separator are negligible; however, these factors must be considered in practical plant application of the theory.
2. The wastage of cells (net growth) is equal to the cell concentration, X_2, in the effluent stream times the flow rate Q.

Both of the foregoing simplifying assumptions do not affect the application of the theory to actual plant evaluation if cognizance is given the conditions specified.

The important equation in Figure 159 is the substrate removal velocity, q, which is a rational measure of the cellular removal activity; that is, the mass of

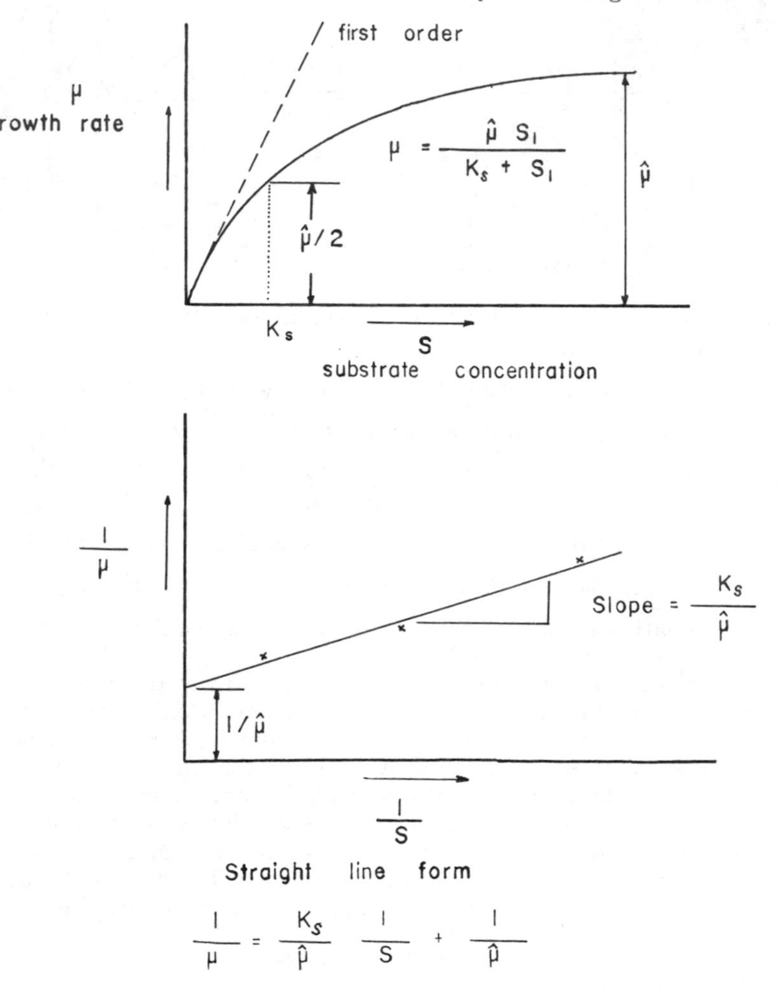

Figure 158. Michaelis-Menton kinetic model.

substrate (BOD_5, COD) removed from the waste stream per unit mass of "active organisms" per unit of time (viz. $\frac{\text{gms. substrate rem.}}{\text{gm. cells-day}}$)

It can be noted that the substrate removal velocity, q, can be transformed to the growth rate, μ, by multiplying by the yield coefficient, Y, as follows:

$$q\ Y = \mu = \frac{\hat{\mu} S_1}{K_s + S_1}$$

$$\frac{\text{gms. subs. rem.}}{\text{gm. cells-day}} \times \frac{\text{gms. cells prod.}}{\text{gm. subs. rem.}} = \frac{\text{gms. cells prod.}}{\text{gm. cells-day}} = \mu$$

thus:

$$q = \frac{\hat{\mu} S_1}{Y(K_s + S_1)} \tag{3}$$

Equation 2 for q can be equated with 3 and solved for $S_0 - S_1$. If one divides both sides of the resulting equation

$$S_0 - S_1 = \frac{\hat{\mu}\, S_1 X_1 V}{Q Y(K_s + S_1)}$$

by S_0 and recognizing that $\frac{S_0 - S_1}{S_0}$ is an expression for process efficiency, the following expression for efficiency can be obtained:

$$E = \frac{\hat{\mu}\, t\, X_a S_1}{S_0\, Y(K_s + S_1)} \qquad (4)$$

SUBSTRATE

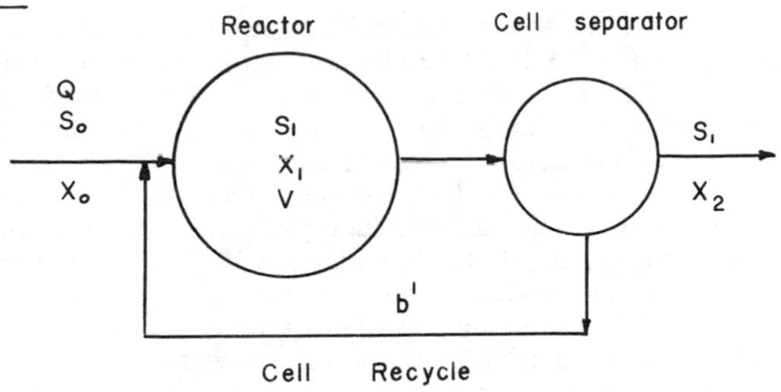

Reactor   Cell separator

Q, S_o, X_o → Reactor (S_1, X_1, V) → Cell separator → S_1, X_2

b'

Cell Recycle

$$\frac{dS_1}{dt} V = QS_o - X_1 V \left\{ f(S) \right\} - QS_1$$

change in substrate mass in reactor   in   removal by cells   out

@ STEADY STATE

$$\frac{dS_1}{dt} = 0 \quad \therefore \quad Q(S_o - S_1) = X_1 V \left\{ f(S) \right\}$$

$$\left\{ f(S) \right\} = \frac{Q(S_o - S_1)}{X_1 V} = q \qquad (2)$$

where $q = \frac{\text{gms substrate removed}}{\text{gms cells - day}}$

or $q = \frac{S_o - S_1}{X_1 \Theta}$

where $\Theta = \frac{V}{Q}$ = hydraulic residence time

Figure 159. Process materials balance.

One can note that the efficiency of a biological process for a given influent substrate concentration is a function of the hydraulic residence time, t, the cell concentration, X_a, the yield coefficient, Y, and the M-M constants.

An expression for process efficiency can be developed from the M-M equation alone. Such an expression for efficiency, E, is shown in Equation 5.

$$E = 1 - \frac{\mu K_s}{S_0 (\hat{\mu} - \mu)} = 1 - \frac{Y q K_s}{S_0 (\hat{\mu} - Yq)} \tag{5}$$

In the foregoing expression q or μ is a function of S_1. Since a given value of S_1 determines q, and for a given reactor volume, X_a, is determined by t and q (viz. $X_a = \frac{S_0 - S_1}{t\, q}$), it is believed that Equation 4 best describes the major parameters.

It should be emphasized that according to Equation 4, once a given effluent concentration is specified, E is determined by the feed concentration S_0, and μ, K_s, and Y are constants in the M-M expression and determined by the microbiological characteristics of the system. Only the cell concentration, X_a, and the residence time, t, are variables; however, only one of the two is independent at a time. Either X_a or t can be selected, but once it is fixed, the other is determined automatically. From this, one can conclude that either the efficiency, E, or the effluent concentration, S_1, should be correlated with the product of the reactor cell concentration, X_a, and residence time, t (viz., E or S_1 vs $X_a t$). While this appears to be relatively simple and straightforward, a perusal of literature in the field indicates that Eckenfelder (4) and his co-workers are of the few to recognize this concept. Moreover, the authors of two recent papers dealing specifically with kinetics of biological treatment systems apparently have not been aware of these facts.

Cells

One of the important characteristics of biological waste treatment systems is cellular recycle and the controlled wasting rates of cells produced during treatment. This permits control of the cell concentration, substrate removal velocity and effluent concentration over considerable limits.

Employing the same flow sheet shown in Figure 159, a materials balance for cells can be written around the process as follows:

$$\frac{dX_a V}{dt} = Q X_0 + \mu X_a V - k_d X_a V - QX_2$$

Δ cell mass in reactor | in | Growth | Decay | Out

Assuming the process is at steady state $\frac{dX_a}{dt} \cong 0$ and that the incoming cells $QX_0 \cong 0$, insofar as active solids in the reactor are concerned (explicit for soluble substrates), the following expression is obtained:

$$\frac{dX_a}{dt} \cong 0 = \mu X_1 - k_d X_1 - \frac{Q}{V} X_2$$

which simplifies to

$$\frac{QX_2}{VX_a} = \mu - k_d \tag{6}$$

The right-hand side of Equation 6 is recognized as the net growth rate of the system (growth—decay); obviously, the left-hand side is the mass of cells leaving the system per day divided by the mass of cells in the system. Equation 6 can be rewritten as follows:

$$\frac{1}{t_c} = Y q - k_d \tag{7}$$

where t_c is the mean "cell age" or mean cell residence time. Obviously the reciprocal of the mean cell residence time is the net growth rate.

If one wishes to express Equation 7 with reference to a cell recycle ratio $b^1 = \frac{X_a}{X_2}$; the following expression is obtained:

$$\frac{1}{b^1 t} = Y q - k_d \tag{8}$$

therefore

$$q = \frac{b^1 t\, k_d + 1}{b^1 t Y} \tag{9}$$

Equating the two expressions for q in Equations 2 and 9, the following expression for the effluent concentration is obtained.

$$S_1 = \frac{S_0\, Y\, b^1 - X_a\, (b^1\, t k_d + 1)}{b^1 Y} \tag{10}$$

Solving Equation 10 for the cell concentration, X_a, and residence time, t, yields the following equations:

$$X_a = \frac{b^1\, Y\, (S_0 - S_1)}{b^1 t k_d + 1} \tag{11}$$

$$t = \frac{Y\, b^1\, (S_0 - S_1) - X_a}{b^1\, X_a\, k_d} \tag{12}$$

The major value of the foregoing equations is to show the interrelationships involved between the physical and the microbiological parameters of the system. It should be noted that the recycle ratio, $b^1 = \frac{X_a}{X_2} = \frac{X_2\,(S_0 - S_1)\,(K_s + S_1) Y}{t\,\hat{\mu} S_1}$, whereas in actual practice it is dependent upon the efficiency of the cell separator, and the effluent concentration adjusts to the conditions imposed on the system.

SYSTEM KINETICS WITH OXYGEN TRANSFER

The foregoing kinetic equations can be modified to include oxygen demand considerations to yield an expression for oxygen transfer requirements. Eckenfelder (4), among others, has shown that the oxygen requirements can be expressed as linear functions of the substrate removal velocity, q, and the endogenous respiration rate k_a, as follows:

$$UV = \frac{(\text{gms. } O_2 \text{ used})}{\text{day}} = h^1\, (\text{Substrate})_{\text{removed}} + i(\text{Cells})_{\text{oxidized}} \tag{13}$$

or $\quad UV = h^1 Q\, (S_0 - S_1) + i k_d X_a V$

$\therefore \quad U = h^1 \frac{(S_0 - S_1)}{t} + \frac{i k_d\,(S_0 - S_1)}{q t}$

where $\quad U = \frac{\text{ppm}}{\text{day}}$

Thus

$$U = \frac{S_0 - S_1}{t}\left[h + \frac{i k_d}{q}\right] \tag{14}$$

The required oxygen transfer rate can be written as a function of the hydraulic residence time, t, and the effluent concentration, S_1, by substituting the M-M expression for the substrate removal velocity, q. Equation 15 reports the oxygen transfer rate for a balanced design in terms of t S_1 and the microbiological constants for the system (K_s, $\hat{\mu}$, Y, k_d, h^1 and i:

$$U = \frac{Y\,(S_0 - S_1)\,(K_s + S_1)}{t\hat{\mu}S_1}\left[\frac{h^1\hat{\mu}S_1}{Y(K_s + S_1)} + ik\right] \tag{15}$$

Equation 15 can be expanded and rewritten in the following form to illustrate better the significance of the parameters as well as the choice between high oxygen transfer rates or increasing the hydraulic residence time:

$$t\,U = \left[\frac{k_d Y k_s}{\hat{\mu}}\right]\left[\frac{S_0 - S_1}{S_1}\right] + \left[\frac{ik_d Y}{\hat{\mu}} + h^1\right]\left[S_0 - S_1\right] \tag{16}$$

Figure 160 shows graphically the relationship of $t\,U$ and $\frac{U}{24}$ (ppm/hr) with effluent concentration (BOD_5) for a selected set of microbiological and process

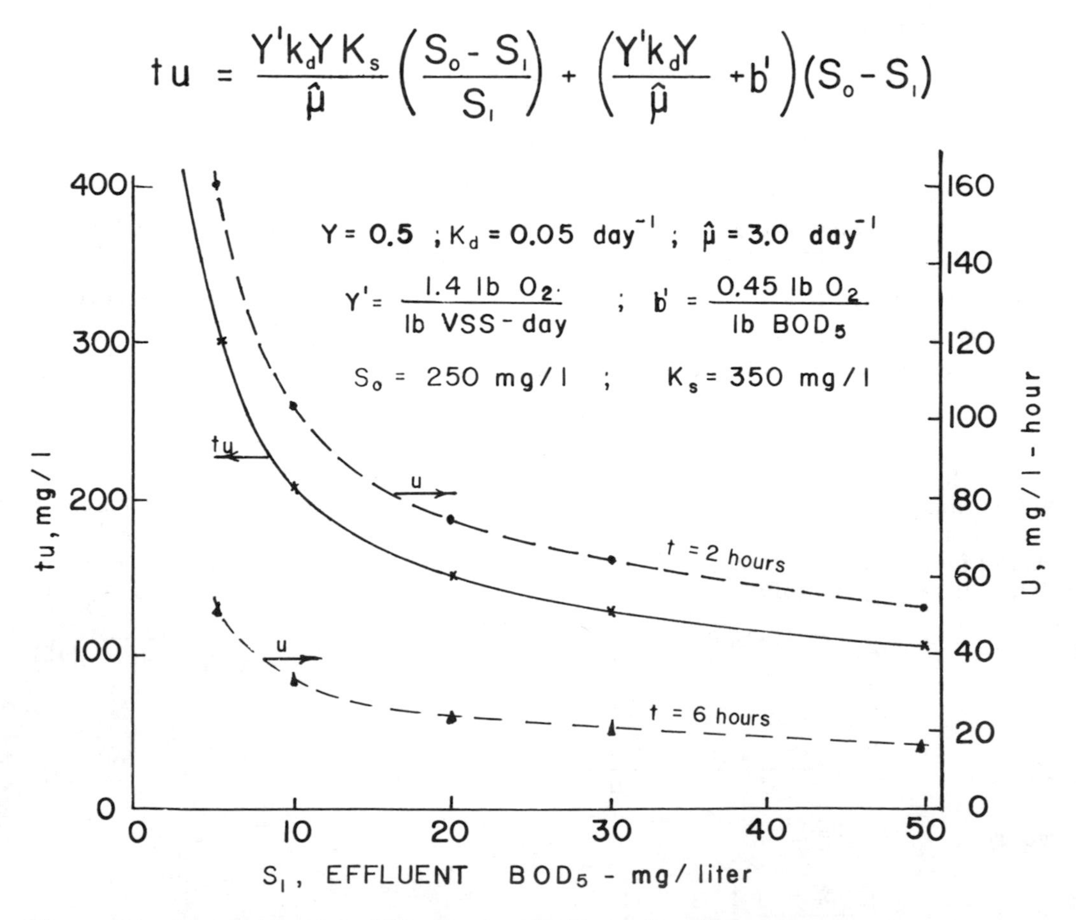

Figure 160. Oxygen transfer—effluent concentration and residence time.

constants which approximate operating conditions in standard rate activated sludge treatment plants. For the assumed constants shown in Figure 160, an oxygen transfer rate of 20 ppm/hr is required to produce an effluent BOD_5 (soluble) of 30 ppm with a t = 6 hours. However, if t is equal to 2 hours, a transfer rate of 60^+ ppm/hr would be required to produce the same effluent BOD. With reasonable estimates of kinetic constants for a given waste it is possible to estimate the oxygen transfer rate requirements for a wide range of influent, effluent, and loading characteristics.

APPLICATION OF KINETIC MODELS

The results of the application of kinetic expressions to experimental or real waste treatment systems can be no better than the availability and accuracy of data on the kinetic constants. Tables 57 and 58 present a summary of most of the data available in the literature for kinetic constants of aerobic and anaerobic treatment systems. Inspection of Table 57, which reports kinetic constants for aerobic systems, indicates that most of the data available are from laboratory studies and pertain to yield (Y), decay (k_d), and oxygen requirement (i and h') constants. Only two studies reported sufficient data to permit computation of the M-M constants for growth and substrate removal. Obviously, more studies are needed to develop data from which one can compute the required kinetic constants.

Table 58 reports most of the kinetic data available in the literature on anaerobic fermentation systems. Again most of these data have been developed in the writer's laboratory during the past eight years by co-workers Stewart (1), Agardy (3), Andrews (5), and Almgren (6). Unfortunately all of these data are the result of laboratory studies. Additional studies are needed to develop more reliable estimates of the kinetic characteristics of anaerobic acid and methane fermentation systems. Once sufficient, accurate kinetic data are available on actual wastes it will be possible to predict performance as well as to guide process design on a rational basis. In addition, such data will permit objective and quantitative evaluation of the economic feasibility of aerobic and anaerobic treatment systems for a given waste treatment problem.

Extended Aeration

The value of theoretical analyses for process evaluation is subject to considerable question without adequate confirmation in practice. As indicated in Table 57, the writer has been engaged recently in the development of kinetic constants for a 15-MGD activated sludge treatment plant, the results of which will be published in the near future. However, one can apply the kinetic theory to operating waste treatment systems such as extended aeration.

In short, an extended aeration plant is one where the net growth rate is made to approach zero. That is, growth is approximately equal to decay; however, it is recognized that there will always be some minimum net growth in an extended aeration system.

Thus

$$\text{Net growth rate} = \frac{1}{t_c} = Yq - k_d \rightarrow 0$$

$$\therefore\ Yq \cong k_d$$

If one uses an average value for the yield coefficient, $Y(\mathrm{BOD})_5$ of $0.5 \frac{\text{gm. VSS}}{\text{gm. BOD}_5 \text{ rem.}}$ and a decay rate of 0.05 day^{-1}, one obtains a substrate re-

TABLE 57

AEROBIC BIOLOGICAL PROCESS CONSTANTS

Authority	Year and Ref.	Substrate	$\hat{q} = \hat{\mu}/Y$		K_s		Y		k_d	$i\ k_d$	h'	Type of Study
			BOD_5	COD	BOD_5	COD	BOD_5	COD				
Heukelekian	1951 (7)	Domestic sewage	–	–	–	–	0.500	–	0.055	–	–	Lab.
Gram	1956 (8)	Skim milk	5.1	–	100	–	0.480	–	0.045	0.065	0.40	Lab.
Stack	1959 (9)	Glucose	3.0	–	355	–	0.420	–	0.087	–	–	Lab.
Downing	1961 (10)	Domestic sewage	–	–	–	–	–	–	–	0.100	0.50	Lab.
Servici-Bogan	1963 (11)	Carbohydrates	–	–	–	–	–	0.34	–	–	–	Lab.
		Aromatics Aliph's	–	–	–	–	–	0.38	–	–	–	Lab.
McWhorter-Heuk'n	1962 (12)	Domestic sewage	–	–	–	–	–	0.33	–	–	–	Lab.
Eckhoff-Jenkins	1966 (13)	Synthetic sewage	–	–	–	–	–	0.44	0.078	–	–	Lab.
Eckenfelder	1960 (4)	Pulp and paper	–	–	–	–	–	–	–	0.089	0.52	Pil. Plt.
		Pharamaceutical	–	–	–	–	0.645	0.37	–	–	–	Pil. Plt.
Dryden	1955 (14)	Chemical	–	–	–	–	0.770	–	0.200	0.200	0.35	Pil. Plt.
Hazeltine	1963 (15)	Kraft pulp	–	–	–	–	–	–	–	0.100	0.50	Field
Pearson-Haas	1965 (16)	Domestic sewage	–	–	–	–	–	0.45	0.050	–	–	Field

TABLE 58

ANAEROBIC BIOLOGICAL PROCESS CONSTANTS

Authority	Year Ref.	Substrate	$\hat{q} = \hat{\mu}/Y$		K_s		Y		k_d	Type of Study	Remarks
			BOD_5	COD	BOD_5	COD	BOD_5	COD			
Stewart *et al.*	1958 (1)	Dextrose, Peptone B. Ex.	–	0.37	–	5,700	–	0.1800	0.025	Lab.	
Agardy *et al.*	1962 (3)	Dextrose, Tryptone B. Ex.	–	0.79	–	6,700	–	0.1140	0.030	Lab.	
	1962 (3)	Dextrose, Tryptone B. Ex.	–	18.50*	–	5,030	–	0.0051*	0.026	Lab.	*DNA, not VSS
Speece *et al.*	1963 (17)	Glucose & Starch	–	–	–	–	–	0.4600	0.088	Lab.	
	1963 (17)	Amino, fatty acids	–	–	–	–	–	0.0540	0.038	Lab.	
	1963 (17)	Nutrient broth	–	–	–	–	–	0.0760	0.014	Lab.	
Andrews *et al.*	1963 (5)	Dextrose, peptone B. Ex.	–	1.33	–	4,200	–	0.1400	0.100	Lab.	Multi stage, acid bact.
	1963 (5)	Dextrose, peptone B. Ex.	–	–	–	–	–	0.1500	0.030	Lab.	Single stage, CH_4 bact.
Almgren *et al.*	1966 (6)	Dextrose, Tryptone B. Ex.	–	0.60	–	2,760	–	–	–	Lab.	Recycle, high t_c
	1966 (6)	Dextrose, Tryptone B. Ex.	–	1.59	–	164	–	–	–	Lab.	Nonrecycle, low t_c, S_0

moval velocity, q, equal to $\frac{0.05}{0.50} \cong 0.10 \frac{\text{lb BOD rem.}}{\text{lb VSS-day}}$. This is about the value of q found in many operating extended aeration systems. Such an analysis gives the theoretical approach some credence as to its applicability to the real world.

If one equates the M-M substrate removal Equation 3 with the expression $q = \frac{\mu}{Y} \cong \frac{k_d}{Y}$ for growth approximately equal to decay, the following relationship is obtained:

$$S_1 = \frac{qYK_s}{\hat{\mu} - qY} \tag{17}$$

Assuming the following constants apply; $\mu = 3.0 \text{ day}^{-1}$, and $K_s = 350$ mg/ℓ BOD_5, S_1 may be computed as follows:

$$S_1 = \frac{(0.1)(0.5)(350)}{3.0 - (0.1)(0.5)} \cong 6 \text{ mg}/\ell$$

The accuracy of this estimated level of soluble effluent BOD_5 for extended aeration plants is not known; however, it appears to be of the right order of magnitude.

Growth Systems—Nutrient Removal

Another example of the possible application of kinetic modeling to the analysis of practical problems is concerned with prediction of the operating conditions to produce maximum cell production (i.e., maximum net growth). If a system is operated in this fashion it should be possible to incorporate essential nutrients in the cells and remove them from the waste stream, thereby increasing the removal of nutrients by the plant.

For a given reactor volume, the net growth is expressed by Equation 5, 6 and 7

$$\frac{1}{t_c} = Yq - k_d = \frac{QX_2}{X_a V}$$

Mass cells produced/day $= QX_2$

$$QX_2 = YqX_aV - k_dX_aV$$

Since $$X_a = \frac{Q(S_0 - S_1)}{Vq} \text{ and } q = \frac{\hat{\mu}\, S_1}{Y(K_g + S_1)}$$

Substituting

$$QX_2 = \frac{YqVE(S_0 - S_1)}{Vq} - \frac{k_d VQ(S_0 - S_1)\, Y\, (K_s + S_1)}{\hat{\mu}\, V\, S_1}$$

where $QX_2 = f(S_1)$,

Taking the partial derivative of QX_2 with respect to S_1, one obtains the following:

$$\frac{\partial QX_2}{\partial S_1} = -\,Q\,Y + \frac{Q\,Y\,k_d\,S_0K_s}{\hat{\mu}\,S_1^2} + \frac{Q\,Y\,k_d}{\hat{\mu}}$$

Letting $\frac{\partial(QX_2)}{\partial S_1} = 0$ and solving for S_1 one obtains the following:

$$S_1 = \sqrt{\frac{k_dS_0K_s}{\hat{\mu} - k_d}} \tag{18}$$

The value of S_1 in Equation 18 is the effluent concentration which gives maximum cell production. From this one can determine q, X_a, and the maximum cell-wasting rate possible for a given waste and residence time. Correspondingly, this operation will likely result in maximum removal of essential nutrients incorporated in the cells. This as well as other possibilities suggested by this example need further investigation.

SUMMARY

A unified kinetic description of both aerobic and anaerobic waste treatment systems is presented. The kinetic model for growth and substrate removal is based upon that of Michaelis Menten, and substrate and cell material balance equations including a decay term constitute the basic kinetic descriptions of the process.

The need for additional laboratory and field determination of the applicable kinetic constants is emphasized. Most of the currently available data on aerobic and anaerobic process constants are summarized. The application of kinetic modeling in interpreting special biological processes such as extended aeration is demonstrated. Also, an analytical approach to maximum growth processes, for possible nutrient removal, is presented.

If aerobic and anaerobic processes are to be evaluated for a specific waste treatment problem on a rational economic feasibility basis, the development of accurate kinetic constants for both processes is an absolute requirement.

REFERENCES

(1) Stewart, M. J. *Reaction Kinetics and Operational Parameters of Continuous Flow Anaerobic Fermentation Processes*. Sanitary Engineering Research Laboratory Publication No. 4. IER Series 90. Berkeley: University of California (June 1958).

(2) Monod, J. "The Growth of Bacterial Cultures," *Ann. Rev. Microbiol., III,* 371 (1949).

(3) Agardy, F. J., R. D. Cole, and E. A. Pearson. *Kinetic and Activity Parameters of Anaerobic Fermentation Systems*. Sanitary Engineering Research Laboratory Report 63-2. Berkeley: University of California (February 1963).

(4) Eckenfelder, W. W., and J. McCabe. *Advances in Biological Waste Treatment.* Proceedings of the Third Conference on Biological Waste Treatment. New York: Pergamon Press (1963).

(5) Andrews, J. F., R. D. Cole, and E. A. Pearson. *Kinetics and Characteristics of Multistage Methane Fermentations*. Sanitary Engineering Research Laboratory Report No. 64-11. Berkeley: University of California (December 1964).

(6) Almgren. H. A. Unpublished Research, Personal Communication (March 1966).

(7) Heukelekian, H., H. E. Oxford, and R. Manganelli. "Factors Affecting the Quantity of Sludge Production in the Activated Sludge Process," *Sewage Ind. Wastes, 23,* 945 (1951).

(8) Gram, A. L. *Reaction Kinetics of Aerobic Biological Processes*. Sanitary Engineering Research Laboratory, No. 2, IER Series 90. Berkeley: University of California (1956).

(9) Stack, V. T., and R. A. Conway. "Design Data for Completely Mixed Activated Sludge Treatment," *Sewage Ind. Wastes, 31*(10), 118–1190 (1959).

(10) Downing, A. L., T. G. Tomlinson, and G. A. Truesdale. "Effect of Inhibitions on Nitrification in the Activated Sludge Process," *J. Inst. Sew. Purif., 6,* 537–554 (1964).

(11) Servici, J. A., and R. H. Bogan. "Free Energy as a Parameter in Biological Treatment," *Proc. ASCE, 89*(S.A. 3), 17–40 (1963).

(12) McWhorter, T. R., and H. Heukelekian. "Growth and Endogenous Phases in the Oxidation of Glucose," *Proceedings of International Conference on Water Pollution Research.* Vol. 2, pp. 419–435. New York: Pergamon Press (1962).

(13) Eckhoff, D. W., and D. Jenkins. "Transient Loading Effects in the Activated Sludge Process." Presented at Third International Conference on Water Pollution Research, Munich (September 1966).
(14) Dryden, F. E., P. H. Barrett, J. C. Kissinger, and W. W. Eckenfelder. "Treatment of Fine Chemical Wastes by High-Rate Activated Sludge," *Proceedings*, 9th Purdue Industrial Waste Conference, Purdue University, Lafayette, Indiana (1954).
(15) Hazeltine, T. R. "Some Recent Advances in the Design of Activated Sludge Systems." Prepublication manuscript presented at the annual meeting of the California Water Pollution Control Federation, Sacremento, California (1962).
(16) Pearson, E. A., and P. Haas. Unpublished Field Investigations (1965).
(17) Speece, R. E., and P. L. McCarty. "Nutrient Requirements and Biological Solids Accumulation in Anaerobic Digestion," *Proceedings*, International Conference on Water Pollution Research, Vol. 2, pp. 305–322. New York: Pergamon Press (1962).

SECTION THREE

WASTE STABILIZATION POND PRACTICES

BASIS FOR WASTE STABILIZATION POND DESIGNS

Earnest F. Gloyna
The University of Texas, Austin, Texas

Waste stabilization ponds have undergone sufficient study and development to be classified as one of the major types of wastewater treatment systems. While some waste stabilization ponds have failed to operate successfully, in general the success of this type of treatment is recognized even though the designs have been largely empirical. Problems with this type of treatment have usually occurred as a result of inadequate engineering, poor maintenance, and lack of operational supervision. An inspection of costs will show that sewage treatment by stabilization ponds is considerably cheaper than other methods as long as the municipality is not too large. The construction and maintenance costs for a waste stabilization treatment plant of 2.5 mgd capacity are frequently less than half the costs of other alternatives.

The design of a waste stabilization pond depends upon the treatment objectives. A pond system may be designed to receive untreated sewage or industrial wastes, primary treatment plant effluents, secondary treatment plant effluents, excess activated sludge, or wastes containing settleable solids.

Waste stabilization ponds may be used to satisfy interim waste treatment requirements, for treatment of small volumes of wastewater in isolated places, or for stabilization of large volumes of wastes. This type of waste treatment process is most suitable for locations where the land is inexpensive, where climatic conditions are suitable, where organic loadings may fluctuate considerably, and where funds are limited.

The treatment process depends upon the effective use of bacteria for degradation of putrescible organic material and the efficient use of algae for oxygenation purposes. The bacteria have the ability to break down complex organic waste materials and release carbon dioxide, which becomes the main source of carbon for the algae. As long as the algae, in conjunction with surface aeration, can provide an excess of oxygen above that required by the aerobic or facultative bacteria, a relatively aerobic environment will be maintained in some sections of the pond. Part of the substrate will be used to make new cells, and the remainder of the substrate will provide the energy that is necessary to further the degradation reactions.

Most waste stabilization ponds develop into some type of facultative system. In this respect, waste stabilization ponds are very similar to rivers and lakes. Aerobic conditions are frequently maintained near the surface and sometimes throughout most of the depth of the pond. Because settleable organic debris are usually present, anaerobic conditions will persist near the bottom.

In ponds receiving optimum waste loads, planktonic algae will be released to streams in the effluent; while, in contrast, in ponds receiving relatively small organic loads, the algae are usually consumed by planktonic phagotrophs, such as *Daphnia* or *Cyclops*, or settle slowly to the bottom where the settled material is consumed by other organisms such as *Chironomas* larvae. These larvae flourish in rich organic sediments when a small amount of oxygen is available (1). In shallow ponds where an algal bloom has developed, some of the algae may become entrapped in floating mats which will settle and thus become part of the bottom sediments, where the algae will ultimately die. Unfortunately, unicellular algae, because of low settling velocities, ordinarily do not settle appreciably and are discharged into receiving streams.

ECOLOGICAL SYSTEM

An understanding of the fundamental principles of algal physiology is important in assisting one to recognize pond performances. Yet, there is a bewildering array of differences in various algae, and the performance of a given culture cannot be predicted on the basis of morphological description alone. For example, an algal "bloom" in two bodies of water may not necessarily be the result of matching environmental conditions (2). The physiological identity of the strains growing in the different locations may not be the same.

Algae have the capacity for both autotrophic and heterotrophic growth. Most species, under appropriate conditions, perform as facultative chemo-organotrophs and in this capacity use sugars or organic acids for sources both of energy and of reduced carbon. These chemo-organotrophs obtain energy from reduced carbon as do most bacteria. However, in stabilization ponds the primary concern is usually with the photosynthetic algae requiring only water, inorganic nutrients, and carbon dioxide. Water becomes the hydrogen donor. Algae utilizing the simpler nutrients are classified as autotrophic-photolithotrophs. Those growing in rich organic substrates are classified as heterotrophic-photolithotrophs. In the latter case, the algae require growth factors to sustain photosynthesis.

Typical of the green algae in waste stabilization ponds are *Chlamydomonas*, *Chlorella*, and *Euglena*. Blue-green algae common to waste stabilization ponds are *Oscillatoria*, *Phormidium*, *Anacystis*, and *Anabaena*. In the operation of a pond *Chlamydomonas* and *Euglena* are generally the first planktonic genera to appear. Blue-green algal mats frequently develop in ponds during the summer and usually rise to the surface. Problems develop when detached patches of benthic algae, such as *Phormidium*, begin to accumulate. *Euglena* show a high degree of adaptability to various pond conditions and are present during all seasons and under most climatological conditions. Probably next in adaptability are *Chlamydomonas*, *Micractinium*, *Ankistrodesmus*, *Scenedesmus*, and *Chlorella*. Frequently *Euglena* and *Chlamydomonas* tend to dominate during the cooler weather, while the various *Chlorococcales* are most numerous during summer months. This latter grouping is an order under the division Chlorophyta containing *Chlorella*, *Ankistrodesmus*, and *Scenedesmus*.

The oxygen evolution and the carbon dioxide absorption by the algae during periods of light may exceed by twenty times the reverse reaction which takes place in the absence of light. During the daytime, the *p*H may be raised materially as compared to periods of darkness. The algae will reduce the alkalinity and mineral content, and there will be a high degree of nitrogen utilization during the ammonia stage. There seems to be a mechanism in the algae for conserving energy by alternating the dominance between photosynthesis during the day and respiration at night.

In general, algae growing in a stream or waste stabilization pond are in a highly competitive environment. One or more of the factors necessary for photosynthesis are interrelated, and unicellular algae, in particular, will react rapidly to changes in the environment. Therefore, it is of importance to examine critically those factors which affect the growth rate: illumination, temperature, and nutrients.

Illumination

Light penetration can be approximated by the use of Beers-Lambert Law, Equation 1. Fortunately, it is not necessary to keep all of the pond aerobic. The algal-bacterial masses are not homogeneous, and design calculations based on light penetration through a homogeneous mixture might be misleading. For example, if one assumes a homogeneous culture of *Chlorella pyrenoidosa* and a photosynthesis-respiration compensation level of 24 ft-C, the maximum depth of the pond must be limited to about 35 cm.

$$I = I_o e^{-kcd} \tag{1}$$

where

I = light intensity after passage through some medium
I_o = original light intensity
k = absorption coefficient
c = concentration of algal cells
d = depth

The diurnal cycle and the oxygenation of a pond are probably influenced much more by variations in algal populations than by variations in light intensity. Also, a depth exists for which the light intensity just equals the light saturation intensity (3). Thus, light that penetrates to greater depths is utilized with increasing efficiency. As an example, *Chlorella* (4) reaches a saturation point at about 600 ft-C (2.5×10^4 ergs/cm^2-sec). A compensation point for growth is experienced at about 24 ft-C (10×10^2 ergs/cm^2-sec). The fraction of light utilized is shown in Equation 2.

$$f = \frac{I_s}{I_o}\left(Ln\,\frac{I_o}{I_s} + 1\right) \tag{2}$$

where

f = fraction of light
I_s = saturation intensity

The heat of combustion for sewage-grown algae is about six calories per milligram. Thus, by calculating the visible solar energy, estimating the fraction of solar energy converted to cell material, measuring the heat of combustion of the cells, and establishing a retention period, the overall efficiency of photosynthetic conversion of solar energy to algal energy can be obtained. Efficiencies range from 2 percent to 9 percent with 5 percent being common. It has been suggested that organic loadings might even be on the basis of one pound of BOD/acre/day (112 mg of BOD/m^2/day) for every two langleys of visible solar energy (5).

Temperature

Temperature is of paramount importance in the design and the performance of waste stabilization ponds. Temperature affects photosynthetic oxygen production as well as other biological reactions. While optimum oxygen production is maintained at about 20°C., limiting lower and upper values appear to be, respectively, about 4°C. and 35°C.

Roughly, chemical reaction rates are doubled for about each 10°C. increase in temperature, and within limits this rule applies to biological reactions, as in Equation 3.

$$\frac{t}{t_o} = e^{c^1(T_o - T)} = \Theta^{(T_o - T)} \tag{3}$$

where

t = reaction time required at any (T) temperature (days)
t_o = original time for reaction at an original (T_o) temperature (days)
c^1 = energy-temperature characteristic of the van't Hoff-Arhenius Equation (0.0693)
T_o = original temperature (°C.)
T = any temperature (°C.)

Thus it is that a paradox presents itself in the operation of ponds in the warmer climates. If the water temperature approaches 35°C., particularly when the ponds are shallow, the beneficial algal population will be severely curtailed. This curtailment of algal activity occurs even though the bacterial population proceeds to use oxygen at an increased rate. In this case, the green algae belonging to the group Chlorophyceae will decrease or disappear. The dominant microorganism remaining when the temperature exceeds 30°C. will be Euglenophyceae. Also, at this temperature gasification will probably cause bottom sediments to rise and Myxophyceae or blue-green algae will develop on the floating sludge mats.

Nutrients

For metabolism to occur, usable food sources must be available in the ponds. In the case of domestic sewage all nutrient requirements are met, but such is not the case with many industrial wastes.

The majority of algal species use only free carbon dioxide in photosynthesis (6). However, there is some indication that a few algae utilize bicarbonate ion (7). Even with a 0.03 percent carbon dioxide concentration which is usually found in air, an optimum rate of photosynthesis can be maintained (8). About six moles of oxygen are produced for every six moles of carbon dioxide reduced. During this process one mole of sugar is synthesized.

Several trace elements are required for algal metabolism. Generally, in waste treatment there is no problem in maintaining an adequate level of trace elements. In laboratory preparations, on the other hand, it is necessary to add trace elements to distilled water preparations, and care must be taken to prevent the formation of insoluble or colloidal materials, especially by elements such as phosphorus and iron. The nutritional thresholds for unlimited algal production have not been defined, but considerable research is under way to define the problem of eutrophication in rivers and lakes. Industrial wastes are frequently deficient in nitrogen and phosphorus. The lack of these two elements retards the formation of protoplasm and reduces the rate of stabilization. The required BOD ratios to phosphorus and nitrogen are respectively about 100:1 and 20:1. However, in a pond where seepage is minimal and detention periods are long, there may be considerable re-use of both nitrogen and phosphorus. The breakdown and reconstitution of carbon are shown in Equations 4 and 5.

$$C_aH_bN_cO_dP_e + (a + \tfrac{1}{4}b - \tfrac{1}{2}d + \tfrac{3}{2}c + 2e)\, O_2 \rightarrow a\,CO_2 + \frac{b}{2}\, H_2O + c\,NO_3 + e\,PO_4^{-3} \quad (4)$$

$$106\, CO_2 + 90\, H_2O + 16\, NO_3^- + 1\, PO_4 + \text{light} \rightarrow C_{106}H_{180}O_{45}N_{16}P_1 + 154\tfrac{1}{2}\, O_2 \quad (5)$$

Roughly 749 grams of dissolved oxygen can be produced according to Equation 5 for each pound of algae synthesized. Equations 6 and 7 present the nutrient balance in terms of millimoles per liter of raw settled sewage and sewage effluent (9).

$$\begin{bmatrix} P = 0.14 \\ N = 2.5 \\ C = 9^* \\ C = 1^{**} \end{bmatrix} + 11\, O_2 \rightarrow \begin{bmatrix} P = 0.075 \\ N = 1.2 \\ C = 8^* \end{bmatrix} + \begin{bmatrix} P = 0.065 \\ N = 1.3 \\ C = 1^* \\ C = 1^{**} \end{bmatrix} + \text{energy} \quad (6)$$

C:N:P = 70:17:1	C:N:P = 106:16:1	C:N:P = 30:20:1
Raw settled sewage	Bacterial sludge	Sewage effluent

*Assimilable carbon
**Nonassimilable carbon

$$\begin{bmatrix} P = 0.065 \\ N = 1.3 \\ C = 1^{*} \\ C = 1^{**} \end{bmatrix} + [(C = 6)] + \text{light} \rightarrow \begin{bmatrix} P = 0.065 \\ N = 1.05 \\ C = 7^{*} \end{bmatrix} + \begin{bmatrix} O_2 = 10 \\ C = 1^{**} \end{bmatrix} \quad (7)$$

C:N:P = 30:20:1 Sewage effluent; Carbon dioxide; C:N:P = 106:16:1 Algal mass

DEVELOPMENT OF DESIGN CRITERIA

Operational experiences and research have provided some information on the environmental factors governing the basic processes of waste stabilization in ponds. These processes can be categorized as aerobic, facultative, and anaerobic.

Aerobic and Anaerobic Designs

In aerobic ponds the waste material is stabilized wholly through the action of aerobic oxidation. These systems may depend on both mechanical aeration and photosynthesis. In algal ponds where photosynthesis provides the aerobic conditions, the designs are based on large ratios of surface area to volume; under these conditions large amounts of algae are grown. In the mechanically aerated ponds sludge removal may be necessary; under these circumstances aeration may be used to assist a flourishing algal-bacterial population, or a pond may approach an activated sludge type operation. The BOD loading in a continuously mixed pond may be very high, that is, as much as 500 lb/acre/day (56 $g/m^2/day$). In principle, aerobic pond design may be based on three concepts: minimum depth with maximum algal production (10), maximum algal production considering a total BOD design load (11), and induced mixing which may support increased aerobic bacterial activity (12).

Methane fermentation is an essential reaction in anaerobic ponds. One of the controlling factors in an anaerobic lagoon system is the narrow *p*H range (6.8–7.2) permissible under methane fermentation. This limitation is very important, since acid production must be followed immediately by methane fermentation. It would seem that a deep facultative pond could provide an anaerobic environment near the bottom, a buffer zone throughout the middle, and even a small aerobic zone near the top. It is not too uncommon to find ponds receiving 400–500 lb. of 5-day BOD/acre/day of untreated wastewater. Even where the loading has reached 1,500–2,000 lb. of BOD/acre/day there have been marked successes. The city of Melbourne, Australia, used a summer detention period of 1.25 days (1,000–2,000 lb. BOD/acre/day) in the anaerobic ponds and 7.5 days in the aerobic units (13). In the winter the detention period is increased by almost a factor of four. The BOD reduction in the summer and winter is reported to be, respectively, 65 percent to 80 percent and 45 percent to 65 percent. Detention longer than five days is not justified on the basis that the performance in the ponds then becomes comparable to facultative or aerobic ponds. Sludge removal, in all probability, will be necessary where suspended solids are high.

The ratio between the area of aerobic and anaerobic units appears to be an important design factor. Ratios between 10:1 and 5:1 seem to be fairly useful for purposes of design. Ponds with a low ratio of 3:1 will be sensitive to short-term changes in the BOD.

Facultative Pond Designs

Facultative ponds are those systems in which the upper layers of the pond are aerobic and the bottom layers are devoid of dissolved oxygen, tending to be anaerobic. Most existing waste stabilization pond installations are of this type. Generally, the criteria, whether empirically derived from research or laid down by regulation, have incorporated the accumulated sediment BOD into the design considerations. Serious odor problems will not develop if adequate depth is maintained and an upper aerobic environment is predominant.

Several concepts have been suggested for the design of facultative ponds (14). The BOD per unit area concept assumes that the BOD loading rate is governed by the usual radiation. In this case, the liquid depth must be limited to the photic zone. A common load is 50 lb. of 5-day BOD/acre/day. However, where ice cover reduces the solar energy input and aerobic conditions must be re-established quickly in the spring, the permissible surface loading may be closer to 15 lb. BOD/acre/day. In this case, reoxygenation by algae is of secondary importance. In temperate zones where there is no ice cover, winter periods may still be critical, but problems can develop in the summer due to high water temperatures as well.

Theory

The functional relationships between the retention time, degradation rate, temperature coefficient, and temperature can be combined (15, 16). The effluent concentration for continuous flow becomes

$$Y_t = \frac{Y}{(V/Q)} \int_{t=0}^{\infty} e^{-Kt}\ e^{-(Q/V)t}\,dt \qquad (8)$$

where

Y_t = effluent 5-day BOD
Y = influent 5-day BOD
t = retention time
V = volume of pond
Q = flow per day
K = degradation rate

Resolving Equation 8 and solving in terms of a retention factor, it is possible to develop Equation 9.

$$Y_t = \frac{Y}{K_T t + 1} \qquad (9)$$

where K_T = degradation rate for some temperature T

As indicated in the typical BOD decay relationship for a batch system, the influent BOD is degraded according to Equation 10.

$$Y_t = Y\,e^{-Kt} \qquad (10)$$

Thus, for a fixed percentage reduction it can be shown that for single ponds the ratios of the degradation constants are equal to the ratios of the retention times (Equation 11).

$$\frac{K_{35}}{K_T} = \frac{t_T}{t_{35}} = \theta^{(35-T)} \qquad (11)$$

where

K = reaction rate for various temperatures
t = reaction times
T = temperatures

Data developed in laboratory ponds (16) operated at 35°C., 24°C., 20°C., and 9°C., show that θ = 1.085 and K_{35} = 1.2 for a synthetic nonsettleable sewage. These experimental results and the theoretical data developed by Marais and Shaw show a fairly significant correlation (Fig. 161).

As equation may be derived by calculating the required volume, which is directly proportional to retention and volume of daily flow. The retention or reaction time, t, is influenced by the quantity of BOD to be stabilized. For proximal deviations from the average BOD of domestic wastewater a straight-line factor, $y/200$, is introduced, where y is the influent 5-day BOD and 200 mg/l is the average BOD value of sewage in the United States. Thus an equation for the volume, including reaction time, becomes

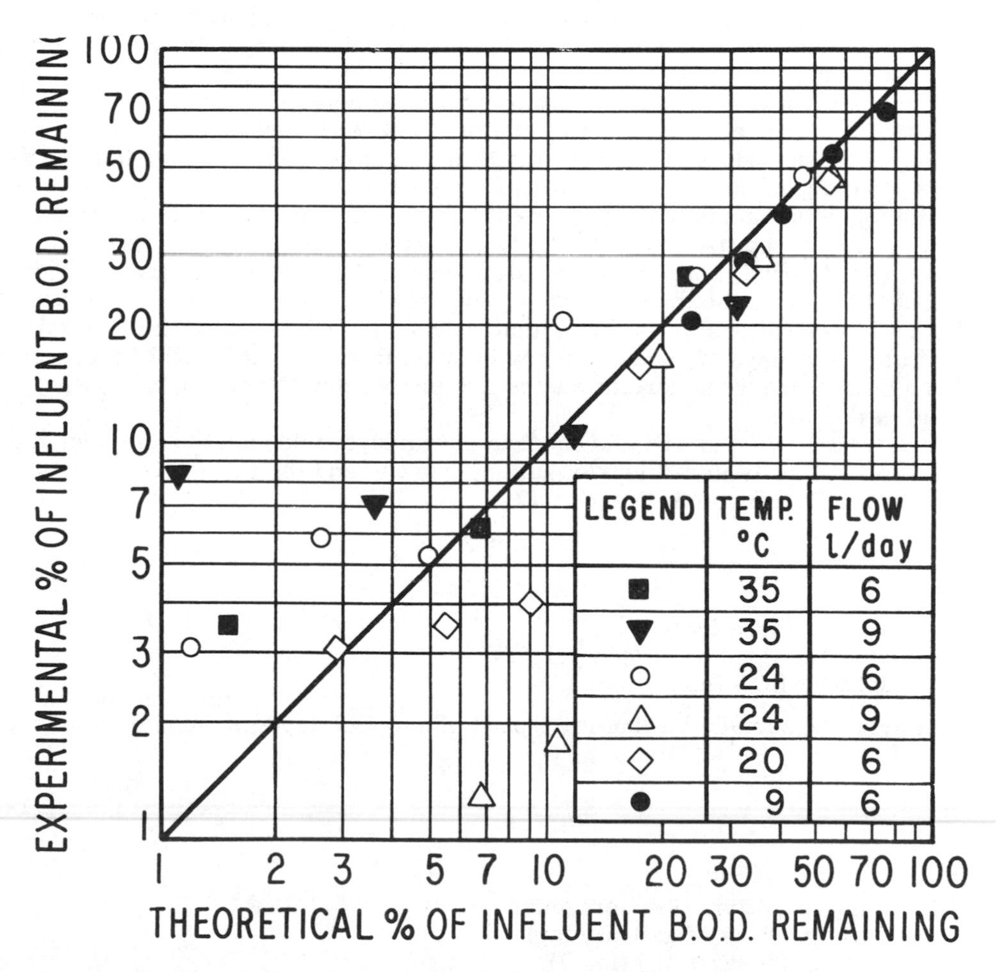

Figure 161. Correlation of experimental and theoretical results.

$$V = fQ \frac{Y}{200} t_o \, \theta \, (T_o - T) \quad (12)$$

where

V = volume
Q = flow
Y = influent 5-day BOD
t_o = reaction time for corresponding temperature (T_o) for waste with BOD of 200 mg/l
T_o = temperature related to reaction time t_o (T_o = 35°C.)
T = temperature for reaction time t (average temperature for coldest month)
f = algal toxicity factor

To obtain ideal conditions the size of the pond can be calculated by choosing a maximum temperature of 35°C., (T_o), an optimum reaction time of seven days (t_o), and a θ of 1.085. To obtain a value for T it is necessary to consider average pond temperatures during the coldest month. Also, for ideal conditions, a minimum depth of 6 feet should be considered.

To compensate for wastes having higher than normal BOD concentrations, it has been found practical to adjust the required volume by a straight-line factor. For proximal deviations, a factor of Y/Y_{avg} has been introduced, where Y_{avg} is equal to 200 mg/l.

The above equations consider the important parameters as related to the biodegradation of a typical domestic wastewater. Where wastewaters contain relatively high concentrations of BOD, adjustments must be made in order to keep the surface area, depth, and volume in proper proportions.

Similarly, adjustments must be made if toxic wastes are added to a system. In case of pronounced toxicity, both the degradation constant, which represents bacteriological activity, and the oxygenation capacity of the algae will be reduced (17). Table 59 shows the toxic effects of several chemicals on *Chlorella pyrenoidosa.* Concentrations are shown which reduced the chlorophyll content by 50 percent after five days of contact. It can be seen that the reaeration capacity of a pond can be reduced when certain wastes are introduced. Much work, however, remains in this area.

Where the retention at 35°C. is equal to seven days, f is equal to one, and T is equal to 15°C., flow is in millions of gallons per day and the volume is in acre feet; Equation 12 reduces to Equation 13.

$$V = 0.56\, QY \quad (13)$$

where

V = volume (acre feet)
Q = flow (millions of gallons per day)
Y = influent BOD (mg/l)

Similarly, the surface loading for a pond of six-foot depth is found by Equation 14.

$$\text{S.L.} = \frac{50\, QY}{V} \quad (14)$$

where

S.L. = surface loading (lbs/acre/day)
Q = flow (millions of gallons/day)
Y = influent (5-day BOD) (mg/l)
V = volume (acre-feet)

TABLE 59

CONCENTRATIONS OF TOXICANT AFFECTING A 50 PERCENT CHLOROPHYLL REDUCTION

Organic Chemical	Toxic Concentration (mg/l)	Organic Chemical	Toxic Concentration (mg/l)
Methanoic Acid	220	3-Butanol	24,200
Ethanoic Acid	350	1-Hexanol	1,275
Propanoic Acid	250	2-Hexanol	3,100
Butanoic Acid	340	Heptanol	525
2-Methyl Propanoic Acid	345	Octanol	250
		Propenoic Acid	120
Pentanoic Acid	280	Butenoic Acid	280
3-Methyl Butanoic Acid	400	2,3 Dihydroxy Butanedioic Acid	480
Hexanoic Acid	320	Hydroxyethanoic Acid	2,700
Heptanoic Acid	180	Sulfanilic Acid	970
Octanoic Acid	220	Methoxyethanoic Acid	580
Ethanedoic Acid	290	2-Oxo Propanoic Acid	880
Propanedioic Acid	460	Ethanoic Andydride	360
Butanedioic Acid	2,200	Propanal	3,450
Pentanedioic Acid	1,200	1-Butanal	2,500
Hexanedioic Acid	900	2-Methyl Propanal	3,450
Heptanedioic Acid	700	1-Heptanal	240
Methanol	31,000	1, 2-Ethanediol	180,000
Ethanol	27,200	1, 2-Propanediol	92,000
1-Propanol	11,200	Phenol	1,060
2-Propanol	17,400	Cresol	800
1-Butanol	8,500	Malthane	160
2-Butanol	8,900	Ortho (pesticide)	320
		DDT in Xylene	120

Example

Determine the retention time, volume, and surface area required to remove 85 to 90 percent of the influent BOD from the primary settled domestic wastes.

Assume the 5-day BOD of the influent is 250 mg/l, and θ is equal to 1.085. Further assume an average minimum monthly temperature of 15°C., a population of 10,000, a flow of 100 gal/person/day, an optimum reaction rate of seven days at 35°C., and a depth of 6 feet.

$$Y_t = [250 - (250 \times 0.90)] \quad = 25 \text{ mg/l}$$

$$t_T = 7\,(1.085)^{(35-15)} \quad = 36 \text{ days}$$

$$\text{Volume} = \frac{100 \times 10{,}000 \times 250\,(1.085)^{35-15}}{43{,}560 \times 7.5 \times 200} \quad = 134 \text{ acre ft.}$$

$$\text{Surface area} = 134/6 \quad = 22.5 \text{ acre}$$

$$\text{Surface loading} = \frac{250 \times 10{,}000 \times 100 \times 8.34}{1 \times 10^6 \times 22.5} \quad = 93 \text{ lb BOD/acre/day}$$

Note: For this problem the surface loading is equivalent to 47 lb BOD/acre/day for a pond having a depth of three feet; this is close to what is recommended by some regulatory agencies. Caution should be exercised in using a shallow pond if the wastewater contains settleable solids.

SLUDGE EFFECTS

A sludge layer can develop in a pond and anaerobic degradation can manifest itself by both gas evolution and release of fermentation products. There products will in most cases exert a considerable BOD. Thus, all BOD data must reflect ultimate first-stage values. Equation 16 shows how the sludge effect can be incorporated into the design calculations (15).

$$Y_{up} = \frac{Y_{ui}}{Kt + 1} \left(f_p + c_p f_s \right) \tag{16}$$

where

Y_{up} = ultimate pond BOD
Y_{ui} = ultimate influent BOD
t = retention for completely mixed system
f_p = fraction of influent BOD to pond liquid
f_s = fraction of influent BOD to sludge layer
d_p = fraction of fermentation products from sludge layer entering pond liquid

It should be recognized that the sludge effect may require several years to reach equilibrium. Also, during summer months increased fermentation may result in the formation of floating sludge mats. Similarly, during the summer the BOD received from the sludge will be high. Unfortunately, little information is available on the fraction of influent BOD, which settles, and the fraction of fermentation products, which either contribute to the BOD load or are released as gaseous products.

As a rule of thumb, it would seem appropriate to use the weighted average of the soluble 5-day BOD of the influent and the ultimate BOD of the settleable solids for the term Y in Equation 12. Furthermore, a weighted average of the reaction rates might also be appropriate.

Select Microorganism

An ecological study conducted in South Africa involving proteolytic bacteria and aerobic, free-living, nitrogen-fixing bacteria provides information on the changes that occur in the population of influent organisms (18). The average number of bacteria capable of proteolysis was found to be $10^{6.5}$ organisms per ml. or one third of the total number of bacteria present in waste stabilization pond water. This fact is important since 55–84 percent of the total organic nitrogen in raw sewage is in the form of proteinaceous material, and conversion to a rapidly available form of nitrogen by proteolytic enzymes is necessary.

An ecological study of the aerobic, free-living, nitrogen-fixing bacteria in stabilization ponds has shown that *Azotobacter* were only found in the aerobic zone, and *Pseudomonas* (capable of fixing nitrogen) were found throughout the ponds. If ammonia nitrogen was present, no atmospheric nitrogen was fixed.

Studies have shown that detention times of 30 to 40 days in multicell ponds will reduce the coliform count to drinking water standards (13). In general, the rate of destruction of coliform bacteria is greater than the rate of die-away of the total bacterial population.

In South Africa *S. typhi* seemed to show a somewhat greater resistance than *E. coli*. Examination of effluent from small urban ponds failed to reveal the presence of either *Salmonella* or *Shigella*. Studies in Auckland, New Zealand, showed that over 99^{+} percent of the coliforms were removed, and all tests were negative for *Salmonella* and *Shigella*.

Snail vectors of bilharziasis were investigated by transplanting them into ponds. In every case the snails died within ten weeks (19). Apparently, death of the snails was not due to a shortage of food.

Larvae of *Ankylostomum duodenale*, ova of *Schistosomum mansoni* and *Enterobius vermicularis*, and *Giardia lamblia* cysts were isolated in the untreated sewage from small urban communities in Southern Rhodesia. However, helminths were not found in the effluents of any pond.

GUIDE TO OPERATORS

In principle, the operation of the waste stabilization pond is simple; however, if there is inadequate supervision, many of the advantages gained through the treatment of wastewaters may be lost. The consideration of maintenance and operation in the design of a waste stabilization pond is of utmost importance.

Waste stabilization ponds, like all wastewater treatment facilities, must be maintained. Regular inspections must be made of the dikes, surface growths, and general pond performance.

Many ponds are equipped with control devices that regulate influent rates, effluent releases, and liquid levels. These devices must be inspected regularly. Stopgates and valves will rust and deteriorate unless properly maintained. Inspection is required for such interconnecting piping and overflows that may be subject to frost action. Use of frost-proof overflow manholes or valve boxes for controlling liquid levels in the pond is a necessity. Multiple influent lines to such structures must be inspected periodically to determine if the overflows will ordinarily come from, at, or near the surface of the pond. The operator must determine periodically if the multiple influent lines to such manholes or structures are at least twelve inches off the bottom to control eroding velocities and to avoid pickup of bottom sediments.

A change in odor or color in all probability forecasts a major change in the performance of a pond system. When the characteristic green color of a pond begins to change or disappear, it is time for the operator to look for causes of this change. For example, changes in the volume, organic load, temperature, light, or turbidity may cause changes in algal activity or predominant genus. A color change from green to black, accompanied by floating mats of bottom material, usually indicates rapid fermentation of the bottom sediments, frequently resulting from changes in the character of the wastewater or pond temperature.

Nuisance midges and mosquitoes have been found to breed in some ponds. Weeds which provide shelter for mosquito larvae can be controlled by maintaining a fairly steep bank. It may be necessary to undertake bank spraying. Also, the introduction of top-feeding water minnows, *Gambusia*, may be worthwhile in secondary or tertiary ponds.

A minimum water depth of about one meter will prevent the emergence of most aquatic plants. The grasses and weeds at the edge can be controlled by mowing or the use of portable flame throwers. The use of herbicides and soil sterilants at the edge of the water has also proven beneficial. These soil sterilants can be put into the bank before the pond is filled.

Erosion can be controlled successfully by the use of concrete mats, soil cement surface, and crushed rock. The embankment should be impervious, and should be compacted with equipment appropriate for the job.

Almost every pond will have a scum or floating algal-mat problem sooner or later. This scum will be blown toward a bank or corner of the pond. If the scum is permitted to collect, serious odor and insect problems will arise. The best preventive measure is to consider this problem during design. The elimination of sharp corners and dead sloughs will prove most fruitful. However, after scum accumulation occurs, the only solution is to agitate the water sufficiently well so that the material will again settle to the bottom or become dispersed.

REFERENCES

(1) Kellen, W. R. "An Ecological Study of Insects in Oxidation Ponds." M. S. Thesis, University of California, Berkeley, California (1956).

(2) Krauss, R. W. "Fundamental Characteristics of Algal Physiology, Algae and Metropolitan Wastes," *Transactions of the 1960 Seminar.* U.S. Public Health Service, Cincinnati, Ohio (USA), 40–47 (1961).

(3) Bush, V. *Algae Culture from Laboratory to Pilot Plant.* Publication 600. Washington, D.C.: Carnegie Institute of Washington (1953).

(4) Phillips, J. N., and J. Myers. "Growth Rate of Chlorella in Flashing Light," *Plant Physiology, 29,* 152 (1954).

(5) Hopkins, G. J., and O. C. Hopkins. *Waste Stabilization Lagoons Symposium on Waste Treatment by Oxidation Ponds.* Nagpur, India: Central Public Health Engineering Research Institute (1961).

(6) Nielsen, E. S. "Carbon Dioxide as Carbon Source and Narcotic in Photosynthesis and Growth of *Chlorella pyrenoidosa,*" *Physiology Plantarium, 8,* 317 (1955).

(7) Osterlind, S. "The Retarding Effect of High Concentrations of Carbon Dioxide and Carbonate Ions on the Growth of Green Alga," *Physiology Plantarium, 1,* 170 (1948).

(8) Davis, E. A., *et al.* Publication 600, pp. 105–153. Washington, D.C.: Carnegie Institute of Washington (1953).

(9) Stumm, W., and J. J. Morgan. *Stream Pollution by Algal Nutrients.* Cambridge, Massachusetts: Harvard University Publication (1963).

(10) Oswald, W. J. "Rational Design of Waste Ponds," *Proceedings of Symposium on Waste Treatment by Oxidation Ponds.* Nagpur, India: Central Public Health Engineering Reserach Institute (1963).

(11) Arceivala, S. J. *Proceedings of Symposium on Waste Treatment by Oxidation Ponds.* Nagpur, India: Central Public Health Engineering Research Institute (1963).

(12) Eckenfelder, W. W. *Proceedings of the 16th Industrial Waste Conference,* Extension Series No. 109, 115–125. Purdue University, Lafayette, Indiana (1961).

(13) Parker, C. D. "Microbiological Aspects of Lagoon Treatments," *J. Water Poll. Cont. Fed., 34,* 149–161 (1962).

(14) Van Eck, H. "Sewage Stabilization Ponds—A Critical Review," *South African Inst. Civil Engr., 9,* 137–153 (July 1958).

(15) Marais, G. v. R. *New Factors in the Design, Operation and Performance of Waste Stabilization Ponds with Special References to Health,* Expert Committee Meeting on Environmental Change and Resulting Impacts on Health, World Health Organization, p. 17 (1964).

(16) Suwannakarn, V., and E. F. Gloyna. "Efect de la Temperatura en el Tratamiento de Aquas Residuales Mediante Estanques de Estabilizacion," *Boletin de la Officina Sanitaria Panamericana.* World Health Organization, Ano 43, LVI, 128–139 (1964).

(17) Thirumurthi, D., and E. F. Gloyna, *Relative Toxicity of Organics to Chlorella Pyrenoidosa.* University of Texas Report No. 11-6503, Austin (November 1965).

(18) Stander, G. J. *Director's Report for 1963.* National Institute for Water Research, Council for Scientific and Industrial Research, Pretoria, South Africa, Report No. WAT 29, p. 22 (July 1964).

(19) Hodgson, H. T. "Stabilization Ponds for a Small African Urban Area," *J. Water Poll. Cont. Fed., 36,* 62 (January 1964).

ADVANCES IN ANAEROBIC POND SYSTEMS DESIGN

W. J. Oswald
University of California, Berkeley, California

A discussion of anaerobic waste ponds as a part of engineered systems for waste disposal should begin with a detailed discussion of the fundamental organic transformations which occur in all types of ponds. It is not really possible to consider one type of pond independently of other types which may be in the same pond system. Although waste solids are characteristically comprised of protein, carbohydrate, fat, and ash, only carbohydrate transformations need be considered, since these predominate. In the following simplified reactions, carbohydrate is typified by the classical formula $(CH_2O)_x$. As described in more detail elsewhere, four principal biological transformations are of concern in ponds.

The first of these is the aerobic conversion of dilute solutions of carbohydrates in wastes into bacterial sludge, carbon dioxide, and water. This reaction, termed aerobic oxidation, occurs in the presence of free oxygen and bacteria somewhat as follows:

$$6(CH_2O)_x + 5O_2 \longrightarrow (CH_2O)_x + 5CO_2 + 5H_2O + \text{energy} \qquad (1)$$

In the absence of free oxygen, conversion of carbohydrate to bacterial cells occurs with formation of organic acids and related compounds as follows:

$$5(CH_2O)_x \longrightarrow (CH_2O)_x + 2CH_3COOII + \text{energy} \qquad (2)$$

Reaction 2 may be termed putrefaction or organic acid formation.

Once produced, organic acids may be decomposed to methane and carbon dioxide during growth of methane bacteria. In this case,

$$2\tfrac{1}{2}\ CH_3COOH \longrightarrow (CH_2O)_x + 2CH_4 + 2CO_2 + \text{energy} \qquad (3)$$

Reaction 3 is termed methane fermentation.

In the presence of oxygen, organic acids may also be oxidized, as indicated in Reaction 1.

During each of the three reactions described above, energy is liberated, although quantities of free energy in the last two cases are small. The microorganisms which grow in these processes are designated as $(CH_2O)_x$ and are themselves subject to decompositions identical to those outlined above.

In the presence of sunlight algae growth occurs in ponds with conversion of carbon dioxide into organic compounds and free oxygen. Sunlight energy is thus fixed in the form of organic matter.

$$(CH_2O)_x + CO_2 \xrightarrow{\text{(Light + Algae)}} 2(CH_2O)_x + O_2 + H_2O \qquad (4)$$

Reaction 4 is essentially the reverse of Reaction 1.

Nitrogen, phosphorus, sulfur, potassium, magnesium, and a large number of other elements in trace amounts are essential to each of the preceding reactions. It is outside the scope of this paper, however, to discuss the reactions and transformation of these substances.

The biological, physical, and chemical environmental requirements of each of the four carbon cycle reactions described are well known. A basis for scientific pond design is thus to select design parameters which will optimize the reaction and interaction of these reactions and will bring about optimum waste stabilization. Specific knowledge of the interaction of the reactions is important to an understanding of systems in which the reactions occur.

In order to illustrate the interaction of environmental factors and the four biological reactions outlined above, a schematic cross section of a stabilization pond is shown in Figure 162. During the spring, summer, and fall, operating stabilization ponds in some localities usually have a well-defined thermocline which divides the pond liquid horizontally, with an upper portion of relatively warm, light water above the thermocline, and a lower portion of relatively cool, heavy water below the thermocline. This is the well-known phenomenon of thermal stratification. A barrier to vertical mixing is formed by the difference in density between bottom and top liquid, but it is only through mixing that oxygen is transported from the surface layer where it is formed into the underlying strata where it is in greatest demand. Although exceptions do occur during strong winds, the liquid below the thermocline rarely contains dissolved oxygen; whereas, the water above the thermocline usually contains dissolved oxygen in varying amounts ranging from zero to an excess of oxygen. In Figure 162 the transition with depth from an aerobic to an anaerobic environment is symbolized by a dotted line. Above the line in an aerobic environment, aerobic oxidation and photosynthetic oxygenation occur. As indicated by comparing Equations 1 and 4,

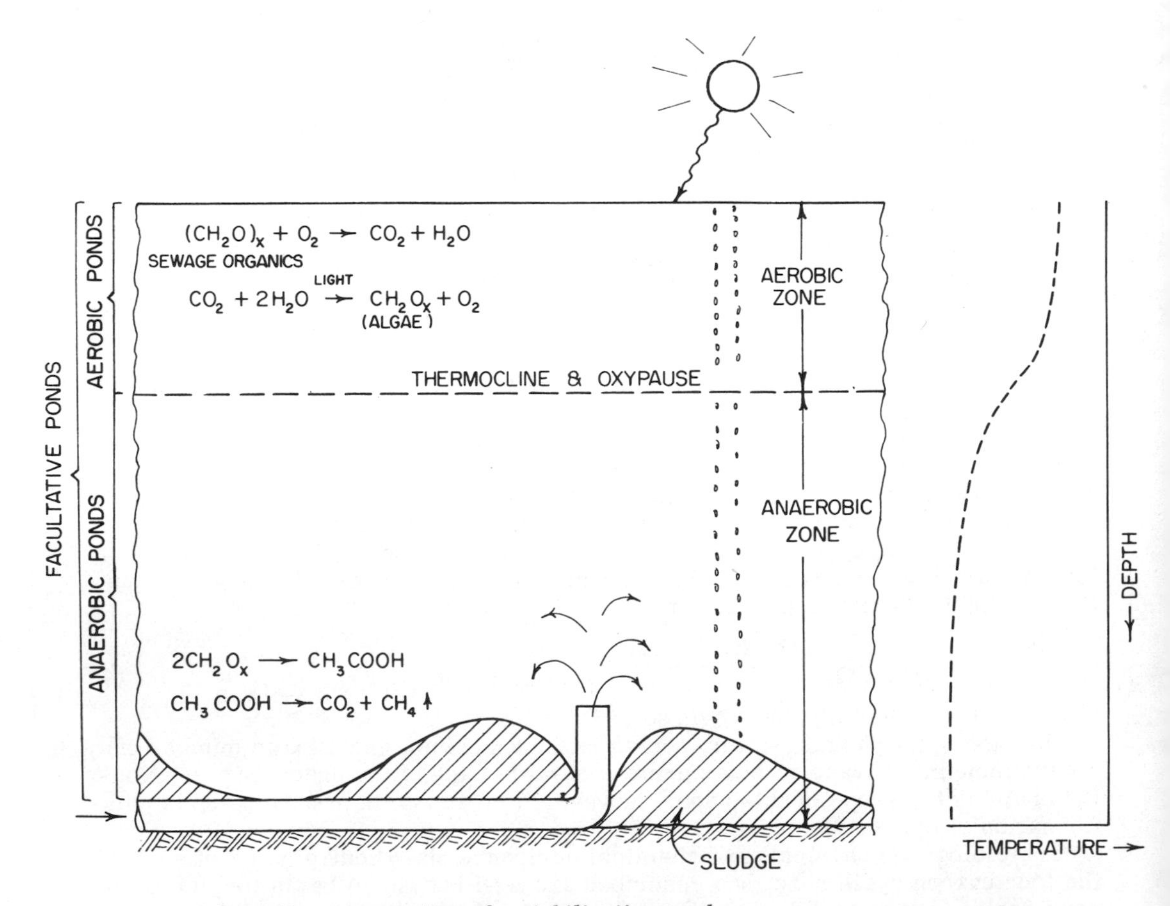

Figure 162. Schematic cross section of a stabilization pond.

these often are linked, cyclical reactions. They are said to be linked because aerobic bacteria depend on algae to produce oxygen, and algae depend on bacteria to produce carbon dioxide and ammonia for their photosynthesis. Below the dotted line in Figure 162 putrefaction and methane fermentation occur. These, too, are linked reactions, since methane fermentation requires organic acids as substrate.

A basis for rational classification of ponds has been derived from the information contained in Figure 162. A pond in which only the reactions above the dotted line--that is, aerobic oxidation and photosynthetic oxygen--occur, may be termed an aerobic pond. A pond in which the anaerobic reactions below the dotted line predominate may be called an anaerobic pond. A pond in which both of the reactions shown below the line occur in the bottom strata is termed a facultative pond.

A pond may be maintained anaerobic by applying a BOD load which exceeds the potential of photosynthesis for oxygen production. In California this critical loading may be as little as 100 lbs/acre/day in winter or as much as 400 lbs/acre/day in summer. When anaerobic ponds become dark and turbid with reduced metal sulfides, light is thus increasingly excluded and algae growth becomes negligible. Where warm conditions prevail, such a pond may be employed as an excellent digester. Even in warm climates without special seeding, a long period is required before digestion becomes well established; meanwhile, the pond may be odorous. Once established, however, methane fermentation will be self-sustaining and will result in about a 70 percent BOD reduction in wastes passed through the pond. During digestion, applied BOD is converted primarily to methane, carbon dioxide, nitrogen, and other gases. A ratio of 10–12 cubic feet of gas per pound of BOD applied is considered a normal gas production for a pond which receives domestic sewage and is degrading the applied load to a satisfactory extent.

SPECIFIC ENVIRONMENTAL INFLUENCES

The influence of a number of specific environmental factors on each of the reactions shown in Figure 162 should now be considered. The specific environmental factors to be considered are microbial population, nutrients, oxygen, time, temperature, *p*H, alkalinity, antecedent reactions, competitive organisms, predators, toxic substances, and oxidation reduction potentials. In the interest of brevity, this information is presented in Table 60. In the table pertinent minimum, maximum, and optimum values are given for each factor and for each major reaction which occurs in ponds. Minimums should not be regarded as the lowest level at which the reactions occur, but rather the lowest level at which the reaction is useful in waste disposal. Optimum is that level at which the specific factor in no way limits treatment. Maximum is the highest level at which the reaction is of any use.

A detailed examination of the information in Table 60 will reveal a number of conflicting environmental conditions for the reactions. Examples are as follows: Organic acids are essential to methane bacteria but methane bacteria require a neutral *p*H. Acid-forming bacteria operate at low temperature and become estabtablished quickly, whereas methane bacteria require months to become established if none are originally present. Algae produce excessive oxygen; methane bacteria cannot tolerate oxygen. Algae may raise the *p*H to 10.8, whereas maximum bacterial oxidation occurs at *p*H 8.3. It thus becomes obvious that a single pond cannot be designed to optimize all the critical reactions. Systems of more than one pond may be designed with great benefit.

TABLE 60

REQUIRED CONDITIONS OR LEVELS FOR INDICATED BIOLOGICAL REACTION IN PONDS

Environmental Factors	Aerobic Oxidation			Algal Photosynthesis			Organic Acid Formation			Methane Fermentation		
	Min.	Opt.	Max.	Min.	Opt.	Max.	Min.	Opt.	Max.	Min.	Opt.	Max.
Population (No. per ml.)	Aerobic bacteria 10^8	10^{10}	10^{12}	Chlorella, Scenedesmus 10^5	10^7	10^8	Heterotrophs facultative 10^8	10^{10}	10^{12}	Mesophilic bacteria Unknown		
Nutrients	Carbohydrate, protein, fat			CO_2, ammonia, P, S			Carbohydrate, protein, fat			Organic acids, alcohols		
Oxygen (mg/l)	1	10	30		Unknown		0	0	1	0	0	0
Time (days)		5–10			30–60			5–10			40–120	
Initial/Active	1/6	1/2	1	2	3	5	1/6	1/2	1	10	40	100+
Temperature, °C.	15	25	40	4	25	40	4	25	40	15	32	40
*p*H	6.5	8.0	10.0	7.0	8.5	10.8	4.3	6.5	7.5	6.8	7.0	7.2
Alkalinity (mg/l)	–	200	–	–	300	–		Unknown		500	2000	–
Antecedent reactions	Photosynthesis			Oxidation			Organic synthesis			Organic acid formation		
Competitive reactions	Sedimentation, methane fermentation			Autoflocculation			Oxidation			Oxidation		
Predators	Unknown			Rotifera, Cladocera			Unknown			Unknown		
Toxic substances	Salts, heavy metals			Copper, chromium			Salts, heavy metals			Oxygen, copper, salt, chromium, heavy metals		
Energy source	Nutrients			Light			Nutrients			Nutrients		
Redox potential $E_n$mv	+0.2	0.5	–	+0.5	Unknown	–	-0.1	–	+0.2	-0.10	-0.5	–

DESIGN FOR ENVIRONMENTAL CONTROL

In the development of pond system designs, environmental conditions should be arranged in the ponds to accentuate desirable reactions and to minimize or negate conflicting reactions. This may be accomplished best by designing systems of a number of ponds in which each pond in the system is designed to optimize a given set of reactions. However, the question arises as to how anaerobic, facultative, and aerobic ponds should be linked together. Which is the optimum order—anaerobic-faculative-aerobic, aerobic-facultative-anaerobic, or aerobic-anaerobic-facultative? The most obvious answer to this question may be drawn from existing knowledge of performance. In general, the effluent from an aerobic pond is of excellent quality, whereas the effluent from an anaerobic pond is of poor quality. The effluent from a facultative pond is often of intermediate quality. Thus, an anaerobic-facultative-aerobic system will give rise to the best effluent. The major problems which arise from this system are the high probability of odors in the anaerobic pond and the poor efficiency of land use in the final or aerobic pond.

Both of these problems can be overcome to some extent through use of recirculation from the final aerobic pond to the primary anaerobic pond. Through recirculation, dissolved oxygen from the aerobic pond commingles or overlays the anaerobic pond, eliminating sulfide odors, while at the same time increased flow due to recirculation carries a larger fraction of the BOD load forward to the facultative pond, thus ensuring increased efficiency of land use in the facultative and aerobic ponds. Although recirculation ponds may be made smaller than unrecirculated ponds with equal performance, a disadvantage of recirculation is the danger that oxygen may be imported in amounts sufficient to stifle methane fermentation in the anaerobic pond; consequently, methods of avoiding contact of this aerobic liquid with the digestion zone require consideration. One method is to perform recirculation only when the water in the aerobic pond is warmer than the water at the bottom of the anaerobic pond. Another method is to design the anaerobic pond bottom to have special digestion chambers in which the sludge to be digested accumulates in some depth, thus protecting itself from the intrusion of oxygen.

Typical examples of this latter concept are shown in Figure 163. In 163A the pond bottom is designed as a mirror image of the normal fallout curve for sludge entering the center of a quiescent pond. In 163B a simplified version of 163A merely utilizes a cone-shaped bottom. In 163C the digestion volume is protected by a submerged baffle system.

Full-scale ponds have been designed and operated on the basis of these three designs with excellent results. The system of 163C, which essentially embodies the Imhoff tank concept, was employed with loads up to 1,000 lbs/acre/day with some success, although this high a loading is not recommended under start-up conditions. Recirculation from an adjacent aerobic pond controlled odors, and BOD removal was on the order of 400 lbs/acre/day. This system is being extended at the present time to include two additional acres of anaerobic pond. The design criteria for an anaerobic pond of this type are a depth of 12–14 feet, loadings of 500–1,000 lbs/acre/day, and recirculation at a rate approximately equal to the influent rate. Recirculant should be applied to the pond surface. The system shown in 163A and 163B has been employed primarily in lightly loaded facultative ponds. However, in the vicinity of the influent, the sedimentation of solids leads to a local loading of approximately 400 lbs BOD/acre/day. Measured rates of gas emission near the center of these ponds exceeds 4,000 cubic feet/acre/day during the summer. This rate of gas emission is equal to a BOD destruction in excess of 400 lbs/acre/day.

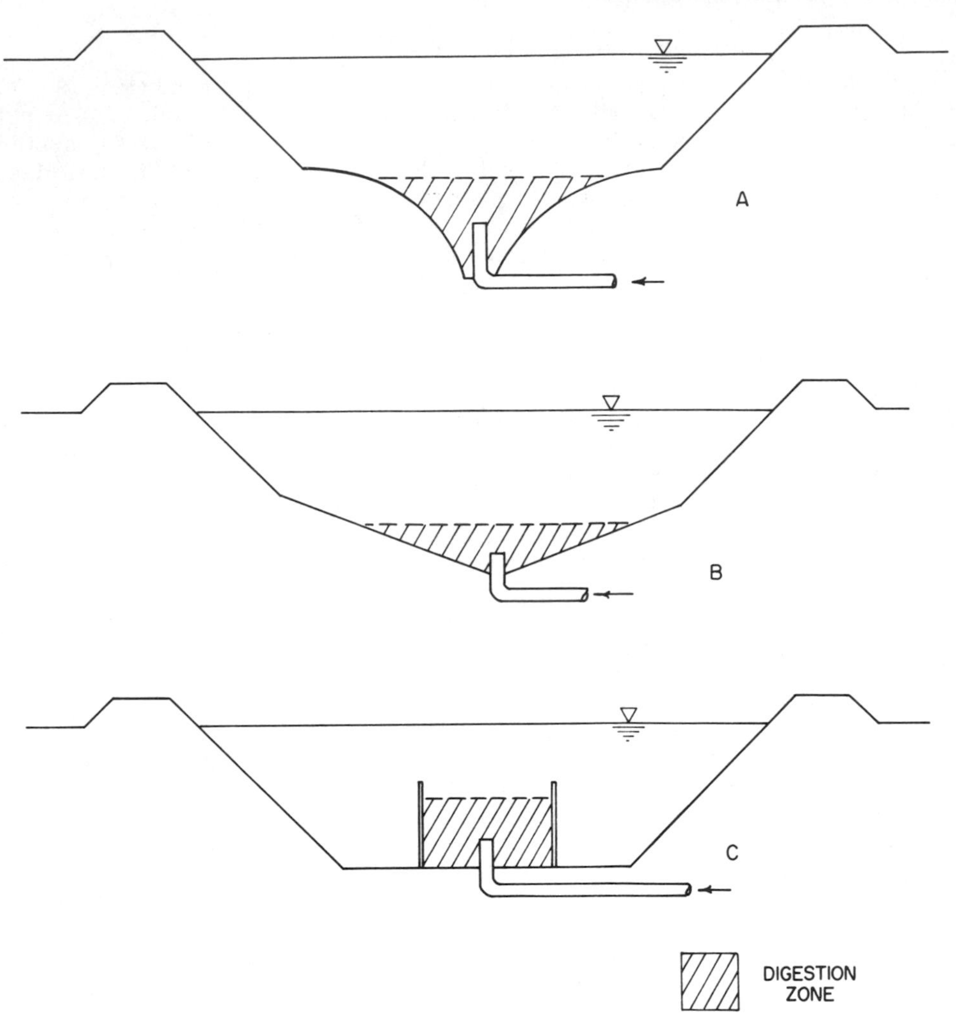

Figure 163. Some methods of creating a digestion chamber in the bottom of a waste pond.

INFLUENCE OF DEPTH ON SYSTEMS

Before going further with a discussion of system-depth relationships, specific definition of certain other basic design criteria is desirable. These criteria, which have been discussed more completely elsewhere (2), are hydraulic load, organic load, and detention period.

Hydraulic Load

The hydraulic load applied to a pond may be computed in the expression

$$L_h = Q/A \tag{5a}$$

in which L_h is the hydraulic load. If Q is the daily volume in acre inches and A is the pond area in acres, L_h will have dimensions of inches per day. As is evident from Equation 5, the hydraulic load is independent of pond depth.

Organic Load

The average organic load may be computed by multiplying the concentration of organic matter or the concentration of biochemical oxygen demand (whichever is desired) by the hydraulic load. Thus,

$$L_o = K(Q/A) \times \text{BOD} \quad (5b)$$

in which the BOD is an expression of the organic content of the applied waste. If L_o is to be expressed in lbs/acre/day and BOD is expressed in mg/liter, the value of K should be 0.226.

Detention Time

The detention of liquid in a pond may be computed from the expression

$$t_D = V/Q \quad (6)$$

in which V is the pond volume and Q is the daily volume introduced to the pond. The detention time thus has the units days.

Inasmuch as the volume of a pond is given by the expression

$$V = lwd \quad (7)$$

in which V is the volume, l the length, w the width, and d the depth of the pond, and inasmuch as the product of lw is the pond surface area, Ad may be substituted for V in Equation 6, yielding the expression that

$$t_D = (A/Q)d \quad (8)$$

in which it is evident that, other factors being equal, detention time varies directly with pond depth. Thus detention time may be increased and organic load held constant by increasing pond depth. It follows then that, other factors being equal, pond depth determines pond detention time.

With this fact in mind attention may now be focused upon the influences of depth upon the basic criteria of performance in ponds, and it may be seen how depth can be varied to give various reactions in a system design.

Depth and Load Distribution

As noted previously, loading intensity is not uniform over the entire pond area. Inlet location, inlet velocity and direction, and differences in pond and waste temperature strongly influence load distribution. In the vicinity of pond inlets, surface loadings become extremely high due to a tendency for solids to settle rapidly under the quiescent conditions normally prevailing below the thermocline. In the Concord, California, ponds, at a time when the average BOD loading was 115 lbs. per acre, the deposition of sludge near the inlet exceeded 1,000 lbs. of volatile matter per acre per day, a ratio of 8.5:1. Near the central inlet at the Woodland pilot plant ponds in California, the volatile deposition was about 9,000 lbs. per acre when the average BOD loading was but 50 lbs. per acre per day, a ratio of 18:1 (1). The difference between Concord and Woodland ratios was caused by recirculation, which was applied in Concord at a rate of twice the waste flow. No recirculation was applied in Woodland. Recirculation in Concord caused a wider distribution of the applied load by increasing the inlet velocity and thus decreasing the ratio of maximum local to average loading.

Although recirculation is effective in load distribution in shallow ponds, the same effect is sometimes attained without recirculation in actively fermenting deep ponds. Studies of temperature, sludge deposition, and gas emission from a deep (8+ foot) anaerobic pond located at Woodland, California (3), evidenced a pattern different from those described above, in that there was more uniform distribution of solids and more uniform gas production over the entire surface area. Although the waste entering this pond was usually warmer than the pond contents, in this case temperature measurements indicated little thermal stratification. Vigorous mixing imparted to the pond by continuously rising gas bubbles from the digestion layer at the pond bottom resulted in complete mixing and broad load distribution. Because of greater bubble path length and larger bubble size, mixing due to rising gas bubbles is greater in deep ponds than in shallow ponds.

As noted previously, for domestic sewage solids, about 10 or 12 cubic feet of gas are evolved for each pound of BOD destroyed. If less gas than this is produced, either decomposition is incomplete or the volatile matter applied is more stable than fresh sewage. Near the center of heavily loaded ponds settleable solids may accumulate at a rate exceeding the rate at which they are broken down to methane. They may be converted to organic acids with reduction of *p*H to such an extent that the *p*H within the sludge falls below that tolerated by the methane bacteria, in which case organic acids accumulate. Excess accumulation of organic acids results in a pond becoming sour, with attendant probable emission of odors from hydrogen sulfide and other substances having vile odors.

In ponds where bubble mixing is incomplete, studies have shown that the ratio of gas production to load intensity varies with respect to distance from the pond inlet, at first rising to a maximum and then declining. This configuration results from the fact that in the vicinity of the inlet, volatile acid production may depress the local *p*H within the sludge bed below that tolerated by the methane bacteria, and methane production decreases or ceases. In deep ponds this effect is less likely to occur, because the added pond volume and detention time provide buffer capacity against sudden changes in *p*H and temperature and because superior sludge and dissolved volatile distribution prevent the initiation of sour conditions in local areas.

As is to be expected, load distribution is significantly influenced by the relative temperature of pond water and wastewater. If sewage entering a pond is warmer than the pond water, it tends to spread over the surface of the cooler water, and settleable solids are dispersed over a wide area. On the other hand, if the sewage is cooler than the pond contents, it quickly finds its way to the pond bottom, and sediment deposition occurs near the inlet. Better sludge distribution, of course, is obtained in the former case.

It is well established that deeper ponds accumulate more heat than shallow ponds, even though a shallow pond may temporarily have hotter surface water during the period when the sun is shining. Excess heat is quickly radiated away from a shallow pond at night, whereas it is retained in a deep pond. The deep pond has a lower average temperature but a more uniform temperature. The nocturnal temperature of a deep pond is greater than that of a shallow pond. Obviously, the warmth of the surface of a shallow facultative pond has little bearing on fermentation rates at the bottom.

Because a pond develops a thermocline during sunny days, a question of thermal lapse rate arises. As reported by Berend (4) and the author (5), near the surface of a pond lapse rates of 2 or more degrees centigrade per foot are observed, but these rarely continue downward for more than 2 feet of depth. Average lapse rates of 1°C. per foot of depth are commonplace in 10- or 12-foot-deep ponds having no source of heat other than sunlight. Lapse rates of this magnitude occur only during periods of high sunlight intensity. In view of the profound effect that temperature has upon the rate of sludge digestion, in view of the decline in temperature with depth, and in view of the fact that most digestion occurs at the pond bottom, extreme pond depths which result in an excessively cool bottom are undesirable if uniform methane fermentation is to be attained.

Depth and Dissolved Oxygen

One of the major reasons for deep ponds is protection of digestion from dissolved oxygen. Observations of dissolved oxygen as a function of depth in waste disposal ponds are rare. Studies, however, have recently been made at Richmond, Esparto, and Woodland, California. Observations have also been made on organisms which indicate the presence of oxygen in ponds at Stockton and Concord, California. Data have also recently become available from Israel (4). The Esparto ponds were intentionally designed to have a center depth of 8 feet in order to have no dissolved oxygen and thus furnish protection of the methane fermentation process from dissolved oxygen. Results of an Esparto study made in September 1963 are shown in Figure 164. It is evident from the figure that the

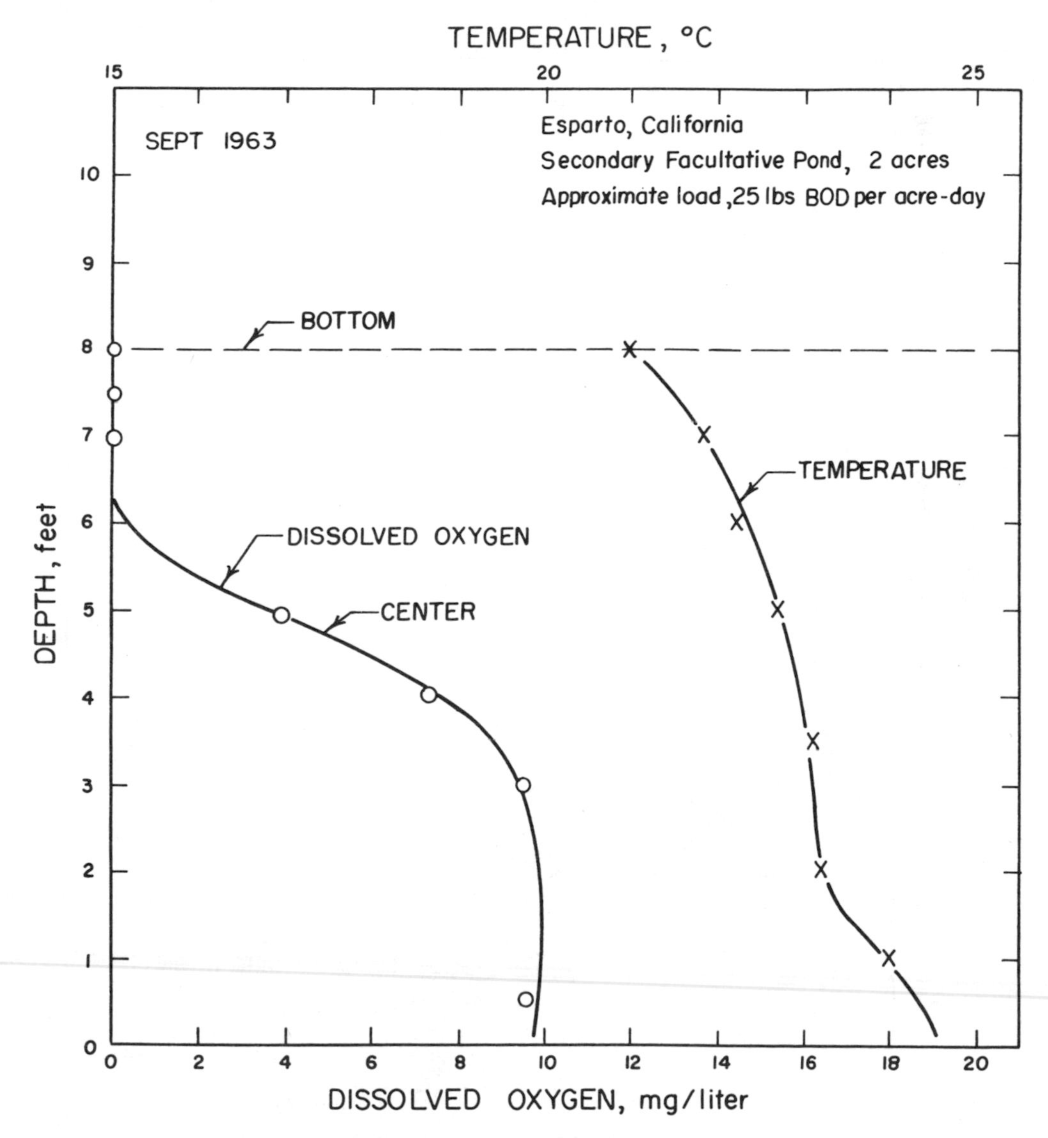

Figure 164. The influence of depth on temperature and dissolved oxygen in a lightly loaded 8-foot-deep stabilization pond.

8-foot design was successful in preventing oxygen penetration to the bottom. Even under the relatively light BOD loading of 25 lbs/acre/day, dissolved oxygen penetrated only to about 6.5 feet of the pond depth, in spite of the fact that surface dissolved oxygen was approximately at saturation, which penetrated to 3.0 feet. From the temperature curve also shown in Figure 164, it is evident that the day's increment in heating amounted to about 1.5°C. and extended downward to about 2.0 feet of depth. Thus, thermal stratification with its attendant inhibition to mixing is credited with preventing the intrusion of dissolved oxygen into the zone of fermentation at the bottom of the Esparto pond.

The available data from a number of sources (2, 4, 5, 6) on dissolved oxygen penetration as a function of depth and BOD loading are assembled in Figure 165.

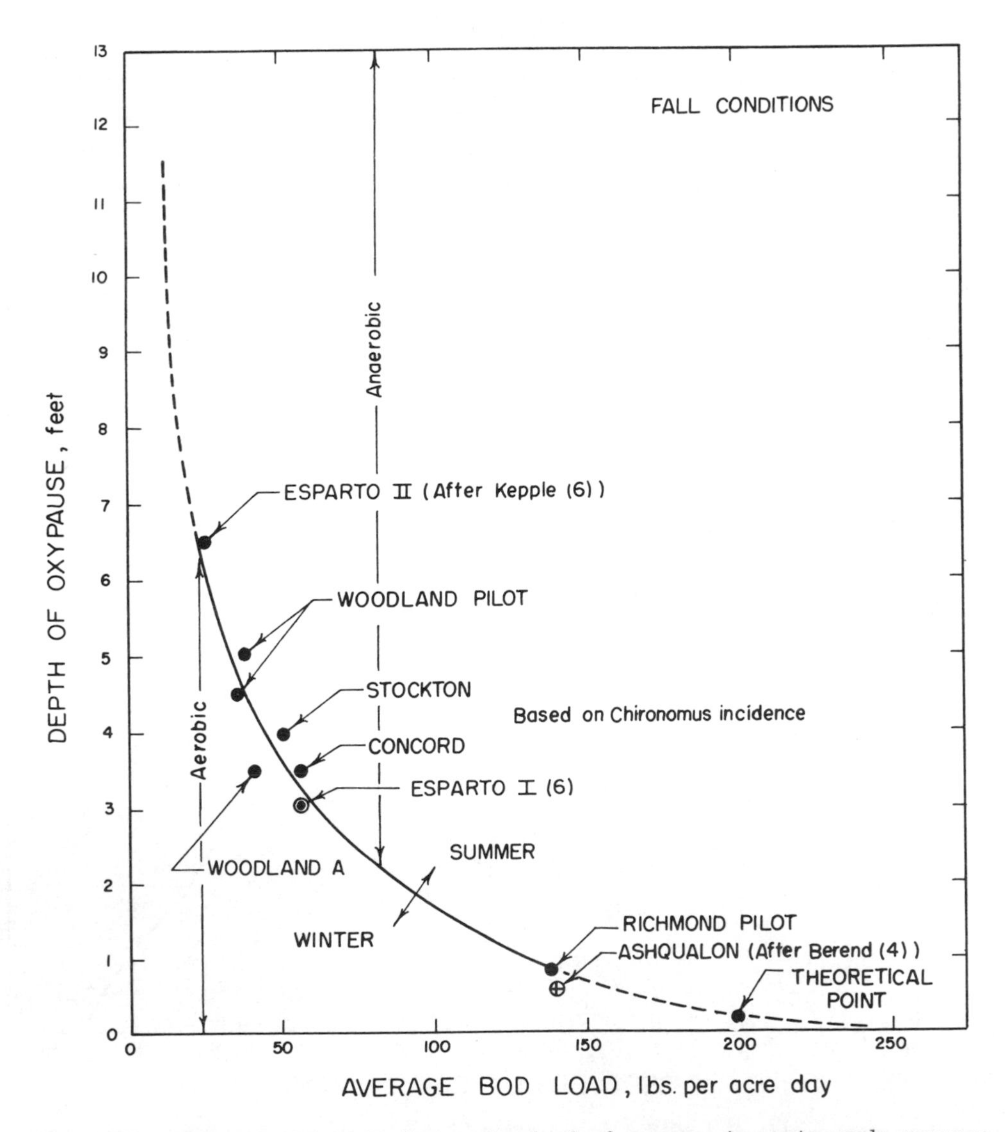

Figure 165. Influence of BOD loading on the depth of oxypause in waste ponds, average conditions.

As is shown in the figure, dissolved oxygen is present to some extent in the surface waters of the ponds in the fall loaded with less than 200 lbs BOD/acre/day, and diminishes to zero at various depths below the surface, depending upon BOD loading, algal growth, and bottom fermentation. As indicated in the figure, the curve moves to the right in summer when loadings of 450 lbs. per acre may still be accompanied by some dissolved oxygen near the surface at midday, and to the left in winter, with the effect that dissolved oxygen may extend to deeper strata in summer than in winter due to increased penetration of sunlight.

From Figure 165 it is evident that effective design methods of obtaining anaerobic conditions at the pond bottom are (a) to increase pond depth, and (b) to increase pond loading, or both. At Murtcaim near Melbourne, Australia, C. D. Parker (7) has described anaerobic-aerobic lagoon systems in which anaerobic ponds are employed in series with aerobic ponds. Melamed's *et al.* (8) analysis of Parker's data is presented in the Dan Region sewage reclamation project, sewage reclamation pond design manual. In this manual it is shown that the Murtcaim primary ponds received BOD loadings of approximately 1,650 lbs. of BOD per acre per day. The secondary ponds were loaded at approximately 300 lbs/acre/day; tertiary ponds, 123 lbs/acre/day, and quaternary ponds, approximately 49 lbs/acre/day. Anaerobic conditions were maintained through intensive loading rather than through increased depth. Comparing these loadings with the information on oxygen penetration shown in Figure 165, it is evident that both the primary and secondary Murtcaim ponds should have been completely anaerobic, as they were reported to be. The tertiary pond should have contained a few mg/l of dissolved oxygen near the surface occasionally, which was also the case. Other ponds contained dissolved oxygen through several feet of the depth, according to Parker.

Depth and Evaporation

Rates of evaporation from waste ponds have never been scientifically studied because other matters such as waste treatment and sterilization effects seemed of more urgent importance. In spite of the lack of formal studies, some qualitative remarks can be made, based on general limnological information and observations. Because algae effectively absorb light and convert it to heat, a body of water containing algae may lose as much as one centimeter of liquid per day from its surface due to evaporation. Evaporation rates should be expected to increase in direct proportion to pond surface temperature and decrease in direct proportion to the relative humidity of the air in direct contact with the water surface. Wind increases evaporation by removing saturated air and by increasing the water surface area by forming waves. Secondary effects are probably caused by the influence of algae on the surface tension of the pond liquid. Recent laboratory studies of evaporation from algae cultures as compared to plain water showed that, other factors being equal, algae may increase evaporation by 10 percent or more (9).

Depth and BOD Removal

The influence of time on BOD removal in a quiescence pond is shown in Table 61. From the table it is evident that removal of BOD at first increases rapidly and then less rapidly with time. The removal shown results from oxidation, bioflocculation, sedimentation, and digestion. Because detention time is increased with increasing depth of pond, it may be said that for equal organic loading, BOD removal will usually be greater in a deep pond than in a shallow pond. Experience has shown, however, that BOD removal is usually high in all types of ponds because quiescent conditions normally prevail, particularly below the thermo-

TABLE 61

NATURAL REDUCTION IN SUPERNATANT BOD IN AN UNDISTURBED POND

Time Days	Percent BOD Removal at Indicated Average Temperature			
	10°C.	14°C.	15°C.	18°C.
0	0	0	0	0
1	23	35	47	33
2	40	61	56	53
4	46	70	67	56
9	57	75	75	81
16	72	89	90	87
32	90	90	95	96
64	94	—	94	—

cline. Consequently, the BOD removal attained is proportional to the detention period. Thus, it may be said that for constant temperature, BOD removal is a direct function of time, which for ponds is a direct function of depth.

Depth and Methane Fermentation

Methane fermentation may be regarded as the *sine qua non* of nuisance-free anaerobic and facultative pond performance. Observations of very shallow ponds and ponds recently activated show that methane fermentation becomes established very slowly if at all in shallow ponds or in layers of sludge lying near the surface. Extensive and interminable variations in temperature, in *p*H, and in oxygen level associated with shallow depths militate against the establishment of methane bacteria.

An example of the sensitivity of the methane fermentation reaction to depth is indicated by observation of gas emission from two stations of the Stockton, California, stabilization pond. At one station where the depth is 4.3 feet and the bottom temperature 24°C., the bubble count (proportional to methane emission) was 20 per minute, whereas where the depth is 6.0 feet and the temperature 22.8°C., the bubble count was 30 per minute. As outlined previously in Table 60, it is evident that in spite of the higher temperature, overall conditions are less favorable for methane fermentation in the shallow portion of the pond. Proximity of dissolved oxygen is believed to be the major cause. At El Centro in Southern California, three ponds having an aggregate area of 50 acres and serving a population of 18,000 persons (secondary treatment) were designed to operate at a depth of 5.4 feet. Because of the intense sunlight, a depth of 5.5 feet at El Centro is equivalent to a depth of only about 3.5 or 4 feet in the average climate. However, because of a lack of water, the operational depth was first established at 3.0 feet. Extreme nuisance conditions developed. Studies reported by Maloney *et al.* (10) indicated that milk whey wastes were in part at fault. These produced a sour sludge which did not digest under the variable pond environment. The result was that organic acids accumulated in the pond, resulting in severe nuisance conditions. Observation of the ponds during this crisis showed a complete lack of methane fermentation, certainly not because of low temperature but probably because of lack of methane organisms, low *p*H, and excessive algae production. Subsequent operation of the El Centro ponds at depths up to 7 feet permitted methane fermentation to become established with greatly reduced nuisance conditions.

Depth-Temperature and Gas Production

The importance of temperature in BOD removal performance of ponds has been evidenced by Hermann and Gloyna (11). Methane fermentation in ponds is strongly influenced by temperature.

In Figure 166 is shown the extent of gas production in the pond and the influence of temperature upon this gas production when the local BOD application was 425 lbs. per acre day. Assuming that 10 cubic feet of gas are evolved for each pound of BOD applied, it is evident that when the bottom water temperature was below about 19°C., decomposible sludge accumulated in the pond more rapidly than it could be converted to gas. On the other hand, above 19°C. both the daily increment and the accumulated sludge were decomposed.

It is concluded from this data that when methane fermentation is well established in a pond and the bottom temperature is above about 19°C., sludge accumulation will not occur. At this temperature, loading and other environmental factors rather than temperature limit gas production. Normally, accumulated sludge itself has such a high oxygen demand that, once deposited, it protects the sludge below from oxygen intrusion. However, during the period when the rate of sludge decomposition is equal to the rate of sludge deposition, such protection

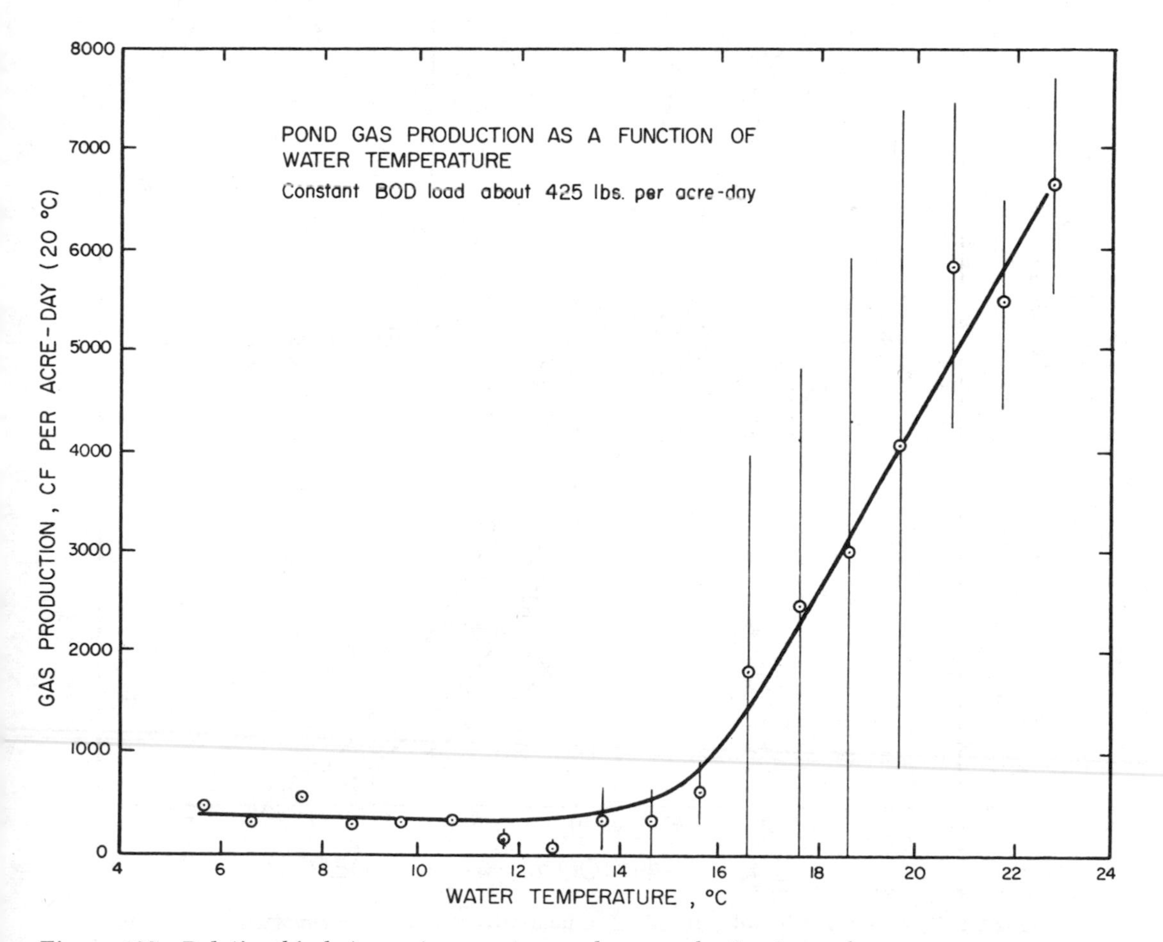

Figure 166. Relationship between temperature and gas production in ponds.

is not available. Under these conditions, pond depth alone provides protection of sludge from the intrusion of dissolved oxygen.

Because pond bottom temperature declines with increasing pond depth, it is obvious that in ponds of extreme depth, bottom temperature may be too low to permit complete methane fermentation of the applied load. Studies should be undertaken to determine at what precise depth the added benefits of increased detention are offset by the detrimental effects of decreased temperature.

Depth and Coliform Destruction

Reduction in the most probable number of coliform bacteria is sometimes of importance. Established relationships between reduction of MPN and time and temperature for domestic sewage are shown in Figure 167. It is evident from

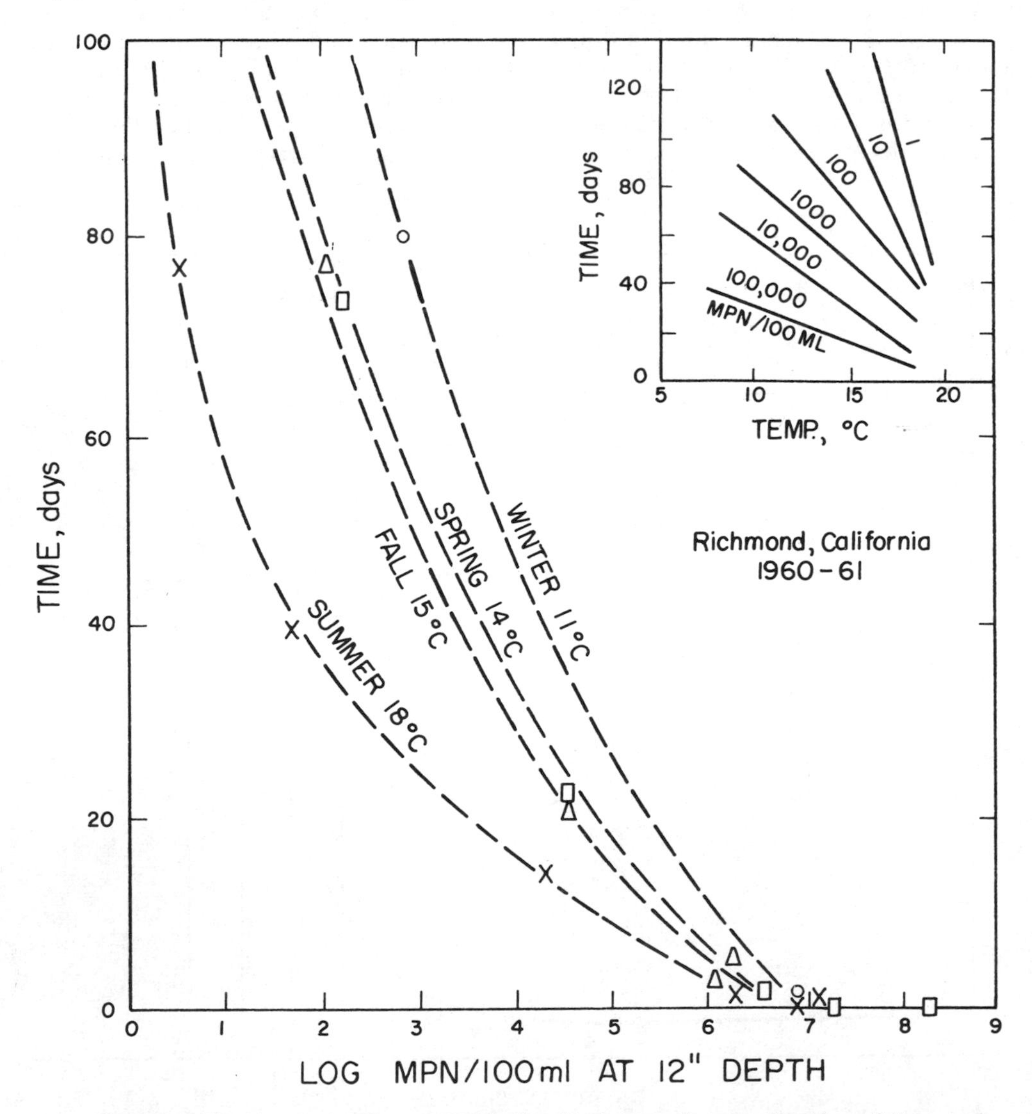

Figure 167. Reduction in coliform MPN in facultative ponds as a function of time and temperature.

the figure that temperature is much more effective than time in reducing MPN. However, a uniform temperature of 18°C. is evidently sufficient to bring about a reduction of MPN from 10^7 per 100 ml. to 10^1 in 45 days. The theoretical reduction in MPN due to higher temperatures in shallow ponds has not been observed, probably due to nocturnal cooling which would tend to preserve the MPN in the same manner as reduced detention periods. For given temperature and loading, doubling pond depth also doubles detention time. According to Figure 167, this brings about a tenfold reduction in MPN. It is therefore concluded that greater MPN reduction is provided by increasing pond depth and detention time than is provided by the increased average temperature attained through use of shallow ponds.

Depth and Algal Growth and Organic Accumulation

It is well established that algal concentration is inversely proportional to pond depth (2). The approximate relationship in simplified form is

$$d\,C_c = 2{,}000 \qquad (9)$$

in which d is the pond depth in inches and C_c is the algal concentration in mg. per liter. In upper layers of deep ponds or in shallow ponds, concentration of algae may reach several hundred parts per million in some cases. The large amount of dissolved oxygen produced by algae in the isolated stratified surface layer of shallow ponds during the day is used by bacteria with very low efficiency. This results from the fact that sedimentation removes BOD quickly from the surface and little BOD remains in the surface strata of liquid where O_2 abounds. Also, the pH in the surface may become high enough to arrest biological activity. Thus oxidation of organic matter is not favored in shallow ponds. In fact, during periods of extremely hot bright weather, the surface of a shallow pond may arrive at a temperature of 35°C., and a pH may attain a level about 11.0. These conditions, occurring together, have repeatedly been observed to bring about a rather sudden precipitation of magnesium hydroxide, calcium phosphate, and other compounds. These compounds tend to act as flocculating agents causing all suspended solids in the entire pond, including algae, to precipitate. Sunlight may then penetrate to the pond bottom with the result that the previously precipitated algal cells resume photosynthesis while lying deposited on the pond bottom. Anaerobic decomposition of deposited sludge at the bottom is halted because of the extreme sensitivity of methane fermentation to oxygen or to an elevated oxidation reduction potential. Buoyed up by oxygen, the previously settled algae float to the surface of the pond and, under wind action, form enormous layers of scum. This sequence of events may be termed pond failure, since no dependable biological activity persists through such a catastrophic period. Such pond failures have been observed to occur numerous times in excessively shallow (less than 4 feet 0 inches) stabilization ponds at Richmond, Concord, Stockton, Chico, Vacaville, St. Helena, El Centro, and Imperial, California. Similar circumstances have been described for the shallow stabilization ponds at Auckland, New Zealand. When the accumulations of dead and decaying algal cell material ferments, it gives rise to vile odors and attendant problems. After a pond failure has occured, algal cells may be accumulated by wind in windrows at one end of the pond. Continued application of BOD loading causes a reduction in pH, and a new growth of algae; the process is repeated on perhaps a two- or three-week cycle. This process repeated month after month results in the accumulation of enormous quantities of unstable organic carbon in a pond. This occurs whenever most of the organic carbon entering the pond is first converted to carbon dioxide and then converted to algae which, once settled, may not be decomposed for months.

Because of high oxygen levels and rapid response to loading, one is often at first impressed by the high degree of BOD removal obtained in shallow ponds. Unfortunately, this is a false and temporary impression, for the BOD is not actually destroyed but only removed as it settles or precipitates to the pond bottom in the form of sludge and algae. When the precipitated organic matter begins to become converted to soluble and volatile organics, the BOD of these materials is added to the BOD applied daily with the waste, resulting in an increasingly high BOD load to the pond. In other words, the shallow pond eventually accumulates organic matter to load itself with BOD to a point beyond the assimilative capacity of the shallow system. It is thus concluded that, unless algae harvesting is practiced, excessive organic accumulation inevitably results when shallow ponds are employed, and that this organic accumulation will eventually overload the pond.

Another effect of shallow ponds is the aging of algal cells. The algae in shallow ponds which have long detention periods will, as a result of lack of nutrients, ultimately stop reproducing cells but continue to produce organic compounds called "shunt products" in large quantities. These algal shunt products are to some extent oxidizable. These materials thus further increase the BOD load to the system. Another problem in shallow ponds is that water containing algae tends to clog the soil much more rapidly than algae-free water. Inasmuch as ponds are often operated to dispose of water into the soil, the presence of algae which clog the soil is detrimental to this objective. Finally, dense concentration of algae will needlessly increase the organic content of water reclaimed from ponds. It is therefore evident that unless algae harvesting is to be practiced, it is more suitable to stabilize waste in deep ponds in which the concentrations of algae do not attain a level sufficiently high to cause precipitation or accumulation of shunt products.

Depth and Odor

Most odors from ponds are caused by the escape from the pond surface of reduced, volatile substances such as volatile organics, ammonia, and hydrogen sulfide. It is preferable therefore to design ponds to foster reactions which prevent the formation of reduced substances, to convert them to nonodorous substances as quickly as they are produced, or to prevent the escape of odorous substances. By far the most reliable of these methods is conversion of odorous compounds to compounds which are nonodorous. Ruling out algae separation for the moment, two mechanisms are readily available: biological oxidation and methane fermentation. From a practical standpoint, biological oxidation cannot be employed in deep ponds because oxidizable substances quickly find their way to the pond bottom where oxygen is lacking and it cannot be employed in shallow ponds because operational conditions result in excessive algae growth. The remaining mechanism is methane fermentation, which is therefore an essential mechanism of BOD reduction and odor prevention in deep ponds. It follows that, other factors being equal, the more complete the methane fermentation, the less odors will be a problem. Shallow, heavily loaded ponds do not provide an environment conducive to continuous dependable methane fermentation or to continuous photosynthetic oxygenation and therefore are more prone to have vile odors.

In order to attain the anaerobic conditions conducive to complete sludge digestion, loads should initially be maintained low enough to permit alkaline digestion to become established.

Depth and Insect Breeding

The 200-acre single stabilization pond at Stockton, California, was constructed without uniform depths, so that areas within the pond have depths of less than five feet. These areas at one time were observed to provide a base for extensive breeding of *Chironomas* (blood worms), which gave rise to clouds of midge flies, the adult stage of *Chironomas*. These midge flies created a severe nuisance by being smashed on the windshields of moving vehicles and by becoming caught and dying in light fixtures. Midge flies breed in stabilization ponds whenever the oxypause (cf. Fig. 165) intersects the pond bottom during an appreciable part of the day. If the ponds are designed to be operated at depths below the oxypause for a given loading, no midge fly nuisance should be expected.

SUMMARY AND CONCLUSIONS

The complexity of actions and interactions in ponds has been great enough to deter scientific investigation, and there has been a tendency to utilize empirical designs having only a superficial basis and doubtful benefits. Recognition of the fact that sedimentation plus four fundamental biological reactions interact in ponds, makes possible a rational design of ponds. While precise formulas remain to be written for the interactions of the variables, the relationships between temperature and methane fermentation, between depth and temperature, and between depth and oxygenation are well established. Because methane fermentation is the *sine qua non* for anaerobic and facultative ponds, designs which maximize temperature uniformity and minimize intrusion of oxygen into the fermentation zone are most successful. In series ponds in which oxygenated water may be recycled, odor in the initial anaerobic pond is easily prevented by overlaying the primary anaerobic pond with oxygenated water. For destruction of coliform organisms, both time and temperature are critical. At the temperatures normally occurring in ponds, increments in time are more easily attained through increasing depth than are increments in temperature through decreased depth.

It is concluded that pond systems having anaerobic, facultative, and aerobic ponds in series with recirculation from aerobic to anaerobic are the most efficient and nuisance-free currently available. However, loadings must be tailored to local conditions and should be conservative for good performance and long functional life. Occasionally, wastes having a high carbon to nitrogen ratio must be oxidized prior to fermentation. In this case aeration should precede fermentation.

Although not discussed in this paper, operations and maintenance are a vital factor in pond performance. Those who would utilize ponds successfully must not ignore operations and maintenance, for if they do, experience indicates that their systems will prematurely fail.

ACKNOWLEDGMENTS

The research reported herein was supported in part by Research Grants RG 2601 from the National Institutes of Health and WP 00026, C1-C4 from the Water Pollution Control Authorities of the United States Public Health Service.

REFERENCES

(1) Oswald, W. J., C. G. Golueke, R. C. Cooper, H. K. Gee, and J. C. Bronson. "Water Reclamation, Algal Production, and Methane Fermentation," *J. Inter. Air Water Poll.*, *7*, 6–7, (August 1963).

(2) Oswald, W. J. "Fundamental Factors in Stabilization Pond Design," *Proceedings*, Third Conference on Biological Waste Treatment, Manhattan College, New York (1960).

(3) Cooper, R. C., W. J. Oswald, and J. C. Bronson. "Treatment of Organic Industrial Wastes by Lagooning." Presented to the International Waste Conference, Purdue University, Lafayette, Indiana (1965).

(4) Berend, J. H. *A Shquelon Deep Oxidation Pond*. Quarterly Report to Tahal, Israel Water Plan (April–July 1964).

(5) Oswald, W. J. "Advances in Stabilization Pond Design," *Proceedings*, Third Annual Sanitary and Water Resources Engineering Conference, Vanderbilt University, Nashville, Tennessee (1964).

(6) Kepple, L. G. *Report on a Study of Three Waste Stabilization Ponds*. Sanitary Engineering Division. Berkeley: University of California (1965).

(7) Parker, C. D. "Microbiological Aspects of Lagoon Treatment," *J. Water Poll. Cont. Fed.*, *34*, 149 (1962).

(8) Amramy, A., B. Caspi, and A. Melamed. *Dan Region Sewage Reclamation Project, Sewage Stabilization Pond Design, Tahal*. Water Planning for Israel Ltd., Tel Aviv, 246 (September 1962).

(9) Golueke, C. G., W. J. Oswald, and H. K. Gee. *Harvesting and Processing Sewage-Grown Planktonic Algae*. University of California, San. Eng. Res. Lab., College of Engineering and School of Public Health, SERL Report No. 64-8 (September 1964).

(10) Oswald, W. J., C. G. Golueke, R. C. Cooper, J. H. Meyers, H. Hintz, and H. K. Gee. "Nutritional and Disease Transmitting Potential of Sewage Grown Algae," First Progress Report, WP 00026 R1-R2-R3, SERL Report No. 64-6 (October 1964).

(11) Hermann, E. R., and E. F. Gloyna. "Waste Stabilization Ponds," *Sewage Ind. Wastes*, *30*, 511, 646, 693 (1958).

WASTE STABILIZATION POND PRACTICES IN THE UNITED STATES

Jerome H. Svore
Federal Water Pollution Control Administration,
U.S. Department of Health, Education, and Welfare, Dallas, Texas

The gradual acceptance of waste stabilization ponds in the Southwest has brought a semblance of design to their use and operation as a secondary treatment facility. The size, shape, and loading varies with the "lay of the land" and the requirements of the stream into which final disposal of the effluent is made.

EARLY OPERATION AND DESIGN

During the late forties, state health departments in the Midwest gradually became interested in lagoons as an accepted method of treating raw sewage. The first such pond with an engineering design still considered acceptable, and having the unconditional approval of the state health department, was completed at Maddock, North Dakota, in 1948. Allowable loadings were arbitrarily extablished on a surface-acre basis at 20 pounds of 5-day, 20°C. biological oxygen demand (BOD). This is considered a light loading in many areas but is the accepted design standard in the Missouri Basin, Upper Mississippi Basin, and Great Lakes States today. The primary reason for this limited loading in Northern states is odor control during the spring ice breakup. This problem of odor control is the single most important item of consideration for the designing engineer in the northern Midwestern states today.

Rates of decomposition are reduced during cold weather, and when ice forms, ponds can become effectively sealed from any reaeration for periods up to several months. When the ice melts in the spring, pond temperatures begin to rise and the organic materials accumulated during the winter months decompose at a higher rate than oxygen can be supplied by reaeration or the limited algae activity at relatively low temperatures. Odors result and persist in direct relation to the loadings imposed on a pond. Some communities have routinely added sodium nitrate as an aid to odor control during this period.

A design rate of 10 pounds BOD/acre/day with a standard 4- to 5-foot depth usually eliminates the odor problem during spring breakup (1). A 20 pound BOD/acre/day loading seems to keep odors at a reasonable minimum, which may persist for a week or two. Loadings of 25 to 30 pounds BOD/acre/day can cause odors for 3 or 4 weeks, while higher loadings of 50 to 60 pounds may cause odors that persist for as long as 3 months (Fig. 168).

Normal domestic sewage loadings of less than 20 pounds/acre/day may cause hydraulic problems during hot, dry summer months because this volume is inadequate to compensate for seepage and evaporation losses. Sufficient lagoon depth under such conditions cannot be maintained to control aquatic growths or adequately disperse the sewage.

A recent survey by the Colorado State Department of Public Health (2) substantiated experience in the Midwest by classifying design, construction, and operation defects into three main categories. Simply stated, they were (a) liquid depth not maintained, (b) water surface inadequate, and (c) primary solids not

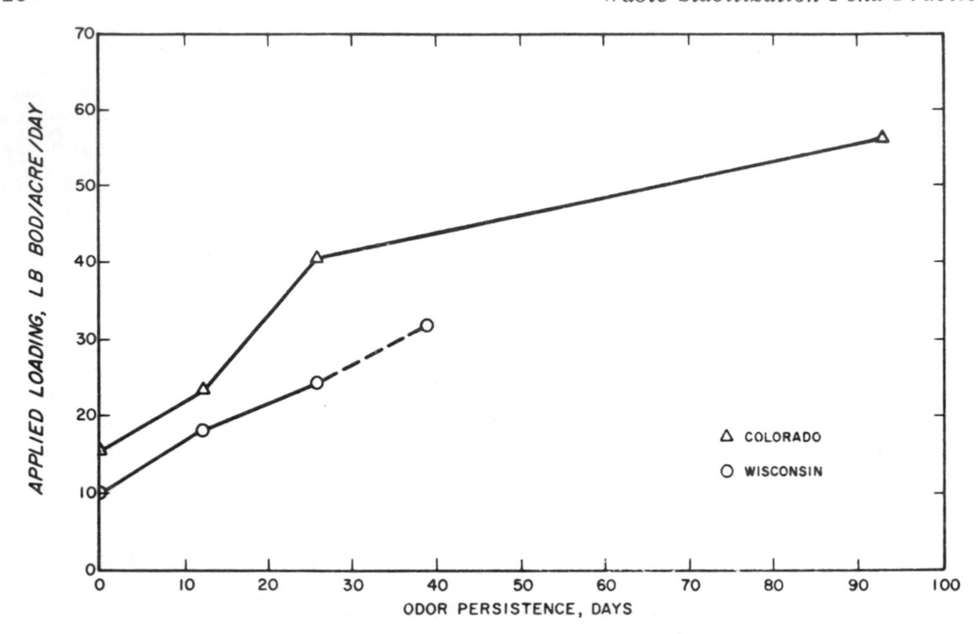

Figure 168. Stabilization pond loading vs. odor persistence after ice breakup.

evenly distributed. All of the Colorado lagoons treated raw sewage, and those found to have spring or year-round odor problems had at least one of these three defects. Of the 65 lagoons surveyed, only 26 complied completely with the state's design standards. Each of the remaining 39 had problems and at least one defect.

Where any spring or year-round odor problem existed, the primary loading rate always exceeded 100 people per acre. This excess varied from 150 to 686 people per acre. Conversely, one lagoon, listed as having a primary loading rate of 572 people per acre, had no objectionable odor problem. Inadequate liquid depth with resulting improper distribution of solids also caused problems, although the theoretical loadings were well below design criteria.

One interesting sidelight of the survey had to do with altitude. An altitude of 5,000 feet has only about 83 percent as much oxygen as is available at sea level for absorption into the lagoon's liquid as dissolved oxygen. Data collected, however, indicated this lower available oxygen in no way affected the spring or year-round odor problems.

EXCESSIVE ALGAE IS A PROBLEM

Average design criteria in the South and Southwest call for loadings up to 50 pounds/acre/day with a trend toward higher figures. Ice coverage combined with springtime recovery is not a problem but the formation of excessive concentrations of blue-green algae during long, hot summer days has caused trouble. Here again, the problem is one of odor control and not treatment efficiency. The difficulty is not universal, and does not occur in all ponds even though the loadings and other design factors are similar. This condition is accepted as an operation problem of no great proportions but calling for maintenance once or twice a week during summer months.

Floating mats of blue-green algae must be broken up before they have an opportunity to decay. Some ponds in Mississippi are now being operated at a six-foot depth (3) in an attempt to control blue-green algae, although the practice is too new to be considered a trend in operation. Considerable success has been experienced throughout the state of Mississippi with the use of an outboard motor boat for stirring the pond and breaking up the blue-green mass. Green algae such as Cladophora has caused an occasional odor problem in the northwestern part of the country (4). Being a clean water form of algae, its presence indicates weak sewage or excessive infiltration. When mats of this material are formed, occasional maintenance is called for and, as in the case of the blue-greens, they should be broken up or removed.

It is current practice in the Midwest and Southwest today to use two ponds in series. Recommended loadings on the first pond are as stated above, 20 to 50 pounds per day. The secondary pond is usually designed on a similar loading but since it receives the treated effluent from the primary, it is considerably smaller in size. The design and operation of the first pond are largely aimed at odor control, with the degree of treatment playing a secondary role. Adequate treatment under this arrangement can be obtained with a smaller primary pond but odor control is not assured. The secondary pond provides a degree of algae control, provides additional treatment, and, in some areas of the Western states, provides the secondary storage needed to prevent any discharge to the stream. It also provides the temporary treatment needed when the primary pond must be lowered or drained for repairs.

EFFICIENCY OF LAGOON TREATMENT

The obvious purpose of any municipal treatment facility is the removal of undesirable materials from a waste before its discharge to a stream. In the Western portion of the country where the annual rainfall rate is considerably below that for evaporation, benefits gained from waste stabilization ponds are not always indicated by an expressed degree of treatment. As an example, the effluent volume of many Western ponds may be only 10 percent of the influent, or even less. With a BOD reduction of 90 percent, as normally measured, the resultant overall treatment measured in ponds of BOD would be 99 percent. This advantage over ordinary treatment must be weighed against the disadvantage of a water resource loss and increased mineral content if re-use for irrigation or industry is contemplated.

Many designers in the Western United States are dedicating considerable effort toward the optimum use of all their water resources. The size of the pond, which is the controlling factor of detention time, may be small if optimum economic BOD removal of low degree is all that is required and there is no concern for odor. This results in the maximum water resource with the lowest salinity content, but a high BOD and bacterial content. In arid areas, longer detention periods will normally result in decreased algal populations, suspended solids, and coliform concentrations, along with an increased BOD removal accompanied by a reduced odor problem. Nevertheless, irrigation's major water quality problem in the Western United States is salinity and its permanent damage to soil. Lagoon design for agricultural re-use must take into consideration this fact as well as the type of crops to be irrigated.

DISINFECTION

Many states require disinfection of all domestic wastes whether from lagoons or conventional treatment plants. Under such requirement, secondary ponds can reduce chlorine usage. One state, Oregon (5), requires the disinfection of all domestic wastes discharged into public waters from May 1 to November 1, or as directed by the State Sanitary Authority. Some municipalities, therefore, make it a practice during this period to operate with no discharge by taking advantage of the additional storage capacity of a secondary pond and the increased losses during periods of high evaporation.

The effectiveness of pond operation as a means of bacterial control is well recognized today and utilized as a standard operation procedure by most states using stabilization lagoons. Results obtained by Public Health Service investigations of a waste stabilization pond at Lebanon, Ohio (6), showed coliform population reductions of 86 percent in winter to 94 percent in autumn. Fecal coliform reductions were between 88 percent and 98 percent. The greatest reduction occured in the numbers of fecal streptococci, which were reduced between the range of 97 to 99+ percent during the four seasons. The quantitative reduction may be greater where effluent volumes are but a small percentage of the influents because of evaporation and seepage losses.

Frequency of sampling was found to be important in establishing reduction percentages. The above results were obtained from geometric mean values, the raw sewage values of which varied greatly during the day. Total coliform densities entering the ponds reached peaks at 6:00 a.m. and noon. Fecal streptococcal maximum values lagged by two hours. The fecal coliform peaks occurred at 8:00 a.m. and 6:00 p.m. The effluent data revealed only a slight tendency toward peak bacterial densities at specific times.

Studies of ponds in Lebanon, Ohio, resulted in limited information on the effectiveness of effluent chlorination. Chlorination of 5 to 10 parts per million (mg/l) seemed to give effective bacterial kill (Table 62). This dosage of the pond effluent disrupts the algal cells normally found, makes them available to bacterial degradation, and may increase the BOD to a slight degree. Breakpoint chlorination applied at a rate of 50 mg/l may result in no change of BOD, as the low residual was not sufficient to disrupt the algal cells. Such a dosage was also accompanied by aftergrowths of bacteria. Several effluent samples chlorinated at 1–10 mg/l gave a relatively straight-line residual, with a 7.5 mg/l giving effective bacterial kill in 30 minutes (Table 63). A dosage of 10 mg/l gave like results in 10 minutes with no aftergrowths in either case.

Recent news releases have referred to the dissemination of pathogenic organisms by stabilization ponds. Such comments seem to run in cycles and it has been the author's experience that they appear with less frequency as the years pass. It is claimed that ducks flying from ponds contaminate other waters. These conclusions have been reached with a complete lack of evidence and no comparable

TABLE 62

COLIFORM IN POND EFFLUENT AFTER CHLORINATION, EXPERIMENT 1

Cl_2 Applied mg/l	Initial MPN/100 ml	Contact Time				
		15 min.	30 min.	60 min.	72 hr.[a]	8 days[a]
		MPN/100 ml				
0	33,000					
5.0		330	45	20	20	20
10.0		20	20	20	20	20
25.0		20	20	20	20	20
50.0		20	20	20	2,300	330
100.0		20	20	20	20	20

[a]Aftergrowth evaluation.

TABLE 63

COLIFORM IN POND EFFLUENT AFTER CHLORINATION, EXPERIMENT 2

Cl_2 Applied mg/l	Initial MPN/100 ml	Contact Time				
		15 min.	30 min.	60 min.	72 hr.[a]	8 days[a]
		MPN/100 ml				
0	7,900					
1.0		13,000	4,900	22,000	13,000	7,900
2.5		7,900	1,700	2,300	330	700
5.0		490	330	790	130	20
7.5		490	20	45	20	20
10.0		20	20	20	20	20

[a]Aftergrowth evaluation.

concern for ducks landing on the thousands of miles of rivers containing higher bacterial concentrations. There is no evidence that ponds emanate pathogenic organisms any more than the usual waste treatment plant.

AERATED LAGOONS

Use of the aerated lagoon for the treatment of domestic waste is showing increased popularity and, although discussed elsewhere in this volume, a few general comments regarding this trend are presented here. The need for aeration is based on the organic loading per unit of volume. As mentioned before, odor problems are minimal in the North and West at a loading of 20 pounds/acre/day (0.09 pounds/1,000 cubic feet/day with a 5-foot depth), and then only during spring breakup. Allowable loadings gradually increase southward with the Gulf Southwest States experiencing little operational problems at 50 pounds/acre/day (0.23 pounds/1,000 cubic feet). Occasional odor problems could be solved by supplemental aeration, beginning with loadings in these ranges and on up to approximately 200 pounds/acre/day (1.0 pounds/1,000 cubic feet/day). Beyond this point, the operation can no longer be considered supplemental aeration, as the oxygen needed provides sufficient turbulence and a resultant turbidity which excludes algae production. This is true up to a loading of approximately 8 pounds/1,000 cubic feet/day, beyond which the treatment must be considered extended aeration and ultimately activated sludge (Fig. 169).

The use of aerated lagoons has not been limited to any one geographic area of the United States. An aerated pilot lagoon was constructed at Eielson Air Force Base, Alaska, in 1964, located approximately 25 miles from the Public Health Service Artic Research Center at College, Alaska. During the winter of 1964–1965, the Center, with the cooperation of the Air Force of the Alaskan Air Command, conducted studies on the pond, which received settled sewage from the Eielson Base (7). The problems associated with lagoon operations in the Northern United States along the Canadian Border, are of course, accentuated in interior Alaska. The Central Valley of Alaska has the coldest winter temperatures in the United States, with the average during this study being -2°F. Extremes for the period were down to -56°F.

The pond operated at a 4.4-foot depth with a surface area of 0.13 acres. Air was provided by a $1\frac{1}{2}$-HP electric motor through 750 feet of weighted aeration tubing spaced at 5-foot intervals. Influent temperatures remained at 20°C. throughout the winter months. It was feared that the pond would freeze solid in

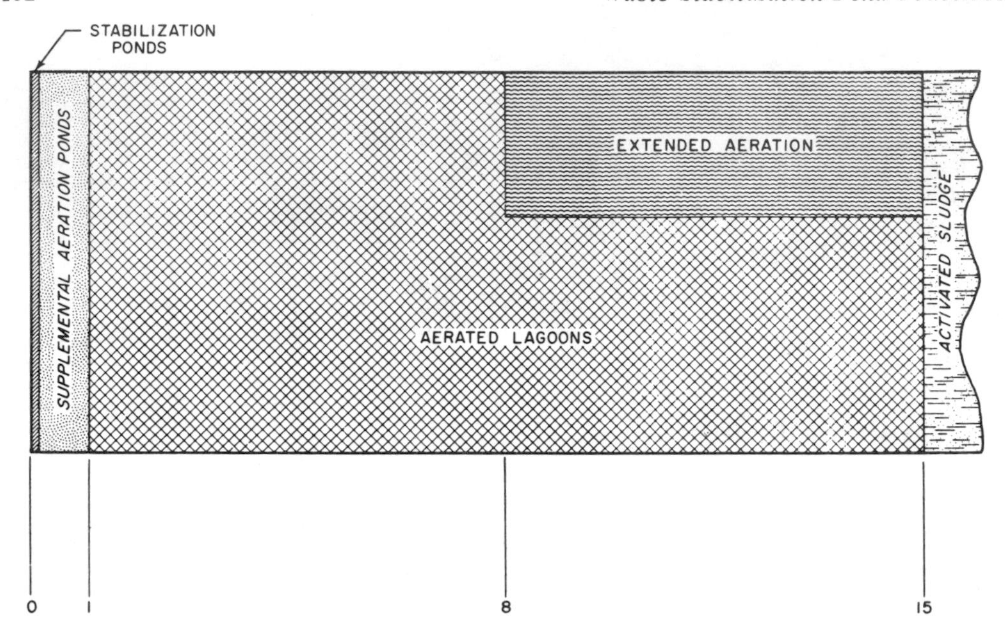

Figure 169. Loading—pounds BOD/1,000 cu ft/day.

this area but this did not happen. Once the ice formed, it gave sufficient insulation to maintain pond effluent temperatures of 1°C. Operational results of this lagoon are difficult to compare with normal lagoon operation. Although it received settled sewage, maximum loading conditions of 26 pounds BOD/acre/day still resulted in a BOD removal of 66 percent. With lighter loadings and longer detention times, the efficiency increased to the 75–80-percent range.

A considerably larger installation in North Dakota (8), covering 3 acres and using two 15-HP blowers gave very acceptable wintertime operation (Plate 11). With a primary cell loading of 400 pounds BOD/acre/day and a secondary cell loading of 100 pounds, the facility gave an average effluent strength of 22 mg/l. In January 1966 the average efficiency of BOD reduction was 92.4 percent.

The operational cost has been approximately $150 per month, which can be justified by a savings in eliminating the purchase of 40 acres of land, a sewage pumping station, and several thousand feet of force main.

DISSOLVED OXYGEN

One major advantage of aeration in cold climates is the resulting high dissolved oxygen content of the effluent. This varied in the Eielson Base lagoon from 4 mg/l to 9 mg/l, and indicates the major advantage of aeration over standard design in the Northern United States during winter months. The optimum in economical, efficient, trouble-free treatment could well be a combination of aerated or nonaerated lagoons using air only when needed.

GENERAL PRACTICE AND PROBLEMS

The trend today is toward better design on the part of the consulting engineer. Ponds continue to be used effectively as temporary treatment for subdevelopments that cannot connect to existing treatment facilities.

Maintenance by the smaller community is still a problem. As with the Imhoff

Plate 11. Aerated lagoon during winter operation in Harvey, North Dakota. Courtesy Otmar O. Olson.

tank of 30 years ago, the pond's simplicity results in its being ignored. When no trouble is experienced, the community pays no attention to the lagoons, provides no maintenance, lets the weeds grow, and adopts an "out of sight, out of mind" attitude. If the facility provides good treatment under such conditions, it is difficult to criticize the community, but certainly all regulatory agencies strongly urge proper maintenance. Most cities routinely mow dikes, control excessive algae, and, in the North, lower the water level during late fall in anticipation of winter storage needs.

An early concern of entomologists was the potential mosquito breeding in sewage ponds. Most states report some mosquitoes present during certain periods of the year at some locations. Mississippi (3) was concerned with the problem and requested assistance from the Communicable Disease Center to survey all of their lagoons during two separate years. In most cases, no mosquito breeding was found. In a few units, breeding was considered light and in one, it was considered moderate. The latter, however, was located near a swamp where breeding was found to be heavy. Some of the Mississippi lagoons had heavy growths of grass and weeds which would seem to invite trouble, but no signs of mosquitoes were found. The reason for this is still unexplained.

Some uninformed individuals still consider lagoons as dangerous, undesirable, and a health hazard. Most consulting engineers, however, consider them as another tool to be used in the continuing fight to control pollution. Whether the lagoons treat settled or raw sewage is of no great concern. When operated in series and properly designed for the job to be done, they can well be the most desirable form of treatment. They have, without question, become the most desirable form of treatment for the fellow who must pay the bill and it is recognized by most pollution control agencies that, in the long run, a properly maintained lagoon will keep more organic material out of a stream per unit of cost than any other kind of treatment.

REFERENCES

(1) Porges, Ralph. "Principles and Practices of Aerobic Treatment in Poultry Waste Disposal Aerobic Stabilization Ponds." Paper presented at Poultry Waste Management Symposium, Lincoln, Nebraska (May 1964).

(2) Horn, James A. *Evaluation of Waste Stabilization Lagoons Located in Colorado.* Colorado State Health Department Report (August 1965).

(3) Johnston, J. E. "Waste Treatment by Lagoons," *The Reporter, Amer. Pub. Works Assoc., 4* (November 1965).

(4) Brinck, C. W. Private Correspondence (November 1965).

(5) Oregon State Board of Health. *Criteria for Design and Utilization of Domestic Sewage Lagoons for Stabilization Ponds* (July 1965).

(6) Horning, William B., Ralph Porges, H. F. Clarke, and W. B. Cooke. *Waste Stabilization Pond Study.* Public Health Service Publication 999-WP-16 (May 1964).

(7) Reid, Leroy C., Jr. *The Aerated Sewage Lagoon in Artic, Alaska.* Public Health Service, Artic Research Center Publication (September 1965).

(8) Olson, Otmar O. "Aerated Lagoon System for Harvey, North Dakota," *Official Bulletin, North Dakota Water and Sewage Works Conference, 7,* 8 (January–February 1966).

WASTE STABILIZATION POND PRACTICES IN CANADA

Charles P. Fisher, W. R. Drynan, and G. L. Van Fleet
University of Waterloo, Waterloo, Ontario, Canada

INTRODUCTION

In Canada, the use of waste stabilization ponds for the treatment of wastewaters was initiated about twenty years ago in the Prairie Provinces. Currently, there are installations in every section of the country, treating wastes from communities of only a few hundred persons or from large cities such as Regina and Winnipeg.

As an aid to this presentation, Canada has been divided into five areas (Fig. 170), each of which represents a region of comparable climatic conditions. On the east coast, the Maritime provinces of Nova Scotia, Prince Edward Island, New Brunswick, and Newfoundland are grouped together into Area I. The second area encompasses the Central provinces of Ontario and Quebec. The Prairie provinces of Manitoba, Saskatchewan, and Alberta form Area III. British Columbia on the west coast forms Area IV. Area V consists of Canada's northernmost regions—the Yukon Territory and the Northwest Territories.

HISTORICAL DEVELOPMENT

The waste stabilization pond form of sewage treatment is becoming increasingly more acceptable, with the number of installations growing almost expo-

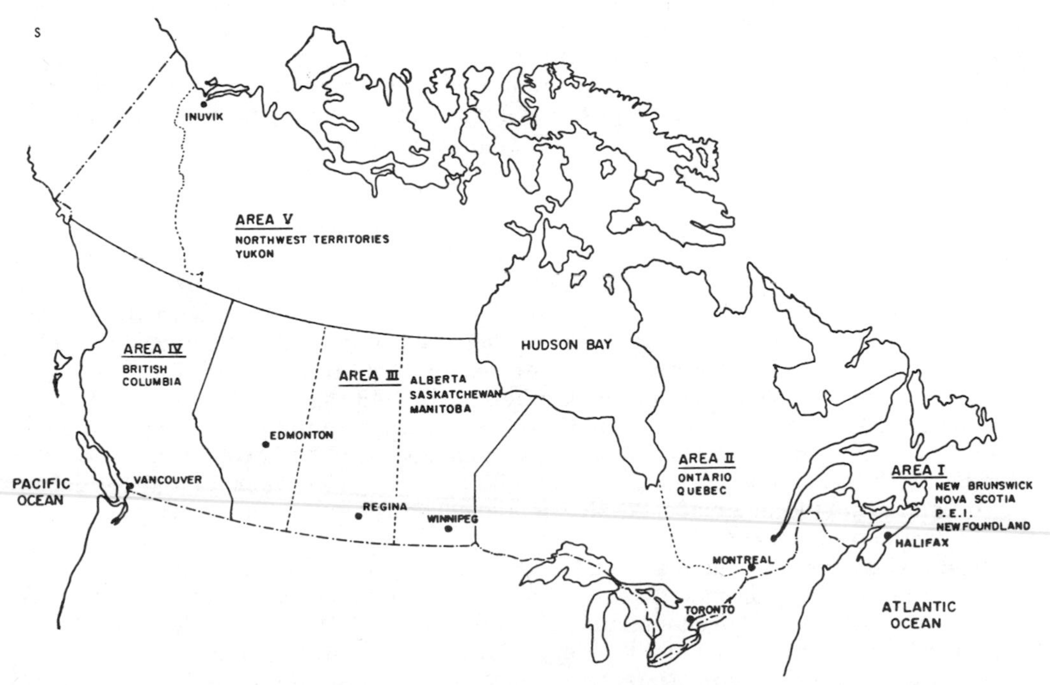

Figure 170. Regions of Canada.

nentially in most provinces. By the end of 1965, there were 275 municipalities in Saskatchewan served by waste stabilization ponds. The first units were constructed in Manitoba in 1955 and by 1961 there were 29 ponds in operation within the province. More than one third of these were multiple-cell systems. Commencing with one pond in 1947, there were 114 in the province of Alberta by 1960.

The first waste stabilization pond in Ontario was constructed at the Ipperwash Army Camp in 1956. By the end of 1964, there were 43 of these installations, which were operated in agreement with the Ontario Water Resources Commission (OWRC). Many other private ponds are operated within Ontario, primarily for the treatment of industrial wastes.

The first ponds in the Maritimes, Area I, were constructed at Charlottetown in Prince Edward Island in 1957 to treat industrial wastes, and at O'Leary, for the treatment of municipal wastes. Ten of the twelve ponds operated within Prince Edward Island in 1965 were used to treat domestic wastes. Provincial authorities in New Brunswick constructed their first pond in 1959. There were, however, nine such ponds in operation by 1963. In Nova Scotia the first waste stabilization pond was installed in 1962 at Berwick, and was designed to treat combined municipal and trade wastes. Presently, a 450-acre pond has been proposed that will be used to serve the Pictou area of Nova Scotia. This proposed pond will be used to treat a mixture of pulp mill and domestic waste from five neighboring municipalities. There were no ponds in operation in the province of Newfoundland as of 1965.

CLIMATIC CONDITIONS

Area I: Maritimes

The climate of the Maritime provinces, which lie between latitudes 43° 30'N on the south and 48°N on the north, is moderated by the Atlantic ocean. This is particularly so in the southeastern regions. Despite this moderation, periodic extremes in seasonal temperatures do occur, primarily as a result of cyclonic storms. As might be expected, January is the average coldest month throughout most of the Maritimes, with temperatures ranging from 5°F. to 25°F., occasionally dropping to as low as -45°F. July is generally the warmest month of the year with average temperatures in the low 60°F. and upper extremes often reaching 100°F.

Mean annual total precipitation decreases in a northwesterly direction from the sea. Along the southern coast of Nova Scotia, the average total precipitation is approximately 55 inches, while the snowfall averages 70 inches (1 inch of snowfall is equivalent to 0.1 inch of precipitation). In northern New Brunswick the average total precipitation is approximately 35 inches, while snowfall averages 110 inches. As a result of the climatic variations across the Maritimes, ponds located in northern New Brunswick have a thicker ice cover and the snow cover is often deeper than in southern areas, thus there are accompanying reductions in algal growth and oxygen production. Windblown snow on pond surfaces often reaches depths of 12 to 15 inches. Maximum ice thicknesses of between 12 and 18 inches have been reported in Prince Edward Island. The ice cover in this region persists from mid-December to early May.

The coastal areas, which are influenced by a marine environment, have a later autumn and spring than inland regions and usually experience highly humid conditions. Westerly winds predominate. Prince Edward Island receives approximately 1,800 hours of sunshine annually. Generally, however, the climate within the Maritimes has permitted satisfactory operation of waste stabilization ponds.

Area II: Central

Most of the waste stabilization pond installations within the province of Ontario are between the forty-second and fiftieth parallels of latitude, which places them adjacent to the Great Lakes. Climatic conditions vary considerably in this area. Mean January temperatures range from 25°F. in the south to less than 5°F. north of Lake Superior. July mean temperatures range between 62°F. and 74°F. The moderating influence of the Great Lakes is evident; however, most regions south of the forty-sixth parallel have experienced occasional extreme summer temperatures in excess of 100°F.

Total annual precipitation varies from 25 to 40 inches, with snow falls ranging from 40 inches in some parts of southwestern Ontario to over 120 inches in the lee of Georgian Bay. Snowfall in the northern part of this region varies between 80 and 100 inches per year.

Northerly ponds are covered with ice and snow from late in October until mid-April. In the south, however, the ponds usually become ice covered in November. Ice cover on these ponds persists until the spring breakup, which occurs in March. Ice thickness varies from 6 to 10 inches in most areas; however, thicknesses of 2 feet have been reported in the northerly regions. The open locations of most ponds result in shallow windswept snow conditions.

In Quebec, the second region of Area II, no waste stabilization pond data were available.

Area III: Prairies

The Prairie provinces extend from the forty-ninth to the sixtieth parallel of latitude. Climatic conditions exhibit a marked effect on waste stabilization pond operation in this region. Winters are long and often severe, while summers are short and often hot. Temperature extremes occur throughout the year. Precipitation is less than in other sections of Canada. There is in excess of 2,300 hours of sunshine annually in southern Alberta and Saskatchewan.

Mean January temperatures vary from 15°F. in southwest Alberta to less than -20°F. in the northern parts of Saskatchewan and Manitoba. Winter temperatures often vary considerably due to the chinook winds. July temperatures range from 55° to 65°F. The mean annual total precipitation ranges between 10 and 20 inches, while the annual evaporation rate at Winnipeg has been estimated to be 26 inches. Snowfall varies from 36 inches in the interior of Saskatchewan to 60 inches in the Rocky Mountain foothills and in the southwestern area of Alberta. Since the winters are long and cold, snow often remains for extended periods of time. Ice cover on the Prairies lasts from mid-November through to about the end of April. Ice thickness often reaches 2 to 3 feet on the ponds. Ice thickness of 54 inches has, however, been observed at Winnipeg and has been reported to be somewhat opaque, with accompanying snow cover of 12 inches. Pond snow cover of up to 18 inches has been reported in Saskatchewan, while 36 inches have been reported in Alberta.

Area IV: West Coast

Climatic conditions in the province of British Columbia vary tremendously from one section of the province to another. The coastal regions are moderated in winter by the warm waters of the Pacific Ocean, which also provides vast amounts of moisture to be carried onto the western slopes of the coastal ranges in quantities in excess of 100 inches annually. Further inland and in the northern regions of the province, precipitation is relatively low.

Although there are more ponds, data are available on three waste stabilization ponds within the province, each located within regions of different climatic conditions. The seasonal variations for these locations serve to show the broad spectrum of climatic conditions in British Columbia.

The city of Courtenay (latitude 49° 43'N) is located on Vancouver Island, approximately 135 miles north of the city of Victoria. Annual average total precipitation varies between 40 and 60 inches, with associated high humidity. Both winters and summers are moderate, with average January and July temperatures of 36°F. and 73°F. respectively.

Ice cover, reportedly, sometimes persists for a duration of two weeks and often attains a maximum thickness of three inches. Snow has reached depths of two feet upon occasion.

Kamloops, British Columbia, is located in the central part of the province, approximately 268 miles northeast of Vancouver (latitude 51°00'N). This district has dry, hot summers with temperatures averaging 69°F. during July but with occasional extremes well in excess of 100°F. Although the temperature often drops below zero during the winter months, the coldest month, January, averages 22°F. This January average temperature is some 14°F. colder than the city of Courtenay, although both cities are approximately at the same latitude.

Ice and snow conditions persist from December through to March, with maximum thicknesses of 6 inches. Kamloops averages 2,094 hours of bright sunshine annually.

The city of Dawson Creek (latitude 55°45'N) is located 730 miles northeast of Vancouver, close to the Alberta boundary. Precipitation in this region varies between 15 and 20 inches annually. Maximum snow depth is reportedly 30 inches.

Summers are quite short with July temperatures averaging about 65°F. Winters are, however, long and cold. January temperatures average 0°F. with ice and snow cover from early November until the end of April. Pond ice thickness varies from 8 to 18 inches.

Area V: North

Only one oxidation pond is found in the Northwest Territories—at Inuvik, which is located (latitude 68°12'N) in the Mackenzie River Valley, about 75 miles inland from the Beaumont Sea. The warmest month is July, during which temperatures average a moderate 58°F. During January, the coolest month, the temperature averages -19°F.

The average annual total precipitation is a modest 9 inches; with two thirds of this total precipitation occurring as snow. Although the snowfall is not heavy, it accumulates due to the extremely long winters. Summer daily temperatures vary from 65° to 75°F. in the mid-afternoon to 40° to 50°F. during the nights. Maximum temperatures of 85°F. have been reported.

Although the ponds are operated year round, there are less than five hours of daily sunlight during the three winter months. Pond surface snow depths of 2 feet have been reported. The maximum ice thickness has on occasions reached a depth of 5 feet and has persisted from September to mid-June.

DESIGN CRITERIA

Waste stabilization ponds in Canada are sometimes designed on the basis of volumetric loading. To accomplish this, a theoretical minimum detention time is used, along with an estimated or observed volumetric per capita flow rate. More commonly, the design is based upon the organic loading, which is usually expressed in terms of the number of pounds of BOD applied per acre of pond surface area per day. In many of the provinces both volumetric and organic loading factors are used to determine pond dimensions.

Area I: Maritimes

The provinces of Prince Edward Island, New Brunswick, and Nova Scotia adhere to suggested design criteria rather than formal standards. To date, only the province of Nova Scotia has "officially" adopted effluent objectives. These objectives are similar to those adopted in Ontario, and are described later.

The suggested design of waste stabilization ponds within the Maritimes is based on an organic loading with a population equivalent of 200 persons per acre. Since most of the ponds in the Maritime Provinces have been designed to serve small communities under moderate climatic conditions, design procedures have been kept simple. Most ponds in the Maritimes are fed from inlets that are center-discharging structures located about one foot above the bottom of the pond. Variable overflow weirs are often employed to maintain liquid levels in the ponds. Where practical, facilities are provided to completely drain the ponds. In Prince Edward Island the per capita water consumption which affects the pond volumetric load, although increasing, is less than in other parts of the country. At the present time, the per capita consumption rate is approximately 40 gallons per day.

Area II: Central

As the design criteria used in Manitoba are similar to those used in Ontario, criteria used in both provinces will be considered jointly with the Ontario Water Resources Commission regulations. These require that the organic design loading rate not exceed 20 pounds BOD/acre/day (100 persons/acre/day). In Manitoba, on the other hand, the permitted design organic loading rate is 40 to 50 pounds BOD/acre/day (200 to 250 persons/acre/day). Substantially higher organic loading is permitted in both provinces for installations that are operated only during the summer. Multiple ponds are recommended in Manitoba when the pond area is greater than 10 acres. When multiple ponds are used, the cells are usually arranged so that they may be operated either in series or in parallel. A winter retention design period of 120 days is required in Manitoba where there is a small dilution factor in the receiving stream.

In both Ontario and Manitoba it is recommended that the influent pipe be located near the center of the pond. When there is gravity flow the inlet may be allowed to discharge horizontally, whereas, when the flow is under pressure a vertical discharge is required. When the discharge is vertical, regulations stipulate that the weir pipe be located 1 foot above the bottom of the pond and discharge velocities not exceed 2 feet per second. One common method of controlling pond depth is by using adjustable, effluent overflow weir structures in Ontario as well as in Manitoba. In Ontario the depth is controlled between 2 and 5 feet, while in Manitoba the controlled depth varies between 1 and 5 feet.

Design criteria in Ontario as well as Nova Scotia have the following objectives:

1. Following initial dilution, the total coliforms (MPN) in the receiving stream should not be greater than 2,400/100 ml. nor should the BOD_5 exceed 4 mg/l for domestic sewage.

2. The effluent BOD_5 and suspended solids concentrations of industrial wastes should not be greater than 15 mg/l.

Area III: Prairies

In Saskatchewan suggested pond design standards are related to organic loading and retention times. Prior to 1961 pond design was based on a loading of 50 lbs BOD_5/acre/day or 120 days retention, whichever gave the greatest surface area.

Since 1961 pond systems have been designed with two cells, operated in series with a total retention time of 180 days. The retention time is determined from the full volume of the secondary cell as well as 2 feet of depth from the primary cell. The first cell is designed on the basis of a maximum organic loading rate of 40 lbs. BOD_5/acre/day. Many of the ponds in the province of Saskatchewan discharge onto or across farmland and receive little or no dilution; consequently, effluent standards have not been established. Ponds are designed to discharge the effluent in the late fall prior to freeze up and again in the spring when dilution from runoff is available.

Design regulations for the province of Alberta are related to the population served (Table 64). When less than 300 persons are served, conventional facultative waste stabilization ponds are permitted; however, when the population is greater than 300 persons more complex systems, using both short and long detention period ponds which are capable of either series or parallel operation, are required.

The short detention period (anaerobic) ponds precede the longer detention period (facultative) ponds in these waste treatment systems. The design detention periods for the anaerobic ponds vary from 2 to 4 days, while the finishing pond detention periods vary from 3 to 6 months. Generally, the primary ponds are designed to be operated without residual dissolved oxygen, while the liquid depth is maintained at about 8 to 10 feet. The finishing ponds are designed as conventional, facultative waste stabilization ponds with a variable depth between 2 and 5 feet.

Design loading rates for waste stabilization pond system in the province of Alberta vary not only for primary and secondary ponds but also for the type of waste to be treated. The maximum design organic loading on the primary ponds is 4,000 lbs. BOD_5/acre/day when the liquid depth is 10 feet. The permissible design organic loading rate of the secondary ponds varies from 30 to 50 lbs BOD_5/acre/day. If the waste to be treated is predominantly domestic, the permissible organic loading on the secondary pond is 50 lbs BOD_5/acre/day. If, however, industrial wastes are to be treated in the system, the design loading rate may be reduced to as low as 30 lbs BOD_5/acre/day.

Design standards require that certain features of physical layout be incorporated. Short detention period ponds must have interconnecting facilities that permit parallel, or parallel-series operation and, as well, there must be provision for bypassing any of the primary cells. Also, the finishing ponds must be designed so that series operation is possible. It is further required that short detention period ponds be designed with inlets and outlets submerged respectively to depths of six and three feet below the liquid surface.

Area IV: West Coast

In British Columbia all waste stabilization pond plans are reviewed by both the Provincial Department of Health and the Water Pollution Control Board prior to

TABLE 64

MULTIPLE POND REQUIREMENTS—PROVINCE OF ALBERTA

Population Equivalents	Number of Short Detention Ponds	Number of Long Detention Ponds
0–300	nil	As required by loading; at least two
300–1,000	3 ponds of equal size	As required by loading; at least two
1,000+	4 ponds of equal size (minimum)	As required by loading; at least two

construction. There are, however, no provincial waste stabilization pond design standards.

Available data on existing ponds in British Columbia indicate that most installations are of the conventional facultative type. A recent installation at Dawson Creek, however, is similar to the multiple-cell design currently in use in Alberta. The system at Dawson Creek consists of four short detention period primary cells, and three long detention period secondary cells, designed to allow for series or parallel operations.

Area V: North

The design of wastewater treatment facilities in the Northwest territories is regulated by the Federal Government. Although there are no Federal design standards for waste stabilization ponds, proposed systems plans are submitted for government review and approval.

There is one waste stabilization pond treatment system in the Northwest Territories to serve the community of Inuvik. Domestic wastes from this community of 1,500 persons are treated in a single conventional facultative pond. The pond is located in a natural depression and has complete winter storage capacity.

OPERATIONAL PROBLEMS AND PRACTICES

Area I: Maritimes

Climatic conditions in the Maritime provinces are moderated through the influence of the marine environment. As a result of this, ice formation is relatively thin and lasts for a shorter period of time than is generally experienced throughout much of inland Canada. Precipitation is moderate, with receiving streams usually able to provide adequate dilution for the effluent discharge. This allows the pond to be operated on the basis of continuous year-round discharge. Emphasis is therefore on organic loading and effluent quality rather than as dictated by storage requirements. In only a few instances is complete summer or winter storage required. In such cases drawdown of ponds takes place during the spring or fall.

Loading Rates

For the most part, only small municipalities are presently serviced by waste stabilization ponds in the Maritime provinces. Consequently, the raw sewage is primarily of a domestic nature. Waste stabilization ponds are of the facultative type with organic loadings ranging from 15 to 35 lbs BOD/acre/day. The higher loadings are associated with operations in the province of New Brunswick.

Efficiencies

BOD and suspended solids reductions vary from summer to winter as well as from system to system. Studies in the Maritimes have been limited to the spring and summer periods only. The results of these studies show that installations in New Brunswick and Prince Edward Island are providing BOD removals in excess of 85 percent. Corresponding suspended solids reductions ranged upward from 70 percent in New Brunswick. Coliform reductions were observed to be in excess of 99 percent at most installations.

Odors

Odors are generally associated with the period of spring changeover from complete ice cover to open water conditions. Most of the ponds under observation during this period produced only slight odors, with some producing none at all. The rest of the year apparently remains odor free. This appears to be consistent with the moderate climatic conditions experienced in the area.

Other Observations

During the summer months the presence of high residual oxygen in the ponds was associated with a proliferous algal growth. Erosion of pond dykes was not considered a serious problem, although excessive seepage and evaporation have created problems at some installations.

Area II: Central

The use of waste stabilization ponds in Ontario has gained wide acceptance only in the last five or six years. There are currently on the order of forty municipal waste stabilization ponds, with a total surface area of about 1,000 acres, in operation in the province. No data were available on the use of ponds in the province of Quebec.

All the oxidation ponds treating municipal wastes in Ontario are of the facultative type and are operated with essentially continuous discharge. More than half of these ponds are comprised of multiple cells connected in series or parallel. Many of the ponds are operated in series in the summer and in parallel during the winter. The relatively high BOD_5 reductions obtained, and high oxygen content maintained during the summer indicate that primarily aerobic conditions are maintained in all ponds in series except under extremely high loadings. Parallel operations are used in the winter in order to reduce BOD loadings at a time when BOD_5 reductions are low. Multiple cells also provide extra storage in order to eliminate discharges during the summer months where such discharges may adversely affect recreational areas. Moreover, the additional storage obtained through the manipulation of cell liquid depth allows regulation of discharges, as required, to receiving streams with intermittent flow.

Loading Rates

In most instances, municipal waste stabilization ponds receive an estimated organic loading between 10 and 20 lbs BOD_5/acre/day. The design loading of 20 lbs BOD_5/acre/day was exceeded in two instances with loadings of 50 and 73 lbs BOD_5/acre/day. A third installation, receiving a large variable flow of industrial wastes along with the domestic wastes, produced an estimated organic loading of 72 lbs BOD/acre/day as compared to the maximum average design figure of 42.9 lbs BOD/acre/day for this facility.

Efficiencies

Municipal installations have been giving an annual average BOD_5 reduction of 90 percent with individual yearly pond averages ranging from 65 to 96 percent. Variations in BOD over the course of a year showed the typical curve, Figure 171, for operations under climatic conditions giving ice cover during the winter months. This curve shows a slow build-up of BOD in the pond concurrent with the formation of ice and subsequent snow cover and a rapid reduction in BOD during the spring recovery period.

Suspended solids reductions varied from 61 to 95 percent with an average reduction of 80 percent. Effluent suspended solids were at their lowest values during the early winter months, rising in late winter to a peak during the spring breakup due to the physical turbulence within the ponds. Algal activity reduces the suspended solids to a median level throughout the summer and fall.

Coliform reductions were observed to be in excess of 99.5 percent where raw sewage concentrations ranged from 40,000,000 to 80,000,000 MPN per 100 mls.

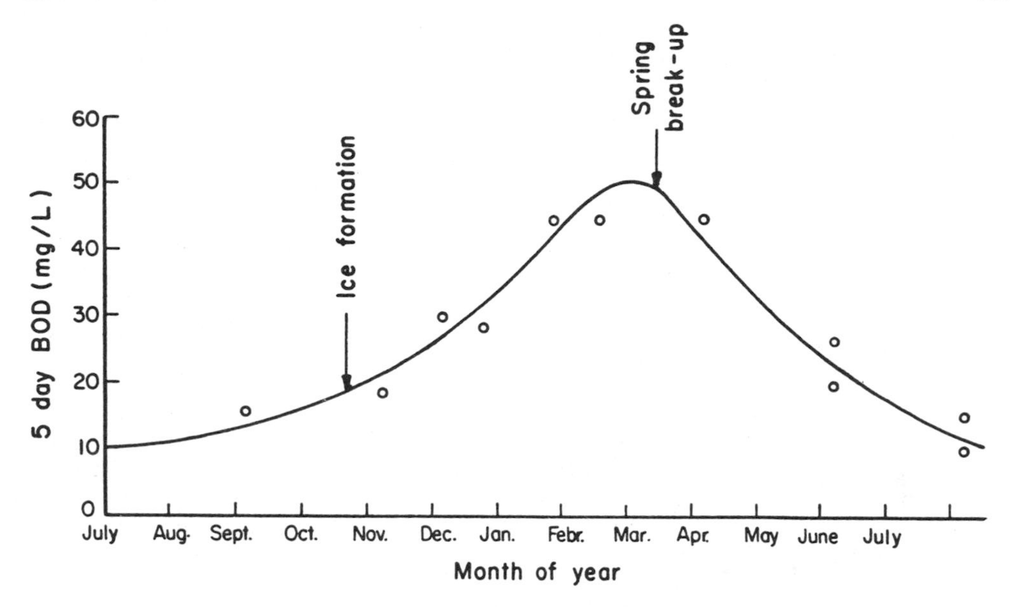

Figure 171. Typical seasonal variation of waste stabilization pond effluent BOD.

Odors

Odors were a serious problem at only one installation. This waste stabilization pond receives a combination of industrial and domestic waste giving an estimated organic loading in excess of 70 lbs BOD/acre/day, almost double the design figure for the two-cell pond with a total area of 70 acres. Generally, odors accompanying the spring recovery period are not a serious problem in Ontario. This may well be due to the relatively isolated locations of the ponds.

Other Observations

Total nitrogen removal in five waste stabilization ponds ranged between 60 and 80 percent, with an average of 70 percent. Free ammonia was reduced, on the average, by 75 percent. Concentrations of nitrogenous compounds were at their lowest levels during the summer months, with nitrite and nitrate concentrations never greater than 1 mg/l in the effluent.

Total phosphorus reduction amounted to an average of 60 percent in five ponds, with greatest reductions evident during the early summer months.

Algae of the genera *Chlorella* and *Chlamydomonas* have been found in some ponds throughout the year from levels as low as 200 areal standard units (a.s.u.) per ml. under ice conditions to 60,000 areal standard units per ml. during the optimum growth periods in late summer.

Physical problems appear to be causing a good deal of concern. Slightly less than one half the ponds on which data are available were encountering problems with weeds. Erosion is a constant problem at some installations and is generally associated with ponds of large surface area and those with inside dyke wall slopes greater than the recommended 4:1 ratio.

In 1963 more than half of the municipal installations had combined sanitary and storm collection systems. As a result, problems developed at some installations due to grit accumulations in the inlet works. In addition, silt banks have been built up in many ponds, with a resultant reduction in operational capacity. At low liquid depth, short circuiting and odor problems can develop. Storm water and sanitary wastewater collection systems should be separated in all new installations. Where practical, older, combined systems are being replaced with separate facilities for collection.

Area III: Prairies

Prairie winters are extremely cold and long, while summers are hot and dry, often accompanied by low precipitation. Climatic conditions such as these do not permit the usual method of continuous pond effluent discharge. Also associated with the low precipitation and hot summers are the receiving streams that are often dry or have very little water available for dilution. Winters, being long and cold, often contribute to severe ice conditions within waste stabilization ponds.

To overcome the severe climatic conditions on the Prairies, ponds are usually provided with 4–6-months volumetric capacity so that they can be discharged during the fall, prior to winter freeze up, and again in the spring when dilution water is available. This practice is usually followed by most governing agencies in the Prairie provinces. Although there are organic loading requirements, the storage requirements often govern pond design dimensions. There are, however, variations of this practice in Alberta, and by the Waste Disposal Division of the Metropolitan Corporation of Greater Winnipeg.

In Alberta most ponds are the faculatative type, and have been designed for either 6- or 12-months volumetric capacity. The more refined systems used in Alberta have, however, the short and long detention period ponds. Where these short and long detention period ponds are used, the long period, or secondary pond, is provided with about 6-months volumetric capacity. Nearly all the waste stabilization ponds in Alberta are discharged either in the fall or in the spring. Where there are receiving streams with sufficient dilution, reduced continuous discharge may be permitted.

Waste stabilization ponds in Manitoba are designed with 4-months retention capacity. The Charleswood system, which serves part of Greater Winnipeg and is comprised of three primary and two secondary cells, is not discharged during the winter. Both the primary and the secondary cells at Charleswood are the conventional facultative type. In this system both the primary and the secondary cells are used for winter storage.

In Saskatchewan, as in Manitoba, existing ponds are generally of the facultative type; many of these are multiple-cell installations, being operated in series with no recirculation.

Loading Rates

As elsewhere in Canada, the organic loading rates of waste stabilization ponds vary with location and type of treatment system. Meat packing and dairy wastes play an important part in organic loadings on the Prairies. In Alberta observed organic loadings of facultative ponds vary from between 19 and 22 lbs BOD/acre/day for single-celled systems to between 50 and 250 lbs BOD/acre/day for multiple-celled systems. The loading rates for anaerobic installations vary from 2.6 to 17.7 lbs BOD/1,000 cu ft/day.

Ponds in the Charleswood system at Winnipeg have varied loading to facilitate efficiency studies. One of the primary cells in the Charleswood system was loaded at an organic loading rate of 50 lbs BOD/acre/day for one year, while the other two primary cells received the excess. During the second year of study, the load to the one primary cell was increased to 80 lbs BOD/acre/day while the excess was distributed to the other two primary cells. Organic loading rates in Saskatchewan vary between 28 and 46 lbs BOD/acre/day.

Efficiencies

Waste stabilization pond removal efficiencies vary with climatic conditions. Since the climatic conditions vary considerably throughout the Prairies, removal efficiencies also vary, resulting in distinct variations between summer and winter operating conditions.

Pond efficiencies, based on BOD reductions, in Alberta vary between 45 and 90 percent. The greatest reduction in BOD naturally occurs during the summer time. In Saskatchewan summer BOD reductions average in excess of 90 percent while wintertime efficiencies average 54 percent. The results of the first-year evaluation study of the Charleswood Treatment System in Winnipeg indicate that the summer-time BOD and suspended solids reduction is equivalent to conventional secondary treatment. During early freeze up, the secondary cells in this system froze to a depth of $1\frac{1}{2}$ feet; thus, there was no further treatment. By the end of the winter, however, the secondary cells had frozen to the full depth of 4.5 feet, while the primary cells had 3.5 feet of ice overlying about 3 feet of liquid. Thus, the overall effect of the ice during the winter period greatly reduced treatment efficiencies.

In Alberta a winter study of suspended solids concentrations in anaerobic ponds showed reductions varying from 64 to 91 percent. In a series-operated system more than 55 percent of suspended solids removal could be expected in the first cell. Suspended solids were observed to decrease with detention time in the entire system. The removal of suspended solids from waste stabilization ponds in Saskatchewan has been estimated at 70 percent during summer operation and 77 percent during the winter. At the Charleswood installation suspended solids reductions through the system varied between 60 and 78 percent during the summer months. No data were available on winter efficiencies. Extensive sludge deposits have developed at many installations where high suspended solids removal was being experienced.

The accumulation of sludge in Alberta ponds was found to range between 0.004 and 0.012 cu. ft./capita/day. Similar data were obtained in Saskatchewan. Measurements of sludge depth in Alberta further indicated that the summer accumulation rate varied from $\frac{1}{3}$ to $\frac{1}{4}$ of the winter accumulation rate. Assuming that the suspended solids concentrations of the raw sewage remained fairly constant throughout the year, the reduction in sludge accumulation must in all probability be associated with accelerated digestion at the height of summer temperatures. An extensive sludge build-up could lead to short circuiting, reduced efficiencies, and odor problems.

Odors

Odors associated with the operation of waste stabilization ponds are not uncommon to installations across the Prairies. A short period of fairly strong odors usually accompanies the spring changeover from complete ice cover to open water conditions. These odors were generally more intense and lasted for longer periods of time where the pond was organically overloaded or where there was an abundance of industrial wastes. Other odor problems have developed from excessive seepage and evaporation, the exposure of sludge mounds, and the high sulfate content in the municipal water supply.

Ice and snow cover accompanied by low winter efficiencies in waste stabilization ponds lead to a build-up of BOD within the ponds. The removal of ice in the spring, generating biological activity and releasing produced gases, is often accompanied by short periods of very intensive odors. These odors are most prominent at facultative installations. Anaerobic, short-detention primary ponds tend to exhibit less intensive spring odors due to a thinner ice cover and shorter period of coverage. These ponds, however, generally produce a relatively low intensity of odors throughout the year, often accompanied by floating sludge, scum, and grease.

Studies on anaerobic short detention period ponds in the province of Alberta concluded that serious odor problems are not necessarily associated with a poor degree of sewage treatment. It was also concluded that the organic loading in anaerobic ponds is not always a criterion as far as odor productions are concerned.

Extensive overloading of facultative ponds in Saskatchewan has resulted in many cases in extending the spring odor period well into the summer months. The Charleswood system in Manitoba was free of spring odors after its first year of operation. However, it was noted that several other systems in the immediate vicinity of Winnipeg, notably those receiving industrial waste discharge, were not by mid-May fully free of noxious odors accompanying spring recovery.

The odor nuisance has been attributed to many causes other than spring breakup of ice. The hydrogen sulfide odor resulting at two Alberta ponds was attributed to the high sulfate content in the town water supplies. At ponds where these odors were observed, there was a distinct correlation with the reduction of sulfates within the ponds. A similar problem was found in Saskatchewan. In all cases the sulfate content in the water supply was greater than 400 parts per million.

Excessive seepage and evaporation at one pond in Saskatchewan created late-summer problems, when a sludge mound at the pond inlet became exposed. The odors disappeared when the solids were submerged by pumping river water into the system.

Ammonium nitrate fertilizer, sodium nitrate, and several commercial products were tested for reduction of odors in Saskatchewan, with no apparent effect. Odor problems were however eliminated at some installations through the introduction of river water or supernatant from other ponds. Chemical treatment was also ineffective in Manitoba and Alberta. In Alberta installation of a multiple inlet distribution pipe along with sludge recirculation lines effectively eliminated noxious odors in one system. The installation was carried out on a primary anaerobic cell, with digested sludge recirculated as seed material for the raw sewage.

Other Observations

Several other operational factors are worth noting. Throughout the Prairies coliform reductions in most installations were in excess of 99 percent. Systems under study in Alberta showed seasonal variations in ammonia nitrogen. Generally higher readings were obtained during the winter months, with summer minimums as low as 5 mg/l in facultative cells.

Algal studies in Saskatchewan indicated concentrations ranging from 5,000 to 400,000 a.s.u. per ml., with lower values being obtained from ice-covered ponds. Photosynthetic sulfur bacteria were present at several installations where the sulphate concentration of the raw sewage was particularly high.

Wave action and runoff caused dyke erosion problems at many large installations. At the Charleswood ponds studies were carried out on dykes constructed with inside slopes varying from 6:1 to 9:1 in order to assess the effect in reducing erosion. One year of operation showed that the flatter slopes did not eliminate the erosion problem. The slopes became terraced with a beach effect evident at various operating depths.

Mosquito control at Charleswood included insecticide applications as well as weed and grass control. Monitoring of larval and adult species was also practised. The effectiveness of these control measures is evident by the fact that no larval development was observed in the ponds, and the number of adult mosquitoes trapped at the pond site was far less than at any other monitoring point in the city.

Area IV: West Coast

In British Columbia waste stabilization pond operating data are available from three ponds, each located within a different climatic region. One of these ponds is located at the city of Courtenay, another at Kamloops, and the other at Dawson Creek. Since winters in the southern coastal region of British Columbia are moderated by the Pacific Ocean, winter storage is not necessary; therefore, little distinction exists between winter and summer pond operating practices.

Waste stabilization ponds in British Columbia are loaded either continuously or intermittently. The loading procedure depends upon the series or parallel operation. The pond system at Kamloops is operated in parallel and each of the two 25-acre ponds is loaded intermittently. There is no recirculation of waste within the Kamloops treatment system. At Dawson Creek the treatment system is operated in series and the ponds are loaded continuously. Although there is no recirculation within the Dawson Creek pond system, the influent may be interchanged between series of connected cells.

Loading Rates

The rate of application of the organic load onto waste stabilization ponds in British Columbia varies with the type of pond and the climate. The anaerobic ponds within the Dawson Creek waste treatment system have been loaded at a rate of 200 lbs BOD_5/acre/day. The organic matter treated in this system consists of a mixture of industrial and domestic wastes. The facultative pond in the treatment systems at Courtenay and at Kamloops each receive an organic load of 42 lbs BOD/acre/day.

Efficiencies

BOD_5 removal efficiencies within waste stabilization pond treatment systems in British Columbia vary between 75 and 90 percent. The systems at Courtenay and Kamloops reportedly have BOD_5 removal rates of 76 and 87 percent, respectively. The treatment system at Dawson Creek has an overall efficiency rate of approximately 90 percent.

Odors

There were very few reports of odor emanating from waste stabilization ponds in British Columbia. The few that were reported were associated with the spring changeover period. There odors were identified as hydrogen sulfide gas. Also, the only odors reported were from anaerobic or deep ponds within the system.

Other Observations

Some erosion problems have occurred at the Kamloops and Dawson Creek installations; however, this appears to be controlled by riprapping the interior face of the dyke. Spraying to control weeds and the use of other chemicals to minimize mosquito breeding is practiced continuously at Kamloops.

Area V: North

A single-cell, facultative waste stabilization pond treatment system is at Inuvik, North West Territories. This pond is used to treat domestic wastes from the community of 1,500 persons. The surface area of this installation is 43.5 acres. The liquid depth varies between 2.0 and 5.7 feet, thus providing a detention period of approximately 6 months.

Loading Rates

This pond is continuously loaded at a volumetric rate of 180,000 Imperial gallons per day. Since the influent BOD_5 is approximately 210 mg/l, the organic load rate is about 8.5 lb BOD_5/acre/day.

Efficiencies

The BOD_5 concentration in the pond effluent has averaged approximately 40 mg/l, thus treatment system efficiency, based on BOD_5 removal, is about 80 percent.

Odors

Odors have been observed from this pond at various times of the year. Usually, these odors have been mild; however, during spring breakup the odors generally increase in strength.

Other Observations

The pond remains green throughout the summer months with an occasional occurrence of blue-green algal blooms. Flies and mosquitoes have been observed during open water periods. During the summer months, when the daylight hours are long, residual dissolved oxygen within the pond has been high.

CONCLUSIONS

The waste stabilization pond form of waste treatment is gaining acceptance in Canada. The trend is to use this form of treatment for treating domestic wastes from large cities.

Generally, the efficiency of this form of waste treatment is influenced significantly in Canada by climatic conditions.

Summertime BOD_5 removal efficiencies vary between 65 and 90 percent, while winter efficiencies vary between 0 and 55 percent. Coliform reduction in excess of 99 percent has been observed within waste stabilization ponds in Canada.

Waste stabilization ponds in the Prairie provinces and in the Northwest Territories, where there are severe winters, are designed for complete winter storage. Elsewhere in Canada ponds are generally continuously discharging. Waste stabilization pond treatment systems, consisting of short detention (anaerobic) ponds in series with long detention (facultative) ponds, are also gaining acceptance in the Prairie provinces.

Pond organic loading rates generally vary between 10 and 45 lbs BOD_5/acre/day.

Odors are commonly associated with the break-up of ice during the springtime on ponds in the Prairie provinces.

REFERENCES

(1) Ballance, R. C. *Report on Condition of Sewage Treatment Facilities in New Brunswick*. New Brunswick Water Authority (September 1963).

(2) Barnes, B. B., and J. Lockhart. New Brunswick Water Authority, Federiction, N. B. Personal Correspondence and Questionnaires (December 1965).

(3) Bates, J. S. "Special Characteristics of Industrial Wastes." Presented at the Pollution Control Course, Nova Scotia Technical College (June 7–11, 1965).

(4) Cameron, A. J. "Sewage Oxidation Ponds, New Brunswick, Canada," *Proceedings*, Symposium on Waste Treatment by Oxidation Ponds, Nagpur, India (October 29–30, 1963).

(5) Champion, D. C., Division of Sanitary Engineering, Prince Edward Island Department of Health, Charlottetown, P.E.I. Personal Correspondence and Questionnaires (November 1965).

(6) Edmonds, W. R., Public Health Engineering Division, Department of National Health and Welfare, Ottawa, Ontario, Personal Correspondence and Questionnaires (November 1965).

(7) Forsberg, C. R., M. D. Prosko, V. J. Sentis, and S. S. Strilchuk. "Aerobic and Anaerobic Waste Stabilization Ponds," University of Saskatchewan (March 1964).

(8) Harris, A. J. "Practical Aspects of Oxidation Ponds." Presented at the Symposium on Waste Water Treatment for Small Municipalities, Ecole Polytechnique, Montreal (November 19–20, 1965).

(9) Higgins, P. M. "Problems and New Developments in the Lagooning of Wastes." Presented to the Canadian Institute of Public Health Inspectors Dominion Conference, Winnipeg, Manitoba (July 13, 1965).

(10) Higo, T. T. *A Study of the Operation of Sewage Ponds in the Province of Alberta.* Edmonton: Department of Public Health (March 1965).

(11) Hogge, H. L., Department of Public Health, Edmonton, Alberta. Personal Correspondence and Questionnaires (December 1965).

(12) Hogge, H. L., and S. L. Dobko. "Use of Sewage Ponds in Alberta, Canada," *Proceedings*, Waste Stabilization Lagoons Symposium, Kansas City, Missouri (August 1960). Public Health Service Publication No. 872 (August 1961).

(13) Hogge, H. L., *et al. A Study of the Operation of Sewage Ponds in the Province of Alberta.* Edmonton: Department of Public Health (September 1961).

(14) Keenan, C. J., British Columbia Pollution Control Board, Victoria, British Columbia, Personal Correspondence and Questionnaires (January 1966).

(15) Penman, A., and P. M. Higgins, The Metropolitan Corporation of Greater Winnipeg, Waterworks and Waste Disposal Division, Winnipeg, Manitoba. Personal Correspondence and Questionnaire (November 1965).

(16) Prescott, M. H., Division of Sanitation, Department of Public Health, Regina, Saskatchewan. Personal Correspondence (December 1965).

(17) Putnam, D. F. *Canadian Regions—a Geography of Canada,* Toronto: J. M. Dent and Sons (Canada) Ltd. (1963).

(18) *Report on Winter Operation of Sewage Lagoons in Manitoba.* Bureau of Public Health Engineering, Province of Manitoba (December 1961).

(19) *Suggested Standards for Sewage Lagoons for the Use of Consulting Engineers Submitting Reports to the Manitoba Department of Health.* Winnipeg, Man. (ES 145) (March 1964).

(20) Thon, J. *Experience with Municipal Waste Stabilization Ponds in the Province of Ontario.* Ontario Water Resources Research Publication No. 7, Toronto (June 1964).

(21) Wigglesworth, A. M., Nova Scotia Water Authority, Halifax, N. S. Personal Correspondence and Questionnaire (December 1965).

EXTRA-DEEP PONDS[1]

Alberto M. Wachs
Israel Institute of Technology, Haifa, Israel

Andre Berend
Water Planning for Israel, Ltd., Tel Aviv, Israel

INTRODUCTION

In order to obtain information on the performance of ponds having depths considerably greater than those generally used, an experimental unit was built by Tahal, Ltd., adjacent to those treating the wastewater of Ashkelon in Israel. The study was related to the feasibility of using lagoons in irregular terrain, with depressions that would cause depths of up to 5 m. to occur in certain zones. In that project (1) lagoons of this type would be part of multi-cell serial systems including polishing ponds of conventional depth, producing effluents suitable for ground water recharge through spreading on dune-sand basins. The shape of the experimental pond is that of an inverted truncated pyramid of square base, with a depth of 5 m. above the latter. The area at the top is close to one half hectare, and because of the slope of the embankments approximately one half of the pond has the maximum depth of 5 m. The inlet and the outlet are at opposite sides of the pond. The pond is fed with the effluent of an anaerobic pond, one of three that receive raw sewage from the city of Ashkelon (Fig. 172). Five sampling columns were anchored by concrete blocks at the bottom of the pond, one of them at the center and the others close to the angles of the square base. To each column five plastic sampling tubes were attached, thus making it possible to obtain samples at 0.5, 1, 2, 3, and 4 meters from the surface. This system has been described in detail elsewhere (2).

THERMAL CHARACTERISTICS AND EFFECTS

Results of temperature measurements corresponding to various depths show that marked thermal gradients exist in the pond during what can be conventionally described as the "warm season." This corresponds mostly to what constitutes usually the "dry season" in Israel, with relatively high temperatures and scanty or no rains. At the time of the study reported here, the "warm season" lasted from sometime in May to sometime in September. The other major period, conventionally described as the "cold season," corresponded to the rest of a twelve-month cycle, and while it lasted only very small or no thermal gradients were observed below the upper layer.

Figure 173 shows temperature profiles corresponding to the average of temperatures measured at different depths during a winter month (January 1963) and a summer month (July 1964). It can be seen that in the latter case a difference of 11°C. exists between the surface and the 4-m. depth, while in the former the temperature remains essentially the same at all depths.

Temperature profiles obtained at two different times within a 24-hour period, the first one in the early afternoon and the other in the small hours of the morn-

[1]The term "extra-deep ponds" was suggested by Professor Gloyna. In this text it refers to ponds having a depth of at least 2.40 m. (8 feet).

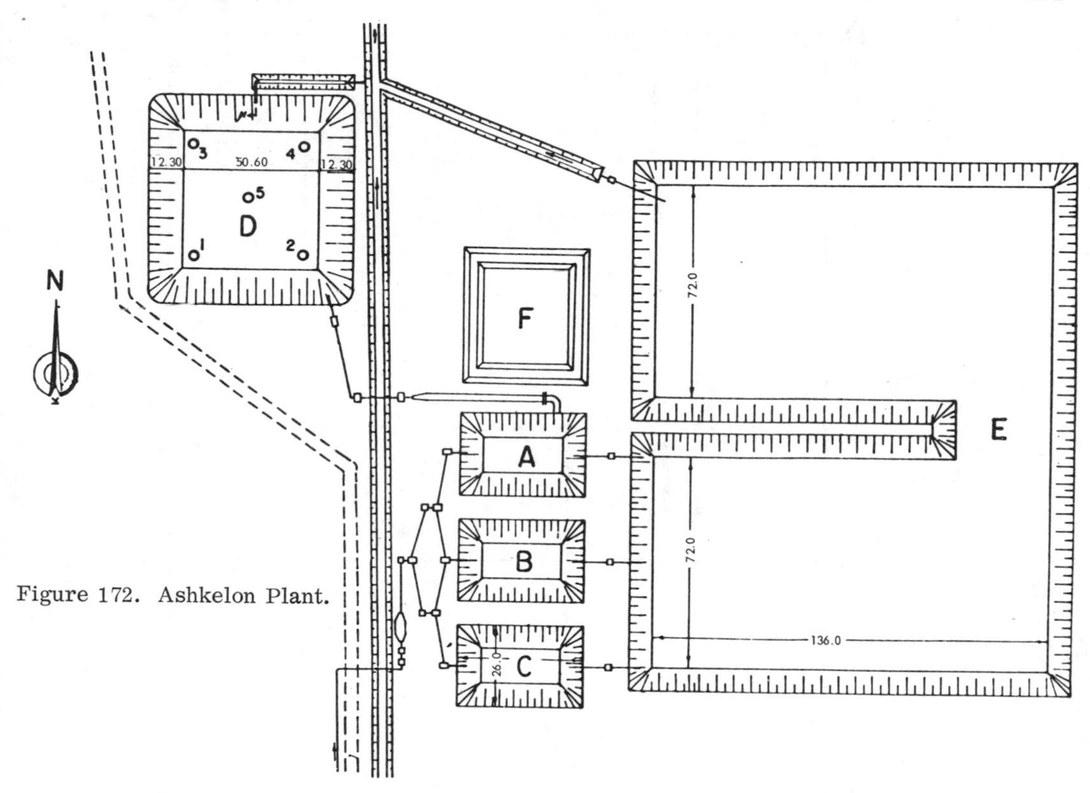

Figure 172. Ashkelon Plant.

ing, are shown in Figure 174 for summer and winter conditions. The Graph A shows that although in the "cold season" the top layer is warmed up at daytime, due to solar radiation, the heat absorbed is not enough to produce a thermal gradient below that layer, and that at night temperatures become practically the same throughout the depth of the pond. In Graph B, corresponding to a "warm season" day, it can be seen that although at night the temperature of the top layer has dropped to that of the subjacent layer (depth 0.5 m.), a marked temperature gradient subsists below that depth.

Of particular importance are the nature and rate of the changes occurring in the pond liquid when "stratification" corresponding to the temperature gradient disappears at the end of the "warm season," in what can be described as a limnological "turnover."

Table 65 shows that when that happened in September 1964, the concentration of sulphides at the surface raised sharply and the *p*H dropped considerably. The net effect of both changes, brought about by the "turnover," was a sharp increase in the concentration of hydrogen sulfide at the upper part of the pond. However, no objectionable odors were recorded at this time.

ALGAE AND DISSOLVED OXYGEN

After the "start-up" period, microalgae were found at all depths during the operation of the pond. *Chlorella* species were present in considerable numbers at all depths and times, while *Euglena* species occurred mostly during the "warm season" and at the upper layer of the pond between the surface and 0.5-m. depth. Other unidentified species, one of them a blue-green algae, were also occasionally observed.

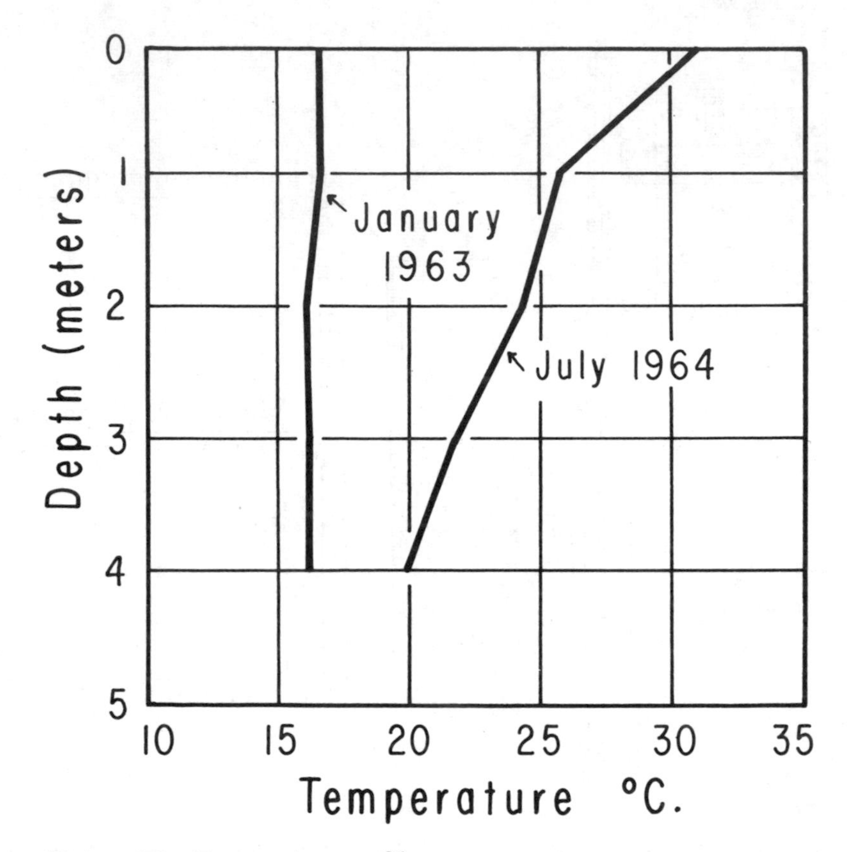

Figure 173. Temperature profiles.

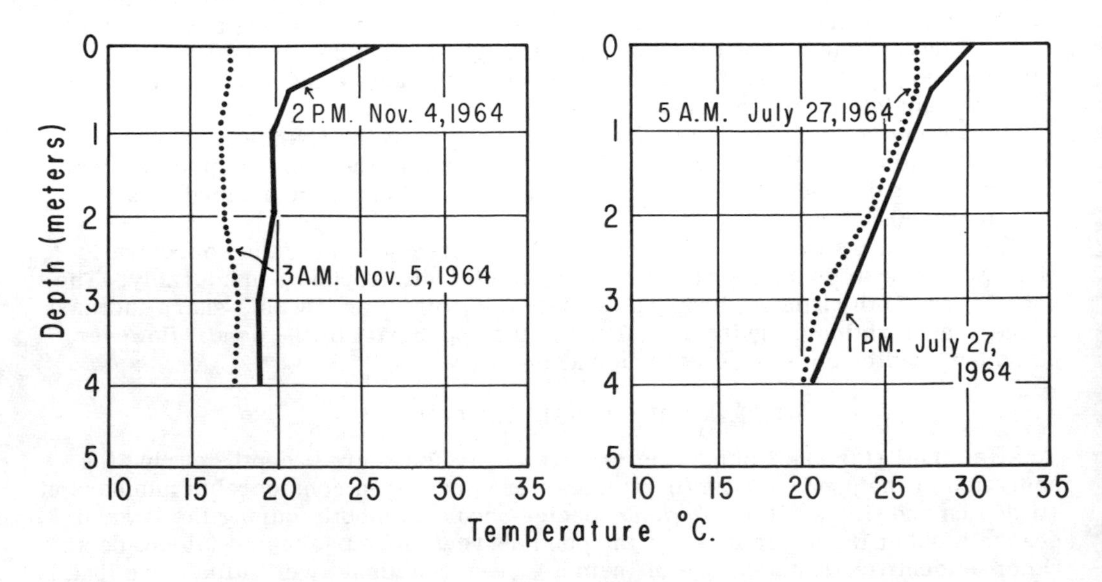

Figure 174. Summer and winter temperature profiles.

TABLE 65

CHANGES IN HYDROGEN SULFIDE CONCENTRATION AT SURFACE OF POND LIQUID*

Date	Temperature °C.	Sulfides mg/l	*p*H	Conversion Factor	Hydrogen Sulfide mg/l
August 24	31.0	0.53	8.8	0.008	0.004
September 2	32.0	0.60	8.6	0.014	0.008
September 9	26.0	8.80	7.5	0.140	1.230
September 14	27.5	4.10	7.3	0.230	0.940
September 24	29.0	0.46	7.8	0.073	0.034
September 30	29.5	0.13	7.8	0.073	0.009

*Data correspond to samples taken at Sampling Station 5 (center of pond).

Because of the presence of mixed algal populations, comprising species of various sizes, the determination of volatile suspended matter could be considered, in this secondary pond, to give more adequate information on total algal concentrations than calculations based on microscopic counts. On the basis of this determination, confirmed in this case by algal counts, it was found that during the "warm season" the concentration of algae at the surface layer of the pond was considerably higher than those at other depths. For surface examples the average value (20 samples) was 111 mg. per liter, while for samples obtained at 0.5 m. below the surface, the average value was 67 mg. per liter. At times when peak concentrations of algae occurred, that difference could be striking, as illustrated in Graph A of Figure 175, showing a drop of more than 100 mg. per liter of volatile suspended solids between the surface and the 1-m. depth in samples taken at 1 p.m. Fluctuations observed during 24-hour periods did not seem to follow regular patterns, but indicate that part of the algae settle to the lower part of the pond.

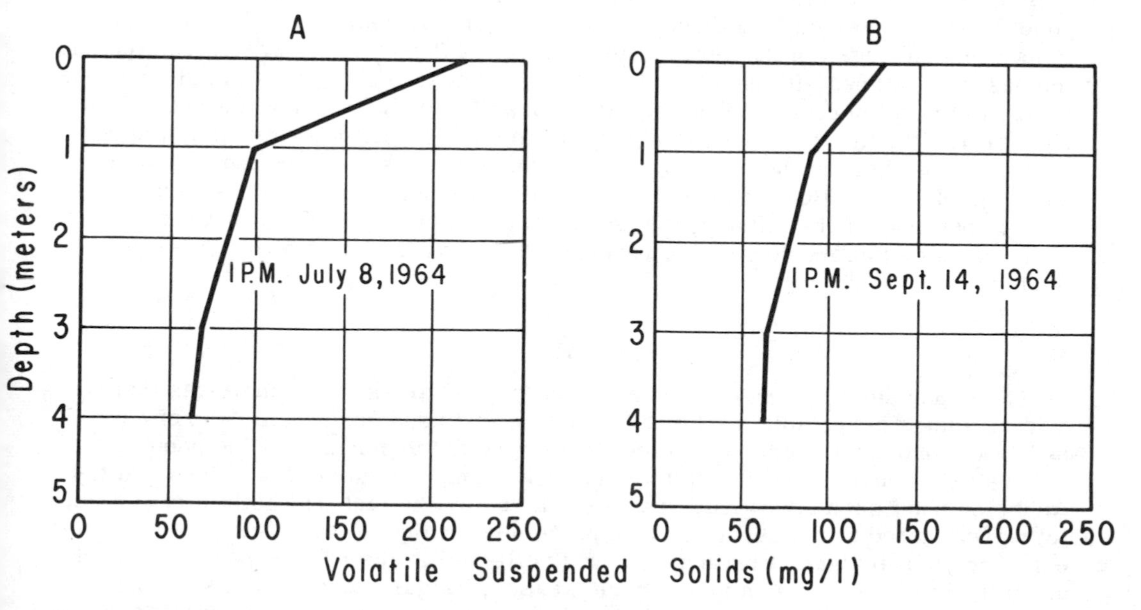

Figure 175. Algal concentration versus depth.

During the "cold season," averages of volatile suspended solids concentrations corresponding to different depths did not show significant differences. Although on certain days during the fall a difference could be observed at daytime between the surface value and the 1-m. depth value, as shown in Graph B, that difference disappeared at night.

Dissolved oxygen, at the loadings and during the "warm season," was found only in the top liquid layer between the surface and 0.5 m. below it. At or near the surface the concentration increased during the hours of morning and early afternoon, reaching, in summer, values that exceeded from two to four times the saturation concentration. Within one or two hours after sunset, the concentration fell to zero.

At the loadings under which the pond was operated during the "cold season," the presence of dissolved oxygen at the surface of the pond was observed only eight times in fourteen observations, and limited then to a few hours of daytime, although a considerable algal population existed throughout that "season" at all depths of the pond.

BOD REMOVAL

Detailed information on the performance of the pond in relation to BOD loadings and removal has been given elsewhere (2). Here some interesting aspects of BOD removal will be reviewed.

During a certain period of operation of the pond in 1963 (March through May), when the applied loading was about 100 kg/hectare/day, the removal of BOD computed on the basis of unfiltered effluent varied around 60 percent. When the loading was increased in June that figure showed a marked decline, possibly due to significant increases in algal population resulting from higher temperatures. It must be remembered that the effluent was withdrawn through an outlet located at the surface of the pond liquid, where algae concentrations were the highest.

When controlled operation of the pond was re-established in the spring of 1964, the BOD of the effluent was determined for both filtered and unfiltered samples. It is of interest to note that although several different loadings were applied to the pond during the period May through September of that year, no significant variations were observed in the percentage removal of BOD when it was calculated on the basis of filtered effluent (Fig. 176). During most of that period the figure was rarely below 80 percent. When the removal was calculated using the BOD of the unfiltered effluent, the result, to a very large extent, was determined by the concentration of algae in the effluent. When a marked peak of algae population occurred in July, the BOD of the unfiltered effluent became in fact considerably higher than that of the influent; the percentage removal of BOD at that time, however, remained above 80 percent when calculated on the basis of the filtered effluent.

SUMMARY

The experience gained with the extra-deep pond at Ashkelon indicates that when loadings acceptable for Israel's climate are used during the "warm season," a pronounced thermal gradient will cause the upper part of the pond to behave as a conventional facultative pond "floating" on an anaerobic one. In the Ashkelon pond such stratification was enhanced by the fact that both inlet and outlet were located at the surface. This placement of the outlet resulted in an effluent very rich in algae, a feature that was reflected in the relatively high BOD of unfiltered samples. During the "warm season," algal concentrations significantly lower were observed at or below 1-m. depths; therefore, an outlet located

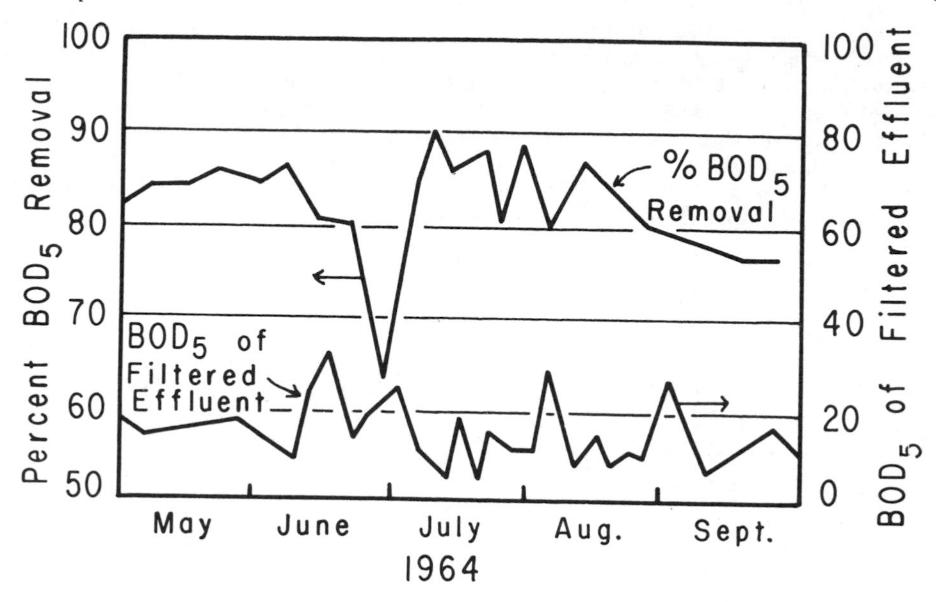

Figure 176. BOD removal.

at such depths could produce a better effluent from the point of view of algal densities, although it would be deficient in dissolved oxygen at all times.

During the "cold season" the gradient disappears. The intensity of mixing of the pond contents when this happens would be dependent mostly on wind force and on the geometry of the system. With the loadings used in the Ashkelon pond, dissolved oxygen was not always present at the upper part during the "cold season," although considerable algal populations existed at all times.

At some time in the fall a "turnover" occurs, resulting in the mixing of the bottom layers with those near the surface. Although this caused an increase of sulfides concentration and a drop in *p*H at the surface of the pond, no odors were recorded.

Throughout a long period comprising part of the "cold season" and all of the "warm season" the percentage removal of BOD was around 80 percent when calculated on the basis of filtered effluent.

REFERENCES

(1) Amramy, A., B. Caspi, and A. Melamed. *Dan Region Sewage Reclamation Project; Sewage Stabilization Pond Design*. Tahal (Water Planning for Israel, Ltd.), report P. N. 246 (1962).

(2) Berend, Andre. M. S. Thesis, Sanitary Engineering Laboratories, Technion, Haifa (in Hebrew) (1965).

(3) Amalorpavam, S. "Factors Involved in the Design of Lagoons as Complete Sewage Treatment Works." Symposium on Waste Treatment by Oxidation Ponds, Central Public Health Engineers Research Institute, Nagpur (1963).

(4) Gloyna, E. F. *Waste Stabilization Pond Concepts and Experiences*. World Health Organization, Wastes Disposal Unit, Publication 1 (1965).

(5) Merz, R. C., J. C. Merrell, and R. Stone. "Investigation of Primary Lagoon Treatment at Mojave, California," *Sewage Ind. Wastes, 29*, 115–123 (1957).

(6) Oswald, W. J. *Feasbility of Deep Ponds for the Dan Region Project*. Report to Tahal, Water Planning for Israel Ltd. (1964).
(7) Oswald, W. J., *et al.* "Water Reclamation, Algal Production, and Methane Fermentation in Waste Ponds," *Inter. J. Air Water Poll.*, *7*, 627 (1963).
(8) Parker, C. D. "Microbiological Aspects of Lagoon Treatment," *J. Water Poll. Cont. Fed.*, *34*, 149 (1962).
(9) Parker, C. D., *et al.* "Performance of Large Sewage Lagoons at Melbourne, Australia," *Sewage Ind. Wastes*, *31*, 133–152 (1959).

WASTE STABILIZATION PONDS FOR AGRICULTURAL WASTES

Samuel A. Hart
University of California, Davis, California

Marvin E. Turner
Kansas State University, Manhattan, Kansas

Today the majority of animals are kept on "factory farms"; hundreds or even thousands of dairy cows, tens of thousands of beef animals, or hundreds of thousands of chickens are kept in close confinement on small acreages. The quantity of manure produced is prodigious, and its disposal is a serious problem.

It is natural that agriculture would also be interested in waste stabilization ponds, and would attempt to treat and dispose of manure within such ponds. However, there is a most significant difference between stabilization ponds used for sewage and industrial wastewater, and ponds used for the disposal of livestock manures. Sewage and other wastewater ponds must accept large quantities of water polluted relatively lightly with waste organic material—sewage contains but about 0.10 percent solids. The primary purpose of such treatment is disposal of the water or its partial purification. Either there is an effluent, or the ponds are sized so that infiltration and evaporation losses equal inflow.

Manure disposal ponds, in contrast, are expected to accept very large amounts of organic solid matter—often containing barely enough water to get the wastes into the pond. The objective is stabilization and disposal of the organic matter rather than water purification. There is usually no effluent and make-up water is frequently required. The BOD loading rate may be as high as 1,000 to 1,200 pounds/acre/day. Because anaerobic conditions predominate, manure disposal ponds are more appropriately compared to open-topped, unheated, municipal sludge lagoons, or perhaps even to conventional sludge digesters, than they are to sewage stabilization ponds.

CHARACTERISTICS (LITERATURE REVIEW)

A number of Midwestern universities are presently conducting research studies on waste stabilization ponds for livestock manure. In the last two years five independent but related and relevant research studies on ponds for manure disposal have been presented or published (1–6). The individual research papers are a rewarding compendium of information on materials balance, predominant species of microorganisms, excess and deficient mineral balances, effects of antibiotics, and climatological variations.

All the studies recognized that manure stabilization ponds depend upon the anaerobic process to accomplish stabilization. In addition, the degraded manure solids must be stored until such time as they are finally removed. The unanimous consensus was that manure pond design should be based on volume considerations rather than on surface relationships so common to wastewater ponds. Clark (5) concluded that the same criteria used in digester loading—pounds of volatile solids/cubic foot/day—could be used. In searching for alternative measures, Clark had difficulty in measuring the BOD of hog manure fed a high antibiotic ration; he therefore also expressed loadings in pounds of COD (chemical oxygen demand)/cubic foot/day. Hart and Turner (4) pointed out that livestock manures usually contain large quantities of hay stems, grain hulls, and similar nondegradable but volatile organic matter which make the volatile solids/cubic foot/day loading parameter inappropriate. Hart and Turner did not have the antibiotic problem to contend with, and were successful in basing manure pond design on pounds of BOD/cubic foot/day. Similar variations in expressing loading rate found in the other published papers make comparison between results difficult.

The designer of a manure stabilization pond must ultimately size the pond to accommodate a certain number of animals. Thus, loadings should be stated in terms of volume of pond per animal; or, for growing animals, in volume per hundredweight. Table 66 is a summary of animal defecation quantity, and Table 67 is a compilation of manure pond loading rates, recalculated from the aforementioned research papers.

DESIGN CRITERIA

The designer of manure ponds for the farm is concerned with the factors which control the design of practical units, which meet four criteria:

1. Odors must be minimal to nonexistant.
2. Fly and mosquito production must be controllable or must not occur.
3. Pollution of subsurface water supplies through infiltration of pond liquor must be prevented.
4. Appearance must be acceptable, or the pond must be screened and hidden.

The first criterion is directly related to the imposed manure loading, the second to loading and good husbandry, the third to the land upon which the pond is placed and proper physical design, and the fourth to location and loading.

Odors and Loading Rates

Odors constitute an immediate, tangible, and powerful limit to manure disposal pond design and operation. Clark (5), in discussing hog waste stabilization ponds, pointed out that "the 'lagoons', without exception, produced a foul odor . . ." He felt that a rate of 60 cubic feet/100 pounds of live weight was completely inade-

TABLE 66

LIVESTOCK MANURE CHARACTERISTICS

Factor	Poultry	Cattle	Swine
Total solids (TS) in feces and urine, lb/animal-day	0.066	10.440	0.795*
Solids content of freshly collected total sample	23.000	18.000	19.000
Volatile solids (VS) as % of TS	77.500	80.300	78.500
Volatile solids, lb/animal-day	0.051	8.400	0.625*
5-day BOD (mg BOD/mg VS)	0.288	0.183	0.320
5-day BOD (lb O_2/animal-day)	0.015	1.540	0.200
COD (mg COD/mg VS)	1.110	1.000	1.200
COD (lb O_2/animal-day)	0.057	8.380	0.750*
Nitrogen, as N, in fresh manure (% of TS)	5.400	3.700	4.000
NH_4 nitrogen (% of total N)	74.000	—	75.000
Phosporous, as P_2O_5 (% of TS)	4.600	1.100	3.100
Potassium, as K (% of TS)	2.100	3.000	1.400
Volatile acids, as acetic (% of TS)	5.800	3.200	4.800

*Clark's values from extensive farm testing are 0.50 pounds total solids, 0.35 pounds volatile solids, and 0.47 pounds COD/150-pound animal/day.

Values are based on a 5-pound chicken (the usual laying hen), a 1,000-pound bovine (small dairy cow or marketable beef animal), and a 100-pound pig (half-grown to market size).

TABLE 67

MANURE STABILIZATION POND LOADING RATES

Researcher(s), Location	Recorded Loading Rate	Recalculated Loading Rate cu ft/animal	Evaluation of Performance
	SWINE		
Clark, Illinois	4–20 ft^2/hog, 3–10 ft. deep	40–60 cu ft/hog	Malodorous, unsatisfactory
	550 hogs/acre-year, 5–7 ft. deep	475 cu ft/hog	Satisfactory!
Dornbush & Anderson, South Dakota	130–170 cu ft/hog	130–170 cu ft/hog	Satisfactory
Hart & Turner, California	45 & 67 cu ft/100-lb pig	45 & 67 cu ft/100-lb animal	Somewhat, but not excessively, odorous
	124 cu ft/100-lb pig	124 cu ft/100-lb animal	Satisfactory
	POULTRY		
Dornbush & Anderson, South Dakota	3.64 ft^2/chicken, less than 2 ft. deep	5.5 cu ft/hen	"Vile odors"
	3.64 ft^2/chicken, 4 ft. deep	14.6 cu ft/hen	Much better
Cooper, California	575 lb BOD/acre-day; 1.09 ft^2/hen, 5–6 ft. deep	6 cu ft/hen	"No odor"
Hart & Turner, California	8.35 cu ft/hen	8.35 cu ft/hen	Very malodorous
	13.6 cu ft/hen	13.6 cu ft/hen	Satisfactory
	49.8 cu ft/hen	49.8 cu ft/hen	Algal-laden pond, satisfactory but overdesigned
	CATTLE		
Witzell *et al.*, Wisconsin	60 ft. top diameter 40 ft. bottom diameter 5 ft. deep—6 bulls	1,547 cu ft/bull	Satisfactory
Hart & Turner, California	795, 1,000, & 1,830 cu. ft. / 1,000-lb. animal	795, 1,000, & 1,830 cu. ft. / 1,000-lb. animal	Satisfactory

quate, and that something like 475 cubic foot/hog was needed to prevent odors. Hart and Turner (4) felt that 67 cubic feet, or even only 45 cubic feet/100 pounds of animal produced conditions not particularly odorous and that a rate of 124 cubic feet of pond/100-pound hog was very satisfactory. Climate, nearness to neighbors, and similar judgment decisions will have to be applied to pond design.

The research results for poultry manure ponds show some of this same variation. Dornbush and Anderson (1) experimented upon a malodorous poultry manure pond in which 5.5 cubic feet of pond volume were alloted per chicken. After increasing the volume to 14.6 cubic feet/bird by deepening the pond and diverting some manure, the odor was much reduced and the pond was considered acceptable. Hart and Turner (3) found that a laboratory poultry manure pond at 13.6

cubic feet/bird was satisfactory, thus substantiating Dornbush and Anderson. But Cooper (6) appraised a Northern California poultry manure pond in which a volume of 6.0 cubic feet was allowed each bird, and the pond was deemed most satisfactory. In all probability, laboratory units do not properly duplicate farm ponds, and the milder climate of California improves biological activity over that of South Dakota. Apparently, 6 to 12 cubic feet of pond volume ought to be allowed per chicken, depending upon the geographical location.

Somewhat more consistency exists in the volume requirements for cattle manure ponds, as reported in the two studies with this manure. Hart and Turner felt that a rate of 800 cubic feet/1000-pound animal (their maximum loading rate) was satisfactory, and suggested that even less volume would probably also work. Witzell *et al.*, in Wisconsin, experimented with a pond in which 1,547 cubic feet were alloted per bull (which must have weighed 1,600 pounds). The climatic difference could well account for this small difference.

When one calculates the proper dimensions to meet his needs, he is amazed as to the large volume. Serious consideration ought therefore to be given to reducing the quantity of manure put into the pond. Such a procedure was followed on the satisfactory hog manure ponds analyzed by Clark, and was part of the procedure indicated by Dornbush and Anderson. For instance, it is often possible to screen out, settle out, or separate out half the fecal matter and handle it in the solid condition. Then only the urine and manure-polluted washwater need go into the pond. Similarly, at certain times of the year it is often possible to spread all the manure onto cropland, using the pond for manure disposal when fields are not available.

In summary, odors are unquestionably a major criterion for manure pond acceptability. As expected, minimal loading (maximum volume per animal) is necessary for non-odorous performance. Diverting manure, and increasing pond volume are the two ways to combat this odor problem.

Fly and Mosquito Production

One of the reasons for considering manure ponds is the hope of reducing fly breeding on the farm. Fresh wet piles of manure are a prime breeding media for many species of nuisance flies. Submerged manure offers no such potential. Hart and Turner appear to have made the most comprehensive study of fly and mosquito production from manure stabilization ponds. They concluded that mosquito production is possible only in very minimally loaded ponds which are impractical for agriculture. They found that manure ponds did support the drone fly larvae, *Tubifera tenax*. The adult drone fly, however, is a flower seeker, does not enter houses or bother humans and animals, and is not presently considered a nuisance fly. Control measures to prevent drone fly emergence were not conducted, but since the larvae must seek a dry environment for pupating, control at the pond bank or on any floating crust appears feasible.

Infiltration Problems

Hart and Turner, who have evaluated the problem of infiltration in their pilot ponds (units 4 feet in diameter and 8 feet deep), found infiltration losses varying from 18.2 to 45 percent of the influent inorganic solids. Admittedly, their ponds were small with a large surface effect, and were placed on a rather permeable sandy loam soil. But biological sealing had been depended upon to quickly control seepage, and this did not occur. After two years of continuous operation, the infiltration loss (total loss less evaporation) amounted to over one half inch per day. The total volume of water gravitating to underground water supplies is likely to be large with any stabilization pond. Although microbes and much of the organic matter is filtered out by passage through soil, salts and taste-producing organic material could well pollute subsurface water supplies. Many states regulate the placement, construction, and operation of sewage and industrial wastewater stabilization ponds to prevent this condition. Unquestionably, agricultural ponds will and should come under similar control. In any event, a manure pond designer is well advised to locate the pond on impermeable soil or to expend the dollars and effort necessary to line the bottom and sides with impermeable barriers.

Appearance

No manure pond can be expected to have pristine beauty, and may even be an eyesore.

Dairy manure is high in lignaceous material—ground hay stems and grain hulls. These quickly float and form a crust on the surface of the pond. This is actually desirable, since the crust dries on the surface, and the appearance is acceptable, if not aesthetic.

Hog manure ponds can vary from a clean-surfaced, black-liquored, swamp water appearance to a crusted-over, foul-appearing hole. If no bedding or detritus is allowed to enter the pond, the appearance will be far more acceptable than if the pond is used as a receiver for all manner of wastes.

Feathers will always float on a poultry manure stabilization pond. But more important, poultry ponds develop a characteristic color, depending upon the loading. At low loadings, the green color of algal-laden water is typical. When the loading is somewhere between 6 and 12 cubic feet per chicken, the pond usually develops a vivid reddish hue. Such units are often called "pink ponds." Cooper (6), who studied this, attributes it to the photosynthetic, anaerobic, sulfur-fixing bacterium, *Thiopedia rosea.* An even more highly loaded poultry manure pond does not turn pink, but remains a foul dank brown, with the inevitable floating crust of feathers.

Manure ponds are usually put on the "back 40," away from the more acceptable farming operations. This is appropriate, and certainly such ponds should be screened and fenced—both for aesthetic purposes and to prevent accidents.

FURTHER CONSIDERATIONS IN DESIGNING AND OPERATING MANURE PONDS

Too many farmers have the idea that stabilization ponds are the utopian answer to manure disposal. Field experience and research results indicate this is not quite so. Unquestionably, ponds are simple and economical to construct and to operate, and when properly designed and maintained, will satisfactorily handle livestock manure.

As pointed out earlier, the pond should be designed on a volume basis. Furthermore, once the volume is decided upon, the pond should be made deep. A deep pond will be more effective in keeping the biologically-active manure solids on the bottom undergoing strict anaerobic degradation. The surface will be less polluted and thus less odorous. Stabilization ponds should be 10 or more feet deep, if infiltration loss is not encouraged by such depths, and if it is safely fenced to prevent accidents.

In the summer a properly operating lagoon will evidence a continual agitation and upwelling of sludge as gasification takes place. This phenomenon does not produce bad odors; rather, digestion, stabilization, and innocuousness are promoted through this action. In winter there is no such sludge lifting, and it is important to have the lagoon deep so that the fresh manure solids can be properly submerged and the surface remain less polluted.

Manure should be discharged to the center of the pond, and preferably under water. This causes maximum mixing of the fresh manure with the active anaerobic culture on the bottom, thus promoting rapid stabilization. Practical considerations generally preclude this, and surface discharge is preferred to prevent ice blockage. An elevated trough is frequently used to convey the manure slurry to the central area of the pond. Wastes should not be discharged to the pond along a bank, because proper mixing is not obtained.

Manure is only stabilized in a pond, it does not disappear. The degraded manure becomes a sludge. Depending on the loading rate, these manures will accumulate and eventually consume a major part of the pond volume. There are field reports, varying from inconsequential build-up to complete filling of the pond in only one or two years. Obviously the build-up is a function of the volume of pond per animal unit, and of the loss of solids through biological degradation and infiltration loss. Hart and Turner made a materials balance on their pilot poultry ponds to evaluate sludge build-up. When infiltration losses are prevented, the degradation loss will be similar to the solids loss in a sludge digester—between 30 and 50 percent of the imposed total solids weight. Further, typical pond sludges vary between 6 and 13 percent solids (87 and 90 percent water). Poultry manure sludge is thickest, and heavier loading rates increase the solids content. On this basis, the sludge blanket build-up can be expected to be about 2 cubic/feet/chicken per year, 20 cubic feet/100-pound hog per year, and 250 cubic feet/1000-pound bovine per year. As the sludge builds up within the pond it becomes heavier in solids content, so that one cannot divide these figures into the design volume to determine cleanout frequency, although it is at least double the value from such a computation.

The typical method used to clean a pond is to pump out the supernatant liquor and as much sludge as possible and spread it on fields by sprinkler irrigation. Heavier sludge is removed by a honey wagon, or the sludge is allowed to dry and then it is mucked out with tractors.

The water level in a manure pond should always be maintained at the design level. Frequently this means that make-up water will be required, and it should be ungrudgingly supplied.

However, the pond should be designed and located so there is no surface effluent, and no uncontrolled runoff of water into the pond. The surface liquor of a manure pond is always high in BOD, often as strong as 1,000 to 1,500 milligrams per liter—more polluted than raw sewage.

The physical construction of a manure pond should consider infiltration, as mentioned before. Side slopes of the banks can be those typical of wastewater ponds, 1 vertical and 2 to $2\frac{1}{2}$ horizontal for the water side, and 1 vertical and $1\frac{1}{2}$ to 2 horizontal for the outside berm. Slope depends on the stability of the soil. Wind-caused waves can erode the banks on large ponds, and protection by ripraping or waterline logs may be appropriate.

Weeds should be controlled along the banks, since such growth harbors insects and further detracts from pond appearance.

There appears to be a definite place for manure stabilization ponds in the management of livestock manure. It is important, however, that the farmer planning to use a pond not expect miracles, but rather recognizes their potential and their limitation. With proper construction, proper loading rate, and proper operation, such manure disposal ponds can be satisfactory.

ACKNOWLEDGMENT

This research was supported in part by Grant EF-265, "Sanitary Engineering of Livestock Manures," from the Division of Environmental Engineering and Food Protection, United States Public Health Service.

REFERENCES

(1) Dornbush, J. N., and J. R. Anderson. "Lagooning of Livestock Wastes in South Dakota." 19th Annual Industrial Waste Conference, Purdue University, Lafayette, Indiana (May 1964).

(2) Witzell, S. A., E. McCoy, and R. Lehner. "What are the Chemical and Biological Reactions when Lagoons are Used for Cattle," Paper 64–417. American Society of Agricultural Engineers, St. Joseph, Michigan (1964).

(3) Hart, S. A., and M. E. Turner. "Poultry Manure Lagoons." Second National Symposium on Poultry Industry Waste Management, University of Nebraska, Lincoln, Nebraska (May 1964).

(4) Hart, S. A., and M. E. Turner. "Lagoons for Livestock Manure," *J. Water Poll. Cont. Fed.*, *37*, 1578 (November 1965).

(5) Clark, C. E. "Hog Waste Disposal by Lagooning," *J. Sanit. Engr. Div. ASCE*, *SA6*, 27 (December 1965).

(6) Cooper, R. C., W. J. Oswald, and J. C. Bronson. "Treatment of Organic Industrial Wastes by Lagooning." 20th Annual Industrial Waste Conference, Purdue University, Lafayette, Indiana (May 1965).

STABILIZATION PONDS IN THE CANNING INDUSTRY

Robert A. Canham
Water Pollution Control Federation, Washington, D.C.

The principal motivation for the use of ponds in the canning industry has been to intercept and hold the waste for long periods of time, usually a season, rather than to allow for continuous discharge to the watercourse. Therefore the concept has been that of lagoons; as a result, most of this discussion necessarily will concern itself with the term *lagoons* instead of *stabilization ponds*. This premise is based on the fundamental differences in design criteria developed for domestic wastewater stabilization ponds and those guiding the installations for canning waste lagoons. This difference centers around the organic and hydraulic loading design factors used for domestic wastewater stabilization ponds which allow for continuous discharge, whereas canning waste lagoons are designed for storage.

The canning industry was one of the early users of the lagoon method of waste treatment. In reality the industry regarded this as disposal rather than treatment. For that matter this philosophy remains in the industry. This fact is important because it demonstrates that in most instances management has not reached the point of realization that treatment of wastewater is a fundamental part of production.

EARLY RESEARCH IN CANNING WASTE

Early published work in methods of treating canning waste dates back to 1910 (1). The earliest work was aimed at utilization of the existing biological and physical methods of treatment otherwise used for domestic wastewater. Examples of this work include reports by Illinois (2), Michigan (3), Wisconsin (4), Ohio (5), New York (6), and Warrick, McKee, Wirth, and Sanborn (7). Although experimental work was carried on in various agricultural states, few full-scale installations developed, because of the resulting unattractive economics and the lack of enforcement. As might be expected most of this work was stimulated by those agricultural states with heavy concentrations of the industry.

The perennial basic problem of the canning industry has been that the processing plant usually is located in a rural community or at best in a small town. Therefore the amount and character of the wastewater is overwhelming in relation to that of the community. The seasonal nature of most of the industry also has imposed a hardship on both the industry and the community as regards the waste. These factors contributed heavily to the problems of developing and implementing suitable waste treatment methods, both from the industry and the regulatory standpoints. They remain today as factors.

EARLY LAGOONS

Lagoons were used in the canning industry as long ago as the early 1930's (8). It was recognized that the utilization of land for organically strong wastes was potentially a favorable method of handling. However, the early attempts, such as that at Markesan, Wisconsin, in 1932 (8), were directed at rapid soil absorption of the wastewater. In some instances where the discharge ponds were in areas of very porous soil or gravel the results were encouraging. Such conditions were limited, however, and as a result at most locations the solids in the waste quickly clogged the soil and the sites became lagoons instead of seepage beds. The first sites were chosen as convenient as possible to the processing plant, and as a result of the high organic content odor became intolerable to the point of total discouragement of the method.

These experiences led to the realization that the concept of massive soil absorption by discharging wastewater into a pond was impractical. Therefore the logical development was toward methods of odor control. When compared with the results and the costs of biological treatment the use of land remained attractive as a method, despite the odor problems.

SOLIDS SEPARATION

One of the earliest requirements for handling the waste prior to discharge to lagoons was the utilization of solids separation at the factory. Various types of screens were developed in the early years and remain in almost universal use today, essentially unchanged. They remove the gross solids and some of the suspended matter but allow great quantities of suspended solids to pass through. Most states specify the provision of screening as the first requirement in their regulations covering canning waste.

In general two types of screens have been used: rotary and vibrating. The rotary screen is a slowly rotating cylinder which receives the waste inside. The liquid passes by gravity through the screen which forms the outside surface of the cylinder. The cylinder is mounted nearly horizontal and those solids retained inside are conveyed to a collector. Vibrating screens use a flat wire surface mounted on a slight slope, and utilize an eccentrically mounted shaft to shake the screen surface. Smaller openings than those in rotary screens are common. For instance, the common range of sizes in vibrating screens is from 20- to 40-mesh, whereas, the openings in rotary screens consistently are larger. The waste is fed to the high end of the screen and the solid separation is accelerated by the vibration. Solids are retained on the top surface and work their way to the free end where they drop off into a conveyor. Blinding can occur by overloading or by unusual characteristics of the waste such as high fiber content. When this happens the screen is of little use.

Rotary screens are somewhat less of a maintenance problem but also are less efficient in terms of solids removal. Conversely, vibrating screens are more troublesome from a maintenance standpoint.

Variations of these basic screen types have been used with limited success but fundamentally little effort has been aimed at improvement of the equipment for forty years. In a recent survey of screening, it was pointed out (9) that it was necessary to refer to reports of work done in 1926–1930 (5, 6) to locate published information on screen performance. These results generally are valid today and emphasize that as a method of treatment screening indeed is unimpressive. For example, the early work reported that in handling pea waste, 20-mesh screens could be expected to remove between 30 and 50 percent of the solids. This performance assumes trouble-free operation, which is unrealistic in practice.

Comparative solids removal data for coarse stationary screening vs. mechanical screening are not readily available, but from a visual examination of waste from various canning operations it is evident that in many instances coarse stationary screens would remove a substantial portion of that done by the mechanical screens. Most of this would be the gross solids but there is reason to believe that this also is about all that can be expected of mechanical screens. Therefore, if mechanical screening is continued as a requirement it appears that the time is far overdue for work aimed at improving their efficiency. Without this it appears reasonable to consider the effects of lagoon treatment without the cost of mechanical screens.

THE SODIUM NITRATE ERA

During the 1930's when it became evident that rapid soil absorption from impoundments could not be generally successful because of soil conditions and resulting odor problems, the search began for methods of odor control. At that time the concept of lagoon treatment changed by necessity to that of storage rather than absorption. The simplicity of the treatment remained attractive and justified extensive investigation toward suitable odor control.

In the early work (8) it was speculated that by maintaining the lagooned waste in an alkaline *p*H range bacterial decomposition could be accelerated and an environment created which would be less attractive to those organisms responsible for hydrogen sulfide. This was attempted by the addition of sodium hydroxide to pea waste under controlled conditions but the results discouraged further investigation.

Development

The use of sodium nitrate as an additive was developed in the early 1940's (10). Sanborn pointed out that the use of sodium nitrate was not an attempt to develop a new method of treatment but rather was a corrective measure for existing lagoons causing odor nuisances. He noted that the ability of nitrates to prevent putrescence in domestic sewage was recognized as far back as 1892, prior to the development of biological filters. Nitrates were used in the late 1920's and early 1930's to correct offensive odor conditions in receiving waters in Massachusetts and New York City (11, 12).

Sanborn's theory was that the sodium nitrate would supply a ready source of oxygen to prevent the waste decomposition from entering the anaerobic phase. He found, however, that as a practical measure the cost of supplying the ultimate oxygen demand from sodium nitrate was prohibitive. Therefore, a compromise was sought, and as a result of extensive studies the threshold dosage was recommended to be the application of sufficient sodium nitrate to supply about 20 percent of the 5-day BOD whn the waste was stored in shallow lagoons.

Sanborn stated that the function of sodium nitrate is three-fold: (a) to furnish oxygen available for aerobic bacterial decomposition during the early stages of decomposition, (b) to stimulate the growth of chlorophyllaceous organisms which in turn produce additional oxygen by photosynthesis, and (c) to maintain an alkaline reaction. It has been recognized that the part sodium nitrate plays in this treatment is complex and not fully understood. Despite the lack of complete understanding of its reaction its value for odor control in canning and other wastes remains. For instance, it was pointed out in discussion (13) that in the chemical reaction only $2\frac{1}{2}$ atoms of oxygen are available for oxidation rather than the 3 atoms found in the sodium nitrate.

Cost and Effectiveness

Shortly after the development of sodium nitrate as an additive lagoons became widespread in the canning industry. The industry followed fairly closely the recommendations for 20-percent oxygen of Sanborn for several years, but in many instances the objectionable odor conditions persisted. Sanborn's work indicated that when 50 percent or more of the oxygen demand was supplied by sodium nitrate complete protection against odor was obtained. His recommendation for the 20-percent level was based on what was thought would be accepted by the industry on a cost basis. The chemical cost for the 20-percent treatment amounted to about one third cent per case of final product in the early 1940's. This cost today would be in the range of one half to one cent per case, depending on variations in delivery cost of sodium nitrate. In retrospect it appears that a more aggressive program of convincing the industry of the necessity for the 50-percent level would have been in order. At that time the cost still would have been less than one cent per case and today not more than two cents. The degree of resistance to what appears to be a small cost for waste treatment when compared with revenue return to the canner of perhaps $2.00 to $3.00 per case is significant.

The decomposition of canning waste in a lagoon follows a two-stage pattern, with or without the addition of sodium nitrate, as shown in Table 68.

During the first few days oxygen is utilized at a rapid rate followed by a much slower decomposition of the organic material.

Only slight acceleration of BOD reduction is demonstrated in Table 68 from the addition of sodium nitrate. Data on corn waste clearly show its slower rate of decomposition, which is attributed to the necessity for first hydrolyzing the starch before eventual decomposition of the waste.

Biological Indicators

The early work led to investigations of the biological indicators during the storage period. Again it is emphasized that these lagoons were designed for storage on a seasonal basis. The lagoons contained the waste for the season's pack, and discharge was effected in the following spring during a period of relatively high stream flow. As a result it was possible to observe a rather complete cycle of decomposition during the stages of stabilization.

During the first stages of decomposition facultative anaerobic and aerobic bacteria were predominant in digesting the concentrated waste. During this period rat-tailed maggots and chironomous larvae were abundant.

During the intermediate stages flagellates and ciliates appeared. These chlorophyllaceous organisms make evident the green color and are abundant during most of the canning season and throughout the storage period following the end of the season. *Chlorella vulgaris*, *Carteria*, *Chlorogonium*, and *Chlamydomonas*

TABLE 68

EFFECT ON 5-DAY BOD OF VARIOUS CANNING WASTE IN LAGOONS IN TERMS OF PERCENT OF OXYGEN DEMAND AS SUPPLIED BY SODIUM NITRATE

	5-Day BOD (mg/l)								
Storage Period (wk.)	Pea Waste			Tomato Waste			Corn Waste		
	0% $NaNO_3$	20% $NaNO_3$	50% $NaNO_3$	0% $NaNO_3$	20% $NaNO_3$	49% $NaNO_3$	0% $NaNO_3$	19% $NaNO_3$	46% $NaNO_3$
0	1,430	—	—	1,800	—	—	2,760	—	—
1	1,360	1,600	1,685	880	1,020	890	2,750	2,480	2,530
2	242	638	456	360	670	550	1,800	1,480	1,940
3	—	—	—	270	380	265	1,580	470	990
4	209	196	—	165	255	225	940	330	510
5	185	201	209	115	140	160	590	135	220
6	—	—	—	150	180	130	455	90	135
7	116	86	85	—	—	—	—	—	—
9	—	—	—	—	—	—	—	50	85
10	—	—	—	14	12	11	—	—	—

appeared to predominate. During one rather short period in the later stages of decomposition various varieties of red microorganisms appear in quantity but decrease with a change in BOD. Algae are effective in maintaining dissolved oxygen when the BOD concentration is below 200 mg/l. Odor is low below this concentration. At BOD's below 200 mg/l cladocera and rotifers appear.

These observations led to the belief that the nitrates act in two principal ways: (a) furnishing necessary oxygen for aerobic decompositions, with a consequent control of the facultative or strict anaerobes; and (b) furnishing an additional supply of nutrient materials for chlorophyll-bearing plankton. During the early stages the first function is predominant. Formation of such compounds as thioalcohols, butyric and valeric acids, indol, skatol, and hydrogen sulfide, with consequent offensive odor production is prevented. Ammonia and carbon dioxide formation is encouraged at the same time. The second function becomes important as the strength of the waste is reduced and the ammonia and carbon dioxide increase. The special types of plankton then formed provide large amounts of dissolved oxygen which is available for further odorless aerobic decomposition. Thus, nitrate is a stimulant to further oxygen production. As pointed out (13), these statements are based on empirical rather than precise data.

These observations reinforced the recommendations that lagoons be shallow in order to take maximum advantage of light penetration and natural aeration.

OTHER METHODS OF LAGOON OPERATION

The persistent odor problems associated with lagoons, even when sodium nitrate is used, led to a series of investigations of controls, addition of other materials, or operational adjustments. All were directed primarily toward odor control and accelerated stabilization rates but none attempted to reduce the loading to approach the design limits of stabilization ponds later developed for domestic waste.

Several of the alternate methods of operation or odor control measures investigated during this period are discussed as follows:

Pure or Selected Cultures

Because of the observation that the odor conditions were not objectionable during times when certain stages of the biological pattern occurred, efforts were made to provide massive inoculations of certain of these organisms to encourage these conditions. For instance, the red algae or nonsulfur purple bacteria referred to above led to work aimed at making these organisms predominant during the earlier stages of operation when the waste concentration was high. These organisims were studied in Minnesota after the correlation of the organism and lack of odor was noted in 1947. The pigmented organisms were identified as belonging to the genus *Rhodopseudomonas* of the group of nonsulfur purple bacteria *Athiorhodaceae*. Some early hope was attained but the eventual results indicated that these organizations did not adapt themselves to the environment associated with the early period of high strength of the waste.

Other unpublished studies were carried on by the National Canners Association with various pure caltures. None produced optimistic results and led to the general conclusion that it is a formidable task to change by artificial means the natural biological environment associated with lagoons.

Odor Masking Agents

Beginning in the late 1940's a variety of chemical agents appeared on the market. Extensive observations were made under controlled conditions to monitor these materials. The compositions of most of these materials were not made available by those marketing them, but they generally fell into two classes: (a) the chlorinated hydrocarbons with concentrated odor materials and (b) products derived from the perfume industry. All materials are highly concentrated. Application generally is made by dripping the material into the waste at the collecting or pump sump at the plant prior to discharge to the lagoon.

The function of these agents appears to be that of providing a pleasant odor by masking the undesirable odors. Some claim to substitute or combine with the existing odors on a selective basis but the reputed tailor-made selection has not been demonstrated satisfactorily.

When these materials appeared, a logical concern was whether the materials would retard the natural biological and chemical stabilization process. With at least one material a retarded effect was demonstrated. As a result there was early concern about the use of these materials. Most, however, did not appear to affect the stabilization process.

Various degrees of effectiveness were reported, from the situation where the combination of the perfume odor and the hydrogen sulfide or pig-pen odor caused a more objectionable odor than the original to that of effective pleasant odor. Because of the difficulty involved in finite evaluation the results invariably were affected by the human element. Therefore the psychological effect of a selling campaign among the neighbors was important.

These materials continue to be used, at a high cost, and with continuing intangible evaluation. Obviously, they are not a panacea but with the prevalence of odor complaint situations many canners probably will continue their use.

Biocatalysts or Enzymes

One of the most controversial materials used in lagoons has been the enzymes or biocatalysts. These also have been on the market since about 1950 and continue to excite the interest of uninformed industries and municipalities. The excitement or anticipation is natural because the theory of accelerated stabilization by the addition of enzymes is sound. Bacterial decomposition of complex organic compounds and even of the relatively simple sugar sucrose is dependent as a first step on the secretion of enzymes by bacteria for the purpose of converting the complex substances into simple compounds suitable for bacterial utilization. It is well known that the enzymatic hydrolysis of starch, for example, is slow relative to the bacterial utilization of the resulting simple glucoses. From a theoretical consideration, therefore, the addition of enzymes might be expected to accelerate the rate of bacterial activity and consequently the rate of stabilization. From a practical standpoint, however, the claims are based, for instance, on the use of actinomycetes in so-called impressive concentrations as additions. In reality the commercially recommended and marketed concentrations of the added actinomycetes may not exceed the concentrations of the same materials found in a small handful of soil from the bottom or sides of the lagoon, or for that matter in the waste itself resulting from soil-grown products.

Extensive tests carried on by the National Canners Association in unpublished work compared several different enzyme products and resulted in the conclusion that the degree of odor control obtained by the application of commercial enzyme products to lagooned pea and corn wastes did not meet expectations. These results were confirmed by published reports on domestic wastewater (14–16). Later the Better Business Bureau issued a release (17) covering prepared biocatalytic and enzymatic products for septic tanks and their failure to benefit the maintenance of septic tanks and cesspools. It also referred to and quoted from a federal publication which pointed out the same results (18). There is enough similarity in the contents and conditions of septic tanks and lagoons to apply the same statements to both. Beginning about 1950 the use of lagoons began to decline when other methods such as spray irrigation began to replace them. However, as late as 1963 it was reported (19) that the canning industry remained as the largest user of the lagoon method in industry by a wide margin. At that time it was reported that there were 238 canning waste lagoons of a total of 827 industrial lagoons in the United States. The nearest industry to this was meat and poultry with 168.

Anaerobic Digestion

Concurrent with the lagoon studies reported above was the work carried on by the National Canners Association on anaerobic digestion, or at least partial anaerobic digestion, in a lagoon system. Work on tomato waste was reported in 1950 and resulted from earlier pilot plant studies (21) on tomato and pumpkin wastes.

The key to the anaerobic digestion system was the utilization, as the first component of the system, of a small lagoon, which was used as a digester with an open surface. The further key feature of the system was the use of mechanical mixing in the digester. This was accomplished by a stationary-mounted "Lightnin" mixer near the inlet end of the digester. The mixer is a direct-drive, electrically powered, three-bladed propeller mixer mounted on a raft. The digester was followed by a series of storage lagoons which had been in use for some years. Figure 177 shows the plan of the system.

The mixer was operated continuously, as the objective was to keep the digester contents in a continual state of motion. Sodium nitrate had been used prior to this work but was replaced by the digestion operation. Operation results were encouraging in that no odor complaints were received, whereas there had been complaints in earlier years. The cost of the mixing operation was about one sixth that of sodium nitrate, and the stabilization of the waste in the system proceeded from an original concentration of about 1,000 mg/l BOD to a final concentration of 57 mg/l in the 52-day period of canning.

This work led to a series of tests with peas and corn in Wisconsin, where the digester portion of the lagoon system was double that of the tomato operation and was followed by a single storage lagoon. Four "Lightnin" mixers were installed on rafts and again were operated continuously. Figure 178 shows this system. The digester volume was about 1,000,000 gallons. Since the system started with no waste, seeding was provided by the addition of about 175,000 gal. of digested solids from a municipal treatment plant.

Because of the physical arrangements it was not possible to adjust the loading which therefore varied with the packing season. This system was operated four years under close surveillance. Decomposition rates in the digester were encouraging but severe odor conditions developed. Table 69 shows the results of the operation as measured by BOD.

BOD loading was reported in terms of lb/1,000 cu ft because of the nature of the digester. If the units are changed to those more commonly understood the digester loadings for pea waste during the four years would have ranged from 870 to 1,700 lb/acre/day or 81.5 to 159 lb/1,000 sq ft/day. The storage lagoon was loaded from 620 to 1,010 lb/acre/day, or 58 to 94 lb/1,000 sq ft/day.

During the corn waste studies the digester loadings varied from 750 to 1,110 lb/acre/day, or 70 to 104 lb/1,000 sq ft/day. The storage lagoon was loaded from 370 to 530 lb/acre/day, or 35 to 49 lb/1,000 sq ft/day.

When it is considered that the loadings imposed on the digester in these studies were perhaps 30 to 70 times those expected of domestic wastewater sta-

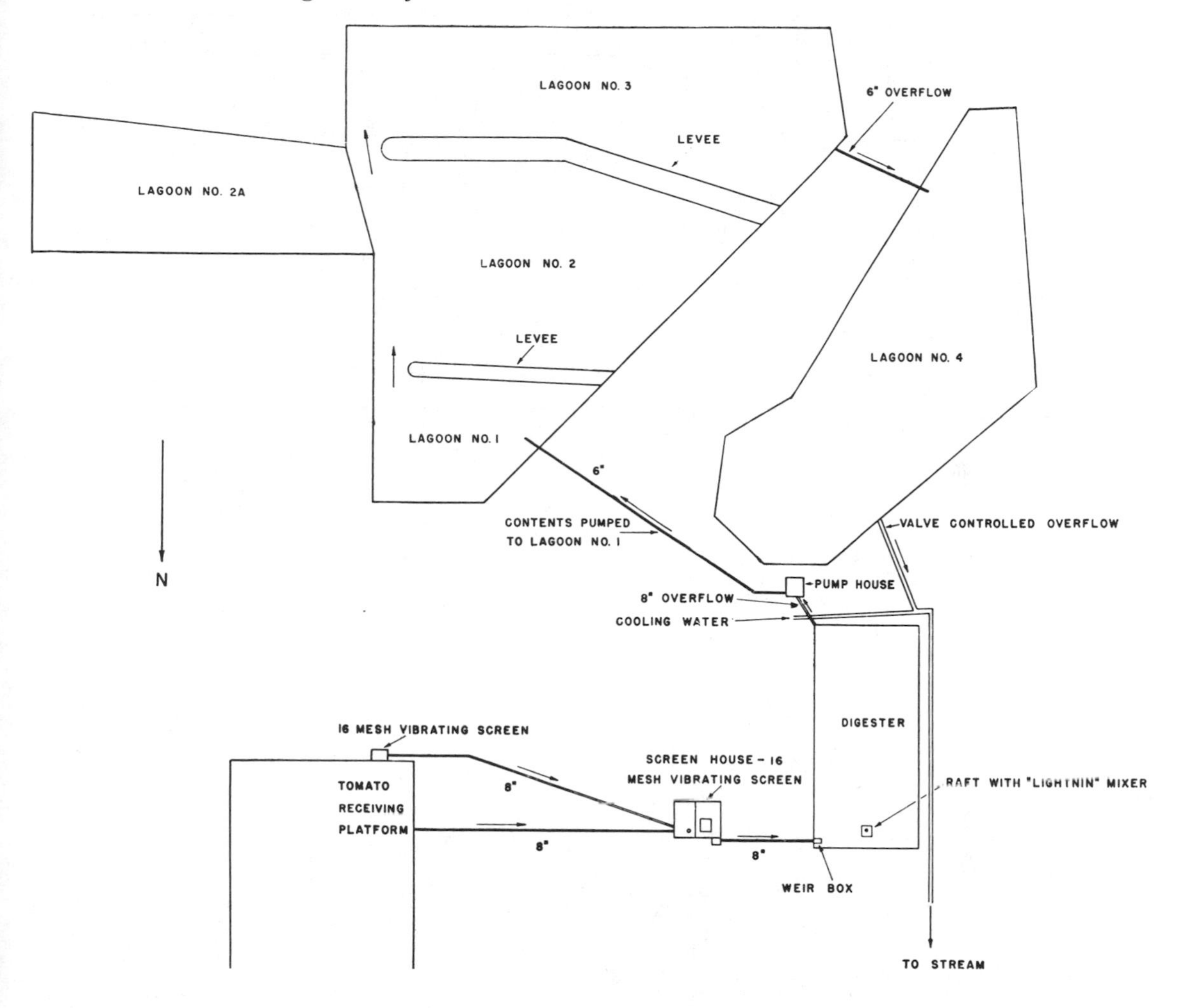

Figure 177. Plan view of combined anaerobic and aerobic lagoon treatment of tomato waste.

bilization ponds, the work done was worthy of attention. The storage lagoon was loaded from 20 to 50 times that of domestic ponds.

The severe odor problem in the digester led to the addition of sodium nitrate. Results with nitrate additions are included in Table 69. Sodium nitrate additions led to the recommendation that with this type system about 0.3 lb. sodium nitrate per pound of BOD should be added for adequate odor control. This, of course, lessens the degree of anaerobic conditions in the digester but is accompanied by corresponding high degrees of BOD removal. Results of the storage lagoon were satisfactory with the modifications provided.

At the time of this work (1950–1953) it was estimated that the costs for the capital investment of lagoons and equipment plus operation costs would amount to \$6.18 per 1,000 cases of No. 2 cans packed. The recommendations for sodium nitrate addition would add about \$5.25 per 1,000 cases, making a total cost of \$11.43 per 1,000 cases, or 1.14 cents per case. Thus, the cost of waste treatment, depending on the variation in market value of the product, may be in the or-

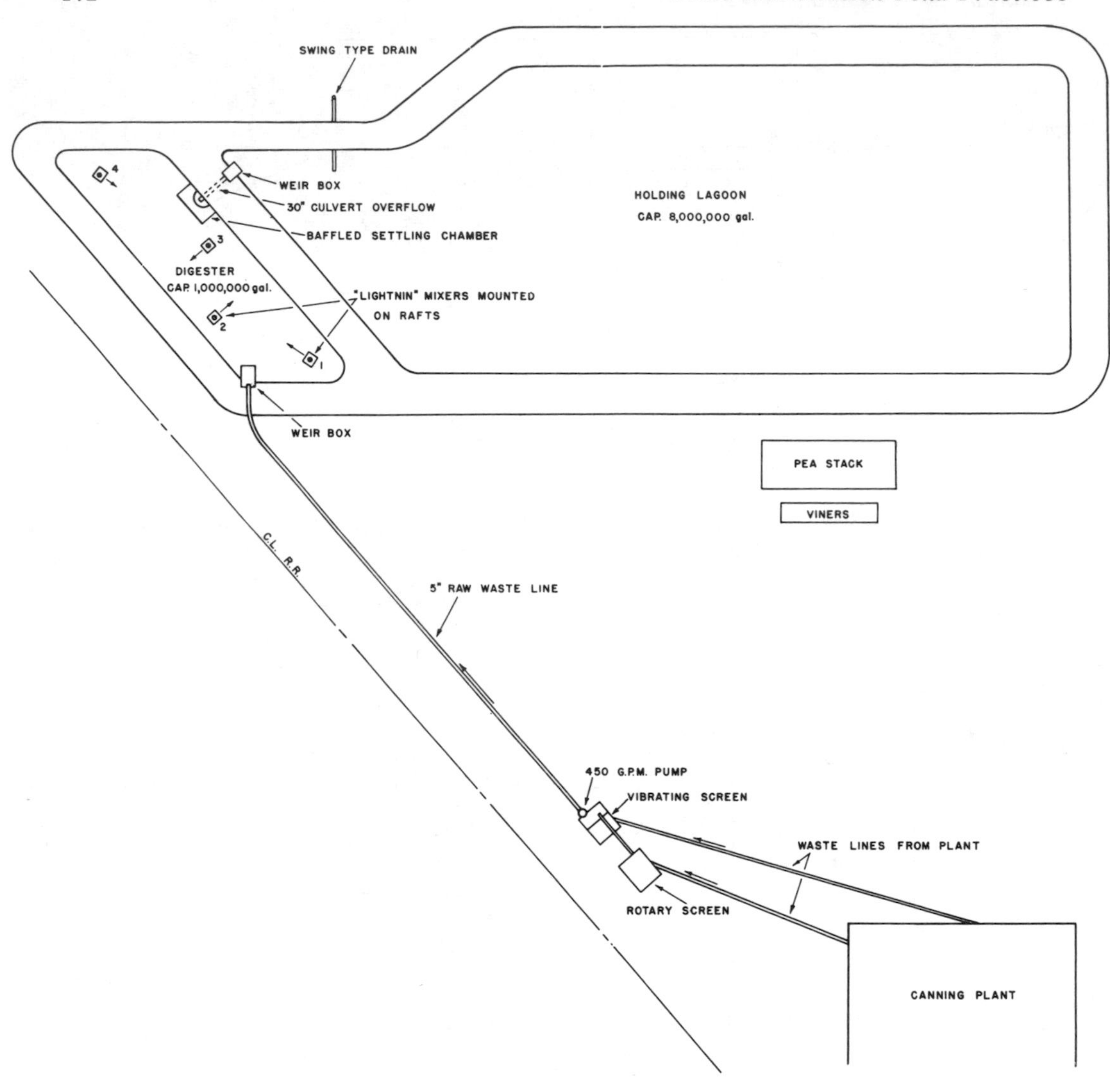

Figure 178. Plan view of waste treatment facilities for combination anaerobic digestion and aerobic storage of pea and corn wastes.

der of a maximum of considerably less than 1 percent of the market value of the product. This amount is hardly exciting when comparing other necessary business costs or the costs of municipal treatment when distributed among the taxpayers.

The value of added air to the digester surface was recognized during the tests after the mixers were adjusted so that one blade agitated the surface as a mechanical mixer. The eventual operation then tended toward a semianaerobic and semiaerobic digester. With the continuous agitation of the digester it was found that operational control was quite important to prevent the intensification of odor. Final conclusions were that with the use of continuously mixed contents and with the addition of controlled amounts of sodium nitrate this system can effect a high

TABLE 69

SUMMARY OF SERIES, OPEN DIGESTER-LAGOON OPERATION FOR PEA AND CORN WASTE

Product	Year	Digester				Storage[a] Lagoon BOD Reduction (%)	Total Treatment (%)
		BOD Loading (lb/1,000 cu ft)	Avg. Detention Period (days)	Raw Waste BOD (mg/l)	BOD Reduction (%)		
Peas	1950	18.2	3.56	790	29	58	77[b]
	1951	22.2	3.31	1,086	22	68[c]	75[c]
	1952	24.7	3.87	1,353	49[d]	85[c]	92[c]
	1953	27.8	2.84	1,545	47[d]	89[c]	94[c]
Corn	1950	12.5	11.30	2,169	25	89[b]	92[b]
	1951	15.3	8.85	2,182	69	68[b]	90[b]
	1952	17.6	10.10	2,614	53[d]	81[b]	91[b]
	1953	17.4	6.09	1,693	53[d]	74[b]	88[b]

[a]No continuous overflow in lagoon.
[b]No storage beyond pack.
[c]Includes 30-day storage in lagoon.
[d]$NaNO_3$ used during this period.

degree of treatment at a reasonable cost. However, the remaining problem of odor is in many localities a factor of sufficient importance to prevent this method's use. Even though the sodium nitrate in the recommended amounts affected a degree of odor control it is judged to be dangerously near the fringe of objectionable conditions. If the operator fails to supply the sodium nitrate for a day or so the results are quickly evident. On the other hand if the amounts of sodium nitrate are increased slightly above the recommended limits it is likely that conditions would be much improved.

Aerated Lagoons

In 1960 the theoretical aspects of aerated lagoons for canning wastes and the criteria for design were presented (2). In field tests the researchers obtained BOD removals of from 50 to 80 percent with an air flow of 0.5 cfm/1,000 gal, detention period of 2 to 5 days, and temperatures of 15 to 30°C. Tomatoes were the principal product handled at the plant. The use of aerated lagoons has spread in the canning industry although not as fast as in some other industries and in municipalities. Even though the area of the ponds may be reduced, there is some tendency in the canning industry to avoid the cost of the aeration equipment and its operation. One philosophy is that a company may be more inclined to purchase more land if equipment and operational costs can be avoided. One of the contributing reasons for this is that the land can be recovered for agricultural or other uses.

Other Variations

From time to time there have been other variations in lagoon design or operation. For instance, there are unusually deep lagoons, there are lagoons which receive the waste including all solids, there are series-and-parallel-operated lagoons, there are lagoons using controlled recirculation. None of these, however, are fundamentally different from the basic principle.

DESIGN CONSIDERATIONS

Various comments already have been made concerning the fact that the canning industry has not adopted the design of lagoons based on standards of organic loading. The controlling criteria have been the minimum area and volume which will hold a season's waste or in many instances most of a season's waste. Many lagoons were designed and built for a season's waste, but with time the operation expanded with more wastewater but the lagoon size remained. Therefore before the end of the season overflows occur. Because of the overloading, this overflow frequently is beyond the limits for the receiving stream.

With the increasing rate of activity in water pollution control the canning industry will find it necessary to improve its treatment facilities. Among the possibilities which should be considered is a design of lagoons using more realistic criteria. These would more nearly approach the accepted standards for other stabilization ponds. For example, a pea operation discharging 1 mgd. may require 180 acres of stabilization ponds. This would be equivalent to a community of about 15,000 people in organic load. The so-called typical pea processing operation, however, is smaller and is nearer to one third that volume, or a plant which would require 60 acres. At an assumed cost of $1,000/acre the cost of the land still is small when compared with the cost of a biological treatment plant. No supplemental treatment aids such as sodium nitrate are assumed for this situation.

Another possibility is the use of somewhat smaller acreage and the use of sodium nitrate in quantities to satisfy at least 50 percent of the BOD. The cost of this may be compared with the larger acreage above, or a compromise may be reached which considers location, distance, and availability of land. Still other choices may be the use of smaller aerated lagoons or combination anaerobic-aerobic digestion systems, or other modifications of operation or design. These choices become local factors, but the importance of management's realization that these alternatives are realistic is paramount. Given the circumstances for providing lagoons along the lines of these criteria there is little reason to question the expected results from both the organic performance and the odor control standpoint.

CONSTRUCTION

Recommendations for construction of earthen lagoons are given by the National Canners Association (8). Burrowing animals are serious problems, as are mosquitoes and weeds. Bank maintenance is an important requirement to provide control of the animals and the weeds. The elimination of weeds is important in controlling breeding areas for mosquitoes. Several authors discussed maintenance in detail (23–25).

SUMMARY

The canning industry was one of the first to utilize lagoons as a method of treating, or rather disposing of its waste. The history of their use in this industry dates back nearly to the turn of the century. Early lagoons were designed as absorption areas with the hope that the wastewater would enter the soil and be forgotten. The combination of soil conditions and waste characteristics caused this theory to fail in practice. Later lagoons were used simply as storage areas for a season's waste. Odor problems persisted and led to the sodium nitrate era. There was rapid growth of this method, but odor continued when not enough sodium nitrate was used because, among other reasons, canners objected to the cost of the material. These factors led to the search for other methods or modifications.

The method then declined in popularity as other land methods such as spray irrigation were used. Despite a decline this industry was reported as late as 1963 to be by far the largest user of the method. The combination anaerobic-aerobic system was studied and is effective for treatment, but the odor remains a problem. Inoculations with pure cultures, odor masking agents, enzymes, and other additives have been tested with varying degrees of success, but are predominantly unsatisfactory. Aerated lagoons were developed with some success but the cost is received with a lack of enthusiasm by the industry. Other variations in operation have been practiced, again with odor a greater problem than organic treatment performance.

The future of lagoons in the canning industry depends on a sharp change in philosophy in the industry management. Given the opportunity for more realistic design criteria there is no doubt that the method can be completely satisfactory. Of course this means a greater expenditure for more land or for more chemicals or air, or a combination of two or more of these circumstances. Far too much of the industry views the problem of waste treatment as a totally unpalatable and expensive requirement which is forced on them instead of adopting the realistic view that treatment cost is a necessary part of production. These more stringent requirements are not the result of aimless bureaucratic action—they are the result of comprehensive studies of quite realistic facts concerning the balance of water supply and demand and its required quality for the expanding country. In a careful analysis of long-range requirements and alternatives it is quite possible that the canning industry will find the lagoon method attractive again, although more costly than its earlier experience indicated.

REFERENCES

(1) *Annual Report.* New Jersey State Board of Health, Trenton, New Jersey (1910).

(2) "The Investigations on the Disposal of Canning Factory Wastes at Washington, Illinois," *Illinois Water Survey Series No. 11.* Illinois Water Survey, Urbana, Illinois (1913).

(3) *Water Pollution Control. Cannery Wastes.* Michigan Department of Health, Lansing, Michigan (1927).

(4) *Treatment of Pea Cannery Wastes.* Special Bulletin, Wisconsin State Board of Health, Madison, Wisconsin (November 1926).

(5) *Progress Report on Cannery Waste Treatment Studies.* Ohio Canners Association and Association of New York State Canners, In., State of Ohio Department of Health, Columbus, Ohio (1927).

(6) *The Treatment of Canning Wastes.* New York State Department of Health, Albany, New York (1930).

(7) Warrick, L. F., F. J. McKee, H. E. Wirth, and N. H. Sanborn. *Methods of Treating Cannery Waste.* Bulletin 28-L, Wisconsin State Board of Health and National Canners Association, Washington, D.C. (December 1939).

(8) Warrick, L. F., T. F. Wisniewski, and N. H. Sanborn. *Cannery Waste Disposal Lagoons.* Bulletin 29-L, Wisconsin State Board of Health and National Canners Association, Washington, D.C. (April 1945).

(9) Canham, Robert A. "Solids Removal in Canning Waste," *Proceedings.* Conference on Waste Disposal. *II*, 2, 19. University of Maryland, College Park, Maryland (March 1965).

(10) Sanborn, N. H. "Nitrate Treatment of Cannery Waste," *The Canner* (March 22, 1941).

(11) Fales, A. L. *J. Ind. Engr. Chem., 21,* 216 (1929).

(12) Carpenter, W. T. *Water Works Sewage, 79,* 175 (1932).

(13) Buswell, A. M. "Reaction of Sodium Nitrate in Stabilizing Organic Wastes," *Sewage Works J., 19*(4), 628 (September 1947).

(14) Heukelekian, H., and M. Berger. "Value of Culture and Enzyme Additions in Promoting Digestion," *Sewage Ind. Wastes, 25*(11), 1259 (November 1953).

(15) McKee, J. E., B. Benas, W. L. Henderson, R. R. Kennedy, and E. A. Pearson. "Biocatalytic Additives in Waste Treatment," *Sewage Ind. Wastes*, *26*(9), 1162 (September 1954).

(16) Pearson, E. A., J. H. Crafts, G. Chanin, W. F. Garber, W. L. Henderson, R. R. Kennedy, and J. E. McKee. "Biocatalytic Additives in Sludge Digestion," *Sewage Ind. Wastes*, *29*(9), 1066 (September 1957).

(17) "Advertising of Septic Tank and Cesspool Additives," *1780*, New York: National Better Business Bureau, Inc., (April 1962).

(18) *Manual of Septic Tank Practice*. U.S. Department of Health, Education, and Welfare, Washington, D.C. (1957).

(19) Proges, R. "Industrial Waste Stabilization Ponds in the United States," *J. Water Poll. Cont. Fed.*, *35*(4), 456 (April 1963).

(20) Canham, Robert A. "Anaerobic Treatment of Food Canning Wastes," *Food Packer*, *31*(5), 32 (May 1950).

(21) Canham, Robert A., and D. E. Bloodgood. "Anaerobic Pilot Plant Operation, Tomato and Pumpkin Wastes," *Proceedings*, Fourth Industrial Waste Conference, Purdue University, Lafayette, Ind., 150 (July 1949).

(22) O'Connor, D. J., and W. W. Eckenfelder, Jr. "Treatment of Organic Wastes in Aerated Lagoons," *J. Water Poll. Cont. Fed.*, *32*(2), 365 (April 1960).

(23) Rapp, W. J., Jr. "Sewage Lagoon Maintenance," *J. Water Poll. Cont. Fed.*, *32*(6), 660 (June 1960).

(24) Myklebust, R. J., and F. C. Harmston, "Mosquito Production in Stabilization Ponds," *J. Water Poll. Cont. Fed.*, *34*(3), 302 (March 1962).

(25) Scovill, R. P. "Mosquito Control in an Industrial Waste Lagoon," *J. Water Poll. Cont. Fed.*, *35*(5), 663 (May 1963).

WASTE TREATMENT IN THE MEAT PROCESSING INDUSTRY

A. J. Steffen
Ralph B. Carter Company, Hackensack, New Jersey

INTRODUCTION

About 60 percent of the wastewater from the 3,140 slaughtering and meat processing plants in the United States is discharged to city sewers. The other 40 percent is discharged into every conceivable type of treatment system, ranging from simple grease recovery by gravity separation to the recently developed anaerobic contact process. In all cases pretreatment measures vary widely, depending upon local requirements and management interests.

Slaughtering and meat processing operations produce a characteristically high organic, highly nitrogenous, biologically degradable wastewater, with relatively high concentrations of suspended and dissolved solids and grease. The waste does not, however, vary as widely in characteristics and concentration as might be expected from the wide range of processing operations and waste conservation practices found in the industry (Table 70). However, there are no average plants and no average conditions; therefore, the figures in Table 70 should not be used without a careful study of plant characteristics and processing program and then only for new plants where analytical data are not available.

In a 1959 survey of 108 plants representing 35 percent of the total quantity of

TABLE 70

APPROXIMATE RANGE OF FLOWS AND ANALYSES FOR SLAUGHTERHOUSES, PACKINGHOUSES, AND PROCESSING PLANTS[a]

Operation	Waste Flow Gallons per 1,000 Pounds Live Weight Slaughtered	Typical Analysis, mg/liter		
		BOD	Suspended Solids	Grease
Slaughterhouse	500–2,000	2,200–650	3,000–930	1,000–200
Packinghouse	750–3,500	3,000–400	2,000–230	1,000–200
Processing Plant	1,000–4,000[b]	800–200	800–200	300–100

APPROXIMATE WASTE LOADINGS[a]

Operation	Pounds per 1,000 Pounds Live Weight Slaughtered		
	BOD	Suspended Solids	Grease
Slaughterhouse	9.2–10.8	12.5–15.4	4.2–3.3
Packinghouse	18.7–11.7	12.5–6.7	6.3–5.8
Processing Plant	6.7[b]	6.7[b]	2.5–3.3[b]

[a]From *An Industrial Waste Guide to the Meat Industry*, Public Health Service Publication No 386, Revised 1965, p. 6.
[b]Per 1,000 pounds finished product.

federally inspected slaughtering, 65 discharged to city sewers, but all had treatment of some type (1). Of these, 71 had some form of primary treatment (screening, sedimentation, grease flotation) and 40 practiced some degree of secondary treatment (13 septic tanks, 2 irrigation, 7 stabilization ponds, 1 trickling filter, 12 activated sludge, and 5 anaerobic contact processes).

Processing plants fall into three general categories: slaughtering plants (abattoirs), processing plants without slaughtering, and packing plants that slaughter and process. Abattoir operations are confined to killing, and possibly rendering. Product is sold fresh or frozen and is processed elsewhere. The abattoir does no canning, smoking, or sausage making. The processing plant converts sides of beef and hogs, sausage trimmings, and by-products to fresh and frozen primal cuts, smoked and canned meat products, sausage, and other finished products. The packing plant combines slaughtering and processing in one location. If a firm operates more than one plant, certain operations may be concentrated at individual plants. Thus, one plant may produce all the canned goods for the firm; another may make shortening in addition to its other operations; and another may concentrate on smoking and sausage manufacture. Tanning, wool pulling, and the manufacturing of glues, soaps, and fertilizers are usually carried on in separate plants.

The size of the plant affects the characteristics of the wastes as well as the volume. Very small abattoirs may not save blood, and some do not provide grease recovery. Some small plants may wet-render but may not have facilities for evaporating the tank water, the liquid by-product of the process. The BOD of tank water and blood will run as high as 30,000 mg/l or more. Most rendering plants are now dry-rendering, which produces no tank water, but "skimmings" from grease recovery tanks are still generally wet-rendered because of the large amount of water in the skimmings.

WASTE CONSERVATION

Where wastewaters are discharged to municipal sewers, the extent of internal waste conservation depends upon the economics of each recovery step and the local municipal requirements. Where the firm treats its own wastes, a decision to recover a by-product is based upon balancing the cost of recovering the ingredients under consideration against the return from the sale of the recovered product plus the resulting savings in the treatment process. In some instances, improvements in waste conservation have not only yielded saleable by-products but have reduced waste strength and volume to such an extent that production could be increased as much as 30 percent without increasing the size of the treatment facility.

The following basic conservation measures will reduce solids, grease, and BOD in typical meat packing operations:

1. Dry-cleaning pens and floors before washing down.
2. Collecting kill blood in a separate blood tank, and squeegeeing the blood floor to the blood sewer before hosing during cleanup. Dual floor drains are provided to permit washing the residual blood to the sewer during cleanup.
3. Retaining casing slimes in casing washing operations. These slimes can be dried and added to animal feed products.
4. Screening paunch manure and hog stomach contents with either rotary or vibrating screens.
5. Separating grease from all grease-bearing wastewaters by means of efficient gravity or air flotation separators.
6. Evaporating tankwater, the liquid residue from wet-rendering. After evaporation to about 35 percent moisture, the liquid "stick" is mixed with tankage and dried.

7. Evaporating blood water, if blood is coagulated rather than dried directly.

In water conservation, the following mechanical conservation procedures can be applied:

1. Water supply valves for hand operations can be self-closing.
2. Sprays in "line operations" can be mechanically linked with the process, to shut off when no product is coming down the line.
3. Plant effluent can be recycled to provide water for inedible purposes such as condensing in the tank house, and spray cleaning of mechanical screens in inedible processing and in waste treatment.

The attitude of plant personnel toward waste conservation is an intangible but important ingredient in every conservation program.

BY-PRODUCT RECOVERY

Blood, casing slimes from stripping operations, and tankwater can be concentrated or dried and utilized in feeds and fertilizers. If the protein values of the feed and fertilizer ingredients produced at the plant are higher than the requirements of the particular fertilizer being produced, some quantities of lower grade materials are sometimes blended with these materials.

The recovery of floatable fat from the wastewater is standard practice To limit the size of recovery basins, grease-bearing wastes are segregated. The basins are generally rectangular, 4 to 6 ft. deep and large enough to provide three quarters' to one hour's detention at maximum flow. The basin may be hand skimmed in small operations but is generally mechanically skimmed in larger plants. In most cases, mechanism for sludge removal is also provided, but some basins are designed to carry settleable solids out with the effluent. The addition of polyelectrolytes has been found to improve grease yields. Air flotation is popular, either by direct aeration or by pressurized air introduced into the influent or a portion of recycled effluent. Alum improves separation but has the disadvantage of producing alum soaps when the resulting scum is wet-rendered.

In recent years the disposal of paunch manure has become a vexing problem. Paunch manure is washed out of the paunch (first stomach of cattle and other ruminants) on the killing floor. The resulting wastewater is generally kept separate from the fat-bearing wastes because it contains very little fat and a large quantity of partially digested hay, grass, and corn. The paunch content of cattle is estimated at 40 to 60 lbs. per head, has a volume of about 1 cu. ft. before dilution, and contains about one fifth to one third pound of BOD (2). The solids are generally concentrated by screening, either with mechanical screens or by leaching through stationary screens. Some use is also made of expellers and presses. In most cases, paunch solids are disposed of directly to farmers as fertilizer or as land fill. In some cases, such as at South St. Paul, Minnesota, and at St. Joseph, Missouri, paunch manure is discharged with the plant wastes to the city sewer for segregation at the municipal treatment plant.

HISTORY OF TREATMENT OF MEAT PROCESSING WASTES

As early as 1916, the Chicago Sanitary District became concerned with the problems of treating the wastes from Chicago's large complex of packing plants and, after an extensive study, reported that the activated sludge process was a feasible answer. The results in the ensuing years have justified these conclusions. In recent years, decentralization of the industry to other cities has reduced the significance of meat packing wastes in the District.

The work of Levine and others at Mason City, Iowa (3), in 1937 led to construction of plants at Mason City and at South St. Paul, Minnesota, employing washable filters in series. These were large plants, particularly at South St.

Paul, where wastes from several plants are treated. This system has also been applied in a new plant at Rochelle, Illinois, which achieves 95 percent BOD removal with three-stage filters following grit removal, mechanical flocculation, and sedimentation. A conventional two-stage high-rate trickling filter plant in Madison, Wisconsin, accomplishes 85 percent removal.

Chemical treatment with chlorine and alum, chlorine and ferric chloride, and ferric chloride alone was also popular for a time (4). A municipal plant in Oklahoma City (Southside), receiving a large proportion of packing plant wastes, used ferric chloride and lime until about 1948 (5). Currently, only small plants are employing chemical treatment, generally as pretreatment to reduce BOD and solids loadings prior to biological treatment. Chemical coagulation may be expected to produce BOD removals ranging from 50 to 70 percent by either flowing-through or batch processes. The batch process is generally preferred because variations in strength and solids concentration during the day can be accommodated by changes in the chemical dosages, batch by batch.

Many of these treatment processes have proved to be unsatisfactory. The high concentrations of proteins in meat processing wastes produce heavy biological growths that tend to clog trickling filters. Reversible washable filters are successful but expensive. Chemical treatment is useful as a pretreatment process for small plants but is expensive and provides limited BOD removal. In some cases, chemical treatment has failed because cooking processes produced wastewaters containing hydrolyzed protein that were not precipitated by chlorine.

Activated sludge treatment was successful when preceded by roughing filters (6), but processing disasters such as spills of blood, casing slimes, or tankwater can upset conventional activated sludge systems.

DISPOSAL BY IRRIGATION

Since meat industry wastes contain relatively high concentrations of nitrogen and phosphorus, disposal by irrigation should be attractive. However, although many systems of ridge-and-furrow, spray-and-broad irrigation are successfully disposing of canning, dairy, and paper mill wastewaters, there are few in the meat industry.

One spray system in Rushville, Illinois, disposes of the effluent from a lagoon receiving meat packing wastes. Another in Madison, Wisconsin, using several types of flood-and-spray irrigation, disposes of trickling filter plant effluent (200 mg/l BOD) from a large packing plant. Eight years of study of the system in Madison showed improved crop yields on all soils tested (7). Miami silt loam removed 50 percent of the nitrogen, 40 percent of the phosphorus, and 60 percent of the potassium. Improved crop growth on these soils was due primarily to the nitrogen. On peat soils the crops removed nearly 80 percent of the nitrogen, 50 percent of the phosphorus, and more than 55 percent of the potassium. In these soils the researchers believed that phosphorus and potassium caused the increase in yield. Application rates were as high as 39,000 gal/day/acre with no leaching of nutrients into a drainage creek 30 ft. away. The irrigation area was cropped with Reed's canary grass and was irrigated by flooding and by movable spray systems. The studies also demonstrated that salt concentrations in packing plant wastewaters can be kept below the optimum allowable limits to prevent soil damage through conservation practices and by separate treatment of the wastes from meat curing.

In New Zealand, 0.5 mgd of raw meat packing wastes are discharged by ridge-and-furrow irrigation onto 80 acres of sheep grazing land (8). The area carries an average of 25 sheep per acre, increasing to 100 per acre in summer. Application is about 50 inches per year.

The only known irrigation system in this country treating raw wastes from a packing plant is at Elburn, Illinois, where 225,000 pgd are sprayed, after grease recovery, onto a 23-acre field planted in alfalfa and brome grass. The spray system consists of 13 conventional irrigation-type spray nozzles, each discharging 14 gmp, on risers about 12 inches above aluminum distribution piping. The spray system covers one sixth of the area and is moved daily, irrigating at 2 in/day, with six days of rest. Crop yields have been so high that the owners have now purchased additional land to make full use of the fertilizing potential of the wastes. During the winter months the spray system was set up on a limited area of 4 acres in order to build an ice pack. The nozzles were extended 4 feet off the ground to facilitate servicing during the winter. The ice pack melted slowly during the first thaw, and the runoff joined that from the farm fields in the area, flowing to a nearby stream which, at the flood stage normally associated with that period of the year, provided more than adequate dilution.

STABILIZATION BASINS OR LAGOONS

Types

The popularity of stabilization basins, for partial as well as complete treatment of meat industry wastes, has increased in recent years, stimulated by developments in the pond treatment of municipal wastewaters and by research in anaerobic fermentation. The following types, including both partial and complete treatment, are currently in active use:

1. Anaerobic (deep) ponds to reduce the strength of wastes prior to discharging to a municipal plant.
2. Complete treatment in aerobic ponds, generally in series and preceded by good grease and solid recovery.
3. Complete treatment in anaerobic-aerobic systems, in series, usually consisting of a single deep anaerobic pond, followed by one or more shallow aerobic ponds in series.
4. Further treatment ("tertiary") following anaerobic contact or conventional aerobic secondary treatment.

Anaerobic (Deep) Ponds for Pretreatment

Dietz (9) reports that a new full-scale anaerobic pond treating packing plant wastes at Union City, Tennessee, which first overflowed in mid-September, 1965, showed 80 percent BOD removal two weeks later at an average loading of 7.9 lbs BOD/day/1,000 cu ft. The pond was seeded with anaerobic sludge from a nearby pilot pond. In recent months loadings have exceeded the design loading of 15 lbs/1,000 cu ft but BOD removals exceed 80 percent. The pond effluent is discharged to a municipal activated sludge plant.

Porges (10) reports data on 29 anaerobic ponds treating meat and poultry plant wastes: a median area of one acre, median depth of 7.3 ft. and median detention time of 16 days. Of the 16 reporting BOD data, loadings ranged from 175 to 6,060 lbs/day/acre (median 1,260), with removals of 65 to 95 percent (median 80%). It is unfortunate that anaerobic pond loadings have been reported on an area basis rather than volume, since the loading of this type of pond is a volume characteristic and has no relationship to surface area.

Aerobic Pond Systems (Complete Treatment)

Reported loadings in conventional aerobic stabilization pond systems range from 50 lb/day/acre (11) treating raw meat packing wastes in South Dakota, to 214 lb/day/acre treating relatively dilute poultry processing wastes in Delaware (BOD 175 mg/l) following primary sedimentation and flow equalization (12). The difference in loading is largely due to primary clarification in the Delaware plant.

Extended aeration in ponds should be useful for meat industry waste treatment but no information is available on existing plants. However, poultry slaughtering wastes are being treated by this process in Canada, in a 15 ft.-deep completely mixed aerated lagoon (13) with 96 percent BOD removal (raw 820 mg/l) in 20 days detention, supplying 390 cu. ft. of air per pound of BOD removed. A plant in North Carolina treating poultry wastes in a combination aerator-clarifier tank rather than a lagoon (14), removes 90 percent of the BOD (raw 665 mg/l) in 24 hours detention, supplying 1,500 cu. ft. of air per pound of BOD removed.

Porges (10) reports a median loading of 72 lbs/day/acre (14 to 250 lbs/day/acre) for 50 aerobic pond systems treating wastes from the meat and poultry industries. Depths ranged from 1.5 to 9.0 ft., with a median of 3.0 ft., and areas ranged from 0.04 acres to 75.0 acres, with a median of 1.3 acres, providing detention of 3 to 326 days, with a median of 70 days.

Anaerobic-Aerobic Pond Systems (Complete Treatment)

The first reported anaerobic-aerobic system, at Moultrie, Georgia (15), has been operating since 1955, treating meat packing waste in an anaerobic pond 14 ft. deep, with a capacity of 4.2 mg., followed by an aerobic pond 19.2 acres in area and 3 ft. deep. The detention time was 6 days in the anaerobic pond and 19 days in the aerobic pond, at a BOD loading of 0.014 lbs/day/cu ft in the anaerobic and 50 lbs/day/ acre in the aerobic stage (four-year average). Indicative of the space saving of this type of pond treatment, the overall BOD surface loading was 325 lbs/day/acre. Sludge is recirculated in the anaerobic pond and effluent is recirculated in the aerobic stage. The BOD of the raw waste averaged 1,100 mg/l, and the effluent averaged 67 mg/l. A second system installed by the same firm at Wilson, North Carolina, consists of an anaerobic lagoon 17 ft. deep with 3.5 days detention, followed by trickling filter treatment in the municipal plant. At each of these plants, grease, paunch manure, and gross solids are removed in pretreatment facilities. To reduce excessive solids concentration in the anaerobic pond, some sludge was removed after two and a half years of service and was dried in a nearby field without nuisance.

Two lagoon systems treating packing wastes in New Zealand, each with about 1.5 days detention in the anaerobic pond and 5 to 7 days detention in the aerobic ponds, produce 90 percent BOD reductions during the annual 6 months kill practiced there. The ponds are recirculated and, at last reports, degasification of the effluent, followed by sedimentation, was planned to provide further BOD removal.

There is evidence that the discharge of paunch manure to anaerobic basins may be beneficial, presumably by forming a scum that resists penetration of air and sunlight. A system in Idaho, consisting of three ponds in series with a total area of 2.8 acres and 8 ft. deep, is so overloaded with a packing plant waste that includes paunch manure and other solids, that it is entirely anaerobic. However, the raw BOD of 1,430 mg/l is reduced to 490 mg/l at a loading of 520 lbs/day/acre. The reduction is only 66 percent, but the high capacity of anaerobic ponds for BOD removal is evident.

Twelve small rural abattoirs in Louisiana (16) are successfully treating the entire plant wastes in three-stage pond systems, each consisting of an anaerobic pond, a transitional pond, and an aerobic pond. The paunch manure, grease, and blood are discharged with the raw wastes without pretreatment of any kind. The paunch manure and grease provide a mat on the anaerobic pond; difficulties in the anaerobic stage of treatment were experienced until this mat developed. Based upon an estimated BOD of 2,000 mg/l and a flow of 800 gal/1,000 lbs of live weight kill, the anaerobic ponds were designed at 30,000 pounds live weight kill/day/acre-foot, the transitional ponds at 150,000 pounds, and the aerobic ponds at

75,000 pounds. The anaerobic pond is 10 to 15 ft. deep, and the transition and aerobic ponds are about 4 ft. deep. There is no recirculation or supplemental heating in the systems. An average of composite samples taken at three plants gave a raw BOD of 2,270 mg/l, anaerobic effluent 183 mg/l, transition pond effluent 85 mg/l, and aerobic pond effluent 56 mg/l, with an overall BOD removal of 98.5 percent.

Porges (10) reports that ten anaerobic-aerobic pond systems treating meat industry wastes averaged 94 percent BOD removal, at BOD loadings ranging from 19 to 1,885 lb/day/acre (median 267).

Design criteria for anaerobic-aerobic systems vary. State regulatory agencies in Illinois, Iowa, Nebraska, Tennessee, Pennsylvania, and Minnesota accept design loadings of 15 lbs BOD/1,000 cu ft of anaerobic pond, allowing 60 percent BOD removal (9), followed by some form of aerobic treatment. Aerobic ponds used in series following anaerobic ponds range from 100 to 150 lbs/day/acre BOD loading (with 60% removal in each stage).

One case in Iowa followed these criteria: anaerobic pond at 11.5 lbs/1,000 cu ft, 60 percent BOD reduction (raw BOD at 1250 mg/l); a mechanically aerated lagoon at 50 lbs/1,000 cu ft, allowing 50 percent BOD removal; and two natural aerobic stabilization ponds, the first at 200 lbs BOD/acre, and the second at 100 lbs/acre, allowing 60 percent removal for each. This total four-stage plant was designed to produce an effluent of 45 mg/l (winter conditions).

Aerobic Ponds for Further Treatment (Tertiary Ponds)

No data are available on aerobic ponds when used in conjunction with conventional aerobic secondary treatment receiving meat industry wastes, but results may be expected to be similar to those experienced with domestic sewage, except that the higher levels of nitrogen and phosphorus would tend to produce more algae. Data on this type of pond following an anaerobic contact-type plant treating packing plant wastes are given in a later section.

Odor Problems

Some odors may be expected. Of thirteen aerobic pond systems treating meat industry wastes, five reported odors at nuisance levels; of ten anaerobic ponds reporting, nine reported nuisance odors; and neither of two anaerobic-aerobic systems reporting on this subject indicated odors of a nuisance level (10).

Odors carry about a mile from a series of three anaerobic cells treating meat packing wastes in Edmonton, Canada, according to a report by D. R. Stanley at the 1965 Ontario Industrial Waste Conference. However, they removed over 70 percent of the BOD and about 75 percent of the suspended solids. Anaerobic ponds are satisfactory for treating meat industry wastes if their location is sufficiently remote in order to avoid odor nuisances.

THE MODIFIED ANAEROBIC CONTACT PROCESS

When digested anaerobically at temperatures of 32° to 34°C., packing plant wastes will produce a quantity of methane gas which, when burned, will raise the waste temperature about six degrees. This is sufficient to sustain the digestion temperature, since the temperature of raw meat packing wastes is normally 28° to 30°C. Most other industrial wastes that satisfy nutrient requirements for anaerobic metabolism are not warm enough to economically justify treatment by this process.

The first full-scale modified anaerobic contact process for the treatment of meat packing plant wastes was placed in operation in December, 1959, at Albert Lea, Minnesota (17–20). The design was based upon pilot scale studies conducted at Austin, Minnesota (21), and upon studies on a first-stage plant designed to treat half the wastewater from the Albert Lea packing plant. Since 1959 other plants of this type have been built at Austin, Minnesota, and at Momence, Illinois. The completed plant at Albert Lea is shown in Plate 12 and Figure 179. Figure 180 shows a schematic flow diagram of the process.

The plants at Albert Lea and Momence are similar in design. Each is equipped with an equalizing tank to equalize the flow over a full 24-hour period. Preliminary treatment consists of gravity grease and solids removal (one half to one hour detention). Digestion takes place in totally mixed concrete digesters into which the raw wastes, preheated to 32°–34°C. are discharged. The detention time in the digesters is 12 to 15 hours based upon the flow of raw wastes. The mixed liquor with suspended solids concentration ranging from 7,000 to 12,000 mg/l is digesting actively as it leaves the digesters to be discharged through vacuum degasifiers to two gravity sludge separation tanks. The degasifiers remove residual gases to facilitate gravity separation.

The vacuum degasifiers are gas-tight steel vessels elevated to receive the di-

Plate 12. Anaerobic contact process plant at Labert Lea, Minnesota.

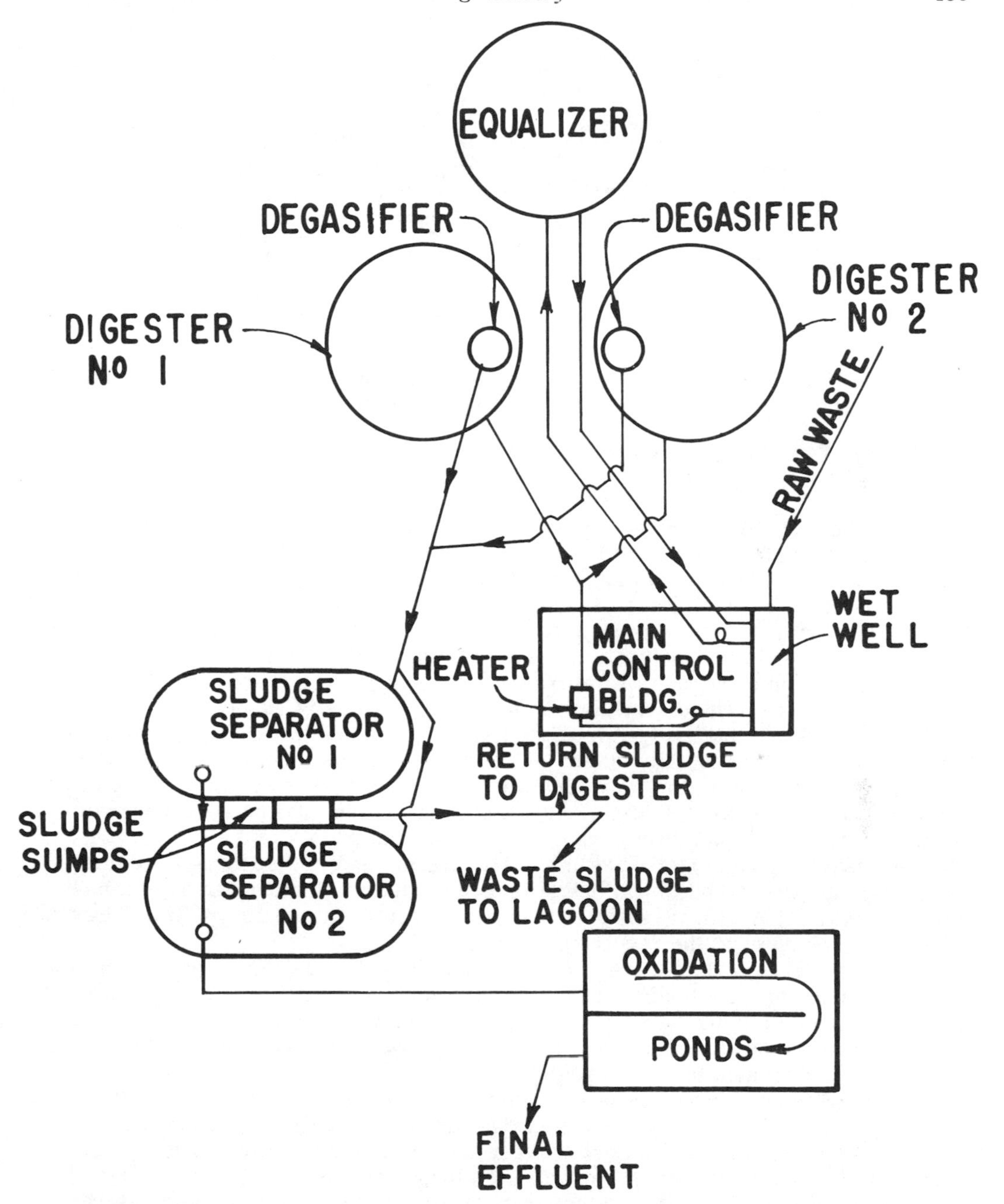

Figure 179. Anaerobic contact process, Albert Lea, Minnesota.

gester effluent, which is drawn up under 20 inches of mercury vacuum by wet vacuum pumps. In the vessel the liquid cascades down over slatted trays to enhance degasification. The gas, as drawn off by the vacuum pumps, is wet, contains high percentages (40 to 60%) of CO_2, and is thus highly corrosive. Corrosion protection consists of a baked phenolic lining and galvanized slats in the degasi-

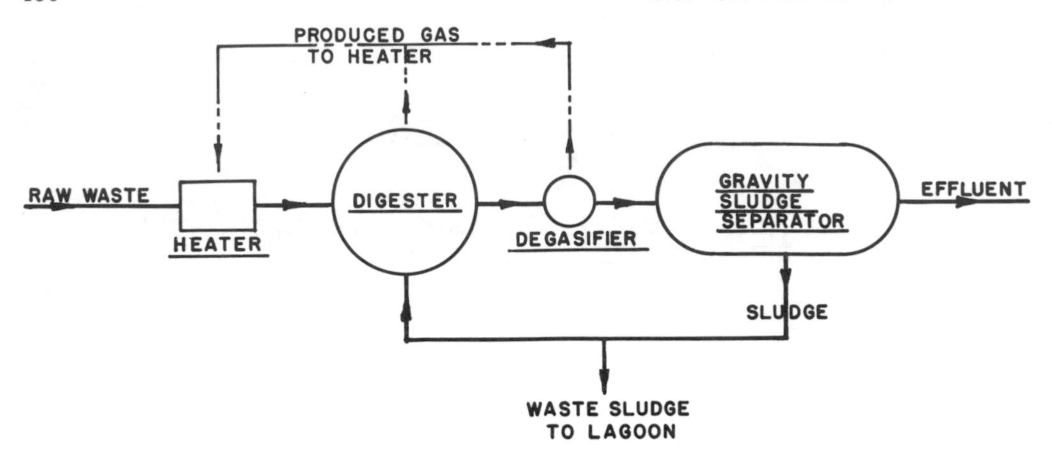

Figure 180. Flow diagram of anaerobic contact process.

fier, stainless steel pumps, and plastic piping. This "vacuum gas" is mixed with the gas generated in the digesters, which contains about 85 to 90 percent CH_4 and 10 to 15 percent CO_2, and is then burned in the boiler.

The plant at Austin utilizes air to purge the residual gases and operates at a lower BOD loading, removing 96 percent of the BOD at loadings of 0.1–0.06 lbs/day/cu ft of digester capacity, treating a raw waste of 1,400 mg/l BOD.

The sludge, in each case, is returned to the digesters as seed to maintain the anaerobic culture. The detention time in the separators is about one hour, based on total flow, including sludge circulating through the system at 3 to 4 volumes per volume of incoming raw waste. The surface settling rate is about 300 gal/day/sq ft based on raw flow only. In spite of the fact that the residual gases are removed in the degasifiers, the sludge is still flocculent and must be removed with suction-type rather than scraper-type mechanism.

The treated effluent overflows into weir troughs and is discharged for final polishing—at Albert Lea to two oxidation ponds, and at Momence to an activated sludge plant. At Austin the effluent may be treated in the municipal trickling filter plant or discharged to the receiving stream.

The ponds at Albert Lea are 3.7 acres in area and 3 to 4 ft. deep; they reduce the BOD of the anaerobic effluent 50 to 70 percent, producing an oxygenated final effluent suitable for discharge into an adjoining lake. Because of reduced BOD removal during the winter months, additional ponds were recently constructed to dispose of the effluent by soil percolation.

The anerobic contact process is similar in many respects to the activated sludge process. As in the activated sludge process, the first phase of treatment is largely stabilization by contact between the organisms and the nutrient in a favorable environment. After contact, the sludge, consisting of organisms and agglomerated organic matter, is separated from the treated liquid and returned to the process to serve as seed for incoming wastes. The organisms digest the organic matter in the sludge mass during the recycling and treating process.

In the anaerobic process at Albert Lea, the sludge age is about 5 days, and the BOD loading is about 0.25 mg BOD/day/mg mixed liquor suspended solids.

Operating data for the Albert Lea Plant, based upon daily analyses of samples composited automatically in proportion to the flow, are shown in Table 71. The relative capacity of the anaerobic process in removing BOD is shown graphically in Figures 181, 182, and 183. It will be noted in Figure 181 that the process

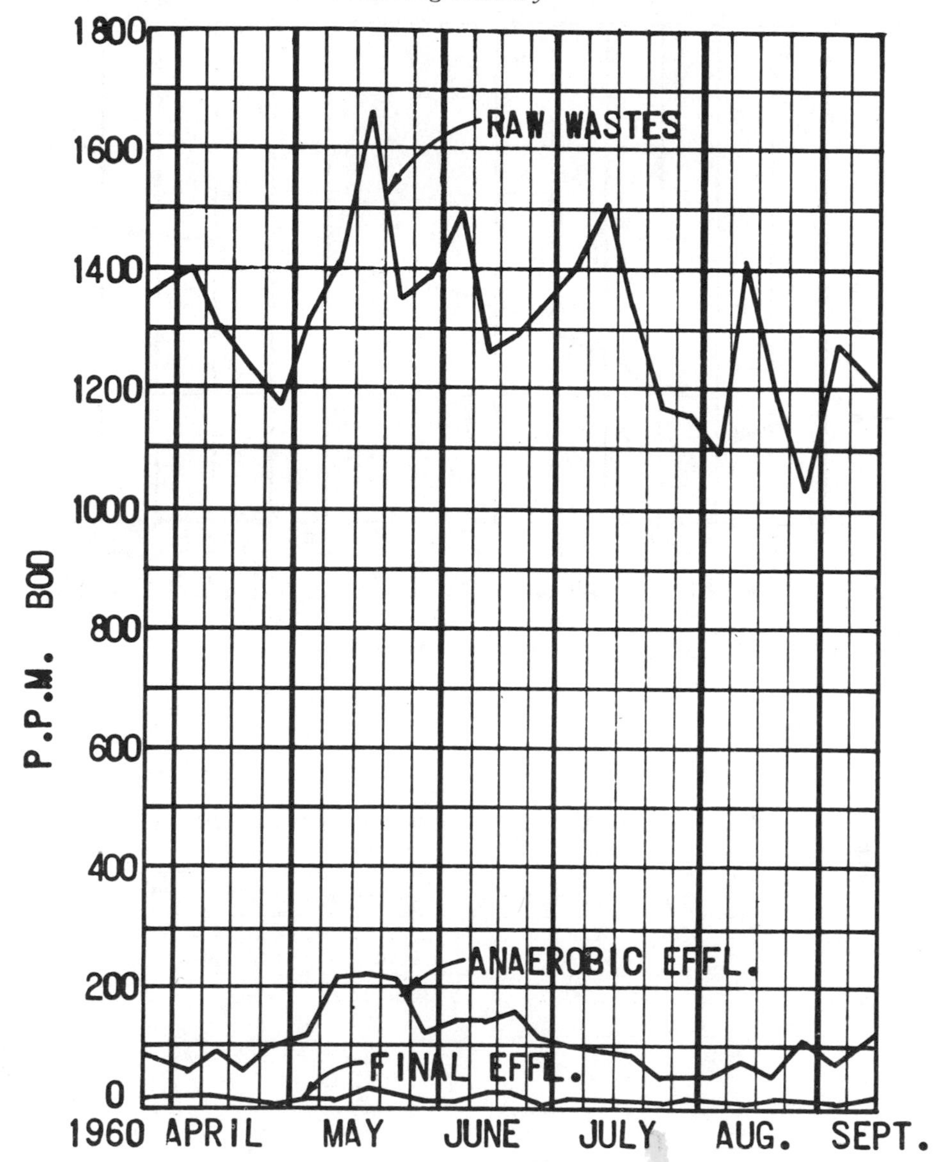

Figure 181. BOD data (weekly averages).

regularly removed 1,000–1,450 mg/l of BOD, while the oxidation ponds removed a much smaller proportion of the load. However, the oxidation ponds act as shock absorbers, producing a final effluent of relatively uniform quality under a wide range of loading. The first pond, which is usually anaerobic, accounts for most of the BOD removal in the pond system. The average BOD loading to the ponds was 410 lbs/day/acre, averaging 129 mg/l BOD and 198 mg/l suspended solids.

Results at Momence show 86 percent BOD removal through the anaerobic unit and 77 percent through the activated sludge plant, yielding 97.0 percent overall BOD removal.

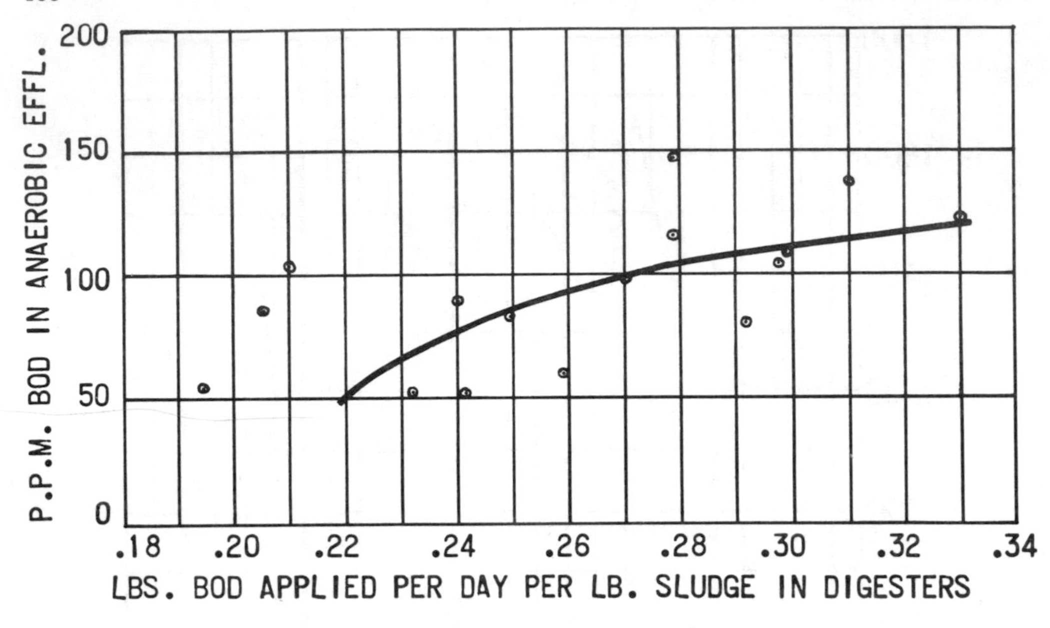

Figure 182. BOD applied per pound sludge vs. BOD in effluent.

TABLE 71

ANAEROBIC CONTACT PROCESS TREATING MEAT PACKING WASTES
ALBERT LEA, MINNESOTA

Average Operating Data—All Killing Days in 1960

	Raw Waste	Anaer. Proc. Effl.	Pond Effluent	Loss in Ponds
Flow gallons	1,410,000	1,410,000	772,000	638,000

	Raw Waste		Anaer. Proc. Effluent		Pond Effl. Corrected for Seepage	
	ppm	lbs.	ppm	lbs.	ppm	lbs.
BOD	1,381	16,220	129	1,517	26	304
Suspended solids	988	11,610	198	2,325	23	268

	Percent Removal			Digester loading lbs/day/cu ft
	Through Anaerobic Unit	Through Ponds	Through Entire Plant	
BOD	90.8	79.8	98.2	0.156
Suspended solids	80.2	88.4	97.6	0.112

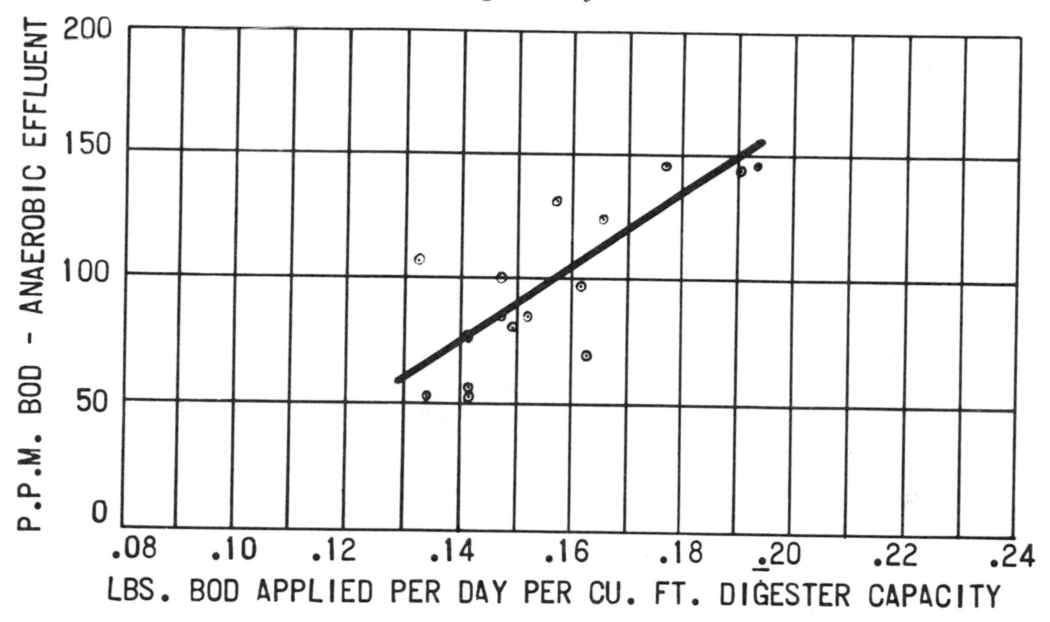

Figure 183. BOD applied per cubic foot digester capacity vs. BOD in effluent.

SUMMARY

Miscellaneous Treatment Processes

Chemical treatment aroused some interest twenty to thirty years ago but is currently limited to pretreatment, producing 50–70 percent BOD removal in adequately designed and properly operated plants.

In the field of aerobic treatment systems, washable trickling filters have been used successfully. Conventional activated sludge treatment has had varied success but has generally required some pretreatment, such as roughing filters to reduce BOD and iron out peaks. Extended aeration systems are in successful use in the treatment of poultry processing wastes in concrete tanks and in lagoon-type construction.

Disposal of raw meat packing wastes by irrigation has been successful in one installation in Illinois and one in New Zealand. This is a practical answer and warrants further study. Disposal of treated effluents by irrigation is more common and less spectacular. Some care is necessary to avoid high sodium concentrations in order to prevent soil damage. Further studies should be conducted to determine suitable crops and to research the possibility of disease transmission from feeding the irrigated crops to livestock.

Pond Systems

Anaerobic ponds serve successfully as "roughing" ponds for meat packing wastes principally because these wastes are warm (28° to 30°C.), have high BOD and organic solids concentrations, and provide proper nutrient balance. These ponds are generally about 12 to 16 ft. deep and, at average loadings of 12 to 15 lbs BOD/1,000 cu ft, require far less land area than aerobic stabilization lagoons. Sludge is often recirculated to the inlet to seed the raw wastes. Because aerobic ponds can accept anaerobic effluents at high BOD loadings without upset, combinations of anaerobic ponds with various arrangements of aerobic ponds have become popular. However, pond systems treating meat industry wastewaters should be located with due regard to possible odor problems.

Anaerobic Contact Process

The anaerobic contact process can remove 90 to 96 percent of the BOD in a waste of 1,400 mg/l, at a digester loading of 0.16 lbs/day/cu ft, with equalized flow. The digester is a completely mixed system, and the mixed liquor is degasified by vacuum before gravity separation of sludge, which is returned to the digesters at ratios ranging between 3:1 and 4:1. The process can be shut down on weekends and for extended periods without loss of treatment efficiency. The anaerobic effluent can be polished in aerobic ponds at loadings of 410 lbs/day/acre with additional removal of about 80 percent of the BOD and 88 percent of the suspended solids.

REFERENCES

(1) *Water in Industry*. New York: National Association of Manufacturers, 65–66 (1965).

(2) Steffen, A. J. "What to Do About Paunch Wastes," *Proceedings*, Third Purdue Industrial Waste Conference, 268–271 (1947).

(3) Levine, M.. F. G. Nelson, and E. Dye. *Experiments on Purification of Packing House Wastes at Mason City, Iowa*. Iowa Engineering Experiment Station Bulletin 130 (February 1937).

(4) Klassen, C. W., and W. A. Hasfurther. "Treatment of Wastes from Small Packing Houses," *Sewage Works Engr.*, *20* (March 1949).

(5) Gold, Donald D. *Summary of Treatment Methods for Slaughterhouse and Packinghouse Wastes*. University of Tennessee Engineering Experiment Station Bulletin 17, 44–45 (May 1953).

(6) Bradney, L, W. Nelson, and R. E. Bragstad. "Treatment of Meat Packing Wastes," *Sewage Ind. Wastes*, *22*, 807 (June 1950).

(7) "Wisconsin Scientists Find Low Salt Wastewater Good for Feeding Crops," *National Provisioner* (December 19, 1959).

(8) Cowie, C. W. "Industrial Waste Treatment and Disposal in New Zealand," *Proceedings*, Fifteenth Industrial Waste Conference, Purdue University, *106*, 9–14 (1961).

(9) Dietz, J. C., and P. W. Clinebell. "Design Considerations for Anaerobic Contact Systems," *J. Water Poll. Cont. Fed.*, *38*, 517–530 (April 1966).

(10) Porges, R. "Industrial Waste Stabilization Ponds in the United States," *J. Water Poll. Cont. Fed.*, *35*, 464–465 (April 1963).

(11) Carl, C. E., and D. C. Kalda. "Waste Stabilization Ponds in South Dakota," *Proceedings*, Symposium on Waste Stabilization Lagoons, United States Public Health Service (1960).

(12) Anderson, J. S., and A. J. Kaplovsky. "Oxidation Pond Studies on Eviscerating Wastes from Poultry Establishments," *Proceedings*, Sixteenth Industrial Waste Conference, Purdue University, 109 (August 1962).

(13) "Aerated Basin Keeps Chicken Processor in Business," *Canadian Muni. Util.* (February 1965).

(14) Teletzke, G. H. "Chickens for the Barbecue—Wastes for Aerobic Digestion," *Wastes Engr.*, *32*, 134–138 (March 1961).

(15) Sollo, F. W. "Pond Treatment of Meat Packing Plant Wastes," *Proceedings*, Fifteenth Industrial Waste Conference, Purdue University Extension Service, *106*, 386 (1961).

(16) Coerver, J. F. "Louisiana Practice and Experience with Anaerobic-Aerobic Pond Systems for Treating Packinghouse Wastes," *J. Water Poll. Cont. Fed.*, *36*, 931 (August 1964).

(17) Steffen, A. J. "Full-Scale Modified Digestion of Meat Packing Wastes," *Sewage Ind. Wastes*, *27*, 1364 (December 1955).
(18) Steffen, A. J. "Treatment of Packinghouse Wastes by Anaerobic Digestion," *Biological Treatment of Sewage and Industrial Wastes*. edited by McCabe and Eckenfelder. New York: Reinhold Publishing Corp. (1958).
(19) Steffen, A. J. "The Modified Anaerobic Contact Process," *Proceedings*, Thirteenth Research Conference, American Meat Institute Foundation, University of Chicago (March 1961).
(20) Steffen, A. J., and M. Bedker. "Operation of Full Scale Anaerobic Contact Treatment Plant for Meat Packing Wastes," *Proceedings*, Sixteenth Industrial Waste Conference, Purdue University Extension Service, *109*, 423 (1962).
(21) Schroepfer, G. J., W. J. Fullen, A. S. Johnson, N. R. Ziemke, and J. J. Anderson. "The Anaerobic Contact Process as Applied to Packinghouse Wastes," *Sewage Ind. Wastes*, *27*, 460 (April 1955).

WASTE STABILIZATION POND PRACTICES IN THE PULP AND PAPER INDUSTRY

Isaiah Gellman
National Council for Stream Improvement,
The Johns Hopkins University, Baltimore, Maryland

Herbert F. Berger
Louisiana State University, Baton Rouge, Louisiana

The use of stabilization basins for the reduction of BOD of pulp and paper mill effluents is the most widely practiced form of secondary treatment employed by the industry today. Twenty-three large kraft mills, at least two large chip board mills, and numerous smaller mills employ this technique. Gehm (1) discussed the reasons for selection of this form of treatment and its evolution from holding ponds designed strictly for controlled discharge to today's efficient biological oxidation systems.

Data obtained from actual Southern kraft mill operations have resulted in the selection of a design value of 50 pounds of BOD_5/acre/day as the loading which will provide at least 85 percent BOD_5 removal. As shown in Table 72, lagoon systems have been operated at loadings from 10 to 300 pounds BOD_5/acre-day. Those which are loaded below 50 pounds/acre-day provide BOD removal in excess of 90 percent, while when loadings are increased BOD removals level off around 60 to 70 pounds/acre-day. Higher removals are also reported, ranging up to 150 pounds/acre-day, but these generally are associated with multiple basin systems arranged in series, in which some volatilization of evaporator condensate constituents occurs. In those cases where high loadings produce removals of more than 60 pounds/acre-day some anaerobic odor production is observed. Sulfides are emitted during basin overflow into connecting channels, and the presence of sulfide oxidizing bacteria is noted in these channels.

TABLE 72

RELATION BETWEEN WASTE STABILIZATION BASIN LOADING, REMOVAL, AND PERCENT REMOVAL

Mill Identification	Pounds BOD/Acre-Day		Percent
	Load	Removal	Removal
1	11	10	92
2	30	27	90
3	52[a]	48[b]	93
4	53[a]	43[b]	80
- - -	- - -	- - -	- - -
5	106	60[b]	55
6	120	40[b]	33
7	275	132	48
8	298	68	23

[a]Mean loading 52.5 lbs/acre-day yielding 86.5 percent BOD reduction.
[b]Mean BOD removal 47.5 lbs/acre-day under order-free conditions.

The ability of nonaerated basins to remove approximately 45 to 50 pounds of BOD/acre daily without production of anaerobic odors correlates well with knowledge of reaeration characteristics of lagoons. Imhoff and Fair (2) published reaeration rates of 43 pounds of oxygen/acre-day for "sluggish streams 6 feet deep, large lakes, and impounding reservoirs," when operated at zero percent dissolved oxygen saturation. Application of such a reaeration rate to 6-feet-deep basins represents a k_2 value of 0.15. The most recent research on stream reaeration by Churchill and his co-workers at T.V.A. (3) shows that sluggish "large streams 6 feet deep" do in fact display a k_2 value of around 0.15 when flowing at 0.5 foot/second. The feature which correlates the reaeration rates of stabilization basins with those for sluggish streams apparently is wind-induced surface velocity. For example, mean summer wind velocities of 7 MPH normally will produce surface currents of 0.5 foot/second.

The last factor to tie down in this analysis is the relation between oxygen transferred and actual oxygen use during BOD reduction. Recent studies by Gellman (4) indicate that k_1 values during BOD measurement of mill effluents, before and after biological treatment, are approximately 0.2. Under these conditions the BOD_5 is approximately 90 percent of the ultimate BOD, so that a given reduction in BOD_5 during treatment is accompanied for all practical purposes by an equal usage of oxygen. It is therefore concluded that removals of 45 to 50 pounds BOD/acre-day correlate in a rational manner with the computed reaeration characteristics of such basins.

Additional evidence is provided by at least one extensive waste stabilization basin system, in which multiple ponds covering 670 acres reduce a total BOD load of 44,000 pounds/day by 95 percent. The last basin in the series-operated system is the largest, covering 470 acres. It receives 20,000 pounds/day and discharges only 2,500 pounds BOD, removing 87 percent of its applied load or 42 pounds BOD/acre-day. This system illustrates the points made above, namely higher than 60–70-pounds BOD removal in the first basins under anaerobic conditions, followed by odor-free removal of 42 pounds/acre in the final basin (consistent with its computed reaeration capacity).

AERATED STABILIZATION BASINS

Laboratory and pilot plant studies of the aerated stabilization basin process by the National Council for Stream Improvement and its member mills have recently led to its rapid acceptance and extensive application. Today, 150,000,000 gal/day receive treatment at eleven installations, and additional treatment is in the offing for another 500,000,000 gal/day at fifteen more mills. While new in terms of application, the process rests on old established principles. In the spectrum of aerobic treatment processes it occupies the ground between low-rate extended aeration activated sludge treatment (24-hour aeration with recycle of secondary sludge) and long-term storage natural stabilization basin treatment. The process is flexible, involving supplemental aeration for periods of 3–20 days with or without nutrient addition, occasionally followed by secondary sedimentation, but without being dependent on sludge recycle for successful operation. Process efficiency can be varied over a wide range from 50 to 95 percent by control of nutrient and air supply, by addition of secondary sedimentation, and most importantly by selection of aeration basin retention time.

One major factor prompting adoption of this process has been the need to upgrade performance of older natural stabilization basins that have become overloaded or are now unable to meet changing receiving-water quality needs. Gehm (1) has shown that such basins can remove 40–60 pounds BOD/acre-day without generating anaerobic odors, and that such removal rates correlate well with natural reaeration rates for shallow basins. Overloading of such basins has been remedied in several ways. For example, both at Riegelwood, North Carolina, and Baltimore, Ohio, mechanical aerators were installed directly in these lagoons to increase BOD removal to 600–1,200 pounds/acre-day. At Naheola, Alabama, an alternate course was followed, namely to install a smaller 40-acre aerated basin to provide substantial pretreatment before discharge into the older 100-acre stabilization basin. In this case this step was in response to both a mill expansion increase in loading and a loss in stream self-purification capacity caused by downstream impoundment.

Land requirements for aerated stabilization basin treatment lie between those for activated sludge aeration tanks and natural stabilization basins. Thus while land usage for aerated basins may equal 2 acres/1,000,000 gallons a day, which is much greater than a typical requirement of 0.04 acre/1,000,000 gallons a day for activated sludge aeration tanks, it is substantially less than the 40 acres/1,000,000 gallons a day normally allotted for natural stabilization basins. Therefore, at locations such as Durham, Pennsylvania, and Covington, Tennessee, advantage was taken of ample land availability to avoid both the high construction and operating costs and the greater process complexity of activated sludge treatment. Recent cost studies indicate that construction and operating costs for aerated stabilization basin treatment are approximately 60 and 40 percent, respectively, of those for activated sludge treatment in the 90 percent BOD removal range.

PROCESS DESIGN FUNDAMENTALS

Gellman (4) showed that the selection of retention time sufficient to provide the desired degree of BOD removal in an aerated stabilization basin may be made through the use of the monomolecular BOD curve, Eckenfelder's (5) first-order equation for a completely mixed system, or the correlation equations of McKinney (6).

On the basis of laboratory and pilot scale studies of a variety of different pulp and paper wastes, Gellman (4) concluded that a continuously mixed first-order type correlation of BOD removal with retention time is probably appropriate, that secondary sludge generation is considerably lower than in activated sludge treatment, and that these solids are well stabilized. External secondary sedimentation produces only a very modest improvement in effluent quality, and it remains problematical whether the same or even greater benefits may not be achieved by putting this extra investment in additional basin retention. One major benefit of the pilot studies has been to permit evaluation of various mechanical aerators under field conditions, helping considerably in design of full-scale treatment facilities.

The tendency of wastes undergoing aeration treatment for extended periods to come toward mean ambient temperatures is well known, and has been documented by Eckenfelder and Rice. This tendency, and interest in application of the process in colder climates and under year-round weather conditions, prompted a recent study of the effects of reduced temperatures on process performance. The results of this study conducted between 2° and 30°C., using five different wastes are shown in Table 73. Very substantial BOD removal occurred even at 2°C., and, while the difference in performance was considerable at 2.5 days retention, the effect was minimized with prolonged retention. It was concluded that the process had utility even under winter conditions that would cool the effluent close to the freezing point.

An important consideration in the design of aerated stabilization basin aeration systems is the relative ease of oxygen transfer, expressed by the alpha value. Studies have shown that while this value ranges from 0.7 to 1.1 for kraft wastes, the general tendency is for this value to approach 1.0 as oxidation proceeds. In

TABLE 73

EFFECT OF TEMPERATURE ON BOD REMOVAL (%) BY AERATED STABILIZATION BASIN TREATMENT

(Average of 5 Pulp and Paper Mill Wastes)

Temperature °C.	Aeration, Days		
	2.5	5	10
30	79	85	88
20	74	82	87
10	70	75	84
2	56	70	79

the absence of experimental data, the use of a value of 0.7 provides an ample margin of safety in meeting oxygen requirements.

Nitrogen and dissolved oxygen requirements have been studied sufficiently by Gellman (4) to establish the adequacy of DO levels of 0.5 ppm and BOD:N ratios substantially greater than that required for activated sludge treatment. Optimal ratios have been found to range from 50:1 with 4 days aeration to 100:1 at 10–15 days, beyond which point nutrient addition is not normally required.

FULL-SCALE APPLICATIONS OF AERATED STABILIZATION BASINS

Gellman (4) described the larger mechanically aerated basins on which data were available. Table 74 summarizes details of these basins.

At least four large kraft mills which are presently under construction in the South plan to include effluent treatment facilities patterned after that shown in

TABLE 74

AERATED WASTE STABILIZATION BASINS IN THE PULP AND PAPER INDUSTRY, MARCH 1966

Location	Flow, MGD	Basins			Depth, Feet	Aerators		
		Retention, Days	No.	Size, Acres		No.	Size, HP	Mounting
Riegelwood, N. C.	35.0	7	1	70.0	11.0	14	60.00	Float
Naheola, Ala.	40.0	3	1	40.0	10.0	9	40.00	Fixed
						1	30.00	Float
Rome, Ga.	10.0	4	5	21.0	7.0	2	60.00	Float
						6	30.00	
Baltimore, Ohio	1.5	4	1	4.0	5.0	4	30.00	Float
Rittman, Ohio	4.0	9	4	3.5	8.0	6	30.00	Fixed
						6	40.00	Fixed
Versailles, Conn.	4.5	4	1	6.0	8.5	5	40.00	Float
Durham, Pa.	2.0	8	2	2.0	12.0	3	25.00	Fixed
						3	10.00	Fixed
Munroe Falls, Ohio	0.3	6	1	0.8	8.0	5	0.75	Float
Covington, Tenn.	0.3	3	1	0.9	3.0	1	7.50	Fixed

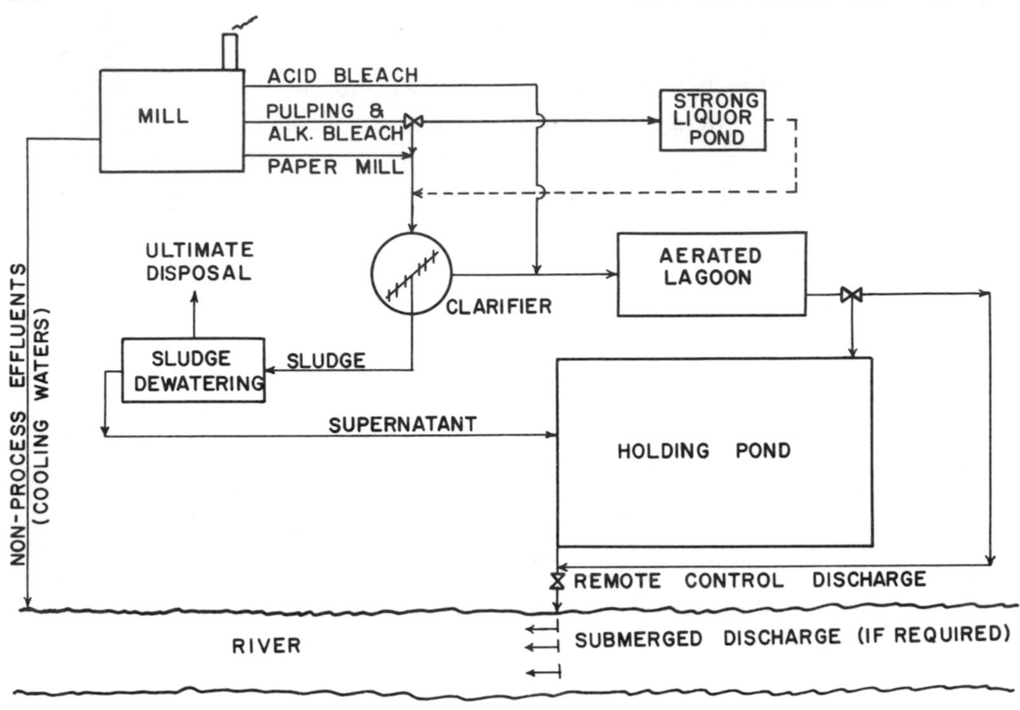

Figure 184. High-degree effluent treatment possibilities—bleached kraft pulp and paper.

Figure 184. In addition, two mills undergoing expansion plan to upgrade their present treatment works along the lines indicated in the flow sheet.

The flexibility inherent in secondary treatment by aerated stabilizations basins makes this unit operation easily alterable to achieve optimum treatment at lowest cost. In a system similar to that shown in Figure 184, retention time, horsepower applied, and nutrients added may be tailored to fit the effluent quality requirements. Also, savings may be effected by seasonal operation of the aerated lagoon, provided the assimilative capacity of the receiving stream in cooler weather and higher flows is shown to be adequate.

REFERENCES

(1) Gehm, Harry W. "The Application of Stabilization Ponds in the Purification of Pulp and Paper Mill Wastes," *J. Water Poll. Cont. Fed.*, *35*, 1174–1180 (September 1963).

(2) Imhoff, K., and G. M. Fair. *Sewage Treatment*. New York: John Wiley and Sons, Inc. (1956).

(3) Churchill, M. A., R. A. Buckingham, and H. L. Elmore. *The Prediction of Stream Reaeration Rates*. Tennessee Valley Authority (1964).

(4) Gellman, I. "Aerated Stabilization Basin Treatment of Mill Effluents," *J. Tech. Assoc. Pulp Paper Ind.*, *48*, 106A–110A (June 1965).

(5) Eckenfelder, W. W., Jr. "Design and Performance of Aerated Lagoons for Pulp and Paper Waste Treatment," *Proceedings*, 16th Industrial Waste Conference, Purdue University, 115–125 (1961).

(6) McKinney, R. E. "Design of Aerated Lagoons," *7th Great Plains Sewage Works Design Conference*, Omaha, Nebraska (March 1963).

(7) Rice, W. D., and R. F. Weston. "Bio-Treatment Design for Pulp and Paper Wastes," *Proceedings*, 16th Industrial Waste Conference, Purdue University, 461–504 (1961).

Index

The following code is used in the Index: *f.* after a page number indicates a figure; *n.* after a page number indicates a note; and *t.* after a page number indicates a table.

D

G

H

Q